SPOTLiGHT on

LITERATURE

GOLD LEVEL

AUTHORS

CANDY DAWSON BOYD
JOYCE BUCKNER
JAMES FLOOD
JAMES V. HOFFMAN
ROBERT J. KEALEY

DIANE LAPP
ROY SINGLETON
CHARLES TEMPLE
ARNOLD W. WEBB
KAREN D. WOOD

Macmillan McGraw-Hill

NEW YORK   FARMINGTON

Macmillan/McGraw-Hill

*A Division of The **McGraw·Hill** Companies*

Cover Art:
*Edward Hopper, **Lighthouse Hill,** 1927. Dallas Museum of Art, gift of Mr. and Mrs. Maurice Purnell.*

Macmillan/McGraw-Hill
1221 Avenue of the Americas
New York, New York 10020

Printed in the United States of America
ISBN 0-02-181013-3/8, L.14
2 3 4 5 6 7 8 9 VHJ 02 01 00 99 98 97

AUTHORS, CONSULTANTS, AND REVIEWERS

Authors

Candy Dawson Boyd
St. Mary's College, California

Joyce Buckner
Omaha Public School System, Nebraska

James Flood
San Diego State University, California

James V. Hoffman
University of Texas, Austin

Robert J. Kealey
Department of Elementary Schools,
National Catholic Association

Diane Lapp
San Diego State University, California

Roy Singleton
University of North Florida, Jacksonville

Charles Temple
Hobart and William Smith Colleges, New York

Arnold W. Webb
Research for Better Schools, Inc.
Philadelphia, Pennsylvania

Karen D. Wood
University of North Carolina, Charlotte

Multicultural and Educational Consultants

Alma Flor Ada, Yvonne Beamer, Joyce Buckner, Helen Gillotte, Cheryl Hudson, Narcita Medina, Lorraine Monroe, James R. Murphy, Sylvia Pena, Joseph B. Rubin, Ramon Santiago, Cliff Trafzer, Hai Tran, Esther Lee Yao

Literature Consultants

Ashley Bryan, Joan I. Glazer, Paul Janeczko, Margaret H. Lippert

International Consultants

Edward B. Adams, Barbara Johnson, Raymond L. Marshall

Music and Audio Consultants

John Farrell, Marilyn C. Davidson, Vincent Lawrence, Sarah Pirtle, Susan R. Snyder, Rick and Deborah Witkowski, Eastern Sky Media Services

Teacher Reviewers

Terry Baker, Jane Bauer, James Bedi, Nora Bickel, Vernell Bowen, Donald Cason, Jean Chaney, Carolyn Clark, Alan Cox, Kathryn DesCarpentrie, Carol L. Ellis, Roberta Gale, Brenda Huffman, Erma Inscore, Sharon Kidwell, Elizabeth Love, Isabel Marcus, Elaine McCraney, Michelle Moraros, Earlene Parr, Dr. Richard Potts, Jeanette Pulliam, Michael Rubin, Henrietta Sakamaki, Kathleen Cultron Sanders, Belinda Snow, Dr. Jayne Steubling, Margaret Mary Sulentic, Barbara Tate, Seretta Vincent, Willard Waite, Barbara Wilson, Veronica York

CONTENTS

Relationships

UNIT 2

SOLUTIONS

Justice
JUSTICE
JUSTICE
JUSTICE

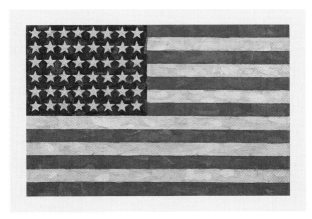

*Detail of **Three Flags,** Jasper Johns. © 1997 Jasper Johns/Licensed by VAGA, New York.*

TURNING points

THE NATURAL WORLD

GENRE FOCUS

Mountains in Four Seasons *(detail)*   *1990*
© *Fumiko Hori   The Sato Museum*

Perspectives

Relat

The Painter's Family   *1911   Henri Matisse   The Hermitage Museum, St. Petersburg*

tionships

Scaffolding
by Seamus Heaney

Masons, when they start upon a building,
Are careful to test out the scaffolding;

Make sure that planks won't slip at busy points,
Secure all ladders, tighten bolted joints.

And yet all this comes down when the job's done
Showing off walls of sure and solid stone.

So if, my dear, there sometimes seem to be
Old bridges breaking between you and me

Never fear. We may let the scaffolds fall
Confident that we have built our wall.

1

Relationships

BEFORE READING

······································

DICEY'S SONG

CONNECT TO LITERATURE

Has anyone ever helped you when you were not expecting help? How did you feel? How did you respond? Share your thoughts with a classmate. As you read "Dicey's Song," note in your journal what Dicey does when she finds herself in just such a situation.

THINKING ABOUT THIRD-PERSON POINT OF VIEW

Every story is told by a narrator, who reveals events from his or her perspective, or point of view. When the narrator of a story is outside the story, meaning he or she is not a character in it, the story is told from the *third-person point of view.* Clues that indicate this point of view include pronouns such as *he, she,* and *they.*

DID YOU KNOW?

Dicey's Song, from which this excerpt is taken, is part of a series of books by Cynthia Voigt about the Tillerman family. The first book, called *Homecoming,* tells how Dicey Tillerman and her younger siblings are abandoned by their mother when she has an emotional breakdown and is hospitalized. Dicey works to keep her family together and to get them to Maryland, where she hopes her grandmother will take them in.

In *Dicey's Song,* Dicey and her family are living with their grandmother near the Chesapeake Bay in Maryland. In making a new home together, each member of the household learns how to reach out to others in new ways.

DICEY'S

With pictures by Jill Enfield

SONG

by Cynthia Voigt

When their mother's emotional breakdown prevents her from taking care of them, Dicey Tillerman, her sister Maybeth, and her brothers James and Sammy courageously find their way on foot all the way from Connecticut to the Chesapeake Bay in Maryland, where they have a grandmother they have never met. They convince her to take them in. A few months later, Dicey writes about what happened to her mother in an English essay assignment. In the essay, Dicey refers to her mother simply as "Mrs. Liza," and she doesn't acknowledge that "Mrs. Liza" is her mother. She is not prepared for her teacher Mr. Chappelle's reaction to the essay.

Dicey looked out the window and made her legs stay still. Outside, wind blew the branches of the two big oaks, ripping off the last of the brown leaves and carrying them away. The sky was a bright blue, and the sun shone with a diamond hardness. The brightness of the sun and the coldness of the wind combined to mark out sharply the edges of her view. She could see each individual brick on the old building, as if the cold made each brick contract into itself. The angles of the main entranceway, the clear edge of the cement sidewalk, the flat lawn, bare and brown now, all looked as if they would be cold to touch.

Dicey crossed her ankles again, containing her impatience. She was wearing jeans and one of the rough old boys' sweaters, a bright red one that hung loose about her torso. She had chosen it because it seemed like the kind of color her Momma's brother Bullet would have liked, if she was right about the kind of person he had been.

Mr. Chappelle was putting off returning their papers until he had told them about the mistakes most of them had made. They were supposed to be writing these things down, the list of misspelled words, the grammar errors, the kind of topic sentence every paragraph was supposed to have. He was explaining and explaining. Everybody was quiet, just waiting for him to get finished. The thing that got Dicey was that he pretended he was doing this stuff first because it was more important than the grades. That was what he said, that the papers were a learning situation, and the grades didn't matter.

But Dicey suspected that he was doing this dull stuff first because he knew that once he handed the papers back nobody would pay any attention to him. It wasn't his fault, it was just the way classes went. You worked hard (or not so hard) for something, and when you got the results that job was over. The teacher might not think it was over, but the students sure did. The grade told you how well you had done (or what you got away with). The grade was what you looked for—not the red circles around mistakes. Sometimes, a teacher wrote a comment, *good work* (or *bad work*), and you looked at that, too. But mostly, everything they had to say they said in the grade. If there was something more important than the grade, Dicey wanted to know why didn't teachers ever say anything about that, like write you a note about it on your paper. If it wasn't worth his time to write down, how could he say it was worth hers?

She sat forward and sat back and sat forward. She looked at the clock—only fifteen minutes left; he'd have to hand the papers back soon.

"Now," Mr. Chappelle said, "you may be interested in seeing your essays." He smiled at his own joke, so a few kids made little fake laughing noises.

"Before I hand them out, there are two I'd like to read aloud to you." Dicey made herself lean back in her chair. She jammed her hands down into her pockets and stretched her legs out in front of her. "To share with you," Mr. Chappelle said, and reached down into his briefcase. He took out the pile of papers. He ran his hand through his red hair and looked around at everyone, his eyes sliding along the rows. He tried another joke. "Both of these essays were written by girls, but I don't want you boys to get <u>discouraged</u>. Everyone knows boys grow up more slowly."

Who *cares*, Dicey demanded silently.

He took up a paper and began to read.

There's this girl I know, you never know what she's thinking, even though everybody thinks they know this girl. You look at her face, but that doesn't tell you anything. Sometimes you know you don't know what's going on inside. Sometimes, you're not sure you don't know. I wonder about this girl. Here's what I've noticed.

Dicey thought this girl could be just about anyone, even Dicey. She could tell by the way the rest of the class was listening, they had the same feeling. The way it was written, it was just like somebody talking.

She's about the laughingest person you're <u>liable</u> to meet, if you live forever. Nothing but sets her off laughing. You could tell her you were flunking every course and about to be booted out of home and into the unemployment lines, and she'd laugh. She'd laugh until you might start laughing too. You could tell her you just got elected president of your class and captain of the football

---

discouraged (dis kûr′ijd) *adj.* disheartened.
liable (lī′ə bəl) *adj.* legally responsible; obligated by law.

team and Prince Charming, all at once, and you know what she'd do—she'd laugh. Everywhere she goes it's nothing but laugh, laugh, until you feel like you're caught out in a rainstorm that won't never end. But I keep finding her crying when she thinks nobody's there to see. I catch her. And when I ask her, "Honey, why you crying so bad?" she never says one word to tell me. I stand there, passing out the Kleenex, and she's whooping and wailing and there's nothing can stop her once she's started.

By this time, Dicey thought she recognized who the person was describing: Mina. Because of the laughing. The crying wasn't anything Dicey had seen, but she guessed this was a pretty close friend of Mina's.

Another thing. She's always talking about you. Not behind your back, but right when you're having your conversation. "How are you, and what do you think, and what do you like?" She's mighty easy to talk with, this girl, because she's always interested in the other person. She listens and she remembers and she'll ask you, two years later, "Remember that fight you had with your father about your allowance? Do you still feel the same way?" I guess she's about the most unselfish person I know. But inside, she's always thinking about herself, patting herself on the back for being a caring, remembering person. She's got about the longest arms you'll ever see for patting herself on the back. So while you're telling her this sad, beautiful love story, and you're saying everything you feel—but everything—she's listening so hard you feel like she's curled up inside your own head and you think there never was such a person for listening to you. All the time, part of her's wondering if she's ever been in love or if she ever will be, and how it'll be for her, and she's thinking how great you think she is. This girl is just about something, and I sometimes wonder if even she knows what's going on.

But, Dicey thought, the only person who could know all that about Mina was Mina. Dicey sat forward in her chair. Was it Mina's paper? She slipped her eye over to where Mina was sitting. The smooth brown cheeks looked as if they'd never heard this before. Mina was looking down at her open notebook. But she wasn't smiling, the way the rest of the class was while they listened. The way Dicey started to smile, figuring out what Mina had done. Dicey was <u>impressed</u> by this paper, the way Mina wrote about herself. Boy was that an idea—that was an idea and a half.

To see her, she's got all the answers. Everybody else has trouble making up their minds. Should I do this? Do I want to wear that? Is it the right answer? Not this girl, she just knows the heart out of everything and everybody. She doesn't hesitate, she just puts her big feet out in front of her and gets going. And worry? That's a word this girl never heard of. It's not in her dictionary. She knows north from south, and she knows which way she wants to go. No regrets, not for her. If she makes a mistake—well she's made a mistake and so what? <u>Confident</u>, you'd call her, and for all you know you're one hundred percent right, there wasn't anybody since the Garden of Eden as confident. But I've seen her do her hair one way then brush it out and do it another. I've seen her sit in one chair and then in another and then move to a bench and finally sit on the ground, until she hopped up to sit in the chair she tried first. I've seen her rip up ten starts on homework papers and only hand one in because she ran out of time to rip it up in.

By this time, the class had figured out that it was Mina the essay was about. They whispered it and looked at Mina. They wondered—interrupting Mr. Chappelle but he didn't seem to mind, he seemed to want them to guess—who'd written it. They asked one another, "Did you?" and answered, "No not me, did you?" Mina just kept staring down, but she was having a hard time not laughing out loud. Dicey was sure Mina had written it about herself, but she didn't know why she was so sure. She just knew it.

And all the time this girl's listening and laughing, all the same. I'm watching her and I don't know what she's thinking, and then I'm thinking, Maybe I do. I guess by now you know who I'm talking about, you know it's me, Wilhemina Smiths.

The class burst out laughing, and praised Mina. Mina looked around and pretended to take a bow. Mr. Chappelle told her to stand up. As she did, she caught Dicey's eye. Dicey pursed her lips into a mute whistle, to try to say how impressed she was. Mr. Chappelle stepped forward and gave

---

impressed (im presd') *adj.* fixed firmly in the mind.
confident (kon'fi dənt) *adj.* firmly trusting; certain.

Mina her paper. Mina didn't even unfold it to see the grade. She just sat down again.

After a minute, the noise in the room, and the occasional laugh, died away.

"Now for a horse of another color," Mr. Chappelle announced. He began to read.

At the first words, Dicey recognized it as hers. She stared at Mr. Chappelle's pale, <u>impassive</u> face as he read about Momma.

Mrs. Liza lived away up north, away out on Cape Cod, away in a town right at the end of the Cape. Her cabin was outside of town, right at the edge of the ocean. The ocean rolled up toward her rickety cabin, like it wanted to swallow it up; but it never did. Maybe it didn't even want to. The wind was always blowing around the cabin, like it too wanted to have that little building gone.

Mrs. Liza had children, but she never had been married, and the man who was her children's father had long ago gone and left her. She worked nights when the children were little, waiting tables in a restaurant, serving drinks in a bar, night-clerking in a motel. She always worked hard and was always willing to take days nobody else wanted, Christmas and Fourth of July, Easter. When the children got older, she switched to a day-time job, checkout in a supermarket. She hadn't had any training for the kind of job that paid well, so she was always thinking about money, hoping she would have enough. Every sweater she owned had holes in it.

She had reasons to turn into a mean woman, but Mrs. Liza just couldn't. She had a face made to smile, and her eyes always smiled with her mouth. She had long hair, the color of warm

■——
impassive (im pas'iv) *adj.* not feeling or showing emotion.

honey in the winter, the color of evening sunlight in the summer. She walked easy, high narrow shoulders, but loose, as if the joints of her body never got quite put together. She walked like a song sung without <u>accompaniment</u>.

Then slowly, so slowly she never really could find out the place where it began, life turned sour on Mrs. Liza. People said things. While she never heard them herself, her children heard them and got older and understood what people meant. Mrs. Liza loved her children, so that worried her. Money worried at her the way waves worry at the shoreline, always nibbling away at the soft sand. Her money seemed to run out earlier each week.

Mrs. Liza stood at the door of her cabin and looked out at the ocean. The ocean looked back at Mrs. Liza and rolled on

---

accompaniment (ə kum′pə ni mənt) *n.* thing that goes along with something else.

toward her. She could see no end to the ocean. The wind that pulled at her hair was always blowing. She looked out at her children playing on the beach and reminded herself to get some tunafish for supper; but she forgot.

Her eyes stopped smiling first, and then her mouth. The holes in her sweaters got bigger. Meanwhile, people talked and she didn't know what to say so they could understand. Meanwhile, quarters and dimes got lighter, smaller. Meanwhile, her children were growing bigger and they needed more food, more clothes. Meanwhile, nothing she did seemed to make any difference.

So Mrs. Liza did about the only thing left to her to do. She went away into the farthest place she could find. They cut her hair short. She didn't notice that, lying there, nor when they fed her or changed the sheets. Her eyes never moved, as if what she was looking at was so far away small that if she looked off for a second, it would be gone.

Mr. Chappelle put the paper down and looked up. Dicey felt proud: it was just about as good as she'd thought it was. It was really good. But everybody was absolutely quiet. Didn't they think it was good, too? She waited nervously. Maybe she just liked it because it was hers, the way you liked anything you had made yourself. Maybe Mr. Chappelle read it because it was so bad, to show the difference between hers and Mina's. Still nobody spoke. Mr. Chappelle was staring down at the paper. He was wearing a green tie.

Dicey didn't care if nobody liked it but her. She remembered how she had felt, writing it down. It was hard, and she kept scratching out sentences and beginning again. Yet it kind of came out, almost without her thinking of it, almost as if it had been already written inside her head, and she just had to find the door to open to let it out. She'd never felt that way about schoolwork before, and she wondered if she could do it again. She made her face quiet, not to show what she was thinking.

At last, Mina broke the silence. "That surely *is* a horse of another color," she said. There was laughter in her voice. "I guess it about beat me around the track—before I even left the starting gate." She looked around the class.

"Oh, yes, it's very well written," Mr. Chappelle agreed.

Dicey kept quiet.

"But who wrote it?" somebody asked, a boy. "And what happened at the end? It sounded like she died. But it didn't say she died."

The voices went on talking.

"It sounded like she was about to die."

"No, she was already dead."

"Where was she?"

"In jail? In a hospital? It said they fed her and changed the sheets."

"But what happened?"

"She couldn't support her family. She was poor, couldn't you tell? And it just got her down."

"Yeah, because she started out happy, didn't she?"

"Why didn't she get married?"

"The guy walked out, weren't you listening?"

"Maybe he didn't want to get married."

"Maybe he didn't want all those kids."

"But it takes two—you know what I mean. It wasn't just *her* fault."

"It wasn't fair what happened to her."

"Fair—what difference does fair make?"

"Did she go crazy? I would."

"And it's a mental hospital at the end? But it sounded like a jail picture, at the end."

"Who wrote it, Mr. Chappelle, tell us. You're the one who knows."

They stopped for his answer: "I do, and I don't," he said.

Dicey bit her lip. Now what did that mean?

"It's like one of the stories in our book," somebody said.

"What do you mean?" Mr. Chappelle asked quickly. "Did you read it in our text?"

How could she have? Dicey thought impatiently.

"No, I mean—it doesn't sound like one of us wrote it. It doesn't sound like anything I could write. I never knew anybody like Mrs. Liza. And even if I did, I couldn't—say it like that. Tell us, did *you* write it?"

Mr. Chappelle came around to the front of the desk. He leaned back against it, half-sitting on it. "No, I didn't. Dicey Tillerman did. Stand up, Dicey."

Dicey stood up. She stood up straight and didn't even lean her hand on her desk. Everybody stared at her. "I shoulda guessed," Mina said. She smiled across the room at Dicey, congratulating.

"What *did* happen to her at the end?" somebody asked, but Mr. Chappelle cut off the question.

"Do you have anything to say?" he asked Dicey. She kept her mouth shut, and her face closed off. She knew now what he was thinking.

"No? But I'm afraid I do. I'm very much afraid I have a great deal to say. I'm not one of your great brains, but I've taught this course long enough to be able to tell the kind of work students can do."

Dicey felt frozen. He wasn't looking at her, but she was looking at him, at his pale, flabby mouth out of which words marched slowly.

"Now I can't say what book this came out of—if it came out of a book. I can't even say for sure that it did come out of a book. Maybe somebody else helped Dicey write it."

He gave her time to say something there, but he didn't look at her. Dicey didn't say a word. In the first place, her tongue felt like it was frozen solid, and her head was a block of ice, and all the blood in her body had chilled and <u>congealed</u>. In the second place, he had more to say. She could guess what that was.

"But even if I can't prove <u>plagiarism</u>, I can still smell it. Besides, there was a restriction on this assignment. It was supposed to be about someone you knew. A real person. On those grounds alone, the essay fails."

Dicey should have known. She should have known this would happen, and everyone would believe him. The silence in the room told her what everyone was thinking. She was the only one standing up, for everyone to look at.

"What I primarily resent is the deceitfulness of it, the cheap trickery, the lies," Mr. Chappelle declared.

---

congealed (kən jēld′) *v.i.* changed from a liquid to a solid by cooling or freezing.
plagiarism (plā′jə riz′əm) *n.* act of copying someone else's work and passing it off as one's own.

"That's not true."

Dicey turned to see who had spoken. She thought she could hear her neck bones crackling, like ice, when she turned her head.

Mina was standing up. She looked around the room, her eyes dark as coffee and puzzled. "How can you believe that?" she demanded of Mr. Chappelle.

"Come now, Wilhemina," he said.

"*I* don't believe it," she declared. Her voice sounded certain.

Mr. Chappelle looked around the classroom. Dicey could have laughed. He didn't quite dare order Mina to sit down, because people listened to her and liked her.

"Dicey wouldn't do that," Mina went on. "She doesn't care enough about what we think to cheat on something."

How did Mina know that? Dicey wondered. She wondered it deep behind her icy face.

"Someone like Dicey—she's too smart to worry about her grades; she doesn't have to worry. And if she cared what we thought—" her hand sketched a circle including all the students— "she'd act different. Don't you think?"

People rustled in their seats. They could think whatever they wanted. Now Dicey understood the C+ in English.

The bell rang, ending class, but Mina spoke before anybody could move to leave. "Stay here, I'll prove it."

"How can you prove it?" Mr. Chappelle asked. He had moved back behind his desk. "I've got these essays to hand out."

"Wait," Mina said.

They could stay or go for all Dicey cared.

"I can prove it," Mina repeated. "Dicey?" She looked across the room at Dicey. Her eyes were filled with <u>sympathy</u>. Dicey didn't need anybody's pity. But behind the liquid darkness of Mina's eyes, Dicey saw mischief. Mina knew she was right, and she was enjoying herself.

"Dicey? Is this someone you know?"

"Yes," Dicey said. She was talking just to Mina.

"Did you write it yourself?"

"Yes," Dicey said.

"What does that prove?" Mr. Chappelle muttered.

---

sympathy (sim′pə thē) *n.* ability to share the feelings of another or others.

"Do you want to hear Dicey lie?" Mina asked him. "Dicey, is this someone you're related to?"

Dicey lifted her chin. She didn't answer. There was no way anybody could make her answer. In her mind, she made a picture: the little boat, she'd have painted it white by then, or maybe yellow—it was out on the Bay beyond Gram's dock and the wind pulled at the sails. Dicey could feel the smooth <u>tiller</u> under her hand, she could feel the way the wooden hull flowed through the water.

---

tiller (til′ər) *n.* bar or handle used to turn the rudder of a boat.

"Dicey," Mina asked, with no expression in her voice, "what are you thinking about?"

"About sailing," Dicey answered. "About a boat and how it feels when you're sailing it." Those might be the last words she spoke in that class, and why should she bother to make them a lie?

Then people did get up and go. They didn't look at Dicey, but they looked at Mr. Chappelle as they walked past his desk and picked out their papers.

Dicey was almost at the door when he stopped her and gave the paper to her. "I'm sorry," he said. "I'll change the grade—to an A+—and I'll change the mid-semester grade too, of course."

Dicey didn't say anything. She didn't care what he said.

"It's my mistake and I'm really very sorry," he said again. "I'm giving you an A for the marking period, of course."

It didn't make any difference to Dicey what he said.

She sat through horrible home ec without any trouble at all. On the outside, she was paring carrots and slicing them thin to boil them at the stoves. She didn't eat any, just scraped them into the garbage. She went to work, without even noticing if Jeff was outside playing his guitar. She did her work hard and fast and answered Millie's questions without thinking. She rode home through a wind like a knife blade, but it didn't make her cold. She put her bike in the barn and leaned her free hand against the boat for a minute before going on into the house. Gram was in the kitchen. Maybeth and James worked in the living room by the fire. Dicey put her books up in her bedroom and then came back downstairs. She peeled some potatoes for Gram, then cut them up into chunks for hash browns. Sammy came through, rubbing his hands and puffing out cold air. Dicey stood at the wooden countertop, slicing the potatoes first, then cutting across the slices, then cutting again <u>perpendicularly</u>. Slice after slice.

Gram was shaking chicken pieces in a brown paper bag. Dicey could hear the sound it made, like somebody brushing out a rhythm on drums. "How was school today?" Gram asked.

"Fine," Dicey said. She cut slowly, carefully, making her squares as even as possible.

---

perpendicularly (pûr´pən dik´yə lər lē) *adv.* straight up and down; vertically.

"How's Millie?" Gram asked. There was a kind of sharpness in her voice, and alertness, but Dicey didn't turn around to read the expression on her face. She heard the chicken pieces shaking, in flour, salt, and pepper.

"Fine."

Gram was staring at her. She could feel it.

"You never said," Gram said without breaking the rhythm of the shaking, "if you got your English grade changed."

"Well," Dicey said. Then she couldn't think of how to finish the sentence.

"Well?" Gram asked after a while. "Was it a mistake? Were you right?"

Dicey picked up the last potato. She cut it into neat slices. She lay the slices down flat in front of her. "Yeah, it was a mistake. Boy was it a mistake." She felt pretty calm again, cold and still.

"What happened?" Gram asked. For a second, Dicey was irritated. It wasn't like Gram to insist on a subject Dicey didn't want to talk about. Usually, Gram understood and stopped asking questions.

"We had an essay to write," Dicey explained. She felt like she was talking to the potato, because that was what she looked at. Behind her, Gram moved around the kitchen, getting things ready. "A character sketch, about a real person and conflict. I wrote one, and thought it was pretty good. He handed them back today. He thought I'd copied mine. Or something. He thought the person wasn't real. He thought I'd taken it out of a book." She slowed her hands down. When she finished with this potato, what was she going to do about what to look at?

Gram's voice came from behind her. "It must have been pretty good, if he thought it came out of a book."

Dicey turned around. Gram was looking at her. "Yeah," Dicey said, hearing how fierce her own voice sounded, "it was."

"Did you tell him?" Gram asked.

Dicey shook her head.

"You mean he thinks you cheated?"

Dicey shook her head again.

"Exactly what happened?" Gram asked, sounding ready to get angry.

"He read a couple of the papers out loud, to everyone. Mine was one. Then he said, he thought I'd cheated but he couldn't prove it. But he said I hadn't done the assignment, because it was supposed to be a real person. So he was flunking it."

"In front of the whole class?" Gram demanded.

"Yeah."

Gram's mouth moved and her eyes burned. That made Dicey feel warm, down deep in her stomach. Gram was angry for Dicey's sake. "Can I read it?" Gram asked.

"Sure."

"Now?"

"OK."

"Will you get it, girl? I've got fat heating."

So Dicey went upstairs to get her essay. She started the potatoes while Gram sat at the table and read. She placed the cubes of potato neatly in the hot bacon fat and turned the gas down to medium once she heard the fat start to sizzle under the layer of potatoes. She checked the lard in the other frying pan, to see if it was smoking hot yet. She got down a jar of tomatoes that Gram had put up that summer. Every now and then she glanced over to see what Gram was doing. Gram read the essay through once, and then again, and then again.

"Well," Gram said at last, "I can see why he thought it came out of a book. I like it, Dicey. I like it very much. Your poor Momma. He couldn't know she was real. It *is* hard to believe. Are you going to tell him?"

Dicey shook her head. "Anyway, he knows," she told Gram. "He said he'll change the grade—as if that mattered— and on the report card too."

"Tell me what happened, Dicey," Gram said.

"Well, there's this girl in our class—we worked together on a science project, and she's about the most popular girl I guess. Mina. He was yelling at me for cheating, and she said she didn't believe it." As she recalled it, Dicey saw the picture she and Mina must have made and she started to smile. "I was standing up, I was the only one. And she stood up too, and she's—she's tall and strong-looking. And her voice—I don't know how to tell you, like an actress."

Gram nodded, listening.

"She said she didn't think I'd cheat or lie. Because I didn't care enough about what people thought. Well, she's right." Dicey grinned now. "Then she said she could prove it. So she asked me a couple of questions—she ought to be a lawyer, really. The bell rang and she told everybody to stay put and they did. Anyway, she proved it, I guess, because before I left he told me about the grades and he said he was sorry."

Gram was laughing. "I wish I'd been there," she said. "I wish I'd seen this. I like the sound of this girl. She your friend?"

"No, not really. I mean—no, not really."

"Hunh," Gram said, getting up from the table and going to the stove. She started putting pieces of chicken into the fat. Dicey stepped back. "Must have been hard on you, though," Gram remarked.

"It doesn't matter," Dicey said.

Then Gram started laughing again. "That teacher sure had his hands full, didn't he, between you and this Mina character. I bet he was sorry the day he assigned that essay." And Dicey joined in now that she could see the scene as if it was part of a movie. "Serves him right," Gram added, "and will you put those tomatoes into a saucepan?"

When James read her essay about Momma, he was impressed. He didn't say so, but Dicey could tell. He asked her why she had left things out, about what their house was like, or Momma losing her job. He asked her why she hadn't told about Momma's kids more. "That's not the way it really was," he protested. "I mean—it is, it's what it felt like. But there was a whole lot more, wasn't there?"

"Yes," Dicey agreed. She thought Gram might bring up the subject of Mr. Chappelle's accusation, but Gram just sat there, knitting away on the start of Sammy's blue sweater. She had finished Maybeth's and then dampened it down and laid it on towels on the dining room table to block it into shape. When it dried, Maybeth could wear it. James went up to bed, and Dicey started to follow him, but Gram asked her to stay a while.

"I've got some reading to do," Dicey protested.

"It won't be long," Gram said. "Sit down, girl."

Dicey sat down cross-legged in front of the fire. Gram sat in an armchair a little farther back from the flames. She was knitting the ribbing, purl two, knit two. Her quick hands moved the yarn back and forth over the needles. Her eyes were dark and her hair, at the end of the day, curled around her head as if nobody ever had combed it.

"I've made a lot of mistakes in my life," Gram began.

"I don't believe it," Dicey answered.

Gram looked up briefly at her and smiled. "Well, I do, and I was there," she said. "After my husband died, I had a lot of time for thinking. And then you-all arrived, and if you think that hasn't added things to think about you're not as smart as I take you for. But especially after he died and I was alone."

She looked up sharply to say, "Don't think I minded being alone."

"I don't," Dicey said, the smile she kept from her face showing in her voice and eyes.

"Good. I didn't mind being alone, and I don't mind you living here. But that's not what I'm trying to say. I'm trying to say—I married John, and that wasn't a mistake. But the way we stayed married, the way we lived, there were lots of mistakes. He was a stiff and proud man, John—a hard man."

Dicey nodded, because Gram had said this once before.

"I stuck by him. But I got to thinking after he died— whether there weren't things I should have done. He wasn't happy, not a happy man. I knew that, I got to know it. He wasn't happy to be himself. And I just let him be, let him sit there, high and proud, in his life. I let the children go away from him. And from me. I got to thinking—when it was too late—you have to reach out to people. To your family too. You can't just let them sit there, you should put your hand out. If they slap it back, well you reach out again if you care enough.

If you don't care enough, you forget about them, if you can. I don't know, girl."

Dicey watched into the fire, where blue-edged flames leaped up toward the chimney.

"I can't say any more that Millie Tydings is stupid," Gram said.

What did she mean by that? Dicey wondered. How did she get to Millie?

"Because Millie is always reaching out. She always had a hand out for me, not that I've taken it much. She's got one out for you, hasn't she, girl. I'm not saying that Millie's thought this out, but she didn't need to. Because there's wisdom in her."

Dicey didn't say anything.

"And I see this paper of yours as a kind of reaching out," Gram said. She stopped then, as if she was finished.

"What do you mean?" Dicey demanded. She wasn't going to let Gram stop there, not until she understood.

"Think about it," Gram said.

"No, you tell me. Reaching out? But for what?"

"I don't know," Gram said. "If I was sure, I'd say. For your Momma, maybe. For all of us, maybe, but I don't think so. I think, maybe, it's reaching out for that school. Somehow. I'm not saying that's what you thought you were doing or what you even wanted to do. But it's how it turned out. And I'm sorry, the way it turned out. Because somebody's slapped your hand back good and hard. But I don't want you to stop reaching, just because it didn't come out the way it should have."

Dicey stared at her grandmother. Her mind was whirling. "That's why Mr. Lingerle—" she began.

Gram's smile flashed across her face, under the golden color the fire painted there. "He's met us halfway, hasn't he?" she observed. "I took him—in the nature of an experiment. You know? I wondered if I could. I like him, don't you?"

"Sure," Dicey said. "We all do. But that's why you told him how poor we are."

"You don't go reaching out with your hand closed up," Gram said. "It worked out all right this time."

Dicey thought.

"It took me so long to learn," Gram explained. "I'd like you to have more of a head start."

Dicey threw back her head and laughed. She didn't know why, except the feelings inside her needed some expression. If she grabbed Gram's hands and started dancing around the room, Gram would think she was crazy, for one, and she'd drop those stitches, for another. She was laughing because she couldn't hug her grandmother, and because she'd figured out something else right then: that Gram was reaching out for her,

Dicey. And Dicey was laughing for another reason, because she had a phone call to make.

She found the address and number in the directory they kept beside the phone. Gram was curious, but didn't ask questions. Dicey knew Gram was curious so she didn't wait to keep her phone call private.

A man answered the phone. "Is Wilhemina there, please?" Dicey asked.

"Do you know what time it is?" the man answered.

"No," Dicey said. "I don't. I'm sorry, is it too late to call?"

"When I was a boy, my mother told me you shouldn't ever call after ten," the voice instructed her.

"I'm sorry," Dicey said again. She bit her lip to keep from giggling. He had a voice like Mina's, just as rich, only deeper. "I didn't know it was after ten."

"It's not exactly, not yet," the voice told her, "but it will be in seven minutes. I'll get Mina, but don't be long."

"Thank you," Dicey said.

"Who shall I say is calling?"

"Dicey Tillerman."

There was a short silence. "Ah," he said. She heard the phone at his end clatter down onto a table.

"Dicey?" Mina's voice came. "I won't, Dad," she called over her shoulder.

"I just wanted to say thank you," Dicey said. "For helping out today."

She could hear the smile in Mina's voice as she answered. "That was some fun, wasn't it?"

"Yes and no," Dicey said.

"I can understand that," Mina agreed. "I was thinking I ought to thank *you* for giving me such a good chance to show off. So I guess we're about even. Talk to you tomorrow, OK?"

"OK," Dicey said. "I really liked yours, you know."

"We'll form a mutual admiration society," Mina answered. "See you."

"See you," Dicey answered. She turned back to meet Gram's eyes. "Wilhemina Smiths," she explained.

"Her father's the preacher, isn't he?" Gram asked.

"She's the one who—"

"I figured that out. I don't know, Dicey—" Gram didn't finish the sentence.

"You'll like Mina, you'll see," Dicey reassured her.

"Of course I will; I already do. But I'm a crazy old bat and my opinion's not worth a flea bite. I'm just wondering what her people will think. What they already think. About me."

"Who says you're a crazy old bat?" Dicey demanded. "James said you're crazy like a fox, he said that right away. You can't fool us, Gram."

"Good," Gram answered. "Are you going to bed or not? I thought you had reading to do."

MEET CYNTHIA VOIGT

"I always wanted to be a writer, always from the age of twelve," says Cynthia Voigt. Like Dicey, Voigt has used her writing to reach out to people, especially to young people confronting the hardships of growing up.

Dicey's Grandma Tillerman tells Dicey, "You have to reach out to people. To your family too." Voigt feels close to both Dicey and her grandmother. So her description of their mutual friendship and understanding is striking and lively. "Dicey is the type of kid I would have liked to have been," she claims, *"and grandmother is the type of old lady I would like to be."*

Voigt has written several novels about the Tillerman family. The first in the saga, and her first novel, is Homecoming. *The second, Dicey's Song, received the Newbery Medal in 1983. Voigt has won many other writing awards as well, but she considers the publication of* Homecoming *to be her most important achievement. "After years of working on my own," she says, "I was suddenly encouraged and accepted by others."*

RESPONDING TO
Literature

THINK • TALK • WRITE

1 What will you remember most about Dicey? Jot some thoughts in your journal.

2 Why does Mr. Chappelle think that Dicey has either copied her essay from another source or had help writing it? Do you think Mr. Chappelle handles his suspicions well? Explain your answer. If you were Mr. Chappelle, how would you have handled the situation?

3 Why does Mina believe that Dicey wouldn't plagiarize? Do you think Mina is right to stand up for Dicey? Explain your response.

4 What do you think Gram would say about this quotation: "Rely on yourself. . . . The victor is the person who can go it alone"? Do you agree or disagree with the quotation? Share your reasons.

5 Do you think people can change as quickly and easily as Dicey seems to change? Tell why or why not.

ACTIVITIES

• **Write About Third-Person Point of View** Write a brief essay about a real person you know, just as Dicey did in "Dicey's Song." Write your essay using the third-person point of view.

• **Role-playing** What might the first meeting of Gram and Mina be like? Get together with two classmates to act out the roles of Gram, Mina, and Dicey.

VOCABULARY PRACTICE

On a separate sheet of paper, write the vocabulary word that fits best with the other words or terms in each row.

discouraged	accompaniment
liable	congealed
impressed	plagiarism
confident	sympathy
impassive	perpendicularly

1 copying   cheating   forging

2 awed   influenced   affected

3 sorrow   support   compassion

4 unfeeling   unmoved   unemotional

5 disheartened   saddened   hopeless

6 solidified   dried   hardened

7 at right angles   upright   vertically

8 harmony   companion   background

9 responsible   obligated   subject to

10 trusting   certain   sure

Legacy II

By Leroy V. Quintana

*G*randfather never went to school
spoke only a few words of English,
a quiet man; when he talked
talked about simple things

planting corn or about the weather
sometimes about herding sheep as a child.
One day pointed to the four directions
taught me their names

El Norte

Poniente   Oriente

El Sur

He spoke their names as if they were
one of only a handful of things
a man needed to know

Now I look back
only two generations removed
realize I am nothing but a poor fool
who went to college

trying to find my way back
to the center of the world
where grandfather stood
that day.

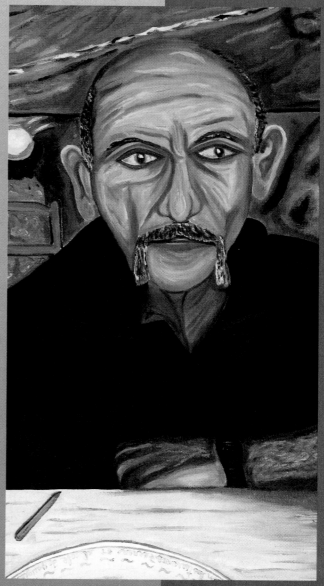

En El Café De Gauguin   1987   Rafael Ferrer

LINEAGE

by Margaret Walker

Woman Peeling Apples   1924   Archibald J. Motley

My grandmothers were strong.
They followed plows and bent to toil.
They moved through fields sowing seed.
They touched earth and grain grew.
They were full of sturdiness and singing.
My grandmothers were strong.

My grandmothers are full of memories
Smelling of soap and onions and wet clay
With veins rolling roughly over quick hands
They have many clean words to say.
My grandmothers were strong.
Why am I not as they?

BEFORE READING

....

ALMOST A WHOLE TRICKSTER

CONNECT TO LITERATURE

Did you ever enter a contest? How did you feel when the winner was announced? Share your thoughts with a classmate. As you read "Almost a Whole Trickster," note in your journal the feelings Pincher experiences during the Fourth of July ice-sculpture contest.

THINKING ABOUT PLOT: COMPLICATIONS

Plot is the sequence of events in a story. Usually a plot has a central conflict, or problem, that the characters struggle to resolve. In their efforts to do so, the characters must deal with *complications,* or setbacks, that make the outcome of the story uncertain.

Complications increase the suspense, or tension, that holds your interest as a reader. New hunches about how the story will end must be tested against complications as they arise. As you read "Almost a Whole Trickster," be aware of the plot complications that characters must deal with.

DID YOU KNOW?

The trickster is a character that appears in a variety of forms in folk literature all over the world. The trickster is usually clever and mischievous, and creates chaos in the lives of ordinary people. Tricksters represent the positive and negative aspects of human behavior. Most trickster tales emphasize the importance of humor.

The trickster in this story is based on a legendary Chippewa folk character, a free spirit who is a master of illusion. In other Native American tales, the Coyote, the Raven, and the Rabbit are trickster figures. Can you think of any tricksters in modern stories?

Gerald Vizenor

The trickster, popular in North American lore, is a clever character who is skilled in the art of illusion. Author Gerald Vizenor has sometimes been described as a bit of a trickster himself. He loves to play with words and to tell stories with unexpected twists and turns. A member of the Minnesota Chippewa Tribe, Vizenor often weaves Native American myths and folklore into his fiction. He is also the author of an award-winning novel, *Griever: An American Monkey King in China.*

Almost a Whole Trickster

by Gerald Vizenor

illustrated by Gary Aagaard
decorative art by Frank Steiner

Uncle Clement told me last night that he knows *almost* everything. Almost, that's his nickname and favorite word in stories, lives with me and my mother in a narrow house on the Leech Lake Chippewa Indian Reservation in northern Minnesota.

Last night, just before dark, we drove into town to meet my cousin at the bus depot and to buy rainbow ice cream in thick brown cones. Almost sat in the backseat of our old car and started his stories the minute we were on the dirt road around the north side of the lake to town. The wheels bounced and the car doors shuddered and raised thick clouds of dust. He told me about the time he almost started an ice cream store when he came back from the army. My mother laughed and turned to the side. The car rattled on the washboard road. She shouted, "I heard that one before!"

"Almost!" he shouted back.

"What almost happened?" I asked. My voice bounced with the car.

"Well, it was winter then," he said. Fine brown dust settled on his head and the shoulders of his overcoat. "Too cold for ice cream in the woods, but the idea came to mind in the summer, almost."

"Almost, you know almost everything about nothing," my mother shouted and then laughed, "or almost nothing about almost everything."

"Pincher, we're almost to the ice cream," he said, and brushed me on the head with his hard right hand. He did that to ignore what my mother said about what he knows. Clouds of dust covered the trees behind us on both sides of the road.

Almost is my great-uncle and he decides on our nicknames, even the nicknames for my cousins who live in the cities and visit the reservation in the summer. Pincher, the name he gave me, was natural because I pinched my way through childhood. I learned about the world between two fingers. I pinched everything, or *almost* everything as my uncle would say. I pinched animals, insects, leaves, water, fish, ice cream, the moist night air, winter breath, snow, and even words, the words I could see, or almost see. I pinched the words and learned how to speak sooner than my cousins. Pinched words are easier to remember. Some words, like *government* and *grammar,* are unnatural, never seen and never pinched. Who could pinch a word like grammar?

Almost named me last winter when my grandmother was sick with pneumonia and died on the way to the public health hospital. She had no teeth and covered her mouth when she smiled, almost a child. I sat in the backseat of the car and held her thin brown hand. Even her veins were

 hidden, it was so cold that night. On the road we pinched summer words over the hard snow and ice. She smiled and said *papakine, papakine,* over and over. That means cricket or grasshopper in our tribal language and we pinched that word together. We pinched *papakine* in the backseat of our cold car on the way to the hospital. Later she whispered *bisanagami sibi,* the river is still, and then she died. My mother straightened my grandmother's fingers, but later, at the wake in our house, she'd pinched a summer word and we could see that. She was buried in the cold earth with a warm word between her fingers. That's when my uncle gave me my nickname.

Almost never told lies, but he used the word *almost* to stretch the truth like a tribal trickster, my mother told me. The trickster is a character in stories, an animal, or person, even a tree at times, who pretends the world can be stopped with words, and he frees the world in stories. Almost said the trickster is almost a man and almost a woman, and almost a child, a clown, who laughs and plays games with words in stories. The trickster is almost a free spirit. Almost told me about the trickster many times, and I think I almost understand his stories. He brushed my head with his hand and said, "The *almost* world is a better world, a sweeter

dream than the world we are taught to understand in school."

"I understand, almost," I told my uncle.

"People are almost stories, and stories tell almost the whole truth," Almost told me last winter when he gave me my nickname. "Pincher is your nickname and names are stories too, *gega.*" The word *gega* means almost in the Anishinaabe or Chippewa language.

"Pincher *gega,*" I said, and then tried to pinch a tribal word I could not yet see clear enough to hold between my fingers. I could almost see *gega.*

Almost, no matter the season, wore a long dark overcoat. He bounced when he walked, and the thick bottom of the overcoat hit the ground. The sleeves were too short but he never minded that because he could eat and deal cards with no problems. So there he was in line for a rainbow ice cream cone dressed for winter, or almost winter he would say. My mother wonders if he wears that overcoat for the attention.

"*Gega, gega,*" an old woman called from the end of the line. "You spending some claims money on ice cream or a new coat?" No one ignored his overcoat.

"What's that?" answered Almost. He cupped his ear to listen because he knew the old woman wanted to move closer, ahead in the line. The claims money she mentioned is a measure of everything in the reservation. The federal government promised to settle a <u>treaty</u> over land with tribal people. Almost and thousands of others had been waiting for more than a century to be paid for land that was taken from them. There were rumors at least once a week that federal checks were in the mail, final payment for the broken treaties. When white people talk about a rain dance, tribal people remember the claims dancers who promised a federal check in every mailbox.

"Claims money," she whispered in the front of the line.

"Almost got a check this week," Almost said and smiled.

"Almost is as good as nothing," she said back.

"Pincher gets a bicycle when the claims money comes."

"My husband died waiting for the claims settlement," my mother said. She looked at me and then turned toward the ice cream counter to order. I held back my excitement about a new bicycle because the claims money might never come; no one was ever sure. Almost believed in rumors and he waited for a check to appear one morning in his mailbox on the reservation. Finally, my mother scolded him for wasting his time on promises made by the government. "You grow old too fast on government promises," she said. "Anyway, the government has nothing to do with bicycles." He smiled at me

and we ate our rainbow ice cream cones at the bus depot. That was a joke because the depot is nothing more than a park bench in front of a restaurant. On the back of the bench there was a sign that announced an ice sculpture contest to be held in the town park on July Fourth.

"Ice cube sculpture?" asked my mother.

"No blocks big enough around here in summer," I said, thinking about the ice sold to tourists, cubes and small blocks for camp coolers.

"Pig Foot, he cuts ice from the lake in winter and stores it in a cave, buried in straw," my uncle whispered. He looked around, concerned that someone might hear about the ice cave. "Secret *mikwam,* huge blocks, enough for a great sculpture." The word *mikwam* means ice.

"Never mind," my mother said as she licked the ice cream on her fingers. The rainbow turned pink when it melted. The pink ran over her hand and under her rings.

We were going to pick up my cousin, Black Ice, from the bus station.

Black Ice was late but that never bothered her because she liked to ride in the back of buses at night. She sat in the dark and pretended that she could see the people who lived under the distant lights. She lived in a dark apartment building in Saint Paul with her mother and older brother and made

treaty (trē′tē) *n.* formal agreement, especially one between nations.

the world come alive with light more than from sound or taste. She was on the reservation for more than a month last summer and we thought her nickname would be *light* or *candle* or something like that, even though she wore black clothes. Not so. Almost avoided one <u>obvious</u> name and chose another when she attended our grandmother's funeral. Black Ice had never been on the reservation in winter. She slipped and fell seven times on black ice near the church and so she got that as a nickname.

Black Ice was the last person to leave the bus. She held back, behind the darkened windows, as long as she could. Yes, she was shy, worried about being embarrassed in public. I might be that way too, if we lived in an apartment in the cities, but the only public on the reservation are the summer tourists. She was happier when we bought her a rainbow ice cream cone. She was dressed in black, black everything, even black canvas shoes, no almost black. The latest television style in the cities. Little did my uncle know that her reservation nickname would describe a modern style of clothes. We sat in the backseat on the way back to our house. We

---

obvious (ob′vē əs) *adj.* easily seen or understood.

could smell the dust in the dark, in the tunnel of light through the trees. The moon was new that night.

"Almost said he would buy me my first bicycle when he gets his claims money," I told Black Ice. She brushed her clothes, there was too much dust.

"I should've brought my new mountain bike," she said. "I don't use it much though—too much traffic and you have to worry about it being stolen."

"Should we go canoeing? We have a canoe."

"Did you get television yet?" asked Black Ice.

"Yes," I boasted, "my mother won a big screen with a dish and everything at a bingo game on the reservation." We never watched much television though.

"Really?"

"Yes, we can get more than a hundred channels."

"On the reservation?"

"Yes, and bingo too."

"Well, here we are, paradise at the end of a dust cloud," my mother announced as she turned down the trail to our house on the lake. The headlights held the eyes of animals, a raccoon, and we could smell a skunk in the distance. Low branches brushed the side of the car and whipped through the open windows. The dogs barked and ran ahead of the car; we were home. We sat in the car for a few minutes and listened to the night. The dogs were panting. Mosquitoes, so big we called them the state bird, landed on our arms, bare knuckles, and warm shoulder blades. The water was calm and seemed to hold back a secret dark blue light from the bottom of the lake. One loon called and another answered. One thin wave rippled over the stones on the shore. We ducked mosquitoes and went into the house. We were tired, and too tired in the morning to appreciate the plan to carve a trickster from a block of ice.

Pig Foot lived alone on an island. He came down to the wooden dock to meet us in the morning. We were out on the lake before dawn, my uncle at the back of the canoe in his overcoat. We paddled and he steered us around the point of the island where bald eagles nested.

"Pig Foot?" questioned Black Ice.

"Almost gave him that nickname," I whispered to my cousin as we came closer to the dock. "Watch his little feet—he prances like a pig when he talks. The people in town swear his feet are hard and cloven."

"Are they?"

"No," I whispered as the canoe touched the dock.

"Almost," shouted Pig Foot.

"Almost," said Almost. "Pincher, you know him from the funeral, and this lady is from the city; we named her Black Ice."

"*Makate Mikwam,*" said Pig Foot. "Black ice comes with the white man and roads. No black ice on the island." He tied the canoe to the dock and patted his thighs with his open hands. The words *makate mikwam* mean black ice.

Black Ice looked down at Pig Foot's feet when she stepped out of the canoe. He wore black overshoes. The toes were turned out. She watched him prance on the rough wooden dock when he talked about the weather and mosquitoes. The black flies and mosquitoes on the island, a special <u>breed</u>, were more vicious than anywhere else on the reservation. Pig Foot was pleased that no one camped on the island because of the black flies. Some people accused him of raising mean flies to keep the tourists away. "Not a bad idea, now that I think about it," said Pig Foot. He had a small bunch of black hair on his chin. He pulled the hair when he was nervous and revealed a row of short stained teeth. Black Ice turned toward the sunrise and held her laughter.

"We come to see the ice cave," said Almost. "We need a large block to win the ice sculpture contest in four days."

"What ice cave is that?" questioned Pig Foot.

"The almost secret one!" shouted Almost.

"That one, sure enough," said Pig Foot. He mocked my uncle and touched the lapel of his overcoat. "I was wondering about that contest—what does ice have to do with July Fourth?" He walked ahead as he talked and then every eight steps he would stop and turn to wait for us. But if you were too close you would bump into him when he stopped. Black Ice counted his steps and when we were near the entrance to the ice cave she imitated his prance, toes turned outward. She pranced seven steps and then waited for him to turn on the eighth.

Pig Foot stopped in silence on the shore, where the bank was higher and where several trees leaned over the water. There, in the vines and boulders we could feel the cool air. A cool breath on the shore.

Pig Foot told us we could never reveal the location of the ice cave, but he said we could tell stories about ice and the great spirit of winter in summer. He said this because most tribal stories should be told in winter, not in summer when evil spirits could be about to listen and do harm to words and names. We agreed to the conditions and followed him over the boulders into the wide, cold cave. We could hear our breath, even a heartbeat. Whispers were too loud in the cave.

"Almost the scent of winter on July Fourth," whispered Almost. "In winter we overturn the ice in shallow creeks to smell the rich blue earth, and then in summer we taste the winter in this ice cave, almost."

---

breed (brēd) *n.* particular strain or variety of a species of plant or animal, produced and maintained by controlled mating.

"Almost, you're a poet, sure enough, but that's straw, not the smell of winter," said Pig Foot. He was hunched over where the cave narrowed at the back. Beneath the mounds of straw were huge blocks of ice, lake ice, blue and silent in the cave. Was that thunder, or the crack of winter ice on the lake? "Just me, dropped a block over the side." In winter he sawed blocks of ice in the bay where it was the thickest and towed the blocks into the cave on an aluminum slide. Pig Foot used the ice to cool his cabin in summer, but Almost warned us that there were other reasons. Pig Foot believes that the world is becoming colder and colder, the ice thicker and thicker. Too much summer in the blood would weaken him, so he rests on a block of ice in the cave several hours a week to stay in condition for the coming of the ice age on the reservation.

"Black Ice, come over here," said Almost. "Stretch out on this block." My cousin brushed the straw from the ice and leaned back on the block. "Almost, almost, now try this one, no this one, almost."

"Almost what?" asked Black Ice.

"Almost a whole trickster," whispered Almost. Then he told us what he had in mind. A trickster, Almost wanted us to carve a tribal trickster to enter in the ice sculpture contest.

"What does a trickster look like?" I asked. The trickster was a word I could not see, there was nothing to pinch. How could I know a trickster between my fingers?

"Almost like a person," he said, and brushed the straw from a block as large as me. "Almost in there, we have three days to find the trickster in the ice."

Early the next morning we paddled across the lake to the ice cave to begin our work on the ice trickster. We were dressed for winter. I don't think my mother believed us when we told her about the ice cave. "Almost," she said with a smile, "finally found the right place to wear his overcoat in the summer."

Pig Foot was perched on a block of ice when we arrived. We slid the block that held the trickster to the center of the cave and set to work with an axe and chisels. We rounded out a huge head, moved down the shoulders, and on the second day we freed the nose, ears, and hands of the trickster. I could see him in the dark blue ice, the trickster was almost free. I could almost pinch the word "trickster."

Almost directed us to carve the ice on the first and second days, but on the third and final day he surprised us. We were in the cave, dressed in winter coats and hats, ready to work when he told us to make the final touches on our own, to liberate the face of the trickster. That last morning he leaned back on a block of ice with Pig Foot; we

---

liberate (lib′ə rāt′) *v.t.* set free; release.

were in charge of who the trickster would become in ice.

Black Ice wanted the trickster to look like a woman. I wanted the ice sculpture to look like a man. The trickster, we decided, would be both, one side a man and the other side a woman. The true trickster, almost a man and almost a woman.

It took us a few hours but in the end the ice trickster had features that looked like our uncle, our grandmother, and other members of our families. The trickster had small feet turned outward, he wore an overcoat, and she pinched her fingers on her female hand. He was ready for the contest—she was the ice trickster on the Fourth of July.

That same night we tied sheets around the ice trickster and towed her behind the canoe to the park on the other side of the lake. The ice floated and the trickster melted slower in the water. We rounded the south end of the island and headed to the park near the town, slow and measured like traders on a distant sea. The park lights reflected on the calm water. We tied the ice trickster to the end of the town dock and beached our canoe. We were very excited, but soon we were tired and slept on the grass in the park near the dock. The trickster was a liberator, she would win on Independence Day. Almost anyway.

"The trickster almost melted," shouted Almost the next morning. He stood on the end of the dock, a sad uncle in his overcoat, holding the rope and empty sheets. At first we thought he had tricked us, we thought the whole thing was a joke, from the beginning, so we laughed. We rolled around on the grass and laughed. Almost was not amused at first, he turned toward the lake to hide his face, but then he broke into wild laughter. He laughed so hard he almost lost his balance in that heavy overcoat. He almost fell into the lake.

"The ice trickster won the ice sculpture contest at last," said Black Ice.

"No, wait, she almost won. No ice trickster would melt that fast into the lake," he said, and ordered us to launch the canoe for a search. Overnight the trickster had slipped from the sheets and floated free from the dock, somewhere out in the lake. The ice trickster was free on July Fourth.

We paddled the canoe in circles and searched for hours and hours but we could not find the ice trickster. Later, my mother rented a motorboat and we searched in two circles.

Almost was worried about the time that the registration would close, so he abandoned the search and appealed to the people who organized the ice sculpture competition. They agreed

to extend the time and they even invited other contestants to search for the ice trickster. The lake was crowded with motorboats.

"There she floats," a woman shouted from a fishing boat. The trickster was almost submerged, only a shoulder was above water. We paddled out and towed the trickster back to the dock. Then we hauled her up the bank to the park and a <u>pedestal</u>. We circled the pedestal and admired the ice trickster.

"Almost a trickster," said Almost. We looked over the other entries. There were more birds than animals, more heads than hips or hands, and the other ice sculptures were much smaller. Dwarfs next to the ice trickster. She had melted some overnight in the lake, but he was still head and shoulders above the other entries. The competition was about to close when we learned that there was a height restriction. Almost never read the rules. No entries over three feet and six inches in any direction. The other entries were much smaller, no one found large blocks of ice in town, so they were all within the restrictions. Our trickster was four feet tall, or at least she was that tall when we started out in the ice cave.

"No trickster that started out almost he or she can be too much of either," said Almost. We nodded in

agreement but we were not certain what he meant.

"What now?" asked Black Ice.

"Get a saw," my mother ordered. "We can cut the trickster down a notch or two on the bottom." She held her hand about four inches from the base to see what a shorter trickster would look like.

"Almost short enough," said Almost. "He melted some, she needs to lose four more inches by my calculations. We should have left her in the lake for another hour."

Pig Foot turned the trickster on his side, but when we measured four inches from the bottom he protested. "Not the feet, not my feet, those are my feet on the trickster."

"Not my ear either."

"Not the hands," I pleaded.

"The shins," shouted Black Ice. No one had claimed the shins on the ice trickster so we measured and sawed four inches from his shins and then carved the knees to fit the little pig feet.

"Almost whole," announced Almost.

"What's a trickster?" asked the three judges who hurried down the line of pedestals before the ice sculptures melted beyond recognition.

"Almost a person," said Black Ice.

"What person?"

"My grandmother," I told the judges. "See how she pinched her

pedestal (ped′ə stəl) *n.* support at the base of a column or statue.

fingers, she was a trickster, she pinched a cricket there." Pig Foot was nervous; he pranced around the pedestal.

The judges prowled back and forth, whispered here and there between two pedestals, and then they decided that there would be two winners because they could not decide on one. "The winners are the Boy and His Dog, and that ice trickster, Almost a Person," the judges announced.

The ice trickster won a bicycle, a large camp cooler, a dictionary, and twelve double rainbow cones. The other ice cave sculptors gave me the bicycle because I had never owned one before, and because the claims payment might be a bad promise. We divided the cones as best we could between five people, Almost, Pig Foot, Black Ice, me, and my mother.

Later, we packed what remained of the ice trickster, including the shin part, and took him back to the ice cave, where she lasted for more than a year. She stood in the back of the cave without straw and melted down to the last drop of a trickster. She was almost a whole trickster, almost.

RESPONDING TO *Literature*

THINK • TALK • WRITE

1 Which episodes do you find most entertaining in this story? Jot some details in your journal to support your opinion.

2 Why is Uncle Clement nicknamed "Almost"? Do you think this is a good nickname for him? Explain your answer.

3 How did the characters' bad luck—the ice sculpture floating away—turn into good luck by the end of the story?

4 Why is a trickster a good subject for an ice sculpture? Explain your answer.

5 Uncle Almost brought to life many Native American traditions for Pincher. Why do you think these traditions are important to Pincher? What cultural traditions play an important role in your life?

ACTIVITIES

• **Write About Plot: Complications** Identify one of the complications in this story. Explain how this complication makes the ending of the story uncertain. List different outcomes your complication could produce and then rewrite the story's ending.

• **Draw a Trickster** Reread the description of the Chippewa trickster at the beginning of this story. Draw a picture of the trickster based on what you read and share your drawing with your classmates.

VOCABULARY PRACTICE

On a separate sheet of paper, write a vocabulary word from the list that best completes each sentence.

treaty   liberate

obvious   pedestal

breed

The new republic had fought hard to __**1**__ itself from its former ruler. Citizens destroyed the statue of the former king by tying ropes to the __**2**__ and pulling the statue over. Their anger was __**3**__. Their leaders had signed a __**4**__ which kept the old king out of the country. The leaders wanted a new __**5**__ of citizen in their republic.

BEFORE READING

TO KILL A MOCKINGBIRD

CONNECT TO LITERATURE

Can you think of someone you admire? What makes you admire this person, and why do you respect these qualities? Share your ideas with a classmate. As you read "To Kill a Mockingbird," note in your journal the qualities that Atticus has—and that Scout doesn't yet understand.

THINKING ABOUT FIRST-PERSON POINT OF VIEW

Point of view is the perspective from which a narrator tells a story. In a story told from the *first-person point of view,* the narrator is a character in the story and uses pronouns such as *I* and *me.* One result of the first-person point of view is that you see things only as the narrator sees them. You experience the story through the narrator's eyes alone. As you read "To Kill a Mockingbird," be aware of how knowing only the narrator's point of view affects your interpretation of events.

DID YOU KNOW?

This selection is an excerpt from the Pulitzer Prize-winning novel *To Kill a Mockingbird.* In the novel, Scout and Jem live with their father, Atticus, and their housekeeper, Calpurnia. When Atticus, a lawyer, takes on an unpopular case, Scout fights to defend his reputation. Hearing this, Atticus forbids Scout to fight anymore.

If you had been a neighbor of the characters in this story, you would have lived in a small town in Alabama in the 1930s. At that time the South was primarily an agricultural area; most people lived on farms or in small towns rather than in large cities. It was also a time of racial segregation, which means that African Americans and whites were expected to go to separate schools and use separate public facilities, including restaurants, rest-rooms, and transportation.

Photographs from the 1962 Universal Studios production of *To Kill a Mockingbird*, with Gregory Peck, Mary Badham, Phillip Alford, and Estelle Evans, based on the novel by Harper Lee.

To Kill a Mockingbird

by Harper Lee

Jean Louise Finch, nicknamed Scout, and her older brother, Jem, live with their father, Atticus, in a small southern town during the 1930s. Their mother has died, and Calpurnia, the family's housekeeper, cares for them. Atticus, a lawyer, has chosen to defend Tom Robinson, a black man unfairly accused of committing a crime against a white woman. Many people disapprove of Atticus's defense of Robinson. Hearing that Scout has gotten into several scraps with schoolmates in order to defend his reputation, Atticus has forbidden Scout to fight anymore.

Atticus was <u>feeble</u>: he was nearly fifty. When Jem and I asked him why he was so old, he said he got started late, which we felt reflected upon his abilities and manliness. He was much older than the parents of our school <u>contemporaries</u>, and there was nothing Jem or I could say about him when our classmates said, "*My* father—"

Jem was football crazy. Atticus was never too tired to play keep-away, but when Jem wanted to tackle him Atticus would say, "I'm too old for that, son."

Our father didn't do anything. He worked in an office, not in a drugstore. Atticus did not drive a dump-truck for the county, he was not the sheriff, he did not farm, work in a garage, or do

---

feeble (fē′bəl) *adj.* lacking physical strength.
contemporaries (kən tem′pə rer′ēz) *n., pl.* people who belong to or live at the same time as another or others.

anything that could possibly arouse the admiration of anyone.

Besides that, he wore glasses. He was nearly blind in his left eye, and said left eyes were the tribal curse of the Finches. Whenever he wanted to see something well, he turned his head and looked from his right eye.

He did not do the things our schoolmates' fathers did: he never went hunting, he did not play poker or fish or drink or smoke. He sat in the livingroom and read.

With these attributes, however, he would not remain as <u>inconspicuous</u> as we wished him to: that year, the school buzzed with talk about him defending Tom Robinson, none of which was complimentary. After my bout with Cecil Jacobs when I committed myself to a policy of cowardice, word got around that Scout Finch wouldn't fight any more, her daddy wouldn't let her. This was not entirely correct: I wouldn't fight publicly for Atticus, but the family was private ground. I would fight anyone from a third cousin upwards tooth and nail. Francis Hancock, for example, knew that.

When he gave us our air-rifles Atticus wouldn't teach us to shoot. Uncle Jack instructed us in the <u>rudiments</u> thereof; he said Atticus wasn't interested in guns. Atticus said to Jem one day, "I'd rather you shot at tin cans in the back yard, but I know you'll go after birds. Shoot all the bluejays you want, if you can hit 'em, but remember it's a sin to kill a mockingbird."

---

inconspicuous (in'kən spik'ū əs) *adj.* not easily seen.
rudiments (rü'də mənts) *n., pl.* basic principles.

That was the only time I ever heard Atticus say it was a sin to do something, and I asked Miss Maudie about it.

"Your father's right," she said. "Mockingbirds don't do one thing but make music for us to enjoy. They don't eat up people's gardens, don't nest in corncribs, they don't do one thing but sing their hearts out for us. That's why it's a sin to kill a mockingbird."

"Miss Maudie, this is an old neighborhood, ain't it?"

"Been here longer than the town."

"Nome, I mean the folks on our street are all old. Jem and me's the only children around here. Mrs. Dubose is close on to a hundred and Miss Rachel's old and so are you and Atticus."

"I don't call fifty very old," said Miss Maudie tartly. "Not being wheeled around yet, am I? Neither's your father. But I must say Providence was kind enough to burn down that old mausoleum of mine, I'm too old to keep it up—maybe you're right, Jean Louise, this is a settled neighborhood. You've never been around young folks much, have you?"

"Yessum, at school."

"I mean young grown-ups. You're lucky, you know. You and Jem have the benefit of your father's age. If your father was thirty you'd find life quite different."

"I sure would. Atticus can't do anything. . . ."

"You'd be surprised," said Miss Maudie. "There's life in him yet."

He did not do the things our schoolmates' fathers did: he never went hunting, he did not play poker or fish or drink or smoke. He sat in the living-room and read.

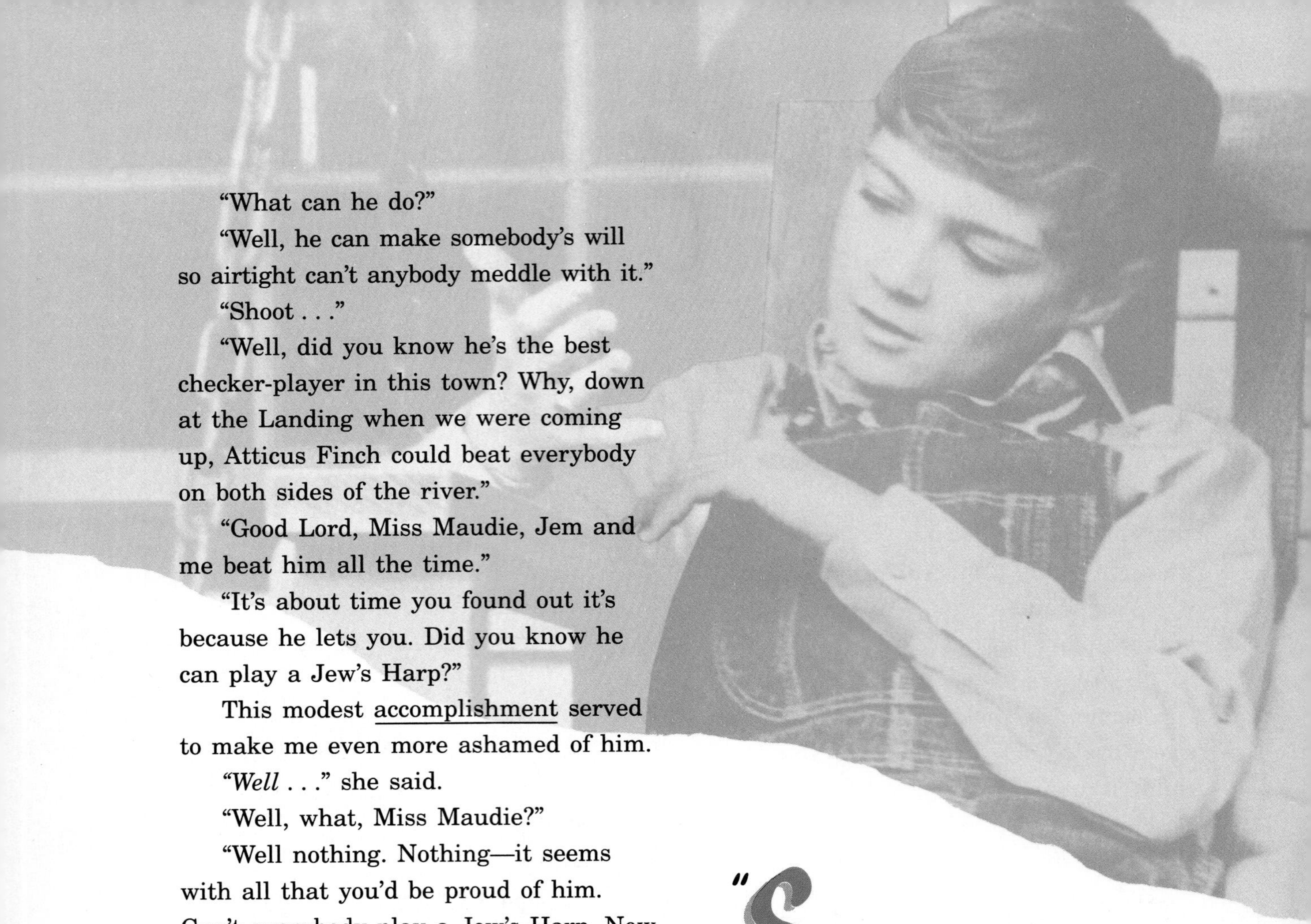

"What can he do?"

"Well, he can make somebody's will so airtight can't anybody meddle with it."

"Shoot . . ."

"Well, did you know he's the best checker-player in this town? Why, down at the Landing when we were coming up, Atticus Finch could beat everybody on both sides of the river."

"Good Lord, Miss Maudie, Jem and me beat him all the time."

"It's about time you found out it's because he lets you. Did you know he can play a Jew's Harp?"

This modest <u>accomplishment</u> served to make me even more ashamed of him.

"*Well . . .*" she said.

"Well, what, Miss Maudie?"

"Well nothing. Nothing—it seems with all that you'd be proud of him. Can't everybody play a Jew's Harp. Now keep out of the way of the carpenters. You'd better go home, I'll be in my azaleas and can't watch you. Plank might hit you."

I went to the back yard and found Jem plugging away at a tin can, which seemed stupid with all the bluejays around. I returned to the front yard and busied myself for two hours erecting a complicated breastworks at the side of the porch, consisting of a tire, an orange crate, the laundry hamper, the porch chairs, and a small U.S. flag Jem gave me from a popcorn box.

When Atticus came home to dinner he found me crouched down aiming across the street. "What are you shooting at?"

"Shoot all the bluejays you want, if you can hit 'em, but remember it's a sin to kill a mockingbird."

---

accomplishment (ə kom'plish mənt) *n.* something done successfully; achievement.

"Miss Maudie's rear end."

Atticus turned and saw my generous target bending over her bushes. He pushed his hat to the back of his head and crossed the street. "Maudie," he called, "I thought I'd better warn you. You're in considerable peril."

Miss Maudie straightened up and looked toward me. She said, "Atticus, you are a devil from hell."

When Atticus returned he told me to break camp. "Don't you ever let me catch you pointing that gun at anybody again," he said.

I wished my father was a devil from hell. I sounded out Calpurnia on the subject. "Mr. Finch? Why, he can do lots of things."

"Like what?" I asked.

Calpurnia scratched her head. "Well, I don't rightly know," she said.

Jem underlined it when he asked Atticus if he was going out for the Methodists and Atticus said he'd break his neck if he did, he was just too old for that sort of thing. The Methodists were trying to pay off their church mortgage, and had challenged the Baptists to a game of touch football. Everybody in town's father was playing, it seemed, except Atticus. Jem said he didn't even want to go, but he was unable to resist football in any form, and he stood gloomily on the sidelines with Atticus and me watching Cecil Jacobs's father make touchdowns for the Baptists.

One Saturday Jem and I decided to go exploring with our air-rifles to see if we could find a rabbit or a squirrel. We had gone about five hundred yards beyond the Radley Place when I noticed Jem squinting at something down the street. He had turned his head to one side and was looking out of the corners of his eyes.

"Whatcha looking at?"

"That old dog down yonder," he said.

"That's old Tim Johnson, ain't it?"

"Yeah."

Tim Johnson was the property of Mr. Harry Johnson who drove the Mobile bus and lived on the southern edge of town. Tim was a liver-colored bird dog, the pet of Maycomb.

"What's he doing?"

"I don't know, Scout. We better go home."

"Aw Jem, it's February."

"I don't care, I'm gonna tell Cal."

We raced home and ran to the kitchen.

"Cal," said Jem, "can you come down the sidewalk a minute?"

"What for, Jem? I can't come down the sidewalk every time you want me."

"There's somethin' wrong with an old dog down yonder."

Calpurnia sighed. "I can't wrap up any dog's foot now. There's some gauze in the bathroom, go get it and do it yourself."

Jem shook his head. "He's sick, Cal. Something's wrong with him."

"What's he doin', trying to catch his tail?"

"No, he's doin' like this."

Jem gulped like a goldfish, hunched his shoulders and twitched his torso. "He's goin' like that, only not like he means to."

"Are you telling me a story, Jem Finch?" Calpurnia's voice hardened.

"No Cal, I swear I'm not."

"Was he runnin'?"

"No, he's just moseyin' along, so slow you can't hardly tell it. He's comin' this way."

Calpurnia rinsed her hands and followed Jem into the yard. "I don't see any dog," she said.

She followed us beyond the Radley Place and looked where Jem pointed. Tim Johnson was not much more than a speck in the distance, but he was closer to us. He walked <u>erratically</u>, as if his right legs were shorter than his left legs. He reminded me of a car stuck in a sandbed.

"He's gone lopsided," said Jem.

Calpurnia stared, then grabbed us by the shoulders and ran us home. She shut the wood door behind us, went to the telephone and shouted, "Gimme Mr. Finch's office!"

"Mr. Finch!" she shouted. "This is Cal. I swear to God there's a mad dog down the street a piece—he's comin' this way, yes sir, he's—Mr. Finch, I declare he is—old Tim Johnson, yes sir . . . yessir . . . yes—"

She hung up and shook her head when we tried to ask her what Atticus had said. She rattled the telephone hook and said, "Miss Eula May—now ma'am, I'm through talkin' to Mr. Finch, please don't connect me no more—listen, Miss Eula May, can you call Miss Rachel and Miss Stephanie Crawford and whoever's got a phone on this street and tell 'em a mad dog's comin'? Please ma'am!"

Calpurnia listened. "I know it's February, Miss Eula May, but I know a mad dog when I see one. Please ma'am hurry!"

Calpurnia asked Jem, "Radleys got a phone?"

Jem looked in the book and said no. "They won't come out anyway, Cal."

"I don't care, I'm gonna tell 'em."

She ran to the front porch, Jem and I at her heels. "You stay in that house!" she yelled.

Calpurnia's message had been received by the neighborhood. Every wood door within our range of vision was closed tight. We saw no trace of Tim Johnson. We watched Calpurnia running toward the Radley Place, holding her skirt and apron above her knees. She went up to the front steps and banged on the door. She got no answer, and she shouted, "Mr. Nathan, Mr. Arthur, mad dog's comin'! Mad dog's comin'!"

"She's supposed to go around in back," I said.

Jem shook his head. "Don't make any difference now," he said.

Calpurnia pounded on the door in vain. No one acknowledged her

---

erratically (i rat′i kəl lē) *adv.* acting or moving in an irregular or confused way.

warning; no one seemed to have heard it.

As Calpurnia sprinted to the back porch a black Ford swung into the driveway. Atticus and Mr. Heck Tate got out.

Mr. Heck Tate was the sheriff of Maycomb County. He was as tall as Atticus, but thinner. He was long-nosed, wore boots with shiny metal eye-holes, boot pants and a lumber jacket. His belt had a row of bullets sticking in it. He carried a heavy rifle. When he and Atticus reached the porch, Jem opened the door.

"Stay inside, son," said Atticus. "Where is he, Cal?"

"He oughta be here by now," said Calpurnia, pointing down the street.

"Not runnin', is he?" asked Mr. Tate.

"Naw sir, he's in the twitchin' stage, Mr. Heck."

"Should we go after him, Heck?" asked Atticus.

"We better wait, Mr. Finch. They usually go in a straight line, but you never can tell. He might follow the curve—hope he does or he'll go straight in the Radley back yard. Let's wait a minute."

"Don't think he'll get in the Radley yard," said Atticus. "Fence'll stop him. He'll probably follow the road. . . ."

I thought mad dogs foamed at the mouth, galloped, leaped and lunged at throats, and I thought they did it in August. Had Tim Johnson behaved thus, I would have been less frightened.

Nothing is more deadly than a deserted, waiting street. The trees were still, the mockingbirds were silent, the carpenters at Miss Maudie's house had vanished. I heard Mr. Tate sniff, then blow his nose. I saw him shift his gun to the crook of his arm. I saw Miss Stephanie Crawford's face framed in the glass window of her front door. Miss Maudie appeared and stood beside her. Atticus put his foot on the rung of a chair and rubbed his hand slowly down the side of his thigh.

"There he is," he said softly.

Tim Johnson came into sight, walking dazedly in the inner rim of the curve parallel to the Radley house.

"Look at him," whispered Jem. "Mr. Heck said they walked in a straight line. He can't even stay in the road."

"He looks more sick than anything," I said.

"Let anything get in front of him and he'll come straight at it."

Mr. Tate put his hand to his forehead and leaned forward. "He's got it all right, Mr. Finch."

Tim Johnson was advancing at a snail's pace, but he was not playing or sniffing at foliage: he seemed dedicated to one course and <u>motivated</u> by an invisible force that was inching him toward us. We could see him shiver like a horse shedding flies; his jaw opened and shut; he was alist, but he was being pulled gradually toward us.

---

motivated (mō′tə vā′tid) *v.t.* moved to effort or action as a result of a mental state, inner need, or outward goal.

"He's lookin' for a place to die," said Jem.

Mr. Tate turned around. "He's far from dead, Jem, he hasn't got started yet."

Tim Johnson reached the side street that ran in front of the Radley Place, and what remained of his poor mind made him pause and seem to consider which road he would take. He made a few hesitant steps and stopped in front of the Radley gate; then he tried to turn around, but was having difficulty.

Atticus said, "He's within range, Heck. You better get him before he goes down the side street—Lord knows who's around the corner. Go inside, Cal."

Calpurnia opened the screen door, latched it behind her, then unlatched it and held onto the hook. She tried to block Jem and me with her body, but we looked out from beneath her arms.

"Take him, Mr. Finch." Mr. Tate handed the rifle to Atticus; Jem and I nearly fainted.

"Don't waste time, Heck," said Atticus. "Go on."

"Mr. Finch, this is a one-shot job."

Atticus shook his head <u>vehemently</u>: "Don't just stand there, Heck! He won't wait all day for you—"

"For God's sake, Mr. Finch, look where he is! Miss and you'll go straight into the Radley house! I can't shoot that well and you know it!"

"I haven't shot a gun in thirty years—"

Mr. Tate almost threw the rifle at Atticus. "I'd feel mighty comfortable if you did now," he said.

---

vehemently (vē′ə mənt lē) *adv.* showing or characterized by intensity of feeling; passionately.

In a fog, Jem and I watched our father take the gun and walk out into the middle of the street. He walked quickly, but I thought he moved like an underwater swimmer: time had slowed to a nauseating crawl.

When Atticus raised his glasses Calpurnia murmured, "Sweet Jesus help him," and put her hands to her cheeks.

Atticus pushed his glasses to his forehead; they slipped down, and he dropped them in the street. In the silence, I heard them crack. Atticus rubbed his eyes and chin; we saw him blink hard.

In front of the Radley gate, Tim Johnson had made up what was left of his mind. He had finally turned himself around, to pursue his original course up our street. He made two steps forward, then stopped and raised his head. We saw his body go rigid.

With movements so swift they seemed <u>simultaneous</u>, Atticus's hand yanked a ball-tipped lever as he brought the gun to his shoulder.

The rifle cracked. Tim Johnson leaped, flopped over and crumpled on the sidewalk in a brown-and-white heap. He didn't know what hit him.

Mr. Tate jumped off the porch and ran to the Radley Place. He stopped in front of the dog, squatted, turned around and tapped his finger on his forehead above his left eye. "You were a little to the right, Mr. Finch," he called.

"Always was," answered Atticus. "If I had my 'druthers I'd take a shotgun."

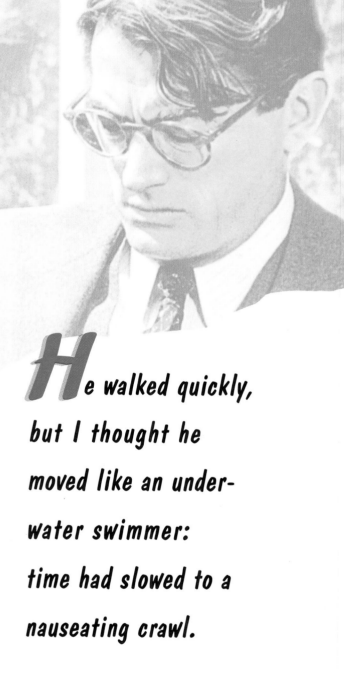

He walked quickly, but I thought he moved like an underwater swimmer: time had slowed to a nauseating crawl.

---

simultaneous (sī′məl tā′nē əs) *adj.* existing, happening, or done at the same time.

He stooped and picked up his glasses, ground the broken lenses to powder under his heel, and went to Mr. Tate and stood looking down at Tim Johnson.

Doors opened one by one, and the neighborhood slowly came alive. Miss Maudie walked down the steps with Miss Stephanie Crawford.

Jem was paralyzed. I pinched him to get him moving, but when Atticus saw us coming he called, "Stay where you are."

When Mr. Tate and Atticus returned to the yard, Mr. Tate was smiling. "I'll have Zeebo collect him," he said. "You haven't forgot much, Mr. Finch. They say it never leaves you."

Atticus was silent.

"Atticus?" said Jem.

"Yes?"

"Nothin'."

"I saw that, One-Shot Finch!"

Atticus wheeled around and faced Miss Maudie. They looked at one another without saying anything, and Atticus got into the sheriff's car. "Come here," he said to Jem. "Don't you go near that dog, you understand? Don't go near him, he's just as dangerous dead as alive."

"Yes sir," said Jem. "Atticus—"

"What, son?"

"Nothing."

"What's the matter with you, boy, can't you talk?" said Mr. Tate, grinning at Jem. "Didn't you know your daddy's—"

"Hush, Heck," said Atticus, "let's go back to town."

When they drove away, Jem and I went to Miss Stephanie's front steps. We sat waiting for Zeebo to arrive in the garbage truck.

Jem sat in numb confusion, and Miss Stephanie said, "Uh, uh, uh, who'da thought of a mad dog in February? Maybe he wadn't mad, maybe he was just crazy. I'd hate to see Harry Johnson's face when he gets in from the Mobile run and finds Atticus Finch's shot his dog. Bet he was just full of fleas from somewhere—"

Miss Maudie said Miss Stephanie'd be singing a different tune if Tim Johnson was still coming up the street, that they'd find out soon enough, they'd send his head to Montgomery.

Jem became vaguely articulate: "'d you see him, Scout? 'd you see him just standin' there? . . . 'n' all of a sudden he just relaxed all over, an' it looked like that gun was a part of him . . . an' he did it so quick, like . . . I hafta aim for ten minutes 'fore I can hit somethin'. . . ."

Miss Maudie grinned wickedly. "Well now, Miss Jean Louise," she said, "still think your father can't do anything? Still ashamed of him?"

"Nome," I said meekly.

"Forgot to tell you the other day that besides playing the Jew's Harp, Atticus Finch was the deadest shot in Maycomb County in his time."

"Dead shot . . ." echoed Jem.

---

vaguely (vāg′lē) *adv.* not definitely or clearly expressed.

articulate (är tik′yə lit) *adj.* spoken clearly in distinct syllables and words.

"That's what I said, Jem Finch. Guess you'll change *your* tune now. The very idea, didn't you know his nickname was Ol' One-Shot when he was a boy? Why, down at the Landing when he was coming up, if he shot fifteen times and hit fourteen doves he'd complain about wasting ammunition."

"He never said anything about that," Jem muttered.

"Never said anything about it, did he?"

"No ma'am."

"Wonder why he never goes huntin' now," I said.

"Maybe I can tell you," said Miss Maudie. "If your father's anything, he's <u>civilized</u> in his heart. Marksmanship's a gift of God, a talent—oh, you have to practice to make it perfect, but shootin's different from playing the piano or the like. I think maybe he put his gun down when he realized that God had given him an unfair advantage over most living things. I guess he decided he wouldn't shoot till he had to, and he had to today."

"Looks like he'd be proud of it," I said.

"People in their right minds never take pride in their talents," said Miss Maudie.

We saw Zeebo drive up. He took a pitchfork from the back of the garbage truck and gingerly lifted Tim Johnson. He pitched the dog onto the truck, then poured something from a gallon jug on and around the spot where Tim fell.

"*I*f your father's anything, he's civilized in his heart."

civilized (siv′ə līzd) *adj.* brought out of a primitive or savage state or condition.

"Don't yawl come over here for a while," he called.

When we went home I told Jem we'd really have something to talk about at school on Monday. Jem turned on me.

"Don't say anything about it, Scout," he said.

"What? I certainly am. Ain't everybody's daddy the deadest shot in Maycomb County."

Jem said, "I reckon if he'd wanted us to know it, he'da told us. If he was proud of it, he'da told us."

"Maybe it just slipped his mind," I said.

"Naw, Scout, it's something you wouldn't understand. Atticus is real old, but I wouldn't care if he couldn't do anything—I wouldn't care if he couldn't do a blessed thing."

Jem picked up a rock and threw it jubilantly at the carhouse. Running after it, he called back: "Atticus is a gentleman, just like me!"

Meet Harper Lee

Harper Lee believed in the old saying that "slow and steady wins the race." While writing *To Kill a Mockingbird,* she completed only a page or two each day. Then she spent more than two years carefully revising it until every sentence sounded just right.

Lee had not originally intended to be a writer. Influenced by her father, a small-town lawyer, she went to law school at a time when very few women pursued law careers. She never completed her degree, but she used her law school experiences as she wrote her novel. Her father became the model for Atticus Finch.

After writing *To Kill a Mockingbird,* Lee never published another work of fiction. But her literary reputation is nevertheless assured. For more than thirty years, her novel has enthralled readers around the world. First published in 1960, it became an instant bestseller. The following year, it received the Pulitzer Prize for Literature. It has been translated into ten languages, and the film based on the novel won three Academy Awards.

RESPONDING TO *Literature*

THINK • TALK • WRITE

1 Would you like to read the rest of this novel? Why or why not? Jot down some ideas in your journal.

2 What does Scout think of Atticus at the beginning of the story? Do you think it is hard or easy on a child to have a parent like Atticus as Scout describes him? Give reasons for your answer.

3 What does Scout hope to discover about Atticus from Miss Maudie and Calpurnia?

4 What effect does Atticus's shooting of the dog have on Jem?

5 How do Jem and Scout differ about what to do with their newfound knowledge of Atticus's marksmanship? With whose position do you agree? Explain your answer.

ACTIVITIES

● **Write About First-Person Point of View** Imagine that you are Scout and write a letter to a friend in another town about the incident with the rabid dog.

● **Make a Collage** Make a collage that shows Atticus's personality. You may use pictures from magazines, newspapers, or any other sources you think of.

VOCABULARY PRACTICE

On a separate sheet of paper, write the vocabulary word that is the best substitute for the italicized word or phrase in each sentence.

contemporaries	motivated
inconspicuous	vehemently
rudiments	simultaneous
accomplishment	articulate
erratically	civilized

1 Jem knew only the *basics* of using a gun.

2 Atticus was a very *refined* and considerate person.

3 Scout argued *forcefully* with Atticus about her ideas.

4 Atticus was the most *well-spoken* lawyer in his town.

5 Atticus embarrassed Scout in front of her *friends of the same age.*

6 Jem was not *moved* to tell anyone that Atticus was a good marksman.

7 Being a good lawyer was Atticus's greatest *achievement.*

8 Atticus was not as *unnoticed* as Scout wished he were.

9 Atticus's shot and the dog's death seemed like they were *happening at the same time.*

10 The rabid dog was moving *irregularly.*

BEFORE READING

THE JOY LUCK CLUB

CONNECT TO LITERATURE

Do you have a skill or a talent? Did you practice a great deal to develop your skill? How does your family feel about your skill? Share your ideas with a classmate. As you read "The Joy Luck Club," note in your journal the ways that Meimei's skill in chess changes her life and her family's life.

THINKING ABOUT PROTAGONIST/ANTAGONIST

The main character of a story is called the *protagonist*. This character is often opposed by another character, called the *antagonist*. Usually the protagonist and antagonist struggle over some problem, and it is this struggle that is the central conflict of the story. Identify the protagonist and antagonist as you read "The Joy Luck Club." How do they resolve their problems?

DID YOU KNOW?

In this excerpt from the novel *The Joy Luck Club,* Amy Tan describes life as a girl in a Chinese American family living in Chinatown.

In the traditional Chinese family structure, allegiance to and respect for one's parents were the most important duties. Children were expected to give way to all of their parents' wishes. Parents even selected husbands and wives for their children.

Traditional Chinese society was based on the teachings of a Chinese philosopher named Kung Fu Tzu, more often called Confucius (551–478 B.C.). For thousands of years, Confucian principles ruled China. Confucianism teaches that each person must play his or her proper role in society, often sacrificing individual needs for the good of the group. Many Confucian ideas were brought to the United States by Chinese immigrants.

THE
JOY
LUCK
CLUB

by Amy Tan

illustrations by
Winson Trang

I was six when my mother taught me the art of invisible strength. It was a strategy for winning arguments, respect from others, and eventually, though neither of us knew it at the time, chess games.

"Bite back your tongue," scolded my mother when I cried loudly, yanking her hand toward the store that sold bags of salted plums. At home, she said, "Wise guy, he not go against wind. In Chinese we say, Come from South, blow with wind—poom!—North will follow. Strongest wind cannot be seen."

The next week I bit back my tongue as we entered the store with the forbidden candies. When my mother finished her shopping, she quietly plucked a small bag of plums from the rack and put it on the counter with the rest of the items.

My mother <u>imparted</u> her daily truths so she could help my older brothers and me rise above our circumstances. We lived in San Francisco's Chinatown. Like most of the other Chinese children who played in the back alleys of restaurants and curio shops, I didn't think we were poor. My bowl was always full, three five-course meals every day, beginning with a soup full of mysterious things I didn't want to know the names of.

We lived on Waverly Place, in a warm, clean, two-bedroom flat that sat above a small Chinese bakery specializing in steamed pastries and <u>dim sum</u>. In the early morning, when the alley was still quiet, I could smell fragrant red beans as they were cooked down to a pasty sweetness. By daybreak, our flat was heavy with the odor of fried sesame balls and sweet curried chicken crescents. From my bed, I would listen as my father got ready for work, then locked the door behind him, one-two-three clicks.

At the end of our two-block alley was a small sandlot playground with swings and slides well-shined down the middle with use. The play area was bordered by wood-slat benches where old-country people sat cracking roasted watermelon seeds with their golden teeth and scattering the husks to an impatient gathering of gurgling pigeons. The best playground, however, was the dark alley itself. It was crammed with daily mysteries and adventures. My brothers and I would peer into

---

imparted (im pär'tid) *v.t.* made known; told.

dim sum (dim'sum') *n.* dish in Chinese cooking, consisting usually of steamed or fried dumplings stuffed with meats, fish, or vegetables.

the medicinal herb shop, watching old Li dole out onto a stiff sheet of white paper the right amount of insect shells, saffron-colored seeds, and pungent leaves for his ailing customers. It was said that he once cured a woman dying of an ancestral curse that had <u>eluded</u> the best of American doctors. Next to the pharmacy was a printer who specialized in gold-embossed wedding invitations and festive red banners.

Farther down the street was Ping Yuen Fish Market. The front window displayed a tank crowded with doomed fish and turtles struggling to gain footing on the slimy green-tiled sides. A hand-written sign informed tourists, "Within this store, is all for food, not for pet." Inside, the butchers with their blood-stained white smocks deftly gutted the fish while customers cried out their orders and shouted, "Give me your freshest," to which the butchers always protested, "All are freshest." On less crowded market days, we would inspect the crates of live frogs and crabs which we were warned not to poke, boxes of dried cuttlefish, and row upon row of iced prawns, squid, and slippery fish. The sanddabs made me shiver each time; their eyes lay on one flattened side and reminded me of my mother's story of a careless girl who ran into a crowded street and was crushed by a cab. "Was smash flat," reported my mother.

At the corner of the alley was Hong Sing's, a four-table café with a <u>recessed</u> stairwell in front that led to a door marked "Tradesmen." My brothers and I believed the bad people emerged from this door at night. Tourists never went to Hong Sing's, since the menu was printed only in Chinese. A Caucasian man with a big camera once posed me and my playmates in front of the restaurant. He had us move to the side of the picture window so the photo would capture the roasted duck with its head dangling from a juice-covered rope. After he took the picture, I told him he should go into Hong Sing's and eat dinner. When he smiled and asked me what they served, I shouted, "Guts and duck's feet and octopus

eluded (i lü′did) *v.t.* avoided or escaped, as by cleverness or trickery; evaded.
recessed (rē′sesd) *adj.* set back or indented from the rest.

gizzards!" Then I ran off with my friends, shrieking with laughter as we scampered across the alley and hid in the entryway grotto of the China Gem Company, my heart pounding with hope that he would chase us.

My mother named me after the street that we lived on: Waverly Place Jong, my official name for important American documents. But my family called me Meimei, "Little Sister." I was the youngest, the only daughter. Each morning before school, my mother would twist and yank on my thick black hair until she had formed two tightly wound pigtails. One day, as she struggled to weave a hard-toothed comb through my disobedient hair, I had a sly thought.

I asked her, "Ma, what is Chinese torture?" My mother shook her head. A bobby pin was wedged between her lips. She wetted her palm and smoothed the hair above my ear, then pushed the pin in so that it nicked sharply against my scalp.

"Who say this word?" she asked without a trace of knowing how wicked I was being. I shrugged my shoulders and said, "Some boy in my class said Chinese people do Chinese torture."

"Chinese people do many things," she said simply. "Chinese people do business, do medicine, do painting. Not lazy like American people. We do torture. Best torture."

My older brother Vincent was the one who actually got the chess set. We had gone to the annual Christmas party held at the First Chinese Baptist Church at the end of the alley. The missionary ladies had put together a Santa bag of gifts donated by members of another church. None of the gifts had names on them. There were separate sacks for boys and girls of different ages.

One of the Chinese parishioners had donned a Santa Claus costume and a stiff paper beard with cotton balls glued to it. I think the only children who thought he was the real thing were too young to know that Santa Claus was not Chinese. When my turn came up, the Santa man asked me how old I was. I thought it was a trick question; I was seven according to the American formula and eight by the Chinese calendar. I said I was born on March 17, 1951. That seemed to satisfy him. He then solemnly asked if I had been a very, very good girl this year and did I believe in Jesus Christ and obey my parents. I knew the only answer to that. I nodded back with equal solemnity.

Having watched the other children opening their gifts, I already knew that the big gifts were not necessarily the nicest ones. One girl my age got a large coloring book of biblical characters, while a less greedy girl who selected a smaller box received a glass vial of lavender toilet water. The sound of the box was also important. A ten-year-old boy had chosen a box that jangled when he shook it. It was a tin globe of the world with a slit for inserting money. He must have thought it was full of dimes and nickels, because when he saw that it had just ten pennies, his face fell with such undisguised disappointment that his mother slapped the side of his head and led him out of the church hall, apologizing to the crowd for her son who had such bad manners he couldn't appreciate such a fine gift.

As I peered into the sack, I quickly fingered the remaining presents, testing their weight, imagining what they contained. I chose a heavy, compact one that was wrapped in shiny silver foil and a red satin ribbon. It was a twelve-pack of Life Savers and I spent the rest of the party arranging and rearranging the candy tubes in the order of my favorites. My brother Winston

chose wisely as well. His present turned out to be a box of intricate plastic parts; the instructions on the box proclaimed that when they were properly assembled he would have an authentic miniature replica of a World War II submarine.

Vincent got the chess set, which would have been a very decent present to get at a church Christmas party, except it was obviously used and, as we discovered later, it was missing a black pawn and a white knight. My mother graciously thanked the unknown benefactor, saying, "Too good. Cost too much." At which point, an old lady with fine white, wispy hair nodded toward our family and said with a whistling whisper, "Merry, merry Christmas."

When we got home, my mother told Vincent to throw the chess set away. "She not want it. We not want it," she said, tossing her head stiffly to the side with a tight, proud smile. My brothers had deaf ears. They were already lining up the chess pieces and reading from the dog-eared instruction book.

I watched Vincent and Winston play during Christmas week. The chess board seemed to hold elaborate secrets waiting to be untangled. The chessmen were more powerful than Old Li's magic herbs that cured ancestral curses. And my brothers wore such serious faces that I was sure something was at stake that was greater than avoiding the tradesmen's door to Hong Sing's.

"Let me! Let me!" I begged between games when one brother or the other would sit back with a deep sigh of relief and victory, the other annoyed, unable to let go of the outcome. Vincent at first refused to let me play, but when I offered my Life Savers as replacements for the buttons that filled in for the missing pieces, he relented. He chose the flavors: wild cherry for the black pawn and peppermint for the white knight. Winner could eat both.

As our mother sprinkled flour and rolled out small doughy circles for the steamed dumplings that would be our dinner that night, Vincent explained the rules, pointing to each piece. "You have sixteen pieces and so do I. One king and queen, two bishops, two knights, two castles, and eight pawns. The pawns can only move forward one step, except on the first move. Then they can move two. But they can only take men by moving crossways like this, except in the beginning, when you can move ahead and take another pawn."

"Why?" I asked as I moved my pawn. "Why can't they move more steps?"

"Because they're pawns," he said.

"But why do they go crossways to take other men. Why aren't there any women and children?"

"Why is the sky blue? Why must you always ask stupid questions?" asked Vincent. "This is a game. These are the rules. I didn't make them up. See. Here. In the book." He jabbed a page with a pawn in his hand. "Pawn. P-A-W-N. Pawn. Read it yourself."

My mother patted the flour off her hands. "Let me see book," she said quietly. She scanned the pages quickly, not reading the foreign English symbols, seeming to search deliberately for nothing in particular.

"This American rules," she concluded at last. "Every time people come out from foreign country, must know rules. You not know, judge say, Too bad, go back. They not telling you why so you can use their way go forward. They say, Don't know why, you find out yourself. But they knowing all the time. Better you take it, find out why yourself." She tossed her head back with a satisfied smile.

I found out about all the whys later. I read the rules and looked up all the big words in a dictionary. I borrowed books from the Chinatown library. I studied each chess piece, trying to absorb the power each contained.

I learned about opening moves and why it's important to control the center early on; the shortest distance between two points is straight down the middle. I learned about the middle game and why tactics between two <u>adversaries</u> are like clashing ideas; the one who plays better has the clearest plans for

---

adversaries (ad′vər ser′ēz) *n., pl.* groups that are hostile toward or competing with each other; opponents or enemies.

both attacking and getting out of traps. I learned why it is essential in the endgame to have foresight, a mathematical understanding of all possible moves, and patience; all weaknesses and advantages become evident to a strong adversary and are obscured to a tiring opponent. I discovered that for the whole game one must gather invisible strengths and see the endgame before the game begins.

I also found out why I should never reveal "why" to others. A little knowledge withheld is a great advantage one should store for future use. That is the power of chess. It is a game of secrets in which one must show and never tell.

I loved the secrets I found within the sixty-four black and white squares. I carefully drew a handmade chessboard and pinned it to the wall next to my bed, where at night I would stare for hours at imaginary battles. Soon I no longer lost any games or Life Savers, but I lost my adversaries. Winston and Vincent decided they were more interested in roaming the streets after school in their Hopalong Cassidy cowboy hats.

On a cold spring afternoon, while walking home from school, I detoured through the playground at the end of our alley. I saw a group of old men, two seated across a folding table playing a game of chess, others smoking pipes, eating peanuts, and watching. I ran home and grabbed Vincent's chess set, which was bound in a cardboard box with rubber bands. I also carefully selected two prized rolls of Life Savers. I came back to the park and approached a man who was observing the game.

"Want to play?" I asked him. His face widened with surprise and he grinned as he looked at the box under my arm.

"Little sister, been a long time since I play with dolls," he said, smiling benevolently. I quickly put the box down next to him on the bench and displayed my retort.

Lau Po, as he allowed me to call him, turned out to be a much better player than my brothers. I lost many games and many Life Savers. But over the weeks, with each diminishing roll of candies, I added new secrets. Lau Po gave me the names. The Double Attack from the East and West Shores. Throwing Stones on the Drowning Man. The Sudden Meeting

---

evident (ev′i dənt) *adj.* easily seen or understood; clear.

obscured (əb skyůrd′) *v.t.* made difficult to understand.

of the Clan. The Surprise from the Sleeping Guard. The Humble Servant Who Kills the King. Sand in the Eyes of Advancing Forces. A Double Killing Without Blood.

There were also the fine points of chess <u>etiquette</u>. Keep captured men in neat rows, as well-tended prisoners. Never announce "Check" with vanity, lest someone with an unseen sword slit your throat. Never hurl pieces into the sandbox after you have lost a game, because then you must find them again, by yourself, after apologizing to all around you. By the end of the summer, Lau Po had taught me all he knew, and I had become a better chess player.

---

etiquette (et′i kit) *n.* forms of proper or polite behavior in society; good manners.

A small weekend crowd of Chinese people and tourists would gather as I played and defeated my opponents one by one. My mother would join the crowds during these outdoor exhibition games. She sat proudly on the bench, telling my admirers with proper Chinese <u>humility</u>, "Is luck."

A man who watched me play in the park suggested that my mother allow me to play in local chess tournaments. My mother smiled graciously, an answer that meant nothing. I desperately wanted to go, but I bit back my tongue. I knew she would not let me play among strangers. So as we walked home I said in a small voice that I didn't want to play in the local tournament. They would have American rules. If I lost, I would bring shame on my family.

"Is shame you fall down nobody push you," said my mother.

During my first tournament, my mother sat with me in the front row as I waited for my turn. I frequently bounced my legs to unstick them from the cold metal seat of the folding chair.

When my name was called, I leapt up. My mother unwrapped something in her lap. It was her *chang,* a small tablet of red jade which held the sun's fire. "Is luck," she whispered, and tucked it into my dress pocket. I turned to my opponent, a fifteen-year-old boy from Oakland. He looked at me, wrinkling his nose.

As I began to play, the boy disappeared, the color ran out of the room, and I saw only my white pieces and his black ones waiting on the other side. A light wind began blowing past my ears. It whispered secrets only I could hear.

"Blow from the South," it murmured. "The wind leaves no trail." I saw a clear path, the traps to avoid. The crowd rustled. "Shhh! Shhh!" said the corners of the room. The wind blew stronger. "Throw sand from the East to distract him." The knight came forward ready for the sacrifice. The wind hissed, louder and louder. "Blow, blow, blow. He cannot see. He is blind now. Make him lean away from the wind so he is easier to knock down."

"Check," I said, as the wind roared with laughter. The wind died down to little puffs, my own breath.

humility (hū mil′i tē) *n.* quality of being humble; lack of pride or arrogance.

My mother placed my first trophy next to a new plastic chess set that the neighborhood Tao society had given to me. As she wiped each piece with a soft cloth, she said, "Next time win more, lose less."

"Ma, it's not how many pieces you lose," I said. "Sometimes you need to lose pieces to get ahead."

"Better to lose less, see if you really need."

At the next tournament, I won again, but it was my mother who wore the triumphant grin.

"Lost eight piece this time. Last time was eleven. What I tell you? Better off lose less!" I was annoyed, but I couldn't say anything.

I attended more tournaments, each one farther away from home. I won all games, in all divisions. The Chinese bakery downstairs from our flat displayed my growing collection of trophies in its window, amidst the dust-covered cakes that were never picked up. The day after I won an important regional tournament, the window encased a fresh sheet cake with whipped-cream frosting and red script saying, "Congratulations, Waverly Jong, Chinatown Chess Champion." Soon after that, a flower shop, headstone engraver, and funeral parlor offered to

sponsor me in national tournaments. That's when my mother decided I no longer had to do the dishes. Winston and Vincent had to do my chores.

"Why does she get to play and we do all the work," complained Vincent.

"Is new American rules," said my mother. "Meimei play, squeeze all her brains out for win chess. You play, worth squeeze towel."

By my ninth birthday, I was a national chess champion. I was still some 429 points away from grand-master status, but I was touted as the Great American Hope, a child <u>prodigy</u> and a girl to boot. They ran a photo of me in *Life* magazine next to a quote in which Bobby Fischer said, "There will never be a woman grand master." "Your move, Bobby," said the caption.

The day they took the magazine picture I wore neatly plaited braids clipped with plastic barrettes trimmed with rhinestones. I was playing in a large high school auditorium that echoed with phlegmy coughs and the squeaky rubber knobs of chair legs sliding across freshly waxed wooden floors. Seated across from me was an American man, about the same age as Lau Po, maybe fifty. I remember that his sweaty brow seemed to weep at my every move. He wore a dark, <u>malodorous</u> suit. One of his pockets was stuffed with a great white kerchief on which he wiped his palm before sweeping his hand over the chosen chess piece with great flourish.

In my crisp pink-and-white dress with scratchy lace at the neck, one of two my mother had sewn for these special occasions, I would clasp my hands under my chin, the delicate points of my elbows poised lightly on the table in the manner my mother had shown me for posing for the press. I would swing my patent leather shoes back and forth like an impatient child riding on a school bus. Then I would pause, suck in my lips, twirl my chosen piece in midair as if undecided, and then firmly plant it in its new threatening place, with a triumphant smile thrown back at my opponent for good measure.

I no longer played in the alley of Waverly Place. I never visited the playground where the pigeons and old men gathered. I

---

prodigy (prod′i jē) *n.* extremely gifted or talented person, especially a child.
malodorous (mal ō′dər əs) *adj.* having an unpleasant odor.

went to school, then directly home to learn new chess secrets, cleverly concealed advantages, more escape routes.

But I found it difficult to concentrate at home. My mother had a habit of standing over me while I plotted out my games. I think she thought of herself as my protective ally. Her lips would be sealed tight, and after each move I made, a soft "Hmmmmph" would escape from her nose.

"Ma, I can't practice when you stand there like that," I said one day. She retreated to the kitchen and made loud noises with the pots and pans. When the crashing stopped, I could see out of the corner of my eye that she was standing in the doorway. "Hmmmph!" Only this one came out of her tight throat.

My parents made many concessions to allow me to practice. One time I complained that the bedroom I shared was so noisy that I couldn't think. Thereafter, my brothers slept in a bed in the living room facing the street. I said I couldn't finish my rice; my head didn't work right when my stomach was too full. I left the table with half-finished bowls and nobody complained. But there was one duty I couldn't avoid. I had to accompany my mother on Saturday market days when I had no tournament to play. My mother would proudly walk with me, visiting many shops, buying very little. "This my daughter Wave-ly Jong," she said to whoever looked her way.

One day, after we left a shop I said under my breath, "I wish you wouldn't do that, telling everybody I'm your daughter." My mother stopped walking. Crowds of people with heavy bags pushed past us on the sidewalk, bumping into first one shoulder, then another.

"Aiii-ya. So shame be with mother?" She grasped my hand even tighter as she glared at me.

I looked down. "It's not that, it's just so obvious. It's just so embarrassing."

"Embarrass you be my daughter?" Her voice was cracking with anger.

"That's not what I meant. That's not what I said."

"What you say?"

I knew it was a mistake to say anything more, but I heard my voice speaking. "Why do you have to use me to

---

ally (al′ī) *n.* person, nation, or group united with another for a common purpose.
concessions (kən sesh′ənz) *n., pl.* acts of granting or conceding.

show off? If you want to show off, then why don't you learn to play chess."

My mother's eyes turned into dangerous black slits. She had no words for me, just sharp silence.

I felt the wind rushing around my hot ears. I jerked my hand out of my mother's tight grasp and spun around, knocking into an old woman. Her bag of groceries spilled to the ground.

"Aii-ya! Stupid girl!" my mother and the woman cried. Oranges and tin cans careened down the sidewalk. As my mother stooped to help the old woman pick up the escaping food, I took off.

I raced down the street, dashing between people, not looking back as my mother screamed shrilly, "Meimei! Meimei!" I fled down an alley, past dark curtained shops and merchants washing the grime off their windows. I sped into the sunlight, into a large street crowded with tourists examining trinkets and souvenirs. I ducked into another dark alley, down another street, up another alley. I ran until it hurt and I realized I had nowhere to go, that I was not running from anything. The alleys contained no escape routes.

My breath came out like angry smoke. It was cold. I sat down on an upturned plastic pail next to a stack of empty

boxes, cupping my chin with my hands, thinking hard. I imagined my mother, first walking briskly down one street or another looking for me, then giving up and returning home to await my arrival. After two hours, I stood up on creaking legs and slowly walked home.

The alley was quiet and I could see the yellow lights shining from our flat like two tiger's eyes in the night. I climbed the sixteen steps to the door, advancing quietly up each so as not to make any warning sounds. I turned the knob; the door was locked. I heard a chair moving, quick steps, the locks turning—click! click! click!—and then the door opened.

"About time you got home," said Vincent. "Boy, are you in trouble."

He slid back to the dinner table. On a platter were the remains of a large fish, its fleshy head still connected to bones swimming upstream in vain escape. Standing there waiting for my punishment, I heard my mother speak in a dry voice.

"We not concerning this girl. This girl not have concerning for us."

Nobody looked at me. Bone chopsticks clinked against the insides of bowls being emptied into hungry mouths.

I walked into my room, closed the door, and lay down on my bed. The room was dark, the ceiling filled with shadows from the dinnertime lights of neighboring flats.

In my head, I saw a chessboard with sixty-four black and white squares. Opposite me was my opponent, two angry black slits. She wore a triumphant smile. "Strongest wind cannot be seen," she said.

Her black men advanced across the plane, slowly marching to each successive level as a single unit. My white pieces screamed as they scurried and fell off the board one by one. As her men drew closer to my edge, I felt myself growing light. I rose up into the air and flew out the window. Higher and higher, above the alley, over the tops of tiled roofs, where I was gathered up by the wind and pushed up toward the night sky until everything below me disappeared and I was alone.

I closed my eyes and pondered my next move.

MEET AMY TAN

When Amy Tan was eight years old, she won a contest with an essay entitled "Why I Love the Library." Her prize was a transistor radio. "This convinced me," Tan said later, "that writing could be a rewarding and lucrative experience, and so I took up reading the thesaurus in addition to fairy tales."

But Tan's parents, both of whom were Chinese immigrants, had other career plans for their daughter. "My parents," says Tan, "believed strongly in education and good English skills as the stepping stones to success in America. I was led to believe from the age of six that I would grow up to be a neurosurgeon by trade and a concert pianist by hobby."

Amy Tan grew up wanting to be as American as possible. She had little interest in her Chinese roots. Years later, when her mother was thought to have had a heart attack, Tan remembered a question her mother had recently asked her: "If I die, what would you remember?"

After that, Tan began paying more attention to her mother's stories and decided to write a book about mothers and daughters. She explains, "Like many American-born Chinese, I've had some difficulties reconciling which parts of me are Chinese and which are American. . . . All of this has somehow found its way into my fiction, which has now become *The Joy Luck Club.*" The novel, her first, earned a 1989 National Book Award nomination. Tan's success may

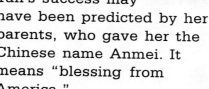

have been predicted by her parents, who gave her the Chinese name Anmei. It means "blessing from America."

RESPONDING TO *Literature*

THINK • TALK • WRITE

1 Who do you like more: Meimei or her mother? Jot down some ideas in your journal.

2 Meimei chooses her Christmas gift carefully. What does this tell you about her as a person?

3 How does the chess board change life for Meimei and everyone else in the family?

4 If you could advise Meimei about how to maintain her own identity and still get along with her mother, what would you tell her?

5 Meimei describes many aspects of life in Chinatown. What would you like to see and do if you were visiting Meimei?

ACTIVITIES

- **Write About Protagonist/Antagonist** Imagine that you are Meimei. Write a diary entry about the problem you are having with your mother.

- **Make a Tourist Brochure** Create a tourist brochure for visitors to Chinatown, using exciting and colorful language. Include drawings and maps based on information in the story.

VOCABULARY PRACTICE

Read each sentence. Decide if the word in color is used correctly or incorrectly. On a separate sheet of paper, write *correct* or *incorrect* and a sentence explaining your answer.

1 The doors were **recessed** in the walls of the building.

2 The **adversaries** were eager to help each other.

3 The modest person is an example of **humility.**

4 His obvious interest in the discussion was **evident**.

5 He **imparted** the secret for years, never telling anyone else.

6 The bushes and rocks **obscured** the entrance to the cave.

7 The criminal **eluded** capture for several weeks before he was arrested.

8 The **malodorous** perfume of the lilies smelled beautiful in the night air.

9 The company made **concessions** to get the striking workers back on the job.

10 You must realize that an **ally** will always work against you.

82

Grandma

BY AMY LING

If you dig that hole deep enough
you'll reach China, they used to tell me,
a child in a backyard, Allentown, Pa.
Not strong enough to dig that hole,
I waited twenty years
then sailed back
half way around the world.

In Taiwan I first met Grandma.
Before she came to view I heard
her slippered feet softly measure
the tatami floor with even step.
The aqua paper door slid open
and there, breathless, I faced
my five foot height, my sturdy legs and feet,
my square forehead, high cheeks, and wide-set eyes.
My image stood before me
acted on by fifty years;
here in my past was my future.

She smiled, stretched her arms
to take to heart the eldest daughter
of her youngest son a quarter century away.
She spoke a tongue I knew no word of
and I was sad I could not understand,
but I could hug her.

SPOT on

AUTOBIOGRAPHY

Think about how you would show others what you look like—the shape of your nose, your mouth, your hairstyle. A photograph would probably capture your appearance most accurately.

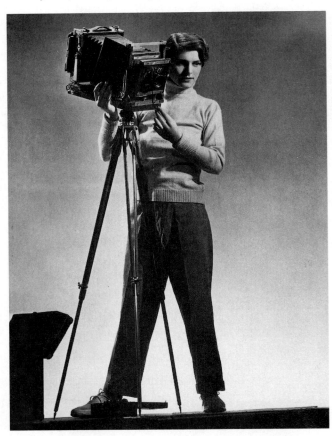

Self-Portrait with Camera   c.1933   Margaret Bourke-White

Examine this self-portrait by photographer Margaret Bourke-White. What might the camera and camera equipment box signify? Does Bourke-White's clothing suggest anything about her?

Think about other self-portraits you have seen. How did the subjects/artists reveal themselves to you? Now think about autobiographies you have read. How did the writers reveal themselves? What do self-portraits and autobiographies have in common?

ELEMENTS OF AN AUTOBIOGRAPHY

An autobiography is the story of a person's life written by that person. Writers of autobiographies often express their personal thoughts and feelings. They also write about the effects of certain events on their lives. Here are some important characteristics of autobiographies.

CHARACTERS are discussed in detail and portrayed realistically.

SETTING is vividly described.

DETAILS are interesting. Writers of autobiographies use objective and subjective details as well as anecdotes to convey their life stories.

- *Objective details* can be proven.
- *Subjective details* are based on personal feelings and opinions and cannot be proven. Most autobiographies contain many subjective details.
- *Anecdotes* are short, often amusing, stories that enliven writing and make a particular point.

CHRONOLOGICAL ORDER is the order in which most writers of autobiographies tell their stories. Usually events are arranged from childhood to adulthood.

POINT OF VIEW is the perspective from which an autobiography is told. Since autobiographies are written by their subjects, they are told from the *first-person point of view,* using the pronouns *I, me,* and *mine.* Readers experience events through the writers' own eyes—knowing only what they think and feel about any given experience.

AUTHOR'S PURPOSE is the author's reason for writing. People often write autobiographies to examine the important events of their lives. Authors frequently give credit to the people and events that have shaped their lives. Writing an autobiography also helps the author understand defeats and triumphs of the past. Often controversial figures write autobiographies to explain or justify their actions.

In the selections that follow, you will explore autobiographies. Your discoveries will help you to understand and enjoy this important type of literature and to write your own autobiography.

AUTOBIOGRAPHY

BARRIO BOY

CONNECT TO LITERATURE

Do you remember your first day of school? How did you feel? What do you recall about the other children and the teacher? Share your recollections with a classmate. In your journal, note a few of your memories of that day. As you read "Barrio Boy," compare your experiences with those described by Ernesto Galarza.

INTRODUCTION TO THE MODEL AUTOBIOGRAPHY

When you read the autobiographies in this unit, you will notice that they have many things in common. For example, the author is the main character in each autobiography. Also, the other characters are real people who had an impact on the life of the author.

As you read "Barrio Boy," use the notes in the margin. These notes will show you how the basic elements of an autobiography are connected to each other. As you read this autobiography, you might like to note your own thoughts and impressions in your journal.

DID YOU KNOW?

The selection you are about to read is an excerpt from *Barrio Boy,* Galarza's autobiography. As a boy, Ernesto Galarza came with his family to the United States from a mountain village in Mexico. Upon settling in this country, Ernesto encountered many new customs and experiences, one of which was his introduction to school.

When Ernesto Galarza was in school, students were not allowed to learn in their own languages. Instead they were expected to learn all their lessons in English. Today many schools offer bilingual education, in which classes are taught both in English and in students' native tongues.

FROM
BARRIO BOY

BY ERNESTO GALARZA

In this excerpt from
Barrio Boy, Ernesto Galarza
recounts his first school experience
in the United States.

Ernesto Galarza, the author, is telling about an event from his own life. The type of writing in which authors give accounts of their own lives is called **autobiographical writing**.

My mother and I walked south on Fifth Street one morning to the corner of Q Street and turned right. Half of the block was occupied by the Lincoln School. It was a three-story wooden building, with two wings that gave it the shape of a double-T connected by a central hall. It was a new building, painted yellow, with a shingled roof that was not like the red tile of the school in Mazatlán. I noticed other differences, none of them very reassuring.

We walked up the wide staircase hand in hand and through the door, which closed by itself. A mechanical <u>contraption</u> screwed to the top shut it behind us quietly.

Up to this point the adventure of enrolling me in the school had been carefully rehearsed. Mrs. Dodson, our landlady, had told us how to find it and we had circled it several times on our walks. Friends in the *barrio* explained that the director was called a principal, and that it was a lady and not a man. They assured us that there was always a person at the school who could speak Spanish.

Exactly as we had been told, there was a sign on the door in both Spanish and English: "Principal." We crossed the hall and entered the office of Miss Nettie Hopley.

Miss Hopley was at a roll-top desk to one side, sitting in a swivel chair that moved on wheels. There was a sofa against the opposite wall, <u>flanked</u> by two windows and a door that opened on a small balcony. Chairs were set around a table and framed pictures hung on the walls of a man with long white hair and another with a sad face and a black beard.

The principal half turned in the swivel chair to look at us over the pinch glasses crossed on the ridge of her nose. To do this she had to duck her head slightly as if she were about to step through a low doorway.

Even though they are based on real people, places, and events, autobiographies share many of the elements of fiction, including developed **characters**.

What Miss Hopley said to us we did not know but we saw in her eyes a warm welcome and when she took off her glasses and straightened up she smiled wholeheartedly, like Mrs. Dodson. We were, of course, saying

---

contraption (kən trap′shən) *n., Informal.* mechanical device; gadget.
flanked (flangkt) *v.t.* located at the side of.

nothing, only catching the friendliness of her voice and the sparkle in her eyes while she said words we did not understand. She signaled us to the table. Almost tiptoeing across the office, I maneuvered myself to keep my mother between me and the gringo lady. In a matter of seconds I had to decide whether she was a possible friend or a menace. We sat down.

Then Miss Hopley did a formidable thing. She stood up. Had she been standing when we entered she would have seemed tall. But rising from her chair she soared. And what she carried up and up with her was a buxom superstructure, firm shoulders, a straight sharp nose, full cheeks slightly molded by a curved line along the nostrils, thin lips that moved like steel springs, and a high forehead topped by hair gathered in a bun. Miss Hopley was not a giant in body but when she mobilized it to a standing position she seemed a match for giants. I decided I liked her.

She strode to a door in the far corner of the office, opened it and called a name. A boy of about ten years appeared in the doorway. He sat down at one end of the table. He was brown like us, a plump kid with shiny black hair combed straight back, neat, cool, and faintly obnoxious.

Miss Hopley joined us with a large book and some papers in her hand. She, too, sat down and the questions and answers began by way of our interpreter. My name was Ernesto. My mother's name was Henriqueta. My birth certificate was in San Blas. Here was my last report card from the Escuela Municipal Numero 3 para Varones of Mazatlán, and so forth. Miss Hopley put things down in the book and my mother signed a card.

As long as the questions continued, Doña Henriqueta could stay and I was secure. Now that they

Consider the details about Miss Hopley's height. Galarza helps you experience Miss Hopley as he experienced her, from a child's **point of view**.

---

formidable (fôr′mi də bəl) *adj.* causing fear, dread, or awe.
mobilized (mō′bə līzd′) *v.* organized or prepared, as for war or an emergency.
obnoxious (ob nok′shəs) *adj.* extremely annoying, disagreeable, or offensive.
secure (si kyür′) *adj.* free from worry, care, or fear.

89

were over, Miss Hopley saw her to the door, dismissed our interpreter and without further ado took me by the hand and strode down the hall to Miss Ryan's first grade.

Miss Ryan took me to a seat at the front of the room, into which I shrank—the better to survey her. She was, to skinny, somewhat runty me, of a withering height when she patrolled the class. And when I least expected it, there she was, crouching by my desk, her blond <u>radiant</u> face level with mine, her voice patiently maneuvering me over the awful idiocies of the English language.

During the next few weeks Miss Ryan overcame my fears of tall, energetic teachers as she bent over my desk to help me with a word in the pre-primer. Step by step, she loosened me and my classmates from the safe <u>anchorage</u> of the desks for recitations at the blackboard and consultations at her desk. Frequently she

---

radiant (rā′dē ənt) *adj.* beaming with joy, contentment, love, or the like.
anchorage (ang′kər ij) *n.* something that fastens or holds securely.

burst into happy announcements to the whole class. "Ito can read a sentence," and small Japanese Ito, squint-eyed and shy, slowly read aloud while the class listened in wonder: "Come, Skipper, come. Come and run." The Korean, Portuguese, Italian, and Polish first graders had similar moments of glory, no less shining than mine the day I conquered "butterfly," which I had been <u>persistently</u> pronouncing in standard Spanish as boo-ter-flee. "Children," Miss Ryan called for attention. "Ernesto has learned how to pronounce *butterfly!*" And I proved it with a perfect imitation of Miss Ryan. From that celebrated success, I was soon able to match Ito's progress as a sentence reader with "Come, butterfly, come fly with me."

Like Ito and several other first graders who did not know English, I received private lessons from Miss Ryan in the closet, a narrow hall off the classroom with a door at each end. Next to one of these doors Miss Ryan placed a large chair for herself and a small one for me. Keeping an eye on the class through the open door she read with me about sheep in the meadow and a frightened chicken going to see the king, coaching me out of my <u>phonetic</u> ruts in words like *pasture*, *bow-wow-wow*, *hay*, and *pretty*, which to my Mexican ear and eye had so many unnecessary sounds and letters. She made me watch her lips and then close my eyes as she repeated words I found hard to read. When we came to know each other better, I tried interrupting to tell Miss Ryan how we said it in Spanish. It didn't work. She only said "oh" and went on with *pasture*, *bow-wow-wow*, and *pretty*. It was as if in that closet we were both discovering together the secrets of the English language and <u>grieving</u> together over the tragedies of Bo-Peep. The main reason I was graduated with honors from the first grade was that I had fallen in love with Miss Ryan. Her radiant, no-nonsense character made us either afraid not to love her or love her so we would not be afraid, I am not sure which. It was not only that we sensed she was with it, but also that she was with us.

Galarza reveals his thoughts and feelings about his teacher. By doing so, he helps you to understand him better.

persistently (pər sis′tənt lē) *adv.* continuing in a firm and steady manner in spite of opposition or difficulty.
phonetic (fə net′ik) *adj.* of or relating to speech sounds.
grieving (grē′ving) *v.* mourning; feeling deep sadness.

Like the first grade, the rest of the Lincoln School was a sampling of the lower part of town where many races made their home. My pals in the second grade were Kazushi, whose parents spoke only Japanese; Matti, a skinny Italian boy; and Manuel, a fat Portuguese who would never get into a fight but wrestled you to the ground and just sat on you. Our assortment of nationalities included Koreans, Yugoslavs, Poles, Irish, and home-grown Americans.

Miss Hopley and her teachers never let us forget why we were at Lincoln: for those who were alien, to become good Americans; for those who were so born, to accept the rest of us. Off the school grounds we traded the same insults we heard from our elders. On the playground we were sure to be marched up to the principal's office for calling someone an <u>offensive</u> name. The school was not so much a melting pot as a griddle where Miss Hopley and her helpers warmed knowledge into us and roasted racial hatreds out of us.

At Lincoln, making us into Americans did not mean scrubbing away what made us originally foreign. The teachers called us as our parents did, or as close as they could pronounce our names in Spanish or Japanese. No one was ever scolded or punished for speaking in his native tongue on the playground. Matti told the class about his mother's down quilt, which she had made in Italy with the fine feathers of a thousand geese. Encarnación acted out how boys learned to fish in the Philippines. I astounded the third grade with the story of my travels on a stagecoach, which nobody else in the class had seen except in the museum at Sutter's Fort. After a visit to the Crocker Art Gallery and its collection of heroic paintings of the golden age of California, someone showed a silk scroll with a Chinese painting. Miss Hopley herself had a way of expressing wonder over these matters before a class, her eyes wide open until they popped slightly. It was easy for me to feel that becoming a proud American, as she said we should, did not mean feeling ashamed of being a Mexican.

The reason for writing an autobiography is called the **author's purpose**. The most common purposes are to describe, to inform, to explain, and to persuade.

offensive (ə fen′siv) *adj.* unpleasant; disagreeable.

MEET
Ernesto Galarza

Ernesto Galarza (1905–1984) was a union leader and writer who spent his life fighting for the rights of Mexican and American farm workers. Galarza was born in an Indian village in western Mexico. When he was six years old, his family migrated north to flee the violence of the Mexican Revolution of 1910. They settled in Sacramento, California, where he attended the school he wrote about in *Barrio Boy*.

After graduating from college and working in Washington, D.C., as an education specialist, Galarza returned to the Sacramento Valley to help farm workers. His reports about the low wages, filthy living conditions, and lack of food in migrant worker camps helped to make conditions better for the workers. He also was a pioneer of bilingual education.

More Autobiographies About Growing Up

- *An American Childhood* by Annie Dillard (Harper & Row, 1987). Annie Dillard grew up in Pittsburgh. There she learned to pitch a baseball, tell a joke, and love books. All of these experiences and more helped her develop into an important American writer.

- *Under the Eye of the Clock* by Christopher Nolan (Dell, 1987). Nolan transcends the inactivity imposed by his mute and paralyzed body in order to express the universal need for love and acceptance.

- *My Indian Boyhood* by Luther Standing Bear (University of Nebraska Press, 1988). In this account, Standing Bear describes his childhood as a member of the mighty Sioux nation during the second half of the nineteenth century.

RESPONDING TO *Literature*

THINK • TALK • WRITE

1 Would you like to read the rest of Ernesto Galarza's autobiography? Tell why or why not.

2 How does Ernesto feel at the beginning of the selection? What story clues help you to know this? Do you think his feelings are justified? Explain.

3 How does Miss Ryan help her students to learn? What qualities do both Miss Ryan and Miss Hopley have that make the students feel good about themselves?

4 What advice do you think Galarza would give to those who work with people who don't speak English?

5 Galarza says, "At Lincoln, making us into Americans did not mean scrubbing away what made us originally foreign." Explain what he means.

ACTIVITY

• **Write About Autobiography** Make two copies of the character-traits web. Complete a web for Ernesto Galarza and one for Miss Ryan.

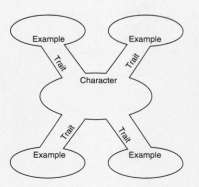

VOCABULARY PRACTICE

On a separate sheet of paper, write whether the words in each pair are *synonyms* (words with the same or similar meanings) or *antonyms* (words with opposite meanings).

1 contraption—device

2 mobilized—prepared

3 obnoxious—pleasant

4 anchorage—fastener

5 formidable—dreadful

6 radiant—sad

7 offensive—disagreeable

8 secure—fearful

9 persistently—repeatedly

10 grieving—laughing

AUTOBIOGRAPHY

I KNOW WHY THE CAGED BIRD SINGS

CONNECT TO LITERATURE

Was there someone important in your child-hood who was not a member of your family? Perhaps this person influenced you in a positive way or made you feel special. Share your thoughts with a classmate. As you read "I Know Why the Caged Bird Sings," note in your journal how one very important person affected the author's life.

Detail of **Allegheny Morning Sky,**
Romare Bearden.

Courtesy Estate of Romare Bearden.

THINKING ABOUT CHARACTERIZATION

The way a writer presents characters is called *characterization.* In direct characterization the writer tells you how a character looks, behaves, and thinks. In indirect characterization, the writer lets you draw your own conclusions about characters based upon how they speak and act and upon how other people react to them. Notice how Maya Angelou paints written portraits of the characters in her autobiography.

HAVE YOU EVER?

In her autobiography *I Know Why the Caged Bird Sings,* Maya Angelou describes her experiences as a child growing up in the South. Prior to the events in the excerpt you are about to read, Angelou went to the big city of St. Louis and then returned to her grandmother's home in the tiny town of Stamps. She is not happy to be back in Stamps. Her mood changes, however, when Mrs. Flowers comes into her life.

Have you ever moped around the house, not knowing what to do with yourself and feeling bad? What did you do? Was there anyone who tried to cheer you up? Think about your experience as you read this selection.

From I Know Why the Caged Bird Sings

BY MAYA ANGELOU

As children, Maya and her brother Bailey were sent to Stamps, Arkansas, to live with their grandmother, whom they called Momma. However, after a visit with her mother in St. Louis, Maya returned to Stamps feeling sad that they were separated once again.

For nearly a year, I sopped around the house, the Store, the school and the church, like an old biscuit, dirty and inedible. Then I met, or rather got to know, the lady who threw me my first life line.

Mrs. Bertha Flowers was the <u>aristocrat</u> of Black Stamps. She had the grace of control to appear warm in the coldest weather, and on the Arkansas summer days it seemed she had a private breeze which swirled around, cooling her. She was thin without the taut look of wiry people, and her printed voile dresses and flowered hats were as right for her as denim overalls for a farmer. She was our side's answer to the richest white woman in town.

---

aristocrat (ə ris′tə krat′) *n.* person who is considered to be superior or outstanding because of wealth, intelligence, or culture.

Mrs. Blanton's October Table *1983 Romare Bearden*

Her skin was a rich black that would have peeled like a plum if snagged, but then no one would have thought of getting close enough to Mrs. Flowers to ruffle her dress, let alone snag her skin. She didn't encourage familiarity. She wore gloves too.

I don't think I ever saw Mrs. Flowers laugh, but she smiled often. A slow widening of her thin black lips to show even, small white teeth, then the slow effortless closing. When she chose to smile on me, I always wanted to thank her. The action was so graceful and inclusively benign.

She was one of the few gentlewomen I have ever known, and has remained throughout my life the measure of what a human being can be.

Momma had a strange relationship with her. Most often when she passed on the road in front of the Store, she spoke to Momma in that soft yet carrying voice, "Good day, Mrs. Henderson." Momma responded with "How you, Sister Flowers?"

Mrs. Flowers didn't belong to our church, nor was she Momma's familiar. Why on earth did she insist on calling her Sister Flowers? Shame made me want to hide my face. Mrs. Flowers deserved better than to be called Sister. Then, Momma left out the verb. Why not ask, "How *are* you, *Mrs.* Flowers?" With the unbalanced passion of the young, I hated her for showing her ignorance to Mrs. Flowers. It didn't occur to me for many years that they were as alike as sisters, separated only by formal education.

Although I was upset, neither of the women was in the least shaken by what I thought an unceremonious greeting. Mrs. Flowers would continue her easy gait up the hill to her little bungalow, and Momma kept on shelling peas or doing whatever had brought her to the front porch.

Occasionally, though, Mrs. Flowers would drift off the road and down to the Store and Momma would say to me, "Sister, you go on and play." As I left I would hear the beginning of an <u>intimate</u> conversation. Momma persistently using the wrong verb, or none at all.

"Brother and Sister Wilcox is sho'ly the meanest—" "Is," Momma? "Is"? Oh, please, not "is," Momma, for two or more. But they talked, and from the side of the building where I waited for the ground to open up and swallow me, I heard the soft-voiced Mrs. Flowers and the textured voice of my grandmother merging and melting. They were interrupted from time to time by giggles that must have come from Mrs. Flowers (Momma never giggled in her life). Then she was gone.

She appealed to me because she was like people I had never met personally. Like women in English novels who walked the <u>moors</u> (whatever they were) with their loyal dogs racing at a respectful

---

intimate (in′tə mit) *adj.* personal or private.
moors (mŭrz) *n., pl.* areas of open land, often covered with heather and having swamps.

distance. Like the women who sat in front of roaring fireplaces, drinking tea incessantly from silver trays full of scones and crumpets. Women who walked over the "heath" and read morocco-bound books and had two last names divided by a hyphen. It would be safe to say that she made me proud to be Negro, just by being herself.

She acted just as refined as whitefolks in the movies and books and she was more beautiful, for none of them could have come near that warm color without looking gray by comparison.

It was fortunate that I never saw her in the company of powhitefolks. For since they tend to think of their whiteness as an evenizer, I'm certain that I would have had to hear her spoken to commonly as Bertha, and my image of her would have been shattered like the unmendable Humpty-Dumpty.

One summer afternoon, sweetmilk fresh in my memory, she stopped at the Store to buy provisions. Another Negro woman of her health and age would have been expected to carry the paper sacks home in one hand, but Momma said, "Sister Flowers, I'll send Bailey up to your house with these things."

She smiled that slow dragging smile, "Thank you, Mrs. Henderson. I'd prefer Marguerite, though." My name was beautiful when she said it. "I've been meaning to talk to her, anyway."

They gave each other age-group looks.

Momma said, "Well, that's all right then. Sister, go and change your dress. You going to Sister Flowers's."

The chifforobe was a maze. What on earth did one put on to go to Mrs. Flowers' house? I knew I shouldn't put on a Sunday dress. It might be sacrilegious. Certainly not a house dress, since I was already wearing a fresh one. I chose a school dress, naturally. It was formal without suggesting that going to Mrs. Flowers' house was equivalent to attending church.

I trusted myself back into the Store.

"Now, don't you look nice." I had chosen the right thing, for once.

"Mrs. Henderson, you make most of the children's clothes, don't you?"

"Yes, ma'am. Sure do. Store-bought clothes ain't hardly worth the thread it take to stitch them."

"I'll say you do a lovely job, though, so neat. That dress looks professional."

Momma was enjoying the seldom-received compliments. Since everyone we knew (except Mrs. Flowers, of course) could sew competently, praise was rarely handed out for the commonly practiced craft.

---

scones (skōnz) *n., pl.* small, often round biscuits.
crumpets (krŭm′pits) *n., pl.* unsweetened batter cakes.
heath (hēth) *n.* open land overgrown with low bushes.
morocco-bound (mə rŏk′ō bound) *adj.* covered in goatskin leather that originally came from Morocco.
chifforobe (shif′ə rōb) *n.* closet for keeping clothes.
competently (kŏm′pi tənt lē) *adv.* in a knowledgeable or capable manner.

Allegheny Morning Sky   *1978*   *Romare Bearden*

"I try, with the help of the Lord, Sister Flowers, to finish the inside just like I does the outside. Come here, Sister."

I had buttoned up the collar and tied the belt, apronlike, in back. Momma told me to turn around. With one hand she pulled the strings and the belt fell free at both sides of my waist. Then her large hands were at my neck, opening the button loops. I was terrified. What was happening?

"Take it off, Sister." She had her hands on the hem of the dress.

"I don't need to see the inside, Mrs. Henderson, I can tell . . ." But the dress was over my head and my arms were stuck in the sleeves. Momma said, "That'll do. See here, Sister Flowers, I French-seams around the armholes." Through the cloth film, I saw the shadow approach. "That makes it last longer. Children these days would bust out of sheet-metal clothes. They so rough."

"That is a very good job, Mrs. Henderson. You should be proud. You can put your dress back on, Marguerite."

"No ma'am. Pride is a sin. And

_____

French-seams (french sēmz) *n.* sewing technique used to reinforce seams.

'cording to the Good Book, it goeth before a fall."

"That's right. So the Bible says. It's a good thing to keep in mind."

I wouldn't look at either of them. Momma hadn't thought that taking off my dress in front of Mrs. Flowers would kill me stone dead. If I had refused, she would have thought I was trying to be "womanish" and might have remembered St. Louis. Mrs. Flowers had known that I would be embarrassed and that was even worse. I picked up the groceries and went out to wait in the hot sunshine. It would be fitting if I got a sunstroke and died before they came outside. Just dropped dead on the slanting porch.

There was a little path beside the rocky road, and Mrs. Flowers walked in front swinging her arms and picking her way over the stones.

She said, without turning her head, to me, "I hear you're doing very good school work, Marguerite, but that it's all written. The teachers report that they have trouble getting you to talk in class." We passed the triangular farm on our left and the path widened to allow us to walk together. I hung back in the separate unasked and unanswerable questions.

"Come and walk along with me, Marguerite." I couldn't have refused even if I wanted to. She pronounced my name so nicely. Or more correctly, she spoke each word with such clarity that I was certain a foreigner who didn't understand English could have understood her.

"Now no one is going to make you talk—possibly no one can. But bear in mind, language is man's way of communicating with his fellow man and it is language alone which separates him from the lower animals." That was a totally new idea to me, and I would need time to think about it.

"Your grandmother says you read a lot. Every chance you get. That's good, but not good enough. Words mean more than what is set down on paper. It takes the human voice to infuse them with the shades of deeper meaning."

I memorized the part about the human voice infusing words. It seemed so valid and poetic.

She said she was going to give me some books and that I not only must read them, I must read them aloud. She suggested that I try to make a sentence sound in as many different ways as possible.

"I'll accept no excuse if you return a book to me that has been badly handled." My imagination boggled at the punishment I would deserve if in fact I did abuse a book of Mrs. Flowers'. Death would be too kind and brief.

The odors in the house surprised me. Somehow I had never connected Mrs. Flowers with food or eating or any other common experience of common people.

---

infuse (in fūz′) *v.t.* instill; inspire.
valid (val′id) *adj.* true; soundly based on facts or evidence.
boggled (bog′əld) *v.i.* hesitated, as from doubt or confusion.

There must have been an outhouse, too, but my mind never recorded it.

The sweet scent of vanilla had met us as she opened the door.

"I made tea cookies this morning. You see, I had planned to invite you for cookies and lemonade so we could have this little chat. The lemonade is in the icebox."

It followed that Mrs. Flowers would have ice on an ordinary day, when most families in our town bought ice late on Saturdays only a few times during the summer to be used in the wooden ice-cream freezers.

She took the bags from me and disappeared through the kitchen door. I looked around the room that I had never in my wildest fantasies imagined I would see. Browned photographs leered or threatened from the walls and the white, freshly done curtains pushed against themselves and against the wind. I wanted to gobble up the room entire and take it to Bailey, who would help me analyze and enjoy it.

"Have a seat, Marguerite. Over there by the table." She carried a platter covered with a tea towel. Although she warned that she hadn't tried her hand at baking sweets for some time, I was certain that like everything else about her the cookies would be perfect.

They were flat round wafers, slightly browned on the edges and butter-yellow in the center. With the cold lemonade they were sufficient for childhood's life-long diet. Remembering my manners, I took nice little lady-like bites off the edges. She said she had made them expressly for me and that she had a few in the kitchen that I could take home to my brother. So I jammed one whole cake in my mouth and the rough crumbs scratched the insides of my jaws, and if I hadn't had to swallow, it would have been a dream come true.

As I ate she began the first of what we later called "my lessons in living." She said that I must always be intolerant of ignorance but understanding of illiteracy. That some people, unable to go to school, were more educated and even more intelligent than college professors. She encouraged me to listen carefully to what country people called mother wit. That in those homely sayings was couched the collective wisdom of generations.

When I finished the cookies she brushed off the table and brought a thick, small book from the bookcase. I had read *A Tale of Two Cities* and found it up to my standards as a romantic novel. She opened the first page and I heard poetry for the first time in my life.

"It was the best of times and the worst of times . . ." Her voice slid in and curved down through and over the words. She was nearly singing. I wanted to look at the pages. Were they the same that I had read? Or were there notes, music,

---

illiteracy (i lit′ər ə sē) *n.* lack of the ability to read or write.

Allegheny Morning Sky *(detail)* 1978
Romare Bearden

lined on the pages, as in a hymn book? Her sounds began cascading gently. I knew from listening to a thousand preachers that she was nearing the end of her reading, and I hadn't really heard, heard to understand, a single word.

"How do you like that?"

It occurred to me that she expected a response. The sweet vanilla flavor was still on my tongue and her reading was a wonder in my ears. I had to speak.

I said, "Yes, ma'am." It was the least I could do, but it was the most also.

"There's one more thing. Take this book of poems and memorize one for me. Next time you pay me a visit, I want you to recite."

I have tried often to search behind the <u>sophistication</u> of years for the enchantment I so easily found in those gifts. The <u>essence</u> escapes but its <u>aura</u>

remains. To be allowed, no, invited, into the private lives of strangers, and to share their joys and fears, was a chance to exchange the Southern bitter wormwood for a cup of <u>mead</u> with Beowulf or a hot cup of tea and milk with Oliver Twist. When I said aloud, "It is a far, far better thing that I do, than I have ever done . . ." tears of love filled my eyes at my selflessness.

On that first day, I ran down the hill and into the road (few cars ever came along it) and had the good sense to stop running before I reached the Store.

I was liked, and what a difference it made. I was respected not as Mrs. Henderson's grandchild or Bailey's sister but for just being Marguerite Johnson.

Childhood's logic never asks to be proved (all conclusions are absolute). I didn't question why Mrs. Flowers had singled me out for attention, nor did it occur to me that Momma might have asked her to give me a little talking to. All I cared about was that she had made tea cookies for *me* and read to *me* from her favorite book. It was enough to prove that she liked me.

---

sophistication (sə fis'ti kā'shən) *n.* quality of having worldly knowledge and experience.

essence (es'əns) *n.* something that makes a thing what it is; necessary and basic part.

aura (ôr'ə) *n.* distinctive character or atmosphere arising from and surrounding a person or thing.

mead (mēd) *n.* alcoholic drink made from fermented honey and water and flavored with herbs.

MEET *Maya Angelou*

After her parents divorced when she was three, Maya Angelou (born 1928) experienced many traumas: separation from her parents, racial prejudice, and abuse. But Angelou never lost faith in herself. She once said, "I believe all things are possible for a human being, and I don't think there's anything in the world I can't do."

As a teenager, she fought to become the first African American "conductorette" on San Francisco's street cars, and won. After graduating from high school, she worked as a singer, dancer, and actress.

Angelou is now one of America's best-known writers. In 1993, she was commissioned to write and read a poem, "On the Pulse of the Morning," for President Clinton's inauguration.

More Autobiographies

- *The Lost Garden* by Laurence Yep (Julian Messner, 1991). Yep's first stories were about visiting aliens who felt "left out." This autobiography tells of a writer's growing acceptance of himself and his family.

- *A Girl from Yamhill: A Memoir* by Beverly Cleary (Dell, 1990). This candid autobiography by a renowned author of children's books also provides a revealing look at life in Oregon in the 1920s and 1930s.

- *A Summer Life* by Gary Soto (University Press of New England, 1990). In short innovative essays, Soto relates the small, very important moments from his boyhood years in Fresno, California.

RESPONDING TO Literature

THINK • TALK • WRITE

1 Which character in this selection did you like best? Jot down some ideas and explanations in your journal.

2 Why does Marguerite admire Mrs. Flowers?

3 How does Marguerite feel about her grandmother in connection with Mrs. Flowers? Do you think Marguerite is justified in feeling this way? Why or why not?

4 Why do you think Mrs. Flowers is interested in Marguerite? How might Marguerite's life have been different if Mrs. Flowers hadn't taken an interest in her?

5 Cultures may differ in the value they place on formal education as opposed to "mother wit." Which do you think is more important and why?

ACTIVITIES

- **Write About Characterization** Imagine that you are Mrs. Flowers. Write a letter to a friend in another town in which you describe Marguerite.

- **Recite a Poem** Mrs. Flowers asks Marguerite to memorize and recite a poem. Choose a favorite poem of yours and memorize all of it or a part of it. Recite it for a small group of classmates.

VOCABULARY PRACTICE

On a separate sheet of paper, write the word or term that best completes each sentence.

1 In a country with no **illiteracy,** everyone can
   a. read **b.** vote **c.** travel

2 If she does a job **competently,** she is
   a. untrainable **b.** capable **c.** lazy

3 If a story **boggled** people's minds, it
   a. confused them **b.** educated them
   c. angered them

4 When you **infuse** a body with blood, you
   a. donate it **b.** put it in **c.** refuse it

5 An example of an **aristocrat** is a
   a. farmer **b.** mechanic **c.** duke

6 People with **sophistication** have great
   a. talent **b.** knowledge **c.** clothes

7 If a passport is **valid,** it will be
   a. accepted **b.** rejected **c.** replaced

8 Someone with an **aura** is surrounded by an
   a. idea **b.** army **c.** atmosphere

9 If you have the **essence** of an idea, you have mastered the
   a. details **b.** core **c.** similarities

10 An **intimate** friendship is very
   a. common **b.** formal **c.** close

AUTOBIOGRAPHY

THE DOG THAT BIT PEOPLE

CONNECT TO LITERATURE

Have you or has someone you know ever had a pet that was more trouble than it was worth? What did you do? Share your ideas with a classmate. As you read "The Dog That Bit People," note in your journal the ways in which the author and his family relate to their difficult pet.

THINKING ABOUT HUMOR

Humor is the quality that makes something funny. Writers create humor by using different techniques, which include exaggeration, amusing descriptions and dialog, and sarcasm.

James Thurber was a famous American humorist. As you read this story, look for comic effects. What is it that makes a scene funny?

DID YOU KNOW?

Standing about twenty-three inches high and weighing from forty to fifty pounds, the Airedale is known as "the king of the terriers." With its boxy shape, long, square muzzle, and dense and wiry coat, this type of dog is among the most intelligent, courageous, and powerful of breeds. While capable of demonstrating great affection, Airedales are generally reserved with strangers.

THE Dog THAT BIT PEOPLE

by James Thurber

Probably no one man should have as many dogs in his life as I have had, but there was more pleasure than distress in them for me except in the case of an Airedale named Muggs. He gave me more trouble than all the other fifty-four or -five put together, although my moment of keenest embarrassment was the time a Scotch terrier named Jeannie, who had just had six puppies in the clothes closet of a fourth floor apartment in New York, had the unexpected seventh and last at the corner of Eleventh Street and Fifth Avenue during a walk she had insisted on taking. Then, too, there was the prize-winning French poodle, a great big black poodle—none of your little, untroublesome white miniatures—who got sick riding in the rumble seat of a car with me on her way to the

This drawing and others in this selection are James Thurber's original illustrations for "The Dog That Bit People."

Greenwich Dog Show. She had a red rubber bib tucked around her throat and, since a rain storm came up when we were half way through the Bronx, I had to hold over her a small green umbrella, really more of a parasol. The rain beat down fearfully and suddenly the driver of the car drove into a big garage, filled with mechanics. It happened so quickly that I forgot to put the umbrella down and I will always remember, with sickening distress, the look of incredulity mixed with hatred that came over the face of the particular hardened garage man that came over to see what we wanted, when he took a look at me and the poodle. All garage men, and people of that intolerant stripe, hate poodles with their curious hair cut, especially the pom-poms that you got to leave on their hips if you expect the dogs to win a prize.

But the Airedale, as I have said, was the worst of all my dogs. He really wasn't my dog, as a matter of fact: I came home from a vacation one summer to find that my brother Roy had bought him while I was away. A big, burly, choleric dog, he always acted as if he thought I wasn't one of the family. There was a slight advantage in being one of the family, for he didn't bite the family as often as he bit strangers. Still, in the years that we had him he bit everybody but mother, and he made a pass at her once but missed. That was during the month when we suddenly had mice, and Muggs refused to do anything about them. Nobody ever had mice exactly like the mice we had that month. They acted like pet mice, almost like mice somebody had trained. They were so friendly that one night when mother entertained at dinner the Friraliras, a club she and my father had belonged to for twenty years, she put down a lot of little dishes with food in them on the pantry floor so that the mice would be satisfied with that and wouldn't come into the dining room. Muggs stayed out in the pantry with the mice, lying on the floor, growling to himself—not at the mice, but about all the people in the next room that he would have liked to get at. Mother slipped out into the pantry once to see how everything was going. Everything was going fine. It made her so mad to see Muggs lying there, oblivious of the mice—they came running up to her—that she slapped him and he slashed at her, but didn't make it. He was sorry immediately, mother said. He was always sorry, she said,

---

incredulity (in'krə dü'li tē) *n.* refusal to believe; doubt.
burly (bûr'lē) *adj.* big, strong, and sturdy.
choleric (kol'ər ik) *adj.* easily irritated or angered.
oblivious (ə bliv'ē əs) *adj.* not aware or conscious; unmindful.

after he bit someone, but we could not understand how she figured this out. He didn't act sorry.

Mother used to send a box of candy every Christmas to the people the Airedale bit. The list finally contained forty or more names. Nobody could understand why we didn't get rid of the dog. I didn't understand it very well myself, but we didn't get rid of him. I think that one or two people tried to poison Muggs—he acted poisoned once in a while—and old Major Moberly fired at him once with his service revolver near the Seneca Hotel in East Broad Street—but Muggs lived to be almost eleven years old and even when he could hardly get around he bit a Congressman who had called to see my father on business. My mother had never liked the Congressman—she said the signs of his horoscope showed he couldn't be trusted (he was Saturn with the moon in Virgo)— but she sent him a box of candy that Christmas. He sent it right back, probably because he suspected it was trick candy. Mother persuaded herself it was all for the best that the dog had bitten

him, even though father lost an important business association because of it. "I wouldn't be associated with such a man," mother said, "Muggs could read him like a book."

We used to take turns feeding Muggs to be on his good side, but that didn't always work. He was never in a very good humor, even after a meal. Nobody knew exactly what was the matter with him, but whatever it was it made him irascible, especially in the mornings. Roy never felt very well in the morning, either, especially before breakfast, and once when he came downstairs and found that Muggs had moodily chewed up the morning paper he hit him in the face with a grapefruit and then jumped up on the dining room table, scattering dishes and silverware and spilling the coffee. Muggs' first free leap carried him all the way across the table and into a brass fire screen in front of the gas grate but he was back on his feet in a moment and in the end he got Roy and gave him a pretty vicious bite in the leg. Then he was all over it; he never bit anyone more than once at a time. Mother always mentioned that as an argument in his favor; she said he had a quick temper but that he didn't hold a grudge. She was forever defending him. I think she liked him because he wasn't well. "He's not strong," she would say, pityingly, but that was inaccurate; he may not have been well but he was terribly strong.

One time my mother went to the Chittenden Hotel to call on a woman mental healer who was lecturing in Columbus on the subject of "Harmonious Vibrations." She wanted to find out if it was possible to get harmonious vibrations into a dog. "He's a large tan-colored Airedale," mother explained. The woman said that she had never treated a dog but she advised my mother to hold the thought that he did not bite and would not bite. Mother was holding the thought the very next morning when Muggs got the iceman but she blamed that slip-up on the iceman. "If you didn't think he would bite you, he wouldn't," mother told him. He stomped out of the house in a terrible jangle of vibrations.

One morning when Muggs bit me slightly, more or less in passing, I reached down and grabbed his short stumpy tail and hoisted him into the air. It was a foolhardy thing to do and the last time I saw my mother, about six months ago, she said she

---

irascible (i ras′ə bəl) *adj.* easily irritated or made angry; irritable.

didn't know what possessed me. I don't either, except that I was pretty mad. As long as I held the dog off the floor by his tail he couldn't get at me, but he twisted and jerked so, snarling all the time, that I realized I couldn't hold him that way very long. I carried him to the kitchen and flung him onto the floor and shut the door on him just as he crashed against it. But I forgot about the backstairs. Muggs went up the backstairs and down the frontstairs and had me cornered in the living room. I managed to get up onto the mantelpiece above the fireplace, but it gave way and came down with a tremendous crash throwing a large marble clock, several vases, and myself heavily to the floor. Muggs was so alarmed by the racket that when I picked myself up he had disappeared. We couldn't find him anywhere, although we whistled and shouted, until old Mrs. Detweiler called after dinner that night. Muggs had bitten her once, in the leg, and she came into the living room only after we assured her that Muggs had run away. She had just seated herself when, with a great growling and scratching of claws, Muggs emerged from under a <u>davenport</u> where he had been quietly hiding all the time, and bit her again. Mother examined the bite and put <u>arnica</u> on it and told Mrs. Detweiler that it was only a bruise. "He just bumped you," she said. But Mrs. Detweiler left the house in a nasty state of mind.

Lots of people reported our Airedale to the police but my father held a <u>municipal</u> office at the time and was on friendly terms with the police. Even so, the cops had been out a couple of times—once when Muggs bit Mrs. Rufus Sturtevant and again when he bit Lieutenant-Governor Malloy—but mother told them that it hadn't been Muggs' fault but the fault of the people who were bitten. "When he starts for them, they scream," she explained, "and that excites him." The cops suggested that it might be a good idea to tie the dog up, but mother said that it <u>mortified</u> him to be tied up and that he wouldn't eat when he was tied up.

Muggs at his meals was an unusual sight. Because of the fact that if you reached toward the floor he would bite you, we usually put his food plate on top of an old kitchen table with a bench alongside the table. Muggs would stand on the bench and eat. I remember that my mother's Uncle Horatio, who boasted that he was

---

davenport (dav′ən pôrt′) *n.* large, upholstered sofa.
arnica (är′ni kə) *n.* medicinal liquid made from the dried flowers and roots of plants.
municipal (mū nis′ə pəl) *adj.* of or relating to the local government or affairs of a community.
mortified (môr′tə fīd′) *v.t.* shamed, humiliated, or embarrassed.

the third man up Missionary Ridge, was splutteringly indignant when he found out that we fed the dog on a table because we were afraid to put his plate on the floor. He said he wasn't afraid of any dog that ever lived and that he would put the dog's plate on the floor if we would give it to him. Roy said that if Uncle Horatio had fed Muggs on the ground just before the battle he would have been the first man up Missionary Ridge. Uncle Horatio was furious. "Bring him in! Bring him in now!" he shouted. "I'll feed the——on the floor!" Roy was all for giving him a chance, but my father wouldn't hear of it. He said that Muggs had already been fed. "I'll feed him again!" bawled Uncle Horatio. We had quite a time quieting him.

In his last year Muggs used to spend practically all of his time outdoors. He didn't like to stay in the house for some reason or other—perhaps it held too many unpleasant memories for him.

Anyway, it was hard to get him to come in and as a result the garbage man, the iceman, and the laundryman wouldn't come near the house. We had to haul the garbage down to the corner, take the laundry out and bring it back, and meet the iceman a block from home. After this had gone on for some time we hit on an ingenious arrangement for getting the dog in the house so that we could lock him up while the gas meter was read, and so on. Muggs was afraid of only one thing, an electrical storm. Thunder and lightning frightened him out of his senses (I think he thought a storm had broken the day the mantelpiece fell). He would rush into the house and hide under a bed or in a clothes closet. So we fixed up a thunder machine out of a long narrow piece of sheet iron with a wooden handle on one end. Mother would shake this vigorously when she wanted to get Muggs into the house. It made an excellent imitation of thunder, but I suppose it was the most round-about system for running a household that was ever devised. It took a lot out of mother.

A few months before Muggs died, he got to "seeing things." He would rise slowly from the floor, growling low, and stalk stiff-legged and menacing toward nothing at all. Sometimes the Thing would be just a little to the right or left of a visitor. Once a Fuller Brush salesman got hysterics. Muggs came wandering into the room like Hamlet following his father's ghost. His eyes were fixed on a spot just to the left of the Fuller Brush man, who stood it until Muggs was about three slow, creeping paces from him. Then he shouted. Muggs wavered on past him into the hallway grumbling to himself but the Fuller man went on shouting. I think mother had to throw a pan of cold water on him before he stopped. That was the way she used to stop us boys when we got into fights.

Muggs died quite suddenly one night. Mother wanted to bury him in the family lot under a marble stone with some such inscription as "Flights of angels sing thee to thy rest" but we persuaded her it was against the law. In the end we just put up a smooth board above his grave along a lonely road. On the board I wrote with an indelible pencil "Cave Canem." Mother was quite pleased with the simple classic dignity of the old Latin epitaph.

---

ingenious (in jēn′yəs) *adj.* made with or showing cleverness, originality, or imagination.
inscription (in skrip′shən) *n.* message or note written on something.
indelible (in del′ə bəl) *adj.* that cannot be removed or taken away.
epitaph (ep′i taf′) *n.* brief statement in memory of a dead person, usually written on a tombstone or monument.

meet JAMES THURBER

James Thurber (1896–1961) often wrote humorous anecdotes about growing up in Ohio and Virginia. As a student at Ohio State University, he was an editor of the college newspaper as well as a writer for the *Sun-Dial,* a monthly humor magazine. He later wrote about this time with typical dead-pan humor: "I showed about as much promise as a writer thirty-two years ago as I did an artist and I am willing to pay enormous sums of money for old copies of the *Sun-Dial* if people want to blackmail me with them."

After college, he worked for a time as a newspaper reporter and began selling his first stories. Later he moved to New York, where he became an editor and contributor to the *New Yorker* magazine. His humorous drawings and stories about his various misadventures remain popular.

More Memories About Animals

- *Travels with Charley: In Search of America* by John Steinbeck (Penguin, 1986). At the age of sixty, John Steinbeck set out with Charley, his French poodle, in a truck named for a horse. They traveled from coast to coast and this book describes what they found.

- *The Moon and I* by Betsy Byars (Julian Messner, 1991). Moon is a snake who shares a sun porch with Betsy Byars and her typewriter. Byars has always been fascinated by snakes, and Moon's presence is felt throughout her autobiography.

- *Woodsong* by Gary Paulsen (Bradbury, 1990). This sometimes thrilling, sometimes humorous account about the author's experiences with his team of dogs on the 1,000-mile Iditarod race across Alaska will enthrall any reader.

114

RESPONDING TO *Literature*

THINK • TALK • WRITE

1 Do you like the Thurbers? Do you think you would like to be a member of their family? Jot down your ideas in your journal.

2 How did the Thurber family get Muggs? If they had it to do over again, do you think the Thurbers would have taken Muggs as a pet? Why or why not?

3 Why do you think Muggs rarely tries to bite Mother?

4 Why do you think the Thurbers never try to get rid of Muggs? Explain your answer.

5 The Thurber family goes out of its way to keep Muggs in a good mood. Would you do this for a pet of yours? Why or why not?

ACTIVITIES

- **Write About Humor** What did you think was the funniest event in the story? Write a letter to James Thurber. Tell him what amused you and why it made you laugh.

- **Tell a Funny Story** Make up a funny situation involving a pet and tell it to the class. Use exaggeration, amusing descriptions, and dialog in your story.

VOCABULARY PRACTICE

Read each sentence. Decide if the word in color is used correctly or incorrectly. On a separate sheet of paper, write *correct* or *incorrect* and a sentence explaining your answer.

1 Mother was **irascible** and smiled at all of us that morning.

2 I was **mortified** when my mistake was printed in the newspaper.

3 The fire chief was one **municipal** officer at City Hall.

4 We all believed him and greeted his story with **incredulity.**

5 I was unable to wash out the **indelible** pencil mark on my shirt.

6 The **burly** man blocked the doorway with his broad shoulders.

7 The **epitaph** written on the birthday card was long and funny.

8 I was **oblivious** and noticed every detail of the crime scene.

9 His **ingenious** plan cleverly connected everyone's goals at once.

10 We were not able to read the **inscription** because the handwriting was unclear.

WRITING

Take some time to recall a key incident in your life. It may be an event that made you especially sad or happy. Write about your key incident.

PREWRITE

One good way to organize your thoughts is to ask yourself the "5 W's and H" questions. Take a look at what one writer did.

What happened? sprained wrist	**Who was involved?** Mr. Rosen, Jaime, and I
When did it happen? during last year's championship baseball game	**Where did the incident take place?** Powell Field
Why did it happen? slid incorrectly into home plate	**How did I feel?** in pain, but also proud because I scored the winning run

Now jot down the "5 W's and H" questions. Answer the questions, keeping your autobiographical incident in mind.

DRAFT

The person who answered the sample questions began his draft this way. Is the paragraph well organized?

This writer wants to introduce the main elements of the autobiographical ----▶ incident in the very first paragraph.

The Great Victory

I'll always remember last year's game at Powell Field. I can still see Mr. rosens signal and Jaime's face as I slid in a cloud of dust. Even though I sprained my rist and were in pain I felt proud that I had won the game for the team

Use the answers to your questions to plan your draft.

116

AUTOBIOGRAPHY

REVISE

You decide how much to revise. Sometimes you may need to rewrite entire paragraphs. Other times a few well-chosen additions or deletions will make all the difference. Take a look at what this writer did.

The writer feels that readers might not understand the kind of game or the importance of it without these additions. Do you agree?

> *championship baseball*
> I'll always remember last year's game
> at Powell Field. I can still see Mr. rosens
> *into home plate*
> signal and Jaime's face as I slid in a cloud
> of dust. Even though I sprained my rist
> and were in pain I felt proud that I had
> won the game for the team

Revise your own draft. How closely does what you wrote match the answers you gave to the "5 Ws and H" questions?

PROOFREAD

The writer proofread this sketch three times. First he looked for spelling errors, then for punctuation and capitalization errors, and finally for grammar errors.

If you are using a computer, run a spellcheck, but don't rely on it entirely. A computer will not catch every spelling error.

> *championship baseball*
> I'll always remember last year's game
> at Powell Field. I can still see Mr. rosen's
> *into home plate*
> signal and Jaime's face as I slid in a cloud
> *wrist*
> of dust. Even though I sprained my rist
> *was*
> and were in pain I felt proud that I had
> won the game for the team.

PUBLISH

What are some ways to share your autobiographical incident with others? Jot down your ideas. Then decide which one is best for your work.

WRITING

EFFECTIVE LEADS AND ENDINGS

ENRICH YOUR WRITING OF **AUTOBIOGRAPHICAL INCIDENTS.**

Effective leads will grab your readers' attention. Effective endings will help your readers know you have said all you want to say.

Read these paragraphs. Which lead grabs your attention? Which ending provides a satisfying close?

Paragraph 1

Lead: I knew that visiting Grandma was the right thing to do. I didn't understand why I was afraid to visit her.

Ending: The visit was fine, and I enjoyed seeing Grandma. I said good-bye to her.

Paragraph 2

Lead: "I know that Grandma has been asking to see me!" I snapped at Mom. As I said this, I wondered why I was in such a panic. Why were the palms of my hands sweating?

Ending: As I walked out of the nursing home, I felt a smile on my face. I knew this would be the start of many happy visits.

PRACTICE 1 Respond on a separate sheet of paper.

1 What details in the second lead drew you into the story? Which ending gives a sense of something important having happened in the story?

2 Rewrite the second set of leads and endings, trying to make it even better. Combine sentences in different ways.

118

COMBINING SENTENCES

REMEMBER THESE RULES ABOUT COMBINING SENTENCES WHEN YOU ARE WRITING **AUTOBIOGRAPHICAL INCIDENTS.**

- Combine sentences by joining simple subjects to make a compound subject or simple predicates to make a compound predicate. You can also join simple sentences to make a compound sentence.

- You can use the coordinating conjunctions *and, but,* and *or* and also the correlative conjunctions *both . . . and, not only . . . but also, whether . . . or, either . . . or,* and *neither . . . nor* to combine sentences. Or, combine information without using any conjunctions.

PRACTICE 2 Turn each set of two sentences into one sentence.

1 Grandma sculpts. Grandma paints.

2 Grandma wanted to sit by the lake during sunset. So did Mrs. Beatty.

3 They served a snack. Vegetables and cheeses made up the snack.

4 We could watch cable TV that night. We could go to the lecture.

EXPANDING SENTENCES

USE THESE RULES ABOUT EXPANDING SENTENCES WHEN YOU ARE WRITING **AUTOBIOGRAPHICAL INCIDENTS.**

- Expand sentences by adding descriptive details such as adjectives, adverbs, and adjective and adverb phrases.

- Expand sentences by using appositives. An *appositive* is a word or group of words that follows a noun and explains something about it. If an appositive identifies the noun it follows, it is essential and is not set off by commas. If it simply provides information about the noun it follows, it is nonessential and is set off by commas.

PRACTICE 3 Expand each sentence as indicated.

1 I walked down the drive. (descriptive details)

2 Sue Wong is the director. The director oversees the work. (appositive)

3 I collapsed into the chair. (descriptive details)

4 I put Grandma's gift in the window. It was an orchid. (appositive)

 **PROJECT 1**

WRITING A POEM

Our friends and family help make us who we are. Try to express your feelings about this subject by writing a poem.

PREWRITE

What kind of poem will you write? If it's a limerick, lines 1, 2, and 5 will rhyme, and it'll be funny. If it's free verse, rhymes aren't necessary. Your poem can tell a story or just describe a person. There are many possibilities. You might want to plan your poem in advance using a diagram like this one:

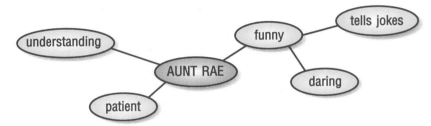

DRAFT There are plenty of ways to begin your draft. You could list some words that rhyme and that describe your subject. Then build lines around the rhyming words.

REVISE Here's your chance to adjust the rhythm of your poem or insert some interesting details.

PROOFREAD Ask a friend to read your poem and check for errors in spelling.

PUBLISH Practice reading your poem out loud a few times. Then perform it for an audience of friends or relatives.

▶ *Proofreading Alert!*

Use commas to separate parts of a sentence. Check page 204 in *Writing and Language Handbook.*

PROJECTS

MAKE A SCRAPBOOK ABOUT RELATIONSHIPS

REMEMBER TO: • PREWRITE • DRAFT • REVISE • PROOFREAD • PUBLISH

Create a warm-hearted picture essay about relationships. Browse old magazines for pictures of relationships. Choose some to cut out. Talk about them with a partner and come up with some captions. Organize your scrapbook into sections by grouping the pictures into categories. The categories will help you write captions. Take a look at the chart.

Friends	Families	People and Pets
Pearl and Fran—pen pals meet at last	Three generations of Wilsons on a picnic	My bird Roscoe on my head

ORGANIZE A DISCUSSION ON RELATIONSHIPS

REMEMBER TO: • PREWRITE • DRAFT • REVISE • PROOFREAD • PUBLISH

Organize a panel discussion to talk about different types of relationships.

Nominate a committee to brainstorm topics. You might use a diagram like the one here to organize your thoughts. Then choose classmates for the panel and elect a moderator. Afterward invite questions and comments from your audience.

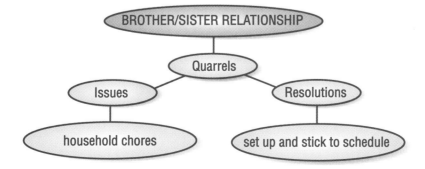

PEER PRESSURE

Peer pressure is the feeling that you have to do a certain thing because all your friends are doing it. You either go along with the group making all the rules or risk being left out. No one wants to be an outsider. Sure, having friends is important. But can you be friends with people who pressure you to do something you know is wrong?

CONSIDER THIS ISSUE: The person you're dating has invited you to a party given by some older friends, and you know the party will extend past your curfew. You don't want to stay out all night, and you aren't looking forward to being pressured to do so. You've explained your feelings to your date, but he/she still wants to go to the party. If you want to continue seeing this person, you have to go along with the group. What do you do?

- Do you do something that's wrong just to please someone else?
- Do you refuse to go to the party and risk breaking up with a person you like?
- Do you go to the party but make up an excuse for having to leave before everyone else?

O I N T S

Read the following viewpoints about how to deal with the issue of peer pressure. Then decide which one is closest to your own opinion. Think of some arguments of your own to support the position you choose.

VIEWPOINT 1

I would refuse to go to the party, even if it meant ending my friendship with my date.

- You shouldn't be forced to do something you know is wrong just to be part of a group.
- You shouldn't go out with someone who doesn't respect who you are and what you believe.
- You lose respect for yourself when you don't stand up for what you think is right.

VIEWPOINT 2

I would go to the party but I would plan to get home just an hour after my curfew.

- Getting home an hour past curfew, even if you don't really want to, isn't such a big deal.
- By compromising, you might be able to keep your relationship.

VIEWPOINT 3

I would go to the party and stay until it was over.

- If you really like someone, you don't embarrass that person in front of friends.
- If your relationship ends because you insist on being home at a certain time, you might not be invited anywhere for the rest of the year.

WHAT DO YOU THINK?

Think about this issue for a few minutes. Do you agree with one of the viewpoints above, or do you have another? Discuss your views with a small group. Then role-play a scene between two teenagers as they try to resolve the situation.

HOME • SCHOOL • COMMUNITY

RELATIONSHIPS: The connections and ties we share with others.

Relationships are the bonds that connect living things. We make these connections with people every day, whether they are family members, friends, and classmates, or doctors, clerks, and others in the community or at school.

These relationships can enrich lives and create complications. In "Barrio Boy," Ernesto Galarza describes how a special relationship with his first-grade teacher helped him take pride in both his Mexican heritage and in his new country. In "The Dog That Bit People," James Thurber describes the difficult relationship his family had with their pet and with other people because of the dog.

We have personal and professional relationships. Sometimes professional relationships begin in **classified ads** in newspapers or magazines. Look at the classified listings to the left.

People place classified ads in magazines or newspapers. These ads appear in a special section in the back of periodicals, where they are arranged under various headings. The ads offer or seek jobs, services, housing, and specific items, such as cars, for sale or rent.

I O N S

THINK • TALK • WRITE

Here are three activities that make use of classified ads. Think of other situations in which classified ads are important. Then choose an activity below or one of your own and talk or write about it.

PROJECT 1

CLASSIFYING ADS Classified ads help you buy or sell a particular item or service. Bring in a page of these ads from a community newspaper or magazine. Identify the headings under which the ads are grouped. Count the number of ads under each heading. Graph your results. Discuss your findings in small groups.

PROJECT 2

WRITE AN AD Write a classified ad for a community newspaper. Before you begin, talk to a representative of the newspaper to find out the cost for different lengths of classified ads. Your ad should offer a particular service, such as dog walking. Remember that classified ads must list all important information in very few lines. Find out how much it would cost to run your ad for four weeks.

PROJECT 3

PLACE AN AD Two factors determine the cost of an ad: the number of words in the ad and the number of times the ad will appear. Find out the classified ad rates charged by a community newspaper or magazine. Work in small groups to make a chart showing ad rates for several newspapers and magazines in your area. Study your chart. In which periodical would you place a classified ad? Why?

getting the sweet

strawberries
from my
fingers
        down
        into the basket
without
        eating all of them
                up
                    is
        the problem

        the solution
                    is
                    not
        to solve
        the problem
until
    you
        are
    full
        of answers

—Arnold Adoff

SOLUTIONS

solutions
solutions
solutions

Blossoming *1934   Paul Klee   Kunstmuseum Winterhur, Switzerland*

SOLUTIONS

BEFORE READING

....
AMANDA AND
THE WOUNDED BIRDS

CONNECT TO LITERATURE

How well do you communicate with your parents and friends? Do you ever have trouble getting people to listen to you? As you read the story "Amanda and the Wounded Birds," note in your journal how Amanda tries to talk to her mother.

THINKING ABOUT PLOT: CLIMAX AND RESOLUTION

The series of events in a story is called the *plot.* As the story builds, complications arise and you become more curious about how the conflict will be resolved. The *climax* in the plot of a story is the point of greatest suspense. At this point, you are able to predict who will triumph in the conflict and how that character will do it.

Following the climax, there may still be some remaining questions about the characters and events of the story. The *resolution* is the part of the plot that ties up any loose ends.

HAVE YOU EVER?

Most likely you're aware of and perhaps have even listened to a few radio call-in shows. But have you ever been tempted to call one of these programs yourself? What do you think it would be like to know you were on the air and that thousands, perhaps tens of thousands, of people were listening to you? Think about that as you read "Amanda and the Wounded Birds."

Amanda and the

*I*t's not that my mother doesn't understand, because she does. In fact, she understands so well, and so much, and so single-mindedly, that half the time she goes around with a glazed look in her eyes and forgets to get her hair cut, and go to the dentist and that we're almost out of toilet paper or tuna fish.

She makes her living understanding, which may make more sense when I tell you that my mother is Dr. Emma Hart. Now, if that doesn't help, then probably, like me until my consciousness was raised, you've always thought of radio as the place to hear the Top 40 or sometimes the weather report when you're heading for the shore on a summer Friday afternoon. But just try twiddling the dial and you'll find her, way over to the left on the band, next to the country and western station.

Maybe what I should do is go back a little and explain. You see, my mother is a psychotherapist, which means that she counsels people and tries to help them find ways of dealing with their problems. She's also a widow. My father died when I was a baby, and sometimes I try to imagine what it must have been like for her, taking care of a baby alone

Wounded Birds

by Colby Rodowsky

illustrated by Vicki Yiannias

and trying to establish a practice all at the same time. One thing I'm sure of is that knowing Mom, she handled it gracefully, and <u>stoically</u>, and with that funny way she has of biting her lower lip so that for all her hanging-in-there attitude she still looks like a ten-year-old kid—the kind you want to do something for because she's not always whining or sniffling. I guess you'd have to say that as much as possible my mother is in charge of her own life, which is the way she tries to get the people who call in to her on the radio to be.

The way the radio program got started was that several years ago the producer was looking for something to put on in the late afternoon when people were mostly fixing dinner or driving carpool or just sitting with their feet up. It wasn't exactly prime time. Then he remembered how he'd heard Mom speak at a dinner once and had thought at the time that putting someone like her on radio would be a real public service. Besides, the ratings couldn't be any lower than they had been for the Handy Home Fixit show he'd had on before. Anyway, he tracked her down, arranged for a test, and then Mom was on the air.

---

stoically (stō′i kə lē) *adv.* in a manner unaffected by pain or pleasure.

I never will forget that first show. I mean, there was my mother's voice coming out of our kitchen radio, sounding slightly frantic and giving those first callers more than they bargained for: I guess she was afraid if she let them off the line there wouldn't *be* any more. That day even the producer called with a question. And the boy in the studio who went for coffee. But Mom hung in there, and calls continued to come in, and then they started backing up, and it wasn't long before people opened by saying, "I didn't think I'd *ever* get through to you." After only a month on the air the Emma Hart show went from one hour to two; and the way I figured it, a lot of people were eating dinner later than they ever had before. Including us.

Mom really cared about the people who telephoned her, and almost right from the beginning she was calling them her "wounded birds." Not on the air, of course, and *never* to anyone but me. I got used to her looking up in the middle of dinner or from watching the late news on TV and saying, "I hope my wounded bird with the <u>abusive</u> husband will get herself into counseling" or "The wounded bird with those children who walk all over her had better learn to <u>assert</u> herself before it's too late." And *I* sure learned not to joke around: once I referred to one of her callers as a fractured canary and almost started World War III.

Not long after this, things really started to happen. First, Mom's show was moved to a better time slot. Then it was syndicated, so that she wasn't just on the air here but in a bunch of other cities, too. The way "Doonesbury" and "Dick Tracy" are in a bunch of newspapers. Now, I have to say that for the most part my mother's pretty cool about things, but the day she found out that the Emma Hart show was being syndicated she just about flipped. She called me from the studio and told me to meet her at the Terrace Garden for dinner, to be sure and get spiffed up because we were going all out.

During dinner Mom spent a lot of time staring into the candlelight and smiling to herself. Finally she said, "Just think of all those people who'll be listening now." And let me tell you, I *was* thinking about them, and it worried me a lot. I mean the way I saw it, there were going to be even more problems: more victims who were <u>downtrodden</u> or misunderstood. More stories about people who had been abused or who had kids on drugs or dropping out, or ne'er-do-well relatives moving in. But when I tried to say that, Mom was suddenly all attention. "Don't be silly, Amanda. It's the same amount of time and the same number of calls—

---

abusive (ə bū′siv) *adj.* harmful; injurious; mistreating with cruelty or roughness.
assert (ə sûrt′) *v.t.* insist upon recognition of.
132 **downtrodden** (doun′trod′ən) *adj.* abused or oppressed, as by those in power.

you'll hardly notice any difference. Only now I'll have wounded birds in Phoenix and Pittsburgh and Philadelphia."

In one way she was right: the show sounded pretty much the same. (Except that *I* found out that when your husband/lover/friend walks out on you it hurts as much in Peoria as it does in Perth Amboy.)

In another way she was wrong: she was busier than she had ever been before, what with traveling and lecturing and doing guest shows from other cities. For a while there, it was as if I was spending as much time at my best friend Terri's as I was at my own house. Then eventually Mom decided I could stay at our place when she had to be out of town, as long as Terri stayed there with me, which wasn't as good or as bad as it sounds, because Terri lives right across the street and her mother has X-ray eyes. I mean we can hardly manage to reach for our favorite breakfast of Twinkies and Oreo ice cream with an orange juice chaser before her mother is on the telephone telling us to eat cornflakes instead—and to wash the dishes.

Sometimes I felt that life was nothing but a revolving door: Mom going out while I was coming in. I know there are some kids who would've thought I was lucky, but the thing about my mother is that she's okay. And I wanted to see more of her. Besides that, I needed to talk to her. I don't know why, but all of a sudden it seemed that things were piling up around me. No major crises, you understand. Nothing that would exactly stop traffic.

I'll give you an example.

Take my friend Terri. I have a terrible feeling that she has a secret crush on my boyfriend Josh. If she does, it would be a disaster, because how could we really be friends anymore? But then again how could Terri and I *not* be friends? I'm not sure *why* I think this, unless it's because she gets quiet and acts bored when I talk about him a lot—the way you do when you don't want to let on about liking someone. I mean she couldn't *really* be bored. Could she?

Then there's Miss Spellman, my English teacher, who has this really atrocious breath and is forever leaning into people as she reads poetry in class. Imagine somebody breathing garbage fumes on you as she recites Emily Dickinson. If something doesn't happen soon I may never like poetry again.

Now, maybe these aren't world problems, any more than the incident with the guidance counselor was, but it bugged me all the same.

Our school has an <u>obsession</u> about students getting into *good* colleges a.s.a.p. and knowing what they want to do with the rest of their lives (Terri and I call it the life-packaging <u>syndrome</u>). Anyway, this particular day I was coming out of gym on my way to study hall when Mr. Burnside, the guidance counselor, stopped me and started asking me all this stuff, like what my career goals were and had I decided what I wanted to major in in college.

What I said (only politer than it sounds here) was that how did I know what I wanted to major in when I didn't even know where I wanted to *go* to college. Mr. Burnside got a wild look in his eyes and started opening and closing his mouth so that all I could see was a shiny strand of spit running between his top and bottom teeth while he lectured me on how I was going about this whole college thing the wrong way. He said I should come into the guidance office someday and let him feed me into the computer—well, not me exactly, but stuff like my grades, extra curricular activities, and whether or not I needed financial aid.

"And what does your mother say?" he asked as he rooted in his pocket for a late pass to get me into study hall. "You'll certainly have it easier than anybody else in your class, or the school either for that matter—living with Dr. Emma Hart." He laughed that horselaugh of his and slapped me on the back. "She'll get right to the *Hart* of it." Another laugh. "Anybody else'd have to call her on the telephone." His laughter seemed to follow me all the way to study hall. I even heard it bouncing around in my head as I settled down to do my Spanish.

"Anybody else'd have to call her on the telephone," he had said.

Why not? I thought as I was walking home from school.

*W*hy not? I asked myself when Josh and I were eating popcorn and playing Scrabble on the living room floor that night.

And pretty soon *why not?* changed to *when?* The answer to that one was easy though, because spring vacation was only a week and a half away and that would give me the perfect opportunity.

The funny thing was that once I'd decided to do it, I never worried about getting through. Maybe that was because I'd heard Mom say plenty of times that they always liked it when kids called into the show, and I guess I figured that unless everybody on spring vacation decided

---

obsession (əb sesh′ən) *n.* state of being occupied or troubled about something.
syndrome (sin′drōm) *n.* group of symptoms that together are characteristic of a particular disease or disorder.

to call the Dr. Emma Hart Show, I wouldn't have any trouble. Besides, I practiced in the shower making my voice huskier than usual and just a little breathless, hoping that it would sound sincere and make an impression on Jordan, the guy who screens the calls and tries for just the right balance of men, women, and kids, with not too much emphasis on busted romances as opposed to anxiety attacks.

The next funny thing was that once I'd made up my mind to call Dr. Emma Hart, I began to feel like a wounded bird myself, and I was suddenly awfully glad that she cared about them the way she did. I had a little trouble deciding what I wanted to ask her on the show, and even before I could make up my mind I began to think of other things that bothered me too. Not problems, but stuff I'd like to talk over with Mom. Like Vietnam, for example. I'd watched *Apocalypse Now* on TV and there was a lot I didn't understand. And what about the sixties?—was Mom ever involved in <u>sit-ins</u> or <u>walkouts</u> or any of that? I somehow doubted it, but it would be important to know for sure. Finally it came to me: what I wanted to ask Dr. Hart about was not being able to talk to Mom because there she was all wrapped up with her wounded birds. Only the whole thing got confusing, one being the other and all.

$\mathcal{A}$nyway, I did it. I put the call in just before eleven on the Monday morning of spring vacation and almost chickened out when Jordan answered. I had met him a couple of times down at the studio, and I could almost see him now, looking like some kind of an intense juggler who is trying to keep everything going at once. I heard my voice, as if it were coming from somewhere far away, giving my name as Claire (it's my middle name) and outlining my problem. When I got finished, Jordan said that he was putting me on hold and not to go away, that Dr. Hart would be with me shortly.

And all of a sudden she was. I mean, there I was talking to my own mother and telling her how I couldn't talk to my mother, and how the things I wanted to talk to her about weren't actually big deals anyway, but still—.

Dr. Hart let me go on for a while and then she broke in and said that it was important for me to know that my concerns were as real as

---

sit-ins (sit'inz') *n., pl.* protest demonstrations in which persons sit in a public place and stay there until their demands are agreed to or considered.

walkouts (wôk'outs') *n., pl.* strikes in which workers leave their working places; walking out of a meeting or the like, especially as an expression of protest.

anybody else's and it sounded as if my mother and I had a pretty good relationship that had just gotten a little off the track and what I had to do was be really up-front with her and let her know how I felt. Then she suggested that I make a date with my mother for lunch so that I could tell her (Mom) exactly what I'd told her (Dr. Emma Hart), and that I should be sure to call back and let her know how it worked out.

After that I said, "Okay," and "Thank you." Then I hung up.

The only trouble was that as soon as Mom got home that day I knew it wasn't going to work.

She was sort of coming unglued. It had been a bad day, she told me. One of her private patients was in the midst of a crisis; the producer of the show was having a fight with his wife and wanted to tell Mom all about it. She had a dinner speech to give Saturday night and didn't have a thought about what to say, and my uncle Alex had called from Scranton to ask Mom to try to talk some sense into his teenage son, who was driving them all crazy.

Then she looked at me and said, "Thank heavens you've got it all together."

Talk about guilt. Right away I was going to break rule number one: I wasn't going to be able to be up-front.

The thing was, I knew I couldn't take what was already one rotten week for Mom and dump all my problems (which seemed to be getting bigger by the minute) on her. Even though I felt like I was going to explode.

By Friday, I knew I needed another talk with Dr. Hart. After all, she'd said to call back, hadn't she?

Getting through Jordan was even easier the second time. All I had to say was that I'd spoken to Dr. Hart earlier in the week and that she'd said to let her know what happened.

"Oh, good, a success story," Jordan said right away, jumping to conclusions. I guess he knew what kind of a week it had been too.

"Hold on; Dr. Hart will be with you soon," he said.

And there was Dr. Emma Hart again. And suddenly there *I* was, unloading about how what she had suggested wasn't going to work.

"Why not?" she wanted to know. "Did you try?"

"Yes—no," I said. Then I was going on again, all about Bad-Breath Spellman, the guidance counselor, and how maybe my best friend had a thing for my boyfriend. She kept steering me back to the subject of my mother and why I hadn't arranged to have lunch with her.

I said that my mother had had a bad week. That she was swamped, preoccupied, distracted, and running behind. And then it happened. I mean, I heard the words sliding off my lips and couldn't stop them. I said, "The thing about my mother is that she has all these wounded birds who have really important problems and they take all the time she has."

A silence ballooned up between us and was so loud I couldn't hear anything else—and if you know anything about radio, you know that the worst thing that can happen is silence. It lasted forever, and while it was going on I gave serious thought to running away from home, or at least hanging up.

When Mom finally spoke, her voice sounded choked, as if she had swallowed a gumball.

"We've been talking to Claire this morning who is really Amanda," she said. "And one of the things we talk a lot about on this show is saying what you have to say—even if that's not always easy. Are you still there, Amanda?"

"Yes," I squeaked.

"If I know Amanda," my mother went on, "she would rather have run away, or hung up, but instead she did something harder. She hung on."

I gulped.

"Amanda is my daughter, and it seems we have some things to talk about, so what I'm going to do is ask my assistant to make a reservation for lunch at the Terrace Garden." Then it sounded as though Mom had moved in closer to the microphone and was speaking just to me. "If you hurry, Amanda, I'll meet you at 1:30. So we can talk."

*A*nd we did: about Bad-Breath Spellman, and Terri, and how it's okay not to know now what I want to do with the rest of my life.

We talked about saving the whales, and our two weeks at the shore this summer, and how some day we're going to Ireland. About books and movies and the time in fourth grade when I got the chicken pox and Mom caught them from me.

And we talked about how we had missed talking to each other and what we could do about it.

We ate lunch slowly, and took ages deciding on dessert, and ages more eating it.

We sat there all afternoon, until the light streaking in the windows changed from yellow to a deep, burning gold and the busboys started setting the tables for dinner.

Meet Colby Rodowsky

A former teacher and librarian, Colby Rodowsky (born 1932) now devotes her time to writing books, short stories, and essays. The mother of five daughters and a son, Rodowsky finds she gets ideas not from her own children but "from the child that I was."

Like Amanda, the characters in her stories often must deal with difficult situations. Although some of her writing is based on her own exploits growing up, Rodowsky says her books are a "combination of reality and imagination."

More Books by Colby Rodowsky

- *Sydney, Herself* (Farrar, Straus & Giroux, 1989). Coming to grips with life's problems is not always as easy as it seems. Sydney, a high-school sophomore, learns this lesson and others as what starts out as a harmless fantasy turns into an obsession.

- *Julie's Daughter* (Farrar, Straus & Giroux, 1985). In this award-winning novel, the author explores the difficult relationship among three women: seventeen-year-old Slug; her mother, Julie, who abandoned Slug as a baby; and their terminally ill neighbor.

- *Fitchett's Folly* (Farrar, Straus & Giroux, 1987). This highly entertaining novel set in Maryland at the turn of the century recounts the coming of age of Sarey-Ann as she copes with the joys and problems of a particularly difficult summer.

RESPONDING TO *Literature*

THINK • TALK • WRITE

1 Do you think the characters in this story are realistic? Jot down your thoughts in your journal.

2 What is Amanda's problem? Do you think her problem is serious? Is it common? Explain your answers.

3 How does Dr. Hart know it is Amanda she is counseling on the phone? Do you think Dr. Hart handles the situation well? Explain your answer. What else might she have done? What would you have done?

4 Do you think Dr. Hart is a good psychotherapist? Explain your reasons. Do you think she is a good parent? Why or why not?

5 In many cultures it would be unacceptable to discuss personal problems on the radio. In such cultures, where do you think people might turn if they needed help with personal matters?

ACTIVITIES

- **Write About Plot: Climax and Resolution** Change the plot of "Amanda and the Wounded Birds" so that it has a different climax and resolution. Rewrite the story from the point at which you made your changes.

- **Create an Advertisement** Create an advertisement for the Emma Hart show. Start out by thinking of a strong visual image for your ad. Then write some copy that will make people want to tune in to the show. Use pictures from magazines or draw your own to capture people's attention.

VOCABULARY PRACTICE

On a separate sheet of paper, write whether the words in each pair are *synonyms* (words with the same or similar meanings) or *antonyms* (words with opposite meanings).

1 assert—insist

2 abusive—kindly

3 stoically—complainingly

4 downtrodden—oppressed

5 obsession—preoccupation

BEFORE READING

HELPING HANDS

CONNECT TO LITERATURE

Have you ever had to depend on someone to help you do some very simple things, such as dressing you or bringing you something to eat? Perhaps there was a time when an injury to an arm or leg kept you from doing for yourself the things you normally would do? Discuss your ideas with a classmate. As you read "Helping Hands," note in your journal how some very special people and animals help improve the lives of individuals with physical disabilities.

THINKING ABOUT AUTHOR'S PURPOSE

Every author writes for a reason; this reason is called the *author's purpose.* Some authors may write to entertain or to explain, while others may write to share personal opinions or to persuade. Often, authors have more than one purpose in mind when writing a particular piece. As you read, consider the purposes Brent Ashabranner might have had in writing this selection.

DID YOU KNOW?

Until very recently, people with disabilities were viewed with a combination of fear and suspicion. Since the early 1970s the Independent Living Movement in Berkeley, California, has tried to provide physically challenged individuals with the same opportunities as those who are not physically challenged. Supporters of Independent Living have fought for federal, state, and local laws that would entitle individuals with physical disabilities to equal access to education, employment, and housing.

Helping

MEET BRENT ASHABRANNER

"Don't try to tell me that what you read as a boy doesn't influence your later life. I grew up in a small Oklahoma town [Shawnee]; but . . . I was hooked on books about foreign places," says Brent Ashabranner. This attraction has inspired many choices during his career. Ashabranner has worked as a Peace Corps volunteer in Africa and India and has lived in Hawaii, Japan, the Philippines, and Indonesia. He knows many people who make a difference all over the world.

Ashabranner is well known for calling attention to people who find solutions to problems that seem impossible. He comments: "Writing about people whose voices need to be heard—immigrants, refugees, immigrant farm workers, Native Americans—is making clear that their lives have value and that they have a right to a decent life. It is work that I love."

Brent Ashabranner's award-winning books include *To Live in Two Worlds*, *Gavriel and Jemal*, and *Into a Strange Land*. All three books were named American Library Association Best Books for Young Adults.

142

Hands

by Brent Ashabranner
Photographs by Paul Conklin

You are thirsty. A cold drink is in the refrigerator ten feet away, but it might as well be ten miles away. You can't move a muscle to reach it. Your nose itches until your eyes water, but you can't lift a hand to scratch. You want to watch a videotape, but all you can do is look helplessly at your VCR across the room and wait until someone comes to put in the cassette.

Your name is Mitch Coffman, and you are a prisoner in your own body. Your mind is clear and sharp; you can talk and move your head, but you can't move any other part of your body. Like almost a hundred thousand other men and women in the United States, you are a quadriplegic, totally paralyzed from the neck down.

Mitch Coffman's entry into the world of the quadriplegic came on a day that should have been a happy one. He was returning from a party to celebrate his thirtieth birthday when his car skidded on a bridge and went into a spin. Mitch was thrown out with an impact that broke his neck.

When Mitch regained consciousness, he came instantly face-to-face with a terrible reality: he had suffered permanent damage to his spine between the third and fifth <u>cervical</u> <u>vertebrae</u>. He would be paralyzed for the rest of his life.

---

cervical vertebrae (sûr′vi kəl vûr′tə brē′) bones of the upper spine.

*M*ary Joan Willard and a capuchin friend

After months of physical therapy, Mitch regained enough movement in his left hand to operate the control for an electric wheelchair. And he was more fortunate than most quadriplegics because he was able to move into a government-subsidized apartment building especially equipped for people with severe physical disabilities. The building has ramps instead of stairs, roll-in showers, light switches and other electrical and kitchen equipment that are easy to reach and operate. Attendants are also on duty at all times. Still, there were endless hours every day and night when Mitch was alone in his apartment waiting, waiting for the simplest tasks to be performed for him.

She could do dozens of other things for him that he could not do for himself.

And then one day a stranger arrived in Mitch's little apartment. She was only eighteen inches tall, weighed but a furry six pounds, and communicated in excited squeaks and endless trills. But she could open the refrigerator door and bring Mitch a cold drink or a sandwich. She could scratch his nose with a soft cloth when it itched. She could put a videotape in the VCR. She could do dozens of other things for him that he could not do for himself.

The stranger was a black and brown capuchin monkey, and her improbable name was Peepers. Almost as important as what she could do for him was the fact that she was there, a companion, a constant presence in the apartment where, for most of the long hours of long days, there had been only Mitch.

"It took us months to learn to live together," Mitch explains as Peepers sits quietly in his lap. "Now I can't imagine living without her."

The modest quarters of Helping Hands: <u>Simian</u> Aides for the Disabled are on the fourth floor of an office building on Commonwealth Avenue in Boston. On my first visit there I could hear monkeys chattering in the training room. I was eager to watch the training, but before that I wanted to talk to Mary Joan Willard, the educational psychologist who started and is director of Helping Hands.

Quantum leaps of the imagination have always fascinated me, and I opened our conversation on that point. "How did you get the idea that monkeys might be trained to do things for paralyzed human beings?" I asked. "What made you think it was possible?"

---

simian (sim′ē ən) *adj.* of, relating to, or resembling an ape or monkey.

Mary Joan explained that after receiving her doctorate in educational psychology from Boston University, she began a postdoctoral fellowship in 1977 at Tufts New England Medical Center in Boston. The fellowship was for <u>rehabilitative</u> study and work with persons who had suffered severe physical injury. In her daily rounds she soon came to know Joe, a patient at the center. One minute he had been a happy, healthy twenty-three year old. The next minute, because of a diving accident, he was a quadriplegic, paralyzed from the neck down. His story was an all-too-familiar one, but he was the first quadriplegic Mary Joan had ever known.

"I was shocked," she said. "I found it inconceivable that someone so young, so full of life was going to spend the rest of his days completely dependent on other people, dependent for a drink of water, for a bite of food, dependent on someone to bring him a book or turn out a light. I am a psychologist, and I kept thinking, There has to be some way to make him more independent.

"I couldn't get him out of my mind. I would sit in my room and think about him lying there in his room, helpless. And then one night it hit me out of the blue. Chimps! Why couldn't chimpanzees be trained to do things for quadriplegics like Joe? I kept thinking about it, and I didn't get much sleep that night."

The next day Mary Joan went to see B. F. Skinner, the famous Harvard psychologist who has done extensive pioneering research with animals, using reward and punishment techniques to alter their behavior. Mary Joan had worked three years for Skinner as a parttime assistant. He might not think her idea was workable, but she knew he would not scoff at it.

Skinner was amused at his assistant's excitement over her new idea; he pointed out that chimpanzees grow to be almost as big as humans, are stronger than humans, and often are bad-tempered. Chimpanzees would be too risky. But Mary Joan was right; Skinner did not laugh. The idea intrigued him.

They are intelligent, easy to train, and form strong bonds of loyalty to their human masters.

Why not, he asked, think about using capuchins, the little creatures traditionally known as organ-grinder monkeys? They are small, usually no more than six or seven pounds and seldom more than eighteen inches tall. They are intelligent, easy to train, and form strong bonds of loyalty to their human masters. Furthermore, they have a long life expectancy, an average of about thirty years.

---

rehabilitative (rē′hə bil′i tā tiv) *adj.* given to restoring good health.

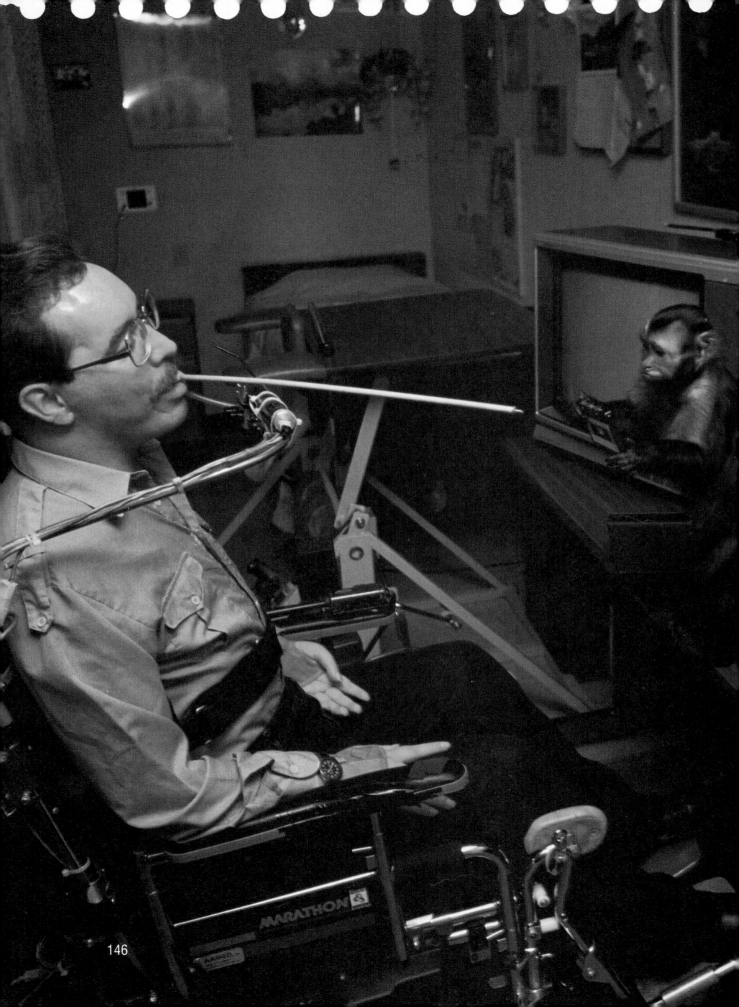

That was all the encouragement Mary Joan needed. She did some reading about capuchins, found out where they could be purchased, then went to the director of postdoctoral programs at Tufts and asked for money to start an experimental capuchin training program.

"He nearly fell off his chair laughing," Mary Joan said, remembering the director's first reaction to her proposal.

But Mary Joan was persistent and persuasive. When the director stopped laughing, he came through with a grant and some training space. The grant was just two thousand dollars, but it was enough for Mary Joan to buy four monkeys, some cages, and hire student trainers at one dollar an hour.

"I thought we could train them in eight weeks," Mary Joan recalled. "I had never touched a monkey! It took us eight weeks just to coax them out of their cages. The monkeys I was able to buy had had some pretty hard treatment. They weren't in a mood to trust any human being."

But a beginning had been made, and patience and dedication paid off in training the monkeys in an astonishing variety of tasks: taking food from a refrigerator and putting it in a microwave oven; turning lights on and off; doing the same with a television set, stereo, heater, air conditioner; opening and closing curtains; setting up books, magazines, and computer printouts on a reading stand.

Using his mouthstick, Mitch gives
instructions to Peepers.

One piece of equipment <u>essential</u> to most quadriplegics is a mouthstick which is used for turning pages, dialing a phone, typing, working a computer, and many other actions which improve the quality of a quadriplegic's life. One problem is that the mouthstick often falls to the floor or onto the wheelchair tray. The monkey helper is quickly taught to pick up the stick and replace it correctly in its master's mouth.

"The capuchins have great manual <u>dexterity</u>, greater than a human adult's," Mary Joan said, "and they're very bright. But we don't try to train them to do tasks where they have to think."

Judi Zazula, an occupational therapist, has been with Helping Hands almost from the beginning. Her title is program director, but Mary Joan describes her as a partner. Judi makes the same point about not putting a monkey in a situation where it has to think about the right way to do something. "Everything," she says, "is planned so that the monkey has just one way to respond if it does the task right."

The basic motivation for a monkey to perform a task correctly is a simple reward system. When it carries out a command as it is supposed to—turning on a VCR or bringing a drink—the trainer, and later the quadriplegic owner, praises the monkey for doing a good job and at the same time gives it a treat, usually a few drops of strawberry-

---

essential (i sen'shəl) *adj.* very important or necessary.
dexterity (dek ster'i tē) *n.* skill in using the hands, body, or mind.

flavored syrup. The quadriplegic releases the syrup by means of a wheelchair control.

There is also a system of punishment because capuchins are endlessly curious and occasionally mischievous. One monkey, for example, began dimming the lights when its owner was reading so that it would get a reward when it was told to turn them up again. More often, however, misbehavior is likely to be opening a drawer without being asked to or throwing paper out of a wastebasket in the hope of finding something interesting.

The monkeys are taught that anything with a white circular sticker pasted on it—such as a medicine cabinet—is off limits. If a monkey violates the off-limits rule, it is warned with a buzz from a small battery-operated device that it wears on a belt around its waist. If it doesn't obey the warning, the quadriplegic master can use remote controls to give the monkey a tiny electric shock. The warning buzz is usually sufficient, and most owners report that they almost never have to use the shock treatment. Judi Zazula points out that buzz-shock collars are also used in dog training.

Late in 1979 Robert Foster, a twenty-five-year-old quadriplegic living near Boston, became the first person to take part in a pilot project to test the <u>feasibility</u> of using a capuchin

monkey aide. Robert, paralyzed from the shoulders down as the result of an automobile accident at the age of eighteen, had been living by himself for several years with the help of a personal care attendant. The attendant lived in the apartment with Robert but worked full time in a nearby hospital. That meant that Robert was alone in the apartment for nine hours or more at least five days a week.

Robert's new helper, a six-pound capuchin female named Hellion, helped to fill the long hours and continues to do so eight years after the experiment began. Robert communicates with Hellion—who deserves a nicer name—by aiming a small laser pointer at what he wants the monkey

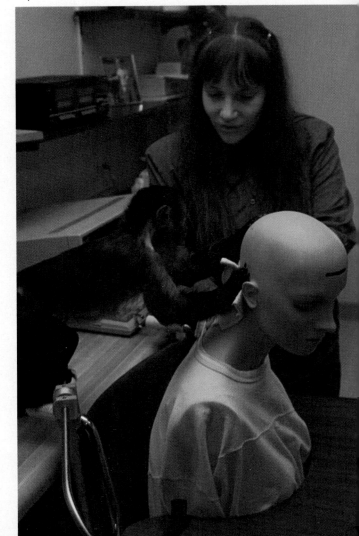

---

feasibility (fē′zə bil′i tē) *n.* ability to be done successfully; practicality.

to bring or do. The laser is mounted on the chin control mechanism of his wheelchair. He also gives her a voice command such as "Bring" or "Open."

Hellion feeds Robert, brushes his hair, tidies up his wheelchair tray, brings him books, and carries out a whole range of other helpful tasks. For his part Robert <u>dispenses</u> strawberry-syrup rewards and tells Hellion how nice she is. Hellion is close by Robert's wheelchair all day, but when he tells her it is time for bed, she will go into her cage and lock the door.

As publicity about simian aides has spread across the country, Helping Hands has been swamped with requests for monkeys. Mary Joan and Judi are proceeding slowly with placements, however, still treating each case as an experiment. A number of additional capuchins have been placed with quadriplegics, and there have been no failures.

Mary Joan has had to spend an increasing amount of her time in fund raising and in administrative details of making Helping Hands a smoothly functioning nonprofit organization. "For the first two years we had to get along on three thousand dollars a year," Mary Joan said. "Fortunately, we don't have to pay student trainers much, and they love the experience."

Several major organizations and agencies concerned with severely disabled persons were interested, but all were <u>skeptical</u>. In the early stages

Practice makes perfect. Someday this monkey will gently rub a quadriplegic's itching nose or cheek.

Mary Joan wrote thirty-nine grant proposals and sent them to philanthropic foundations and government agencies, but not one was approved. But she persisted and, as evidence mounted that the capuchins could do the job, a trickle of financial support began. Now the Veterans Administration, National Medical Enterprises, the Educational Foundation of America, and the Paralyzed Veterans of America give some financial help to Helping Hands.

"A robot won't sit in your lap and put its arms around you."

Money is also received through private contributions, but fund raising still requires time that Mary Joan would rather be giving to other parts of the program.

Lack of money was not the only problem in the early days of the program. Some critics said that the idea of monkeys serving as helpers was demeaning to the quadriplegics as human beings. Some medical authorities said that mechanical equipment—robotics is the technical term—could be developed to do a better job than monkeys.

To the first criticism, Mary Joan points out that no one thinks it is beneath the dignity of a blind person to

---

dispenses (di spen′səz) *v.t.* gives out in portions.
skeptical (skep′ti kəl) *adj.* showing doubt.

have a dog serve as a guide. As to robotic equipment, she agrees that for some quadriplegics mechanical tools may be best. But she points out that no piece of equipment can provide the companionship and sheer pleasure that an affectionate capuchin can.

"A robot won't sit in your lap and put its arms around you," Mary Joan said.

Developing a reliable supply of trainable monkeys was a problem that Helping Hands solved through the cooperation of Walt Disney World in Florida. A capuchin breeding colony has been established on Discovery Island in this world-famous recreational-educational center, and it will produce most of the monkeys needed in the quadriplegic program. Other monkeys are received through private donation, and Helping Hands has become a safe haven for monkeys that have been <u>confiscated</u> by government agencies because of mistreatment or having been brought into the country illegally.

Trial-and-error testing proved to the Helping Hands crew that early so-cialization was necessary to train a monkey that would be affectionate and happy when it became part of a hu-man household. The answer has been the creation of a foster home program. When the monkeys from Walt Disney World are young babies, six to eight weeks old, they are placed with foster families. These volunteer families agree

to raise the monkeys in their homes for about three years and then turn them over to Helping Hands to be trained as aides to quadriplegics.

The carefully selected volunteer families agree to spend ten hours a day with their primate babies for the first six months—ten hours with the monkey outside its cage. This means that the foster mother and father and older children are actually carrying the baby monkey as they go about their household routines. Older mon-keys require less time, but members of the household still must spend at least four hours daily with the young capuchin if it is to become a truly "humanized" primate.

Over sixty-five monkeys are now living with foster families.

Being a foster parent to a young monkey may sound like fun, and in many ways it can be a delightful experience. But it is time-consuming and demanding, and the time inevita-bly comes when the monkey must be given over to Helping Hands. "Everyone knows this moment of part-ing is coming, and most people handle it well," Mary Joan said, "but for some it is very hard. We have been offered

---

confiscated (kon'fis kā' tid) *v.t.* seized by authority.

*J*udi Zazula teaches one of her bright pupils to place a tape in a cassette player.

as much as five thousand dollars to let a family keep a monkey. But, of course, we can't do that."

If for any reason a monkey does not successfully complete its training at Helping Hands, it is offered to its foster care family as a pet. Should the foster care family be unable to take it, Helping Hands maintains a carefully screened list of other families who have applied for a monkey pet. The "unsuccessful" monkey will be placed in the kind of human home environment to which it is accustomed.

"One of the first things I was asked to design was the nose scratcher."

Over sixty-five monkeys are now living with foster families. More than a hundred additional families have passed the screening test and are waiting to receive their foster "children."

Judi Zazula is a rehabilitation engineer. Together with Doug Ely, a solar research specialist for Arthur D. Little, Inc., she has designed most of the special equipment needed in the Helping Hands program: the laser pointer, chin and other wheelchair controls, and equipment that the capuchin's tiny hands can hold and manipulate.

"One of the first things I was asked to design was the nose scratcher," Judi told me and added, "The monkeys helped design a lot of the equipment."

She explained that by watching the monkeys as they carried out their tasks, she and Doug Ely could tell when a piece of equipment needed changing or when some new device was necessary.

Almost all of the monkeys selected for training are females because they tend to be gentler and more affectionate than males. Even so, to preclude the possibility of a capuchin aide hurting anyone, the teeth are extracted from the trainee monkeys when they reach maturity at about three-and-a-half to four years.

This operation has no harmful effects on the monkey or on her ability to eat and digest her food. All Helping Hands monkeys, from soon after they go into foster care, have a diet which is 85 percent commercial monkey food (Purina Monkey Chow). After teeth extraction the food pellets are softened a bit with water, and the monkey can eat them with no difficulty. The rest of the diet usually is fruit—bananas, apple slices, peaches—which the monkey, even without teeth, can eat easily, especially as her gums harden.

The training of a monkey usually takes about eight months. A session with the student trainer may last from half an hour to an hour, but it might be

---

preclude (pri klüd') *v.t.* prevent or make impossible.

as short as ten minutes depending upon the monkey's personality. There may be several training sessions a day.

"Every monkey is different," Judi said. "Every one has her own personality and her own strengths and weaknesses."

Judi's biggest job within Helping Hands is to match the right monkey with the right quadriplegic who is being considered to receive one. A training log is kept on each monkey, and Judi pores over every page until she knows everything that can be known about a particular capuchin's personality and about her strengths and weaknesses.

"The quadriplegic who can control a monkey is an expert in a very unusual way."

Then Judi visits the quadriplegic. She stays at least two days and gets to know as much about the person as she can and about the environment where the monkey is going to live and work for the rest of her life. Judi even makes a video of the quadriplegic's living quarters so that they can be duplicated in the final training of the monkey the quadriplegic will receive.

"I am totally consumed with getting the right monkey in the right place," Judi said to me. "By the time they leave this training room, they are my children. I always think, what kind of life will they have out there? I want to make sure it will be the best and most useful life possible."

Judi has come to know dozens of quadriplegics very well, and she has thought a great deal about the total loss of hope that they suffer. "A spinal cord injury is an especially terrible thing," Judi said, "because it usually happens to young people, and it usually occurs at a happy moment in life— a car accident after a junior-senior prom or having fun diving into a swimming pool or playing football. Then everything is lost in a split second. The person comes to and his or her world has collapsed and a nightmare begins.

"Most people thinking about something like that happening to them say, 'I wouldn't want to live; I'd rather be dead.' But these people aren't dead. Slowly, if they begin to believe that they can do things and affect things, they begin to think that it is worth hanging around."

Both Mary Joan and Judi know very well that the success of Helping Hands depends upon how effective simian aides are in performing tasks that help quadriplegics lead better and more productive lives. But they also believe passionately that having a capuchin helper adds an interest and

spice to quadriplegics' lives that can make a huge psychological difference. The companionship is important, but beyond that their ability to control the monkey makes them special. They can do something few other people can do.

As part of her master's degree work, Judi made a study of how people react to a quadriplegic with and without a monkey helper. When one quadriplegic she was using in her study was at a shopping center without his monkey, only two strangers stopped to talk with him in the course of an hour. When the monkey was sitting beside him on the wheelchair, seventy-one people took time from their shopping to speak to the quadriplegic during about the same amount of time.

"The quadriplegic who can control a monkey is an expert in a very unusual way," Judi said, "and that makes him interesting to other people."

One quadriplegic had this to say: "When I go outdoors in my wheelchair, all that people see is the wheelchair. But when I go out with my monkey, the only thing they see is the monkey. Nobody notices the chair at all."

Mary Joan Willard has a sense of history and a vision of the future. In terms of need and demand, Helping Hands may seem slow in getting trained monkeys to the thousands of quadriplegics who want them. But she points out that the possibility of training dogs to guide the blind had been debated and <u>advocated</u> for a century before the Seeing Eye program began early in this century.

"Compared to that, we are doing all right," Mary Joan said to me.

Mary Joan's immediate goal for Helping Hands is to place forty simian aides a year and to move beyond that as fast as the job can be done properly. Costs for training, equipment, and placement are approximately nine thousand dollars for each Helping Hands monkey. If a <u>recipient</u> is able to meet these costs from insurance payments or other personal resources, he or she is expected to do so; however, no one selected to receive a monkey is refused for inability to pay. For most quadriplegics, costs are met from U.S. Veterans Administration and state rehabilitation program funds or from private research or charitable organizations.

Of one thing Mary Joan Willard is sure. "I see this as a life's work," she told me.

Judi Zazula feels the same way. "I can't imagine getting the satisfaction out of anything else that I get from this work," she said.

Judi was recently married to Doug Ely, her long-time partner in equipment development. Instead of a flower girl, Judi decided to have a flower primate. Hellion, the first monkey to become a simian aide in the Helping Hands program, carried a little bouquet of flowers.

Judi Zazula and one of the monkeys in training.

---

advocated (ad′və kā′tid) *v.t.* pleaded in favor of; supported.

recipient (ri sip′ē ənt) *n.* person who receives.

RESPONDING TO *Literature*

THINK • TALK • WRITE

1 Which person in the selection do you admire most? Write notes in your journal to support your opinion.

2 How long does it take Mitch and Peepers to learn to live together? Why do you think it takes this long?

3 What is the average life expectancy of capuchins? Why was their life expectancy important in deciding whether or not they would be suitable helpers?

4 If a monkey disobeys a warning, what can the human master do? Do you think this is right? Explain your answer.

5 Would you like to be a foster parent to a young monkey? Why or why not?

ACTIVITIES

• **Write About Author's Purpose**
Write briefly about why you think Brent Ashabranner wrote "Helping Hands." Be sure to give reasons to support your ideas. Compare your ideas with those of a classmate.

• **Create a Promotional Brochure**
What did you learn about the Helping Hands program from this selection? Make a brochure for people interested in the program.

VOCABULARY PRACTICE

On a separate sheet of paper, write the vocabulary word from the list that best completes each sentence.

rehabilitative	skeptical
essential	confiscated
dexterity	preclude
feasibility	advocated
dispenses	recipient

1 His injury will _____ his attendance at the meeting.

2 The senator _____ a bill to open day care centers.

3 The teacher _____ the toys and would not give them back.

4 The capuchins have the _____ to open jars and dial phones.

5 Oxygen is _____ to life on Earth.

6 The _____ of the award accepted the prize last week.

7 Scientists did a study to check the _____ of capuchins doing the work.

8 _____ therapy made it possible for her to walk again.

9 The machine _____ stamps when you insert the money and push the button.

10 He may be innocent but I am still _____ about his honesty.

fable for

WHEN THERE'S NO WAY OUT

by May Swenson

Grown too big for his skin,
and it grown hard,

without a sea and atmosphere—
he's drunk it all up—

his strength's inside him now,
but there's no room to stretch.

He pecks at the top
but his beak's too soft;

though instinct or ambition shoves,
he can't get through.

Barely old enough to bleed
and already bruised!

In a case this tough
what's the use

if you break your head
instead of the lid?

Despair tempts him
to just go limp;

Maybe the cell's
already a tomb,

and beginning end
in this round room.

Still, stupidly he pecks
and pecks, as if from under

his own skull—
yet makes no crack . . .

No crack until
he finally cracks,

and kicks and stomps.
What a thrill

and shock to feel
his little gaff poke

through the floor!
A way he hadn't known or meant.

Rage works if reason won't.
When locked up, bear down.

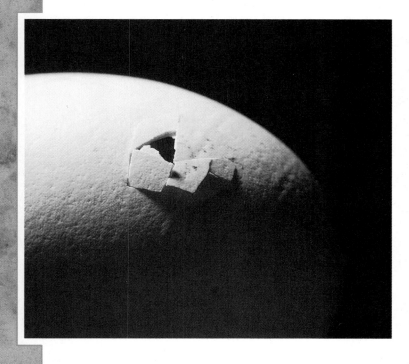

WHAT DO WE DO WITH A Variation?

BY JAMES BERRY

River of Darkness *1986* *Frank E. Smith*
Evans-Tibbs Collection

What do we do with a difference?
Do we stand and discuss its oddity
or do we ignore it?

Do we shut our eyes to it
or poke it with a stick?
Do we clobber it to death?

Do we move around it in rage
and enlist the rage of others?
Do we will it to go away?

Do we look at it in awe
or purely in wonderment?
Do we work for it to disappear?

Do we pass it stealthily
or change route away from it?
Do we will it to become like ourselves?

What do we do with a difference?
Do we communicate to it,
let application acknowledge it
for barriers to fall down?

BEFORE READING

....

HATCHET

CONNECT TO LITERATURE

Have you ever been alone in an unfamiliar place? How did you feel? What thoughts ran through your mind? In your journal jot down some ideas about your experience. As you read "Hatchet," compare your feelings and thoughts to Brian's.

THINKING ABOUT MOOD

Mood is the general feeling of a literary work. Some works may have a mood of dread and terror, while others may have one of peace and contentment. Authors can create mood in several ways, but typically they do so through the details of setting. Usually, engaging and dramatic plot events make a story most interesting. But as you read to find out what will happen next in the plot, your interest can be heightened if you visualize the setting and feel the mood, or atmosphere, that the author creates.

DID YOU KNOW?

This excerpt is from the book *Hatchet* by Gary Paulsen. Paulsen, a rugged outdoorsman himself, usually writes about young people who must struggle to survive in harsh environments. *Hatchet* tells how thirteen-year-old Brian survives in the Canadian wilderness after a plane crash strands him with only his ingenuity and a hatchet.

Although Canada is the world's second largest country, more than half of its land surface is made up of mountain and wilderness areas. Extremely rugged terrain and an arctic climate make much of Canada unsuitable for settlement. In fact, only about 11 percent of the land has been settled, with more than 80 percent of Canada's population living within 200 miles of the U.S. border. Only a few Native Americans, some mounted police, and some prospectors live in the remaining vast wilderness areas of the country.

HATCHET

by Gary Paulsen   illustrated by Jim Himsworth III

Before Brian boards a two-seater plane to visit his father in northern Canada, he hooks onto his belt the hatchet his mother has given him as a going-away present. Brian's parents are divorced, and his mother now has a boyfriend. On the plane, as Brian is deciding to keep this fact a secret, the pilot suffers a heart attack and dies. Brian takes over the controls and executes a rough landing. He finds himself alone and lost in the wilderness with only the hatchet and his own ingenuity to help him survive. He manages to construct a shelter but soon discovers that many more problems lie ahead.

At first he thought it was a growl. In the still darkness of the shelter in the middle of the night his eyes came open and he was awake and he thought there was a growl. But it was the wind, a medium wind in the pines had made some sound that brought him up, brought him awake. He sat up and was hit with the smell.

It terrified him. The smell was one of rot, some musty rot that made him think only of graves with cobwebs and dust and old death. His nostrils widened and he opened his eyes wider but he could see nothing. It was too dark, too hard dark with clouds covering even the small light from the stars, and he could not see. But the smell was alive, alive and full and in the shelter. He thought of the bear, thought of Bigfoot and every monster he had ever seen in every fright movie he had ever watched, and his heart hammered in his throat.

Then he heard the slithering. A brushing sound, a slithering brushing sound near his feet—and he kicked out as hard as he could, kicked out and threw the hatchet at the sound, a noise coming from his throat. But the hatchet missed, sailed into the wall where it hit the rocks with a shower of sparks, and his leg was instantly torn with pain, as if a hundred needles had been driven into it. "Unnnngh!"

Now he screamed, with the pain and fear, and skittered on his backside up into the corner of the shelter, breathing through his mouth, straining to see, to hear.

The slithering moved again, he thought toward him at first, and terror took him, stopping his breath. He felt he could see a low dark form, a bulk in the darkness, a shadow that lived, but now it moved away, slithering and scraping it moved away and he saw or thought he saw it go out of the door opening.

He lay on his side for a moment, then pulled a rasping breath in and held it, listening for the attacker to return. When it was apparent that the shadow wasn't coming back he felt the calf of his leg, where the pain was centered and spreading to fill the whole leg.

His fingers gingerly touched a group of needles that had been driven through his pants and into the fleshy part of his calf. They were stiff and very sharp on the ends that stuck out, and he knew then what the attacker had been. A porcupine had stumbled into his shelter and when he had kicked it the thing had slapped him with its tail of quills.

He touched each quill carefully. The pain made it seem as if dozens of them had been slammed into his leg, but there were only eight, pinning the cloth against his skin.

He leaned back against the wall for a minute. He couldn't leave them in, they had to come out, but just touching them made the pain more intense.

So fast, he thought. So fast things change. When he'd gone to sleep he had satisfaction and in just a moment it was all different. He grasped one of the quills, held his breath, and jerked. It sent pain signals to his brain in tight waves, but he grabbed another, pulled it, then another quill. When he had pulled four of them he stopped for a moment. The pain had gone from being a pointed injury pain to spreading in a hot smear up his leg and it made him catch his breath.

Some of the quills were driven in deeper than others and they tore when they came out. He breathed deeply twice, let half of the breath out, and went back to work. Jerk, pause, jerk—and three more times before he lay back in the darkness, done. The pain filled his leg now, and with it came new waves of self-pity. Sitting alone in the dark, his leg aching, some mosquitos finding him again, he started crying. It was all too much, just too much, and he couldn't take it. Not the way it was.

I can't take it this way, alone with no fire and in the dark, and next time it might be something worse, maybe a bear, and it wouldn't be just quills in the leg, it would be worse. I can't do this, he thought, again and again. I can't. Brian pulled himself up until he was sitting upright back in the corner of the cave. He put his head down on his arms across his knees, with stiffness taking his left leg, and cried until he was cried out.

He did not know how long it took, but later he looked back on this time of crying in the corner of the dark cave and thought of it as when he learned the most important rule of survival, which was that feeling sorry for yourself didn't work. It wasn't just that it was wrong to do, or that it was considered incorrect. It was more than that—it didn't work. When he sat alone in the darkness and cried and was done, was all done with it, nothing had changed. His leg still hurt, it was still dark, he was still alone and the self-pity had accomplished nothing.

At last he slept again, but already his patterns were changing and the sleep was light, a resting doze more than a deep sleep, with small sounds awakening him twice in the rest of the night. In the last doze period before daylight, before he awakened finally with the morning light and the clouds of new mosquitos, he dreamed. This time it was not of his mother, not of the Secret, but of his father at first and then of his friend Terry.

In the initial segment of the dream his father was standing at the side of a living room looking at him and it was clear from his expression that he was trying to tell Brian something. His lips moved but there was no sound, not a whisper. He waved his hands at Brian, made gestures in front of his face as if he were scratching something, and he worked to make a word with his mouth but at first Brian could not see it. Then the lips made an *mmmmm* shape but no sound came. *Mmmmm—maaaa.* Brian could not hear it, could not understand it and he wanted to so badly; it was so important to understand his father, to know what he was saying. He was trying to help, trying so hard, and when Brian couldn't understand he looked cross, the way he did when Brian asked questions more than once, and he faded. Brian's father faded into a fog place Brian could not see and the dream was almost over, or seemed to be, when Terry came.

He was not gesturing to Brian but was sitting in the park at a bench looking at a barbecue pit and for a time nothing happened. Then he got up and poured some charcoal from a bag into the cooker, then some starter fluid, and he took a flick type of lighter and lit the fluid. When it was burning and the charcoal was at last getting hot he turned, noticing Brian for the first time in the dream. He turned and smiled and pointed to the fire as if to say, see, a fire.

But it meant nothing to Brian, except that he wished he had a fire. He saw a grocery sack on the table next to Terry. Brian thought it must contain hot dogs and chips and mustard and he could think only of the food. But Terry shook his head and pointed again to the fire, and twice more he pointed to the fire, made Brian see the flames, and Brian felt his frustration and anger rise and he thought all right, all right, I see the fire but so what? I don't have a fire. I know about fire; I know I need a fire.

I know that.

His eyes opened and there was light in the cave, a gray dim light of morning. He wiped his mouth and tried to move his leg, which had stiffened like wood. There was thirst, and hunger, and he ate some raspberries from the jacket. They had spoiled a bit, seemed softer and mushier, but still had a rich sweetness. He crushed the berries against the roof of his mouth with his tongue and drank the sweet juice as it ran down his throat. A flash of metal caught his eye and he saw his hatchet in the sand where he had thrown it at the porcupine in the dark.

He scooched up, wincing a bit when he bent his stiff leg, and crawled to where the hatchet lay. He picked it up and examined it and saw a chip in the top of the head.

The nick wasn't large, but the hatchet was important to him, was his only tool, and he should not have thrown it. He should keep it in his hand, and make a tool of some kind to help push an animal away. Make a staff, he thought, or a lance, and save the hatchet. Something came then, a thought as he held the hatchet, something about the dream and his father and Terry, but he couldn't pin it down.

"Ahhh . . ." He scrambled out and stood in the morning sun and stretched his back muscles and his sore leg. The hatchet was still in his hand, and as he stretched and raised it over his head it caught the first rays of the morning sun. The first faint light hit the silver of the hatchet and it flashed a brilliant gold in the light. Like fire. That is it, he thought. What they were trying to tell me.

---

wincing (win'sing) *v.i.* drawing back or away as if from something painful, dangerous, or unpleasant; flinching.

Fire. The hatchet was the key to it all. When he threw the hatchet at the porcupine in the cave and missed and hit the stone wall it had showered sparks, a golden shower of sparks in the dark, as golden with fire as the sun was now.

The hatchet was the answer. That's what his father and Terry had been trying to tell him. Somehow he could get fire from the hatchet. The sparks would make fire.

Brian went back into the shelter and studied the wall. It was some form of chalky granite, or a sandstone, but imbedded in it were large pieces of a darker stone, a harder and darker stone. It only took him a moment to find where the hatchet had struck. The steel had nicked into the edge of one of the darker stone pieces. Brian turned the head backward so he would strike with the flat rear of the hatchet and hit the black rock gently. Too gently, and nothing happened. He struck harder, a glancing blow, and two or three weak sparks skipped off the rock and died immediately.

He swung harder, held the hatchet so it would hit a longer, sliding blow, and the black rock exploded in fire. Sparks flew so heavily that several of them skittered and jumped on the sand beneath the rock and he smiled and struck again and again.

There could be fire here, he thought. I will have a fire here, he thought, and struck again—I will have fire from the hatchet.

Brian found it was a long way from sparks to fire. Clearly there had to be something for the sparks to ignite, some kind of tinder or kindling—but what? He brought some dried grass in, tapped sparks into it and watched them die. He tried small twigs, breaking them into little pieces, but that was worse than the grass. Then he tried a combination of the two, grass and twigs.

Nothing. He had no trouble getting sparks, but the tiny bits of hot stone or metal—he couldn't tell which they were—just sputtered and died.

ignite (ig nīt') *v.t.* set on fire.

tinder (tin'dər) *n.* any substance that burns easily, especially something used to start a fire from a spark, such as twigs.

kindling (kind'ling) *n.* small pieces of dried wood or twigs.

He settled back on his haunches in <u>exasperation</u>, looking at the pitiful clump of grass and twigs.

He needed something finer, something soft and fine and fluffy to catch the bits of fire.

Shredded paper would be nice, but he had no paper.

"So close," he said aloud, "so close . . ."

He put the hatchet back in his belt and went out of the shelter, limping on his sore leg. There had to be something, had to be. Man had made fire. There had been fire for thousands, millions of years. There had to be a way. He dug in his pockets and found the twenty-dollar bill in his wallet. Paper. Worthless paper out here. But if he could get a fire going . . .

He ripped the twenty into tiny pieces, made a pile of pieces, and hit sparks into them. Nothing happened. They just wouldn't take the sparks. But there had to be a way— some way to do it.

Not twenty feet to his right, leaning out over the water were birches and he stood looking at them for a full half-minute before they registered on his mind. They were a beautiful white with bark like clean, slightly speckled paper.

Paper.

He moved to the trees. Where the bark was peeling from the trunks it lifted in tiny tendrils, almost fluffs. Brian plucked some of them loose, rolled them in his fingers. They seemed <u>flammable</u>, dry and nearly powdery. He pulled and twisted bits off the trees, packing them in one hand while he picked them with the other, picking and gathering until he had a wad close to the size of a baseball.

Then he went back into the shelter and arranged the ball of birchbark peelings at the base of the black rock. As an afterthought he threw in the remains of the twenty-dollar bill. He struck and a stream of sparks fell into the bark and quickly died. But this time one spark fell on one small hair of dry bark—almost a thread of bark—and seemed to glow a bit brighter before it died.

---

exasperation (eg zas′pə rā′shən) *n.* the state of being greatly irritated.

flammable (flam′ə bəl) *adj.* able to be set on fire easily; combustible.

The material had to be finer. There had to be a soft and incredibly fine nest for the sparks.

I must make a home for the sparks, he thought. A perfect home or they won't stay, they won't make fire.

He started ripping the bark, using his fingernails at first, and when that didn't work he used the sharp edge of the hatchet, cutting the bark in thin slivers, hairs so fine they were almost not there. It was painstaking work, slow work, and he stayed with it for over two hours. Twice he stopped for a handful of berries and once to go to the lake for a drink. Then back to work, the sun on his back, until at last he had a ball of fluff as big as a grapefruit—dry birch-bark fluff.

He positioned his spark nest—as he thought of it—at the base of the rock, used his thumb to make a small depression in the middle, and slammed the back of the hatchet down across the black rock. A cloud of sparks rained down, most of them missing the nest, but some, perhaps thirty or so, hit in the depression and of those six or seven found fuel and grew, <u>smoldered</u> and caused the bark to take on the red glow.

Then they went out.

Close—he was close. He repositioned the nest, made a new and smaller dent with his thumb, and struck again.

More sparks, a slight glow, then nothing.

It's me, he thought. I'm doing something wrong. I do not know this—a cave dweller would have had a fire by now, a <u>Cro-Magnon</u> <u>man</u> would have a fire by now—but I don't know this. I don't know how to make a fire.

Maybe not enough sparks. He settled the nest in place once more and hit the rock with a series of blows, as fast as he could. The sparks poured like a golden waterfall. At first they seemed to take, there were several, many sparks that found life and took briefly, but they all died.

Starved.

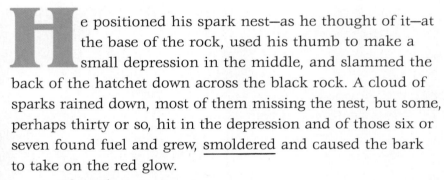

---

smoldered (smōl′dərd) *v.i.* burned and smoked with little or no flame.

Cro-Magnon man (krō mag′non man) member of a prehistoric group of humans distinguished by a well-developed brain, tall, erect stature, and the use of stone implements.

He leaned back. They are like me. They are starving. It wasn't quantity, there were plenty of sparks, but they needed more.

I would kill, he thought suddenly, for a book of matches. Just one book. Just one match. I would kill.

What makes fire? He thought back to school. To all those science classes. Had he ever learned what made a fire? Did a teacher ever stand up there and say, "This is what makes a fire . . ."

He shook his head, tried to focus his thoughts. What did it take? You have to have fuel, he thought—and he had that. The bark was fuel. Oxygen—there had to be air.

He needed to add air. He had to fan on it, blow on it.

He made the nest ready again, held the hatchet backward, tensed, and struck four quick blows. Sparks came down and he leaned forward as fast as he could and blew.

Too hard. There was a bright, almost intense glow, then it was gone. He had blown it out.

Another set of strikes, more sparks. He leaned and blew, but gently this time, holding back and aiming the stream of air from his mouth to hit the brightest spot. Five or six sparks had fallen in a tight mass of bark hair and Brian centered his efforts there.

The sparks grew with his gentle breath. The red glow moved from the sparks themselves into the bark, moved and grew and became worms, glowing red worms that crawled up the bark hairs and caught other threads of bark and grew until there was a pocket of red as big as a quarter, a glowing red coal of heat.

And when he ran out of breath and paused to inhale, the red ball suddenly burst into flame.

"Fire!" He yelled. "I've got fire! I've got it, I've got it, I've got it . . ."

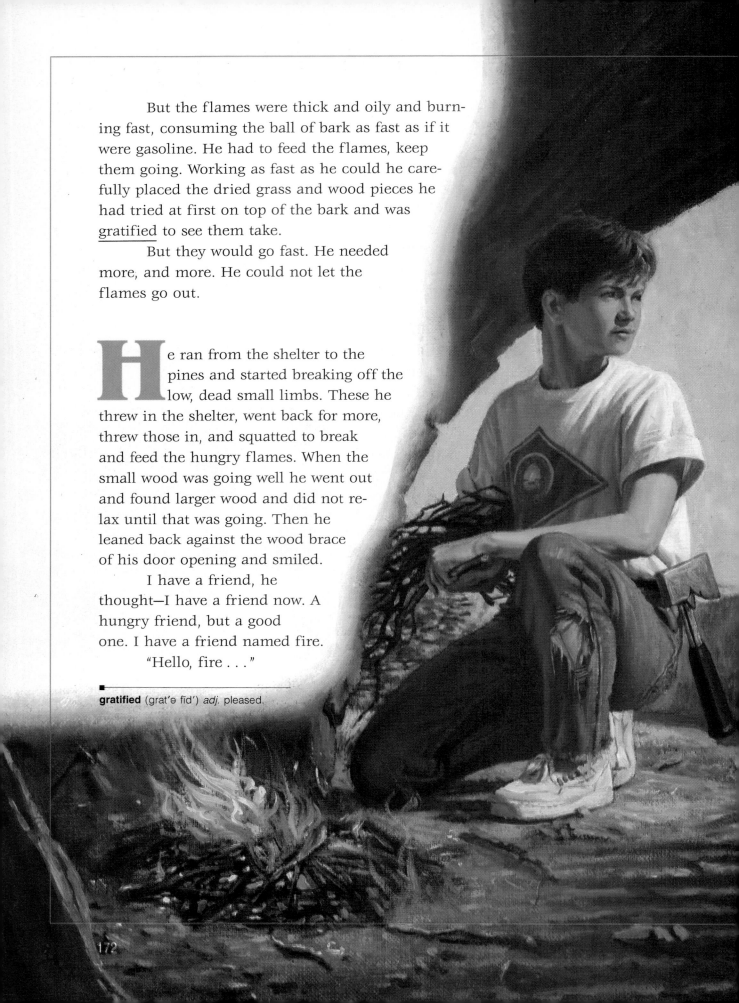

But the flames were thick and oily and burning fast, consuming the ball of bark as fast as if it were gasoline. He had to feed the flames, keep them going. Working as fast as he could he carefully placed the dried grass and wood pieces he had tried at first on top of the bark and was <u>gratified</u> to see them take.

But they would go fast. He needed more, and more. He could not let the flames go out.

He ran from the shelter to the pines and started breaking off the low, dead small limbs. These he threw in the shelter, went back for more, threw those in, and squatted to break and feed the hungry flames. When the small wood was going well he went out and found larger wood and did not relax until that was going. Then he leaned back against the wood brace of his door opening and smiled.

I have a friend, he thought—I have a friend now. A hungry friend, but a good one. I have a friend named fire.

"Hello, fire . . ."

gratified (grat′ə fīd′) *adj.* pleased.

Meet

Gary Paulsen

Gary Paulsen understands firsthand the ache and fear that can take over when life takes a nosedive and there's no one around with a safety net. His father was a career military officer, and Paulsen moved around constantly. He says, "School was a nightmare because I was unbelievably shy, and terrible at sports. I had no friends. . . . "

One day, in twenty-below temperatures, teenage Paulsen walked into the public library to get warm, and the librarian offered him a library card. "She didn't care if I looked right, wore the right clothes, dated the right girls, was popular at sports—none of those prejudices existed at the public library.

When she handed me the card, she handed me the world."

Many years later, when Paulsen had become a successful writer, he again found himself in peril without a safety net. This time, it was during the Iditarod, a 1200-mile dogsled race in the middle of Alaska. "I had no idea what I was in for. You don't sleep for seventeen days. . . . You are not allowed any outside assistance. If you make a mistake, you are left to die. . . . After about eight miles of navigating the Arctic Circle, you start to feel scared. After twelve miles, you realize that you are nothing and dogs are everything. To survive, you must be in deep harmony with your team."

Paulsen's experiences in the Iditarod convinced him that "Macho is a lie. . . . Core toughness and compassion are the opposite of macho. The absence of fear comes with knowledge, not strength or bravura. More people should be telling this to young people, instead of 'climb the highest mountain and kill something.' "

Three of Gary Paulsen's novels, *Hatchet, The Winter Room,* and *Dogsong,* have been selected as Newbery Honor Books.

Cover art for *Hatchet* and *Dogsong* by Neil Waldman

RESPONDING TO Literature

THINK • TALK • WRITE

1 Do you think you would like to have Brian as a friend? Why or why not? Write your reasons in your journal.

2 How does Brian feel after the porcupine attack? Do you think his feelings are justified? Explain your reasoning.

3 According to Brian, what is the most important rule of survival? Do you agree with him? What other rules might you add?

4 How do you think Brian feels after he gets the fire going? How might these feelings affect his outlook on his chances of survival?

5 How do you think Brian's experience in the wilderness will affect him in the rest of his life? Explain your answer.

ACTIVITIES

• **Write About Mood** Imagine that the setting of the story was a deserted tropical island instead of the Canadian wilderness, and that Brian had only a book on astronomy instead of a hatchet. Write one episode of the story, paying particular attention to creating a mood.

• **Draw a Picture** Some say a picture is worth a thousand words. Draw a picture of Brian's cave. Use colors and visual details that express the mood of "Hatchet."

VOCABULARY PRACTICE

Refer to the word list to answer each of the questions below. Write your answers on a separate sheet of paper. Use each word only once.

wincing   flammable

ignite   gratified

exasperation

1 Which word describes what Brian was trying to do when he struck his hatchet against the stone to create sparks?

2 Which word is associated with physical pain?

3 Which word explains why the dried bark and leaves were able to burst into flames?

4 Which word names Brian's feeling when he could not get the sparks to start a fire in the leaves?

5 Which word describes how Brian felt when the fire began to warm the cave?

BEFORE READING

WITH BERT & RAY BY WILLIAM

CONNECT TO LITERATURE

Have you ever known people who were unable to take pleasure in the good fortunes of a friend? Perhaps there was a time when you couldn't bring yourself to congratulate a friend on his or her accomplishment. Or maybe you have been disappointed when a friend failed to congratulate you for a job well done. In your journal, jot down details of your experience. As you read "With Bert & Ray by William," compare your experience with that of William and his mother.

THINKING ABOUT COLLOQUIALISMS

Colloquialisms are expressions in local or regional dialect. They can be used in conversations in literature to help bring characters to life. Colloquial language refers to informal speech, not the written language. E. L. Konigsburg uses entertaining and original expressions to help bring William's personality to life on the page.

DID YOU KNOW?

In the course of the story William and his mother visit the Smithsonian Institution. The Smithsonian had its beginning in 1829 when James Smithson, a British scientist, left his fortune to the United States to establish an institution for the "increase and diffusion of knowledge among men." The result of that donation is the Smithsonian Institution, which was established by Congress in 1846.

The Smithsonian Institution houses some of the most important scientific, historical, and cultural collections belonging to the United States. In addition to the parts of the Smithsonian that are located in Washington, D.C., the Institution has divisions in other parts of the country, including Massachusetts and New York.

Antiques supplied by Artifax, New York, New York

176

WITH
BERT & RAY

BY WILLIAM

BY E. L. KONIGSBURG

IF I HAVE TO START AT THE BEGINNING OF things, I guess I would have to start with Pa. Or the end of Pa, I should say. I had long ago heard the expression of someone being *dead drunk*. Well, that was Pa. Or the end of Pa. He died dead drunk when I was six, and that was that many years ago. Half my life ago. For a long time before he died, he couldn't get anyone to sell him any more insurance, and I can't say that I blame them. Anyway, the little bit he did have, didn't hardly pay for his funeral, and the little bit that Ma got from the Social Security didn't hardly carry us from one month to the next.

So what Ma did, after Pa had been dead for three years and we had some powerful dentist bills mounted up, was to sell off all his stuff. Wasn't any of it she wanted around the house anyways. He had hunting guns and duck decoys and all the issues of *National Geographic* back to when it was started. Pa could pitch a classic fit if anyone ever did touch his stacks of *National Geographics*. He never read the blame things, just stacked them up in a corner of the bedroom and made misery for anyone who got them the tiniest bit out of order.

Ma and I put GARAGE SALE signs up at the light poles on the street leading to our house, and people snuck around to our back door trying to get in and buy some of Pa's things even before eight A.M., the time we said we was starting. They paid right good money for some of the stuff Pa collected, the guns in particular, and even them fancy Jack Bean bottles. We was sold out before noon, and we had brought in two months' worth of dentist bills from that stuff of Pa's.

Two of the people who came to the sale were Bert and Ray, this couple who have an antique store over in the section of town called Huntington. Bert and Ray were at our sale early, and they were kinda thrilled about the duck decoys and the prices Ma had put on them. We had made them odd numbers like the stores do. We put two ninety-five and like that on them, except for the biggest one that we made an even four dollars. They didn't touch the *National Geographics* or the Jack Bean bottle collection or any of the old camping equipment, but they sure did tuck them decoys under their arms real quick and paid Ma exactly what she asked for them and gave her a card, saying that she should please to call them whenever she did another house sale. Ma took the card and said that she sure would call them if she ever did another. I was <u>speculating</u> about what else Ma could sell until I realized that Ma is just a timid soul who says "scuse me" to the chiffonier when she bumps into it.

Next thing I know, we are over in the Huntington section of town, having our dentist appointments, and right there on Elmhurst Avenue where we stood, waiting on the bus, there was a house that had a sign out front, a neat, lettered sign saying, HUNTINGTON ANTIQUES, *Bertram Grover and Raymond*

---

speculating (spek′yə lā′ting) *v.i.* thinking carefully or seriously.

Porterfield, Proprietors. Right up on the front door was attached another sign, a littler one, and this one just said, OPEN. Ma remembered that that was exactly the name on the card given her by the couple that had bought them decoys on the day of our sale. She took the card out from her pocketbook, and sure enough, even the style of the lettering on the card matched that what was on the sign.

"C'mon, Ma," I said, "let's pay them a visit."

"Aw, William," Ma said. "It's not nice to pay a call so unexpected."

"C'mon, now, Ma," I said. "This here is a place of business, and heck, you don't need no appointment to walk into a open business unless'n it's a dentist." I marched right up onto the porch and beckoned to Ma to follow, and she did. I pushed on the doorbell that was right next to the small sign that said OPEN.

Took a pretty minute or two for them to open the door and Ma was ready to back on down, but I wouldn't let her. I told her to stand right there by the door. I noticed that the porch was fixed up right nice with wicker chairs and lots of plants in pots. On the wicker rocker was a little sticker, white with a red border that said one hundred forty dollars and then I found another sticker on a chair that said one hundred thirty dollars. Each pot that had a plant inside it had a numbered price, too. I didn't have time to point any of this out to Ma, because there at the door appeared Ray, who was smiling and welcoming us in.

Bert was standing in the front hall, and he pointed the way into their parlor, and Ma and me sat down on this here sofa with legs so skinny they didn't look like they could hold up the sofa cushions let alone Ma and me. Bert and Ray asked us to have some tea with them, and I must say that they served it up real fine in little cups you couldn't hardly fit your finger through the handle. I put my cup and saucer down on a end table and picked up a ashtray and saw one of them little white stickers with a red border on it and written on it was some letters and then a price, twenty-five dollars. It wasn't a very big ashtray neither. I got up from that skinny-legged sofa and began to wander around their parlor, and whatever I took to picking up had a red and white sticker and some letters and some number wrote on it.

"What're these here letters for?" I asked.

Ray kinda winked at me and said that that was a big secret, that that there was their code, saying how much they paid for something. Knowing that, it wasn't too much trouble figuring things out because sitting right there on their sideboard was one of Pa's decoy ducks, and I picked it up kinda casual and saw that it said RIB, and right under that code was written twenty-five dollars. Well, I knowed that we had not charged them but one seventy-five for that there decoy. All of the decoys was marked twenty-five dollars, even though we charged different amounts, up to four full dollars for them. I just lifted each duck sort of casual like and, remembering what we had charged, I memorized that EAB was two ninety-five, PAB was three ninety-five and UNN was four dollars even. I had already spotted RIB at one seventy-five.

Bert and Ray asked Ma if she often managed house sales, and Ma said no. Then they told her that if she ever wanted help with any, they would be happy to give it to her if she would just let them in first. Ma said she'd be more than happy to let them in first, not quite understanding everything they were asking and telling.

We left their place, and I couldn't hardly wait a minute to write down the number and the letters of that there secret code. I took the card that had our next dentist appointment reminder, and I done my figuring on it.

If EAB was two ninety-five, then E was the second letter and A was ninth and B was fifth.

So I wrote all the numbers in a row and in order and I fitted the letters with their numbers like this:

1 2 3 4 5 6 7 8 9 0
R E P U B   I   A N

Weren't but one word could fit into all that, and that word had to be REPUBLICAN, which Bert and Ray probably were.

Thing that happened not long after that was that Ma got a call from Ray, saying that there was the contents of this house to sell. Some old lady had died, and the family that was left wanted Bert and him, Ray, to handle the whole thing, but that since they had opened their Huntington Antiques Shop, they didn't want to do that kind of business anymore. So they was calling Ma to see if she wanted to handle it. They said that they would come on over to the dead lady's house with her to help her and teach her what to do if she'd just remember that she was supposed to let them in first.

Ma said sure she'd like to help them, not even knowing what was in it for her, but she wanted to thank them for having her and me to tea. She asked Ray if I, William, could help, too. I guess she figured that I ought to since I had had some tea, too, and Ray told her yes, that certainly William could help. He told her that they would lend her one of their standard contract forms to use until she could get some of her own printed up. And Ma said thanks for that, not even knowing for sure what she was thanking for, but living with Pa for as long as she had, she had got into the habit of being thankful for just any kind of common courtesy.

The contract when it came said that Ma was to get twenty cents on the dollar of whatever money she took in from the sale of household goods.

Bert and Ray showed us how you have to go around and put these prices on everything, even old bath towels so wore out that

you'd be right ashamed to hang them on a clothesline, which these people didn't because they had a clothes dryer. And I didn't think any self-respecting person would leave such a kitchen when they died. You would think that Cockroaches United was having a county convention. Ray taught Ma how to tag and mark everything, and Bert taught her how to keep track of what was sold to who and how to do the book work, and they taught me how to clear out the cupboards and drawers and wash the stuff that needed it.

Then Bert and Ray went around the house and concentrated hard on putting the prices on a silver pitcher and a cut glass bowl and other stuff from the china closet. There was also a couple pieces of furniture, one sofa whose guts was pouring out, that he consulted about in some big book called *Nutting*. "I'll just check *Nutting*," he kept on saying. And Ma and me, we'd smile and nod and empty the drawers and closets and clean out the roach doo-doo. Ma and me have a plum good <u>capacity</u> for work, which neither of us inherited from Pa, I can tell you.

It's not hard to guess what Bert and Ray bought when they were the first allowed in on the sale. That big cut glass bowl was tucked under Ray's armpit and the big silver pitcher was under Bert's almost before the door was full open.

The sale turned out real good. We cleared out that whole houseful of stuff, and the heirs were right pleased and so were Ma and me. We made two hundred forty-three dollars and thirty-eight cents for our work, and that was the start of our career managing house sales. The work turned out to be pretty good and a lot steadier than either of us would ever have guessed. When you think about it, though, people are always dying, and something has to be done with all their stuff. Even people like Pa and his *National Geographics* and his Jack Bean bottles. And house sales are most always weekend affairs so's I could help Ma most all the time.

Ma and me got so's people would call us direct and not go through Bert and Ray, and we got so's we could price things out pretty good ourselves. Just ask me what a pillowcase brings at an estate sale or what pie tins go for, and without even having to think about it, I can tell you fifty cents if not worn and twenty-five cents if not rusty.

---

capacity (kə pas′i tē) *n.* ability or power to do something.

And there's something else you learn right quick. People will buy most anything at an estate sale. Was a time once when Ma was having these bad cramps, and I was right worried about her, and I made her to take her medicine and tuck it into the bathroom cabinet while the sale was going on. Doncha know, some old lady come by and insisted on buying Ma's cramp pills, and Ma sold them to her for twenty-five cents over what she had paid for them, and she had already swallowed three. I said to Ma, why did you sell them to her, why didn't you tell her real forceful like that you needed them? And Ma answered me that the lady was giving her worser cramps just from insisting. But Ma's like that, the giving-in type. How else can you explain her putting up with Pa all those years?

And I want to say one more thing about Bert and Ray because fair is fair. They may have helped us to price some things that they were gonna be let in first to buy, but they never did anything real bad. Like if we had had some duck decoys again, they wouldn't mark them only four dollars and then turn around and sell them for twenty-five. They would mark them just right, that is twelve dollars and a half apiece and then sell them for twenty-five. What I'm saying is this, they never gave theirselves the benefit of the doubt.

Ma and me got so's we could tell the antique dealers from the regular people, and the dealers all understood how it was with us and Bert and Ray, and we all got along pretty good because most dealers have someone who lets them in first. Ma and me got so's we could make up the newspaper ads ourselves, and we had signs painted, little sandwich boards that said ESTATE SALE, real neat and professional, that we would set at the street corners and one on the sidewalk in front of the house itself.

Ma and me even developed a little bit of a social life from our business of estate sales. We also got so's we'd have Bert and Ray over to supper at least once every other week.

They both had always loved antiques they said, but they had had other careers before. Bert was retired from the marines, and Ray was retired from the civil service; but Ma told me that you can retire from those things and still be young. I wouldn't say that Bert and Ray were young. I'd say that they were middle-aged, about what the average TV father appears to be. Each one had different specialities in antiques, and they got along pretty good with each other, except sometimes when they'd be fighting before they got over to our house, and then Ma would consider it her duty to cheer them up with her good cooking and sweet ways.

They had us over to tea about as often as we had them over to supper, and they and Ma talked on the phone a lot. Bert and Ray would tell Ma what good buys they got and what fantastic pieces they had bought or sold. As soon as something crossed the threshold of their shop, it became a fantastic piece. But I was glad that they found company with each other, and Bert and Ray provided Ma with some of the best gossip this side of *People* magazine, except all their gossip was local, not national.

Ma and me came to see how getting in first was pretty important to an antique dealer. Because the thing of it is this—the hardest part about antiques is finding them and buying them at a good price. Selling them is pretty easy except for some things and those things aren't necessarily the ugliest. Sometimes ugly sells real good. It depends on the style of ugly. After a while Ma got so's she could price out the cut glass and the silver and the furniture, too. She had gathered together a little library of books, including the famous *Nutting*. She didn't ever do the pricing if Bert and Ray were around and if they showed even by a quick look in their eyes that they wanted to keep in practice. Ma always let them because she told me she didn't want to hurt their feelings none, and she didn't want to give them the idea that she had forgot from whence all her new career had sprung.

A lot of dealers came to Ma and promised her things if she would let them in first, but she never even thought about it twice. She was loyal, but seeing the way she had stuck with Pa way past normal endurance, anybody'd guess that.

Meanwhile, Bert and Ray started going up North to some of them big antique shows in places like Philadelphia and Lexington. They got so they were considering taking out a ad in *Antiques* magazine, and considering the price of that magazine and how many colored pictures is in it, a person's got to be pretty fancy to run an ad in there. But them and us never lost our relationship of buyer and seller, and Ma always swooned for them over their fantastic pieces.

---

threshold (thresh'ōld) *n.* point of entry.

184

In the meantime while Bert and Ray were getting fancier, we were, too. Our house started changing, and for the better. We were upgrading, you could say. It started when Ma couldn't sell a set of dining room chairs unless she'd of come way down on the price, and she just couldn't. She knew they was worth what she was asking, so she decided, heck, we could use them as good as anyone, and then it happened with other things, too. We got a nice set of dishes the same way, and Ma got me a Polaroid, bought it outright at one of her sales. Surprised me with it for my birthday. We also got a Pontiac station wagon at a good price. It was left in a garage, and the lawyers said that it was to be sold as part of the contents of the estate.

In our ads we always said "contents of the estate." We never called them house sales anymore.

One day when Ma and me were invited over to Bert's and Ray's for tea they had just come back from a buying trip up to Kentucky and some other horse country, I think. We no sooner got in the front door good when Ma spotted this piece of furniture leaning over by the wall to the left of the archway that leads to their parlor. Ma went on over to it and studied on it awhile and said, "I just love your *panetière,* Bert. Wherever did you find it?"

"*Panetière?*" Bert said. "What *panetière?*"

"That there cupboard," Ma said, pointing to the piece of furniture leaning against the parlor wall.

"This'n," I said. "Ma called it a *panetière.*"

Then Ma looked at the ticket and said, "I see that y'all made a good buy. A right good buy."

I glanced on down at the ticket and saw that they had paid UNNN for it which was forty dollars American, and they had marked it up to a hundred twenty-five.

Ray came in from the kitchen just then, and Bert said to him, "It seems that we made a good buy on our *panetière*, Ray."

And Ray said, "Our what?"

"Your *panetière* right there," I said, pointing to that same cupboard leaning against the parlor wall.

Ray got real upset, and so did Bert, and they said that they didn't think it was fair that we should know their code, and I asked them how did they expect us not to know, seeing's how Ma always let them in first and knew whatever it was they had paid for whatever it was they had carried out under their respective armpits. They smiled, both of them did, but I could tell that they sorta hurried us through the tea. I peeked back in the door after we left, and I saw them pulling the tag off of that there *panetière,* which they didn't even know they had until Ma called it to their attention.

Next week Ma had Bert and Ray over to supper and Ray announced, "Bert and I sold our *panetière* for four hundred dollars to Mrs. Sinclair, the lady who just built that big house by the golf course. She's doing everything in French, and we called her and told her that we had an <u>authentic</u> eighteenth century bread cupboard, and she didn't even know it was a *panetière* until we told her. She bought it like that," he said, snapping his fingers.

"Fancy that," I said, "a genuine eighteenth century *panetière,* and Mrs. Sinclair didn't even know it."

Bert said, "Well, some of these people who have big houses need to be educated in good taste."

Ma just smiled and told them how glad she was for them that they had turned a nice profit. "Well," Ray said, "it's not hard to do if you buy right and know what you're selling." Ma gave me a look that said "hush," and I didn't say nothing about they never would have thought that they had nothing but a old kitchen cupboard if Ma hadn't been reading a whole lot of books besides *Nutting.*

Bert and Ray were in Philadelphia doing one of their fancy shows when the call came that they would like Ma to come handle the Birchfield estate. Mrs. Birchfield was the widow of one of the richest men in town. At one time, half the town owed her money, and the other half were her relatives. Ma said that she'd be most willing to handle that estate, and we went there, the two of us, full of high hopes, expecting to find treasure like in the palace of an OPEC <u>shah</u> of an oil producing country.

What we found was the same old grease pool in the kitchen and the same old roaches in the cupboards, none of which were

---

authentic (ô then′tik) *adj.* being what it appears to be; genuine; real.
shah (shä) *n.* title of the former hereditary ruler of Iran.

panetières, I can tell you. The towels and the sheets were such that Ma thought she best sell them direct to the rag man. And save! That Mrs. Birchfield had so many peanut butter jars that it was hard to believe that Peter Pan never did get old.

Ma said, "Some people just don't know how to live."

The furniture was mostly good. Ma knew that. If you recovered it, it would be right pretty. Some ancestor of Mrs. Birchfield had knowed quality and had bought it. Besides the furniture, there was a nice silver coffee <u>urn</u> and a brass clock that chimed and some big old china <u>tureens</u> and bowls that must have been what the family ate off of before Mrs. Birchfield discovered jelly glasses and peanut butter jars. Ma knew that there was some fine stuff in there even if it was all tarnished, and she was glad that Bert and Ray would be back from Philadelphia in time for her to let them in first.

Ray was in a bad mood when they got to the sale, and Ma knew it, and she tried to cheer him up by showing him the very best things first, and he bought the brass clock and a coupla tureens. Then Ma saw that he was being more cheery and she showed him this big Chinese screen that was made in four panels. Ma had found it wrapped in a old bedspread in the back of Mrs. Birchfield's bedroom walk-in closet. "I put a hundred twenty-five on this, Ray," she said.

Ray looked at it and laughed. "I wouldn't have that thing if you gave it to me. It's a piece of junk."

Ma looked at it real good and said, "I think it's something good, Ray."

Then Ray called Bert over, and they both said that they wouldn't have it even if Ma gave it to them, that they both thought it was a piece of junk. Bert added that when he was in the marines, every other sailor that hit the port of Hong Kong bought at least two of these things for his wife. After they both spoke on how junky that screen was, they didn't seem so mad at each other anymore, and Ma looked glad that she had at least helped them to make peace with each other by agreeing over disagreeing with her.

Ma couldn't sell that screen the whole time we had the Birchfield estate sale, and when it was over, she deducted the full

urn (ûrn) *n.* closed vessel having a spigot, used for making, heating, or serving hot drinks.
tureens (tə rēnz') *n., pl.* deep dishes with covers, used for serving food, especially soup.

amount of one hundred twenty-five dollars from her commission, and she carried it on home with her and set it up in the corner of our dining room where, since our dining room was not even room-sized, she could not open it all the way.

The next day after school we carried it into the parlor and there we spread it out in front of the sofa. There were four panels, and each panel told part of a story of some Chinese ladies washing clothes and doing other dainty things. Ma said that the women were washing silk. She sure had been doing a lot of reading since Pa died and we had started in the estate sale business.

She asked me to leave the screen up, right there in our parlor, blocking our sofa. The next day when I came home from school, she was sitting on a little stool in front of that there screen contemplating it some more. "William," she said, "I got a feeling in my bones that this is something really good. The next weekend we don't have a estate sale, we're gonna carry this downstate and see if them fancy dealers down there don't want it."

"What you gonna ask for it, Ma?"

"Gonna ask five hundred dollars for it, William," she answered.

I didn't do nothing but swallow.

The next weekend we carried the screen, wrapped in a bed of old bedspreads from Mrs. Birchfield's, to four different shops and didn't anyone want it.

Come the following Monday, Ma got herself over to the library and began some more reading that didn't stop until Saturday, at which time she was more convinced than ever that what she had was something real good. So the weekend after that, we loaded the thing back onto its bed of Birchfield bedspreads and headed North this time. We visited five antique shops and one interior decorator's, but didn't anyone want it.

Had it not come up spring vacation for the sixth grade, I don't know if I would've done the next thing. Spring vacation in the sixth grade means a bus trip to our nation's capital of Washington, D.C., and Ma was real proud that we had some money to send me. I took some pictures of that China silk screen with my Polaroid. I remembered that Ma had told me that in her researching at the library she had seen pictures of some screens like ours at the Freer Gallery in Washington, D.C. She said, though, that ours was prettier, and she thought that it might could be older.

In *my* research I found out that the Freer Gallery was part of the Smithsonian and that the Smithsonian was part of our student tour of Washington, D.C. The whole Freer Gallery was China and other Oriental art.

There was a couple of things about the Smithsonian that I didn't know, and the main one of them was that it's so big, and it's not just one building, and the third one I didn't know was that they don't ever take a sixth grade student tour to the Freer Gallery part. I don't think they ever even took a sixth grade student tour there where the school was all Chinese and Oriental. The Freer is a whole quiet building that hardly anyone goes to.

We didn't.

We went to Aeronautics and Space, and we had a buddy system. The buddy system in our school means that each person has to hold onto one other person going into and going out of places so that the chaperones had only half as much to keep track of. Now, in the buddy system at our school, they usually have a girl-boy arrangement because things stay quieter that way.

It's hard to break away from the buddy system, and much as I didn't want to cause no trouble on my first field trip ever, I felt more for Ma and how bad she wanted to know about that China silk screen. So I told my buddy Carita that I had to answer a call of nature, and she blushed, even though I said it to her gentlemanly the way I did, and I left Aeronautics and Space and dodged school buses and school groups and made my way over to the Freer.

---

chaperones (shap′ə rōnz′) *n., pl.* older people who attend and supervise a social gathering of young people.

As busy and noisy as Aeronautics and Space was, that's about how quiet the Freer was. Was about like the way you'd figure it'd be in downtown Mars.

Was a lady right up front at a desk and I told her that I had some business with the person who studied on China silk screens, and the lady smiled at me, like the smile would have been a pat on the head had she knowed me better. She asked me, "Now, what business would you be having with the curator of Chinese art?"

I told her, "I got one."

She pretended that she was looking for it in front of and in back of me, and said, "Where?"

She gave me that smile again, and I could see that she was mighty unlikely to do business with me, so I took the Polaroids out of my pants pocket. I had put them between two pieces of cardboard so's they wouldn't get mashed on the bus trip. I spread them out in front of her on top of the desk there and said, "I might be interested in selling, and I think you might be interested in buying."

She looked at my Polaroids, and I could tell that she didn't know what it was that she was seeing, and I was beginning to lose patience. They were about to miss me at Aeronautics and Space. "Listen, ma'am," I said, knowing full well how ladies liked to be called ma'am by a accent like mine. "Listen, ma'am," I repeated, "I don't have a right awful amount of time, and I would like to talk to someone in charge of these here Chinese silk screens."

"Our curatorial staff is really quite busy," she said.

And I said, "Back to home, we have a expression, ma'am."

"What's that?" she asked.

"Why, back to home we always say that there's some folk who don't know that they're through the swinging doors of opportunity until they've got swat on their backside."

She picked up her telephone.

A lady came down the hall, a magnifying glass swinging from a chain around her neck. Her name was Mrs. Fortinbras, only don't pronounce the *s*. She looked at my pictures through that magnifying glass, and I felt real proud that someone was taking that much of care with them. She took off her glasses and then she studied on me for a while. Finally, she said, "These photographs are not entirely clear and there are fingerprints on a couple of

curator (kyŭ rā′tər) *n.* manager of exhibits at a museum.

190

critical places, but it looks as if you might have a very fine screen there. If you ever want to bring it in and have it examined directly, it can be arranged by our staff."

I thanked her real kindly, and I asked her to write her name on the back of one of the pictures and that is how I knowed about that silent *s*.

I put the pictures back between the cardboard and then back inside my pocket, and I said to the lady at the desk, "I'll be back."

She didn't look a bit like she was glad that I had kept the door of opportunity from swatting her on her backside.

I caught up with my group somewheres between Leonardo da Vinci and the bathrooms in the National Gallery, and I didn't tell the first person about what I had been up to. I saved it all for Ma because she deserved to know it first.

Ma was out loud happy when I gave her my news, and she stopped trying to sell the screen altogether after that. Both of us was waiting, just waiting, for something to happen, and we knew it would when school was out for the summer.

I told Ma that I thought we ought to pay the Freer a visit, and she was right surprised at how firm I was about it, but she didn't hesitate much either. She loaded us and the Chinese screen into the station wagon and drove us all the way north to Washington, D.C.

"Do you remember the name of the lady, William?" she asked.

I told her yep, that it was Fortinbras with a *s* on the end that you're not supposed to pronounce and that I had had her to write it on the back of a Polaroid.

"Good boy," Ma said.

We got ourselves to the Smithsonian, that part they call the Freer Gallery, and Ma, she found herself a parking space that wasn't too awful far so's we could walk it. We marched us up to the desk there and asked to see Mrs. Fortinbras right off, and I handed the woman, who was a different one this time, the Polaroid with the name writ on the back so's there'd be no mistake about who it was we wanted and so's to cut down on the delays.

The woman behind the desk asked what was it about, and I said, "Same thing's as is on the other side of that there picture. Mrs. Fortinbras and I talked about it last spring."

She asked Ma and me to wait, and she got on her telephone, and we waited for only near a half-hour before Mrs. Fortinbras came on down the hall, still wearing that magnifying glass on a chain around her neck.

I said, "Hey," to her and she said, "Hello," back and then I said, "This here is my ma," and Mrs. Fortinbras stuck out her hand for Ma to shake it, and Ma did. Ma shook it real good.

First thing Ma said was, "We brung the screen."

"Where is it?" Mrs. Fortinbras asked.

"In the wagon," Ma said. "Should we of carried it in?"

Mrs. Fortinbras said, "Suppose you drive your wagon over to the delivery entrance, and I'll have our men bring it to one of the examining rooms."

Ma said "Shucks, I lift heavier than that any time I do a estate sale. William and me'll just carry it on over from the parking lot, seeing's that I found a good spot not too far from here."

Mrs. Fortinbras said that they'd let us put the wagon in the employee lot if we drove it around like she said to do.

So we backed the wagon on up to the delivery, and two men came and lifted out that screen that was resting in its bed of washed bedspreads from Mrs. Birchfield's, and that made us feel that already it was important, just like Ma had thought all along.

We went along with the screen to the examination room where Mrs. Fortinbras was waiting and where the two men lifted it onto a examination table. Mrs. Fortinbras said that she would do the examining of it her own self. Ma and I sat around and waited while Mrs. Fortinbras went over the thing with her magnifier, and then she turned to us and asked would we leave it with her for a few days so's they could run some tests, and we said, "Sure." Came time for us to sign a receipt that we had left it of our own free will, and Mrs. Fortinbras asked us what valuation we put on it, for insurance purposes, and Ma said, "Ten thousand dollars." For the life of me I don't know where she come up with that figure since all's we paid was REBNN, that is, a hundred twenty-five.

We decided to leave our wagon in that employee parking lot all day and use our time for me to show Ma all the things that had been showed to me in the spring. And that Ma is a real good appreciator. She said to me, "You know, William, I do think that had I been city born, I might could get a job in one of these here museums. I think I could of. I got some real delicate feelings about some of these here things." And it would make you sad to think of Ma wasted in our little old town until you saw Ma's face as she looked at the things in the museum. That face just had to make a person happy.

We drove on back to our motel, and we looked for any messages, but there wasn't any. And the whole next day, too, there wasn't. We didn't sit around waiting. We went to visit at Congress and take a tour of the White House.

The third day we couldn't decide should we call over at the Freer or wait one more day when a call came right through to our room. It was Mrs. Fortinbras. She said that she was making a recommendation to the Museum that they buy—she said purchase—the screen at the price what Ma said, ten thousand dollars.

Want to know what Ma said? She said, "Since I been waiting here, Mrs. Fortinbras, my customer back home said that he would double his offer. So's I'm afraid I'll have to ask twenty. Thousand, that is." That's what Ma said, cool as well water.

Mrs. Fortinbras talked over the phone some more, and I heard Ma saying, "I'll do that, Mrs. Fortinbras. Sure, I understand."

I was dancing around the room, that's how anxious I was to know what was going on.

When Ma hung up, she told me that Mrs. Fortinbras said she needed a written offer from her customers back home.

"Yeah, Ma," I said. "Who might that be, seeing's how we couldn't peddle the thing for a even five hundred?"

"Why, Bert and Ray," Ma answered. "I'm sure if I call them, they'll come up with a written offer just like Mrs. Fortinbras needs."

"What do you think we have there in that screen, Ma?"

"Some genuine Chinese painting done along about the time that Marco Polo went to China. You know Marco Polo, William?" she asked.

"Sure," I said. "But I can't remember when he went to China."

"Long about the year 1260," Ma said. "I been doing some reading."

When Ma put a call through to Huntington Antiques, Bert answered the phone, and Ma told him pretty quick what it was she was calling about. And the first hint I had that Bert wasn't too happy about Ma's getting into the museum and all was that he said that he wasn't sure he could send her a written offer because what if the government held him to it. The Smithsonian was a government affair. Ma said that gosh, she hadn't thought about how the Smithsonian was a government affair. I took the phone from her and said to Bert as how he was making his promise to Ma, not to any government, and he oughtta know Ma wouldn't hold him to no twenty-thousand-dollar promise. He kept on saying "government," and I kept on telling him that it was between him and Ma, and he could ask Ralph Nader if'n he didn't believe me. I wouldn't let go—even though it was long distance—'til he got my point. Finally, he said he'd send Ma a offer in writing saying he was dying to pay twenty thousand dollars for the Chinese screen. Ma took the phone back and said to him that he should send a telegram. She said that she would pay him back. She figured it'd be cheaper than living in the motel, which was right expensive.

We got the telegram and carried it on over to the Museum, and Mrs. Fortinbras told us that the committee that decides whether or not to buy things wouldn't be meeting until early next month. Would Ma mind leaving the screen? Ma asked was the Museum considering matching the offer we had from Huntington Antiques, and Mrs. Fortinbras said yes, it was. They were prepared to pay twenty thousand dollars for the screen, and Ma said that that being the case, she was prepared to leave it for them to look at some more.

We got a telegram from the Museum when we'd been back home eight days. It said that the committee had voted to purchase the Chinese silk screen and please to send them a bill and please to keep quiet about it until the Museum itself made the announcement.

I just pretended that I hadn't even read that last part of the telegram, and I called up the newspaper and told them, and a writer from the newspaper came on over to the house and listened to Ma's story and published two of my Polaroids besides, not even complaining that they were a little out of focus or that they had fingerprints on them in the wrong places.

We must have got a hundred phone calls the day that story came out in the paper. There was people who had umbrella stands and others who had statues and some who had paintings, but all of them was sure that they had themselves a museum piece and would Ma please to come on over to their place to look at it. One lady told Ma she would love to have her to come over and look at a Rembrandt painting she wanted to sell except she couldn't tell Ma who she was because she had to keep it a secret so's she wouldn't get robbed. Ma said she understood.

I told Ma that what I couldn't understand was why Bert and Ray hadn't called us up to congratulate us. A lot of other dealers had. Ma said that she understood why they had not, and she was feeling pretty sad about it.

I asked Ma if she thought that they was jealous about the money, and I reminded Ma that she had offered the screen to them first for a hundred twenty-five. Ma said that the money was just a little bit of it. "What do you suppose is the big part of it then, Ma?" I asked.

"It's hard for me to know the words for saying it, William," she said. "I know what it is that's bothering them. It's the same thing that bothered them about the *panetière,* but I don't know the psychological words for it."

Bert and Ray finally called the next day, and I heard what Ma told them. Ma said, "It seems like I got took pretty good, Bert. I found out that that there screen I sold the Museum for twenty thousand dollars was really worth twenty-five thousand. Guess I just still got a lot to learn."

Well, that was it.

Bert and Ray come on over to the house that night and teased Ma about how she got took by the Freer Gallery, and Ma just laughed at herself right along with them.

Well, that was it.

Bert and Ray just couldn't stand being beat out by Ma, who had been their student just a few years ago. Bert and Ray couldn't stand that Ma already knew more about antiques than they did, not only because she studies on them, but also because she's got all these delicate feelings about things that you can't hardly help but notice when you watch her looking at something or touching it so gentle.

But Ma's been so wore down by everything, including living all them years with Pa, that she figures won't nobody love her if she shows that she knows one thing more than they do.

But I look back on how good she stuck by her guns with that screen when all them dealers and one decorator laughed us out of their shops, and I figure that if she can stand by her guns with strangers, she soon will be able to with people who have us over to tea. And I figure that I got six more years before I finish school and have to go off and leave her, and I'm going to work on her. I pushed her up them steps to Huntington Antiques, and I got her to go to that Freer, and I figure that I can help her to find out how being grateful to Bert and Ray is something she should always be, but outgrown them is something she already is. By the time I leave home, she's gonna be ready to face that fact and live with it. She'll need it, being's she won't have me around to push her here and there anymore.

196

MEET
E. L. KONIGSBURG

"Why, back to home we always say that there's some folk who don't know that they're through the swinging doors of opportunity until they've got swat on their backside."

—William

As E. L. Konigsburg prepared to be a chemist, she had no inkling of the swat that would launch her amazing writing career. After she started teaching, Konigsburg made a surprising discovery: "I began to suspect that chemistry was not my field. Not only did I always ask my students to light my Bunsen burner, having become match-shy, but I became more interested in what was going on inside of them than what was going on inside the test tubes.

That interest in her students prompted Konigsburg to start writing. Her subject?—the young people she had taught and the ones she was raising. Always experimenting, she read what she wrote to her own children, and "their reaction determined what happened next." Konigsburg offers this advice to anyone who wants to be a writer: "The difference between being a writer and being a person of talent is to apply the seat of your pants to the seat of your chair and finish. Don't talk about doing it. Do it. Finish."

E. L. Konigsburg is the first author to have one book, *The Mixed-up Files of Mrs. Basil E. Frankweiler,* win the Newbery Award and another book, *Jennifer, Hecate, Macbeth, William McKinley and Me, Elizabeth,* win the Newbery Honor in the same year. *Throwing Shadows,* a volume of short stories that includes "With Bert and Ray by William," was a 1979 American Library Association Notable Book and a School Library Journal Best Book of the Year.

RESPONDING TO Literature

THINK • TALK • WRITE

1 Did you find this story entertaining? Would you like to read other stories by E. L. Konigsburg? Jot down your thoughts in your journal.

2 What does William's mother do when Bert and Ray finally call about the deal she made with the Freer Gallery? Why do you think she does this?

3 How does William describe his mother's personality at the beginning of the story? Do you think she changes by the story's end? Explain your answer.

4 How does William feel about his mother at the end of the story? Do you think his feelings are justified? Explain your answer.

5 What kind of a person does William seem to be? What leads you to think as you do?

ACTIVITIES

- **Write About Colloquialisms** Ma and William use many colloquialisms. List some examples from the story. Then substitute a more formal phrase for each colloquialism.

- **Role-playing** With a classmate, role play a scene between Ma and William. Decide what the two of you will talk about and act out your scene, remembering to use colloquialisms in your conversation.

VOCABULARY PRACTICE

On a separate sheet of paper, write the vocabulary word from the list that has the same or almost the same meaning as the word italicized in each sentence.

speculating **authentic**

capacity **chaperones**

threshold

1 He stood at the *doorway* of the ancient house and peered inside.

2 The *supervisors* helped us to clean up after the dance.

3 He had been *thinking* about the job offer for many days.

4 She really has no *ability* for this kind of work.

5 This is the *genuine* Chinese silk screen.

THE ARMFUL

BY ROBERT FROST

For every parcel I stoop down to seize
I lose some other off my arms and knees,
And the whole pile is slipping, bottles, buns—
Extremes too hard to comprehend at once,
Yet nothing I should care to leave behind.

With all I have to hold with, hand and mind
And heart, if need be, I will do my best
To keep their building balanced at my breast.
I crouch down to prevent them as they fall;
Then sit down in the middle of them all.
I had to drop the armful in the road
And try to stack them in a better load.

The Flower Seller   1942   Diego Rivera   Private Collection

SPOT on

FOLKLORE

As a child, you probably once said to an adult, "Tell me a story." Then as the tale unfolded, you most likely sat with eyes glued to your storyteller, listening to every word with undivided attention. Try to recall this experience as you look at the picture below.

Old Father, the Story Teller *1960 Pablita Velarde Collection of the artist*

What do you think is taking place in this painting? What details suggest what is happening?

How would you describe the people gathered around the man? Why do you describe them in this way?

Think about stories that are passed along from grandparent to parent to child. What do these stories have in common? How are they different? How is the storytelling experience captured in this painting?

LIGHT

TYPES OF FOLKLORE

The *folklore* of a culture includes the stories, songs, and poems that have been handed down from generation to generation. Works that survive by word of mouth become part of the culture's *oral tradition*.

FOLK TALES entertain readers or listeners. They are not meant to be true. Usually the main characters are farmers or laborers shown to have better values than their more wealthy, powerful neighbors.

FAIRY TALES are about fanciful characters with unusual abilities.
- *Characters* include giants, monsters, dragons, fairies, talking animals, trolls, gnomes, evil beings, and kindly godmothers.
- *Events* include transformations, wishes, things happening in threes, superhuman strength or ability, trickery, and magic.

TRICKSTER TALES describe how clever people or animals take advantage of foolish people or animals. Trickster tales are well known in Native American and African American folklore.

TALL TALES are humorous stories that exaggerate characters and events beyond belief.

FABLES are brief stories that teach a lesson through a *moral*—a principle involving right and wrong. Most fables have animal characters that behave like people.

MYTHS are set in ancient times and explain important natural events.
- *Greek and Roman myths* describe the actions of gods, goddesses, and mortal heroes and heroines.
- *Creation myths* explain how Earth was formed.

LEGENDS are stories that usually describe real historical figures in fictional situations.

In the selections that follow, you will read three different types of folklore. What you learn will add to your understanding and enjoyment of this type of literature. It will also help you in writing a folk tale of your own.

FOLKLORE

....

BENDING WILLOW

CONNECT TO LITERATURE

Did you ever wonder why your town is located where it is? Did you ever wonder how it got its name? In your journal, write some questions about your town's founding, and jot down some possible answers. Then as you read "Bending Willow," note how the folk tale explains the location of Bending Willow's village.

INTRODUCTION TO THE MODEL FOLK TALE

When you read the folklore in this unit, you will find that the selections are made up of similar elements. For example, each piece has a fictional main character and includes extraordinary events.

As you read "Bending Willow," use the notes in the margin. The notes will help you see the structure of the folk tale and show you how its elements are related to each other. As you read the folk tale, you might like to note your own thoughts and impressions in your journal.

DID YOU KNOW?

Folklore consists of stories that have been passed down by word of mouth over many generations. Folklore exists in every culture and often reveals a great deal about the values or customs of the culture from which it comes.

Much Native American folklore tells about living in harmony with nature, showing respect for the wisdom of one's elders, and putting the needs of family and tribe before one's own needs. These tales were often used to teach; if a child misbehaved, he or she would be told a "lesson story" that showed the correct way to act.

Bending Willow

By Ethel Johnston Phelps

Long ago, the young Indian maiden Bending Willow lived in the wigwam of her parents, not far from the great falls called Niagara. The tribe was at peace, the waterfowl and fish from the river were plentiful. But Bending Willow was very unhappy.

Although several young warriors sought her in marriage, the most persistent and most unwelcome suitor was the chief, a cruel old man rightly named No Heart. His hair was as gray as a badger and he had already buried three wives. However, he had great power in the tribe, and when he declared that he would take Bending Willow for his next wife, her parents dared not refuse him.

Bending Willow had another reason for sadness; she had no living brother or sister to help or advise her. They had died from the mysterious sickness that so

203

often attacked members of the tribe. Since her close friend, Laughing Water, had been taken, Bending Willow felt very much alone.

The tribe blamed an evil spirit loose in the village for the mysterious sickness. Chief No Heart <u>proclaimed</u> that the marriage celebration of a chief would drive away this evil spirit. Then he set the day for the ceremony.

When Bending Willow was told of this, she ran into the forest to be alone and think. She would not marry Chief No Heart. She did not believe the mysterious sickness would disappear if the marriage took place. At last she could think of only one solution: she must leave the village and escape to the lands across the wide river.

Early the next morning before dawn, when all were sleeping, she dragged her father's canoe to the edge of the river, stepped into it, and paddled swiftly out into the current.

The night was still dark, with very few stars gleaming in the blackness above her, and the current at this time of the year was much stronger than she had expected. She paddled with all her strength for some time without success. Instead of making her way across the wide river, she found herself at dawn headed toward the rapids.

The paddle was torn from her hands as the canoe tossed about wildly, like a withered branch, on the white-crested waves. The roar of the great falls filled her ears.

■
proclaimed (prə klāmd′) v.t. announced officially; declared publicly.

Folk tales reveal a great deal about the people who tell them. Folk tales are a way of conveying cultural values, such as a belief in spirits, from one generation to the next, usually through oral retellings.

Iroquois-type canoe model Iroquois
Peabody Essex Museum, Salem, Massachusetts

Swiftly but surely she was borne toward the rocks at the edge of the great falls.

She raised her eyes to the distant star still gleaming steadily in the morning grayness above. If only the Star Maiden would lift her up to the heavens!

"I would rather be up in the sky forever than down at the bottom of the river!" she thought.

For one moment only she saw the bright white and green foam of water. Then she felt herself lifted on great white wings above the rocks. The water divided, and she passed into a dark cave behind the foaming spray.

In the cave was a small creature with a white face and hair of soft white mist, like the mist that rises from the base of the falls. It was the water spirit, Cloud-and-Rain, who had rescued her and taken her into his lodge. The door of his lodge was the green wave of Niagara, and the walls of the cave were of gray rock <u>studded</u> with white stone flowers.

Cloud-and-Rain gave her a warm wrapper and seated her on a heap of <u>ermine</u> skins in a far corner where the dampness was shut out by a magic fire. He brought her fish to eat and delicate jelly made from mosses only the water spirits can find.

When she was rested, Cloud-and-Rain told her he knew her story. "No Heart is not a wise leader for your people," he said. "The campsite of the village is a bad one. It is too close to the swamp. When the sickness came, he did not listen to the elders' advice to move."

"You know of the mysterious sickness!" cried Bending Willow. "It has taken my brothers and sister and my friend Laughing Water. No one knows what evil spirit brings it or how to drive it away!"

"There are herbs to help and knowledge of how to use them. That I can teach you." Cloud-and-Rain was

Very often, supernatural creatures and events play a large role in folk tales.

---

studded (stud′əd) *v.t.* scattered or spread over.
ermine (ûr′min) *adj.* of the white winter fur of a weasel, whose fur is brown during the rest of the year.

silent for a time. "Yes, there are many things I can teach you that will help your people. The water of your village is bad, poisoned."

"Poisoned?" Bending Willow stared at him in per-plexity. "What evil spirit did that? I do not understand."

"Listen carefully if you would save the lives of your tribe," said the water spirit Cloud-and-Rain. "A great serpent lies underneath the ground of your village. He poisons the springs from which you draw the water to drink. When people die, the serpent is pleased, and more and more poison seeps into your springs. Even now the spring that No Heart uses is fouled, and he will soon die."

"If you can teach me how the village can get rid of this evil serpent, I will stay with you gladly," said Bending Willow.

"When you return," said Cloud-and-Rain, "you must persuade your people to move their camp. Let them come to dwell nearer to me, in the high upland."

Bending Willow stayed three months with Cloud-and-Rain. He taught her much medicine skill, and showed her the herbs to cure sickness.

One day when he came in from fishing, he said to her, "Chief No Heart is dead. This night I will throw a bridge from the foot of the waters across the falls to the high hills. You must climb it without fear, for I will hold it firmly until you are on the land."

When the moon rose, casting a gleam of silver on the waters, Cloud-and-Rain caused a gentle wind to raise the spray until it formed a great white arch reaching from his cave to the distant hills. He led Bending Willow to the foot of this bridge of mist and helped her start off. Higher and higher she climbed, brave and confident, until she descended the misty arch onto the high upland.

Wooden spoon with squirrel effigy (1850) and corn-washing basket (1910) Iroquois New York State Museum, Albany

---

perplexity (pər plek′si tē) *n.* state or condition of being filled with uncertainty, confusion, or bewilderment.

seeps (sēps) *v.i.* spreads or flows slowly, as through openings or pores.

When she returned to the village, the tribe welcomed her joyfully. No one blamed her for leaving the tribe to escape marriage with No Heart. They listened quietly when she told them of the water spirit Cloud-and-Rain, and of the medicine wisdom he had taught her. But they would not agree to move their village to the uplands.

"The swamp is a protection against enemy attack," they said. "And there are plentiful fish and waterfowl here."

"The upland farther down the river is safer," she answered. "The water is pure. There are many herbs and plants to cure sickness. Here the water springs are poisoned by an evil serpent spirit who lies hidden under the ground." But they shook their heads in disbelief.

When the tribe would not accept the wisdom she had brought from the water spirit, Bending Willow at first felt discouraged. But the months she had spent with Cloud-and-Rain had given her confidence and courage, as well as wisdom. She spoke to her mother and other women of the village separately. Several of them were persuaded that the water spirit's advice was <u>sound</u>.

Bending Willow led the women to the high uplands to draw their water from the clear springs bubbling out from the rocks. Then the women carried the water carefully back to the village. They did this for several months. Neither the women nor any of their families who used this water fell ill. Of those using the village water, some sickened—and among them were strong warriors as well as two of the new chief's children.

This was enough to convince the new chief. The tribe held a council and voted to move. They took down their lodgepoles and moved the village to the uplands.

There the tribe lived in peace and good health. Bending Willow shared her knowledge of herbs with the women of the tribe. And before many months had passed, she happily married a young warrior of her choice.

> Typically, folk tale heroes and heroines must overcome obstacles to achieve their goals.

> Notice that Bending Willow uses her "confidence and courage, as well as wisdom" to persuade her people. Through their folk tales, cultures reveal what they consider to be desirable and undesirable personal traits.

> Another characteristic of folk tales is that good is rewarded and evil is punished.

sound (sound) *adj.* stable or safe; reliable.

Meet Ethel Johnston Phelps

Although Ethel Johnston Phelps (born 1914) started writing stories as a child, it wasn't until the 1970s that she published her first book, a collection of folk tales about resourceful heroines. The success of that work prompted Phelps to gather a second collection of similar tales, entitled *The Maid of the North,* from which "Bending Willow" is taken.

Phelps sees folk and fairy tales as "adventure stories with a moral." In retelling the tales, she hopes to add to our knowledge of the great oral literatures of the past.

More Native American Tales

- *They Dance in the Sky: Native American Star Myths* by Jean Guard Monroe and Ray A. Williamson (Houghton Mifflin, 1987). According to Native American mythology, in the Beginning Time, humans and sky spirits moved frequently between the sky and the earth. This collection includes star myths from many Native American nations.

- *Native American Stories* told by Joseph Bruchac (Fulham, 1991). Bruchac, a master storyteller, has collected Native American folklore that focuses on the interrelationship between people and nature.

- *The Girl Who Married a Ghost and Other Tales from the North American Indian* collected by Edward S. Curtis (Four Winds, 1978). Curtis traveled throughout the United States in the early 1900s photographing the vanishing Native American cultures. His photographs and the tales he gathered have been collected in this book.

Iroquois-type moccasins Museum of Mankind, British Museum, London

Copyright The British Museum

RESPONDING TO *Literature*

THINK • TALK • WRITE

1 Were you sympathetic to Bending Willow's plight? Did you think she was right to leave her village? Write a few lines about this in your journal.

2 Why does Bending Willow stay with Cloud-and-Rain? What might this tell you about the values of her people?

3 How would you describe the personality of Bending Willow? Explain your answer.

4 Many folk tales contain a lesson. What do you think might be the lesson of "Bending Willow"? Why do you think this?

5 What did you learn about Bending Willow's tribe from this folk tale? Use story details in your response.

ACTIVITY

• **Write About a Folk Tale** Copy and complete a story map like this one for "Bending Willow."

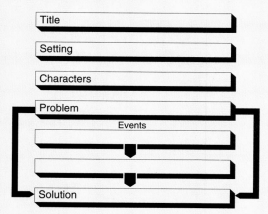

Title

Setting

Characters

Problem

Events

Solution

VOCABULARY PRACTICE

On a separate sheet of paper, write an answer to each of the following questions.

1 Would a tribal announcement be **proclaimed** or **studded?** Explain your answer.

2 What **seeps** into the village's drinking water? What effect does it have?

3 Do you think the decision to move the village was **sound?** Why or why not?

4 Do you think Bending Willow's tribe listened to her story with **perplexity?** Why or why not?

5 Would a clear night sky be **studded** or **sound** with stars? Explain your answer.

FOLKLORE

PAUL BUNYAN'S CORNSTALK

CONNECT TO LITERATURE

What do Davy Crockett, Johnny Appleseed, and Pecos Bill have in common? They are all heroes of American tall tales. Think about some of the tall tales you have read about or heard. Then list the characteristics of these tales. As you read "Paul Bunyan's Cornstalk," see how many characteristics from your list you can find in the story.

THINKING ABOUT A FOLK HERO

A *folk hero* is typically a character who is strong, courageous, and capable of doing extraordinary things.

The folk heroes found in American tall tales often use superhuman powers to accomplish wonderful deeds. Frequently these heroes will be responsible for the creation of some well-known landmark or for the occurrence of some famous event.

DID YOU KNOW?

It is not clear how the story of Paul Bunyan began. It may have been based on tales told by French Canadian lumberjacks. However, Paul Bunyan may be the product of advertising, newspapers, and children's books. There is no written mention of Bunyan before a 1910 newspaper story. In 1914 a logging company began to use Bunyan as a symbol and distributed booklets about the giant lumberjack. Two children's books appeared in the 1920s, and since then Paul Bunyan has been one of America's favorite tall-tale heroes.

PAUL BUNYAN'S CORNSTALK

RETOLD BY
HAROLD COURLANDER

Paul Bunyan was the fellow who invented the ax with two edges so a man could stand between two trees and chop them both down at the same time. As it turned out, Paul was the only man who could do that trick, but the other lumberjacks used the double-bitted ax anyway, because they didn't have to sharpen the blades so often. Paul Bunyan also had other tricks. Most lumberjacks used to cut off the tops of the pines before they felled them. But when Paul was in a hurry, he'd wait till a tree started falling; then he'd get set with his ax and lop off the top of the tree as it came down.

---

lumberjacks (lum′bər jaks′) *n., pl.* people who cut down trees and get logs ready for transportation to the sawmill.

Nothing Paul Bunyan ever did was small. He had an ox named Babe, who used to help him with his logging work. Babe was just about the most phenomenal ox in Michigan. His color was blue, and he stood <u>ninety hands</u> high. If you happened to hang on the tip of one horn, it's doubtful if you could have seen the tip of the other, even on a clear day. One day when Paul had Babe

Even the storms that Paul was in were big. The biggest of all was the one they call the Big Blue Snow. It snowed for two months straight, and the way the drifts piled up only the tops of the tallest pines were showing. Lumberjacks went out that winter on their snowshoes and cut off all the pine tops. It saved them a lot of time when spring came around. Babe the blue ox didn't get a

out plowing, the ox was stung by a Michigan deerfly about the size of a bushel basket. Babe took off across the country dragging the plow behind him, right across Indiana, Illinois, and Missouri, with the deerfly bringing up the rear. After a while Babe <u>veered</u> south and didn't stop till he got to the Rio Grande. The plow that Babe was hitched to dug a <u>furrow</u> four miles wide and two hundred miles long. You can check it in your own geography book. They call it Grand Canyon nowadays.

wink of sleep, though, from December till the first of March. It seems that standing out there in the weather the way he was, the snow that fell on his back melted and ran down his tail, and once it got there it froze into ice. Babe's tail kept getting heavier and heavier,

ninety hands: thirty feet.

veered (vîrd) *v.i.* changed in direction or course; shifted; turned.

furrow (fûr′ō) *n.* long, narrow groove or channel made in the ground by a plow.

and it drew on his hide so hard it just pulled his eyelids wide open and kept them that way. Babe never did get his eyes closed until the spring thaw came and melted the ice off his tail.

But the Big Blue Snow wasn't anything compared to the big <u>drought</u> that started in Saginaw County and spread out as far as the Alleghenies in the East and the Rockies in the West. It all

vines. It grew so fast it just darted around like a Massauga rattlesnake. It climbed into any place where there was an opening. People had to keep their windows closed. The ones that didn't had to cut their way out of their beds with a brush knife. Sometimes that vine would grow into one window and out another between sunset and sunrise. Things weren't too bad until the vine

started with Paul Bunyan's vegetable garden. Paul planted some corn and some pumpkins. One of those cornstalks was six feet high before the others had sprouted. In two weeks it was tall as a house and growing like crazy. About the time it was as big as a fifty-year-old pine, people began to come in from all over the county to see it. It was growing out of the ground so fast it was pulling up stones that even the frost couldn't <u>heave</u> out. Same kind of thing, more or less, happened to one of the pumpkin

blossomed and the pumpkins came out. They were about the size of <u>hogsheads</u>— the *little* pumpkins, that is—and when the vine whipped back and forth looking for someplace to grow it just snapped the pumpkins around like crab apples on a string. People had to be mighty alert to keep from getting hit by those

■ _____

drought (drout) *n.* long period of dry weather; prolonged lack of rainfall.

heave (hēv) *v.* lift or raise with force or effort.

hogsheads (hôgz′hedz′) *n., pl.* large barrels holding from 63 to 140 gallons of liquid.

pumpkins. One man lost a team of horses that way, and half a dozen good barns and one silo were stove in.

But the real problem started when the corn and pumpkin roots began to soak up all the water out of the ground. Farms for sixty miles around went dry—fields, springs, and wells. The pine woods turned yellow from lack of moisture. The Au Sable River just turned into a trickle, and pretty soon there wasn't anything there but dry mud. The next thing that happened was that the water in the Great Lakes began to go down. It went down so fast in Lake Huron it left the fish hanging in the air. When things began to look real bad, folks came and told Paul Bunyan he'd just have to get rid of his corn and pumpkins. Paul was reasonable about it. First he went after the pumpkin vine. He spent four hours racing around trying to catch hold of the end, and finally did it by trapping it in a barn. He hitched Babe up to the end of the vine, but as fast as Babe pulled the vine grew. Babe ran faster and faster, and he was near Lake Ontario before he had the vine tight enough to pull it out.

Then Paul sized up his cornstalk. He figured he'd have to chop it down. He sharpened up his ax and spit on his hands. He made a good deep cut in that stalk, but before he could chip out a wedge the stalk grew up six feet, cut and all. Every time he made a cut it would shoot up out of reach before he could swing his ax again. Pretty soon he saw there wasn't any use going on this way. "Only way to kill this stalk is to cut off the top," he said. He hung his ax in his belt and started climbing. In about two hours he was completely out of sight. People just stood around and waited. They stood around two and a half days without any sight of Paul. Lars Larson called, "Paul!" but there was no answer. Erik Erikson and Hans Hanson called, "Paul!" But there wasn't any word from Paul Bunyan. So they waited some more. Two more days went by. No word from Paul. They decided that if everyone yelled at once maybe the sound would carry. So all together the two thousand eight hundred men and boys hollered, "Paul!" And sure enough, they heard his faint voice from up above.

"When you going to top that cornstalk?" they yelled back at him.

"Hasn't that top come down yet?" Paul hollered back. "I cut it off three days ago!"

And it was the truth, too. The stalk stopped growing, the water in the Great Lakes stopped falling, the Au Sable River began to run, the springs began to flow again, and things came back to normal. But it was a narrow escape.

---

silo (sī′lō) *n.* tall, cylindrical tower of metal or other material for the storage and fermentation of green fodder.

stove (stōv) *v.i.* smashed; broken.

MEET
HAROLD COURLANDER

Harold Courlander (1908–1996) was a native of Indianapolis, Indiana. After graduating from the University of Michigan in 1931, Courlander began a career that brought him into contact with many peoples of the world. At various points in his life, Courlander was a historian in Ethiopia; an editor for the U.S. Office of War Information in New York and Bombay, India; a press officer for the United Nations, and a senior political analyst for the U.S. Information Agency, Voice of America.

Between the years 1939 and 1972, Courlander studied the folklore and folk music of a number of cultures. He is best known for the collections of folk tales that resulted from this work.

More American Folklore

- *American Tall Tales* by Adrien Stoutenburg (Puffin, 1976). Read about the incredible exploits of eight mighty American heroes, including Paul Bunyan, who swagger through the pages of this book.

- *American Tall Tales* by Mary Pope Osborne (Knopf, 1991). Among the American tall tale heroes you will meet in this irresistibly funny collection is Sally Ann Thunder Ann Whirlwind, the fictional wife of Davy Crockett, who could outdo any varmint around.

- *The People Could Fly: American Black Folktales* retold by Virginia Hamilton (Knopf, 1985). Simply told adaptations of old slave tales in an outstanding book of African American folk tales.

RESPONDING TO *Literature*

THINK • TALK • WRITE

1 What did you like best about "Paul Bunyan's Cornstalk"? Jot down some ideas in your journal.

2 According to the story, how was the Grand Canyon created?

3 What clues can you find that show the story is a tall tale?

4 How would you characterize Paul Bunyan? Give reasons to support your ideas.

5 Do you think you would like to be a neighbor of Paul Bunyan's? Why or why not?

ACTIVITIES

● **Write About a Folk Hero** Make up a folk hero of your own and write a tall tale about him or her. As you write, keep in mind the characteristics typical of folk heroes: strong, brave, capable of doing extraordinary things.

● **Interview a Folk Hero** With a small group of classmates prepare and conduct an interview with Paul Bunyan or another folk hero. One person in the group will be the hero and the others will ask questions. Take a few minutes before the interview to list ideas about things you might ask.

VOCABULARY PRACTICE

On a separate sheet of paper, write the word from the vocabulary list that best completes each sentence.

veered   heave

furrow   stove

drought

1 The rock _____ in the window, and bits of glass covered the floor.

2 The ox pulled a plow and made a _____ in the rich soil.

3 The flying ducks _____ to the left.

4 As the farmers looked at their dried-up crops, they were sure this was the worst _____ they had ever seen.

5 The hero was strong enough to _____ the car into the air.

FOLKLORE

THESEUS

CONNECT TO LITERATURE

Journeying into the unknown can be exciting. In action-adventure movies, the characters usually have to overcome great obstacles. In real life you also may have had to face the unknown—perhaps, for example, in changing schools or moving to a new place. How did you meet the challenge? As you read "Theseus," note in your journal how he behaves. How are you similar to him? How are you different?

THINKING ABOUT CHARACTER: MOTIVATION

Like real people, *characters* in stories have their own personalities. One character might be brave; another one might be timid. Characters also have to have *motivations,* or *reasons,* for what they do. There are many different motivations, including love, pride, and fear.

As you read "Theseus," try to figure out the motivation for the actions of each of the characters. Understanding the characters and their motivations will increase your enjoyment of the story.

DID YOU KNOW?

Scholars believe that the sources of some myths may be events that actually happened thousands of years ago. In the nineteenth century, a man named Heinrich Schliemann used clues in the *Iliad,* a story by the ancient Greek poet Homer, to locate the long-buried ruins of the city of Troy. He found jewels, weapons, and other items from many periods in history. Not too long after Schliemann's discovery, Sir Arthur Evans uncovered what is called the Palace of Minos on the island of Crete. Because the palace has so many hidden passageways, Evans believed that it was the inspiration for the legendary Labyrinth of Greek mythology.

THESEUS

Retold by Nathaniel Hawthorne

Theseus   Floor mosaic from a Roman villa in Cyprus   3rd century A.D.

In the old city of Troezene, at the foot of a lofty mountain, there lived long ago a boy named Theseus. His grandfather, King Pittheus, was the <u>sovereign</u> of that country. His mother's name was Aethra. As for his father, the boy had never seen him. But from his earliest remembrance, Aethra used to go with Theseus into a wood and sit upon a moss-grown rock which

---

sovereign (sov′rən) *n.* supreme ruler of a monarchy.

was deeply sunken into the earth. Here she often talked with her son about his father. She said that he was called Aegeus and that he was a great king and ruled over Attica and dwelt at Athens, which was as famous a city as any in the world.

"Mother," asked the boy, "why cannot I go to Athens and tell King Aegeus that I am his son?"

"That may happen by and by," said Aethra. "You are not yet big and strong enough to set out on such an errand."

"And how soon shall I be strong enough?"

"You are but a boy," replied his mother. "When you can lift this rock and show me what is hidden beneath it, I promise you my permission to depart."

Often after this did Theseus ask his mother whether it was yet time for him to go to Athens. Still his mother pointed to the rock and told him that for years to come he could not be strong enough to move it. Again and again the boy would tug and strain at the huge mass of stone. Meanwhile the rock seemed to be sinking farther and farther into the ground. The moss grew over it thicker and thicker.

But difficult as the matter looked, Theseus was now growing up to be such a vigorous youth that,

in his own opinion, the time would quickly come when he might hope to get the upper hand of the lump of stone.

"Mother, I do believe it has started!" cried he after one of his attempts.

"No, no!" his mother hastily answered. "It is not possible you can have moved it."

It was not more than a year afterwards when they were again sitting on the moss-covered stone. Aethra had once more told him the story of his father.

"Mother," he exclaimed, "I never felt half so strong as now! I feel myself a man! It is now time to make one earnest trial to remove the stone."

Then Theseus bent himself in good earnest to the task and strained every sinew. The great rock stirred! Yes, it was raised slowly from the bedded moss and earth and was turned upon its side. While taking breath, he looked at his mother, and she smiled upon him.

"Yes, Theseus," she said, "the time has come, and you must stay no longer at my side. See what King Aegeus left for you."

Theseus looked and saw that the rock had been placed over another slab of stone that somewhat resembled a roughly made chest.

Within lay a sword with a golden hilt, and a pair of sandals.

"That was your father's sword," said Aethra, "and those were his sandals. When he went to be king of Athens, he bade me treat you as a child until you should prove yourself a man by lifting his heavy stone. That task being accomplished, you are to put on his sandals in order to follow in your father's footsteps and to gird on his sword."

When his grandfather, the wise King Pittheus, heard that Theseus intended to present himself at his father's palace, he earnestly advised him to go by sea.

"The roads are very bad by land," said the venerable king, "and they are infested with robbers and monsters. Let him go by sea!"

But when Theseus heard of robbers and monsters, he was eager to take the road along which they were to be met with. Therefore, he bade a respectful farewell to his grandfather, thanking him for all his kindness, and after affectionately embracing his mother, he set forth.

Many adventures befell Theseus on the road to Athens. He quite cleared that part of the country of the robbers about whom King Pittheus had been so much alarmed. One of these was named Procrustes, and he was indeed a terrible fellow. In his cavern he had a bed on which, with great pretense of hospitality, he invited his guest to lie down. But if they happened to be shorter than the bed, this wicked villain stretched them out by main force. Or if they were too long, he lopped off their heads or feet. Thus, however weary a man might be, he never liked to lie in the bed of Procrustes. Another of these robbers, named Scinis, must likewise have been a great scoundrel. He was in the habit of flinging his victims off a high cliff into the sea. Theseus tossed him off the very same place.

Thus by the time he reached his journey's end, Theseus had done many valiant feats with his father's golden-hilted sword and had gained the renown of being one of the bravest young men of the day. His fame traveled faster than he did and reached Athens before him. As he entered the city, he heard the inhabitants talking at the street corners and saying that Theseus, the son of their own king, would turn out as great a hero as the best of them.

■

venerable (ven′ər ə bəl) *adj.* deserving respect or reverence, as by reason of age, character, or position.
pretense (prē′tens) *n.* false show or appearance, especially for the purpose of deceiving.
valiant (val′yənt) *adj.* brave; courageous.

Grand Stairway/Hall of the Colonnades at Palace at Knossos, Crete   c.1600 B.C.

their own hands. Thus these nephews of King Aegeus, who were the cousins of Theseus, became his enemies. A still more dangerous enemy was Medea, the wicked enchantress, for she wanted to give the kingdom to her son Medus.

It so happened that the king's nephews met Theseus and found out who he was just as he reached the entrance of the royal palace. They pretended to be his friends. They proposed that he should come into the king's presence as a stranger to try whether Aegeus would recognize him. Theseus consented, but while he waited at the door, the nephews ran and told the king that a young man had arrived who intended to get possession of his crown.

"Aha!" cried the old king. "What would you advise me to do with him?"

"Leave that to me, your Majesty," replied Medea. "Invite him to drink a goblet of wine. Let me put a single drop of this powerful medicine into the goblet."

King Aegeus, like most other kings, thought any punishment mild enough for a person who was plotting against his life and therefore gave orders that the young stranger should be admitted into his presence. The goblet was set on a table beside the king's throne.

He little suspected, innocent youth that he was, that here in this very Athens a greater danger awaited him than any which he had encountered on the road. The father of Theseus was almost worn out with the cares of government and had thus grown aged before his time. His nephews intended to get all the power of the kingdom into

Advancing to the foot of the throne, Theseus attempted to make a little speech, but he was almost choked by the tender feelings that swelled into his throat.

"Young man," said the king, "you are welcome! Do me the favor to drink the contents of this goblet."

So saying, King Aegeus took the golden goblet from the table and offered it to Theseus. Theseus held out his hand to take the wine. But before he touched it, King Aegeus trembled. His eyes had fallen on the gold-hilted sword that hung at the young man's side. He drew back the goblet.

"That sword!" he cried. "How came you by it?"

"It was my father's sword," replied Theseus, with a <u>tremulous</u> voice. "These were his sandals. It is only a month since I grew strong enough to lift the heavy stone and take the sword and sandals and come to Athens to seek my father."

"My son! My son!" cried King Aegeus, flinging away the fatal goblet. "Yes, these are Aethra's eyes. It is my son."

And now Prince Theseus was taken into great favor by his royal father. The old king was never weary of hearing him tell about his childhood and his many efforts to lift the stone.

One morning when Prince Theseus awoke, he fancied that he must have had a sorrowful dream. For it appeared as if the air was full of a melancholy wail. And when he listened more attentively, he could hear sobs and groans. He put on his clothes quickly and, hastening to the king, inquired what it all meant.

"Alas! My son," said King Aegeus, heaving a long sigh, "this is the woefullest anniversary in the whole year. It is the day when we annually draw lots to see which of the youths and maidens of Athens shall go to be devoured by the horrible Minotaur."

"The Minotaur!" exclaimed Prince Theseus. "What kind of a monster may that be? Is it not possible to slay him?"

But King Aegeus shook his venerable head and gave him an explanation of the whole affair. It seems that in the island of Crete there lived a certain dreadful monster called a Minotaur, which was shaped partly like a man and partly like a bull and was altogether a hideous sort of a creature. King Minos, who reigned over Crete, laid out a vast deal of

---

tremulous (trem′yə ləs) *adj.* marked or affected by trembling; shaking.

money in building a habitation for the Minotaur and took great care of his health and comfort merely for mischief's sake. A few years before this time, there had been a war between Athens and Crete in which the Athenians were beaten and compelled to beg for peace. No peace could they obtain, however, except on condition that they should send seven young men and seven maidens every year to be devoured by the pet monster of the cruel King Minos. For three years past this <u>grievous</u> calamity had been borne. And now the fatal day had come again.

When Theseus heard the story, he straightened himself up so that he seemed taller than ever before.

"Let the people of Athens this year draw lots for only six young men instead of seven," said he. "I will myself be the seventh. Let the Minotaur devour me, if he can!"

The old king shed tears and begged Theseus not to leave him <u>desolate</u> in his old age. Theseus, however, felt that he was in the right and would not give up his resolution. But he assured his father that if the Minotaur devoured him, it should not be without a battle for his dinner. So a vessel was got ready and rigged with black sails. Theseus, with six other young men and seven maidens, came down to the harbor to embark.

Just as Theseus was going on board his father thought of one last word to say.

"My beloved son," said he, "the sails of this vessel are black, since it goes on a voyage of sorrow and despair. I shall creep daily to the top of yonder cliff to watch if there be a sail upon the sea. And if by some happy chance you should escape the jaws of the Minotaur, then tear down those dismal sails and hoist others that shall be bright as the sunshine. Then I will know that you are coming back victorious."

Theseus promised that he would do so. Then the mariners trimmed the vessel's black sails to the wind, which blew faintly off the shore. But by and by when they had got fairly out to sea, there came a stiff breeze from the northwest that drove them along merrily. Soon the high blue mountains of Crete began to show themselves among the far-off clouds. The vessel went bounding onward until it glided between the headlands of the

---

grievous (grē′vəs) *adj.* causing deep sorrow or great pain.

desolate (des′ə lit) *adj.* left alone; without companionship.

224

port. No sooner had they entered the harbor than a party of the guards of King Minos came down to the waterside and took charge of the fourteen young men and <u>damsels</u>. Surrounded by these armed warriors, Theseus and his companions were led to the king's palace and ushered into his presence. Now Minos was a stern and pitiless king. When his eyes rested on Theseus, the king looked at him attentively because his face was calm and brave.

"Young man," asked he with his stern voice, "are you not appalled at the certainty of being devoured by this terrible Minotaur?"

"I have offered my life in a good cause," answered Theseus, "and therefore I give it freely and gladly. But thou, King Minos, art thou not thyself appalled who hast committed this dreadful wrong year after year? I tell thee to thy face that thou art a more hideous monster than the Minotaur himself!"

"Aha! Do you think me so?" cried the king, laughing in his cruel way. "Tomorrow at breakfast time you shall have an opportunity of judging which is the greater monster, the Minotaur or the king! Take them away, guards, and let this free-spoken youth be the Minotaur's first morsel!"

Near the king's throne stood his daughter Ariadne. She was a beautiful and tender-hearted maiden and looked at these poor doomed captives with very different feelings from those of the iron-breasted King Minos. And when she beheld the brave, spirited figure of Theseus bearing himself so calmly in his terrible <u>peril</u>, she flung herself at the king's feet and begged him to set all the captives free, especially this one young man.

But the king would hear not a word in their favor. The prisoners were led away and clapped into a dungeon. The seven maidens and six of the young men soon fell asleep, but Theseus was not like them. He felt conscious that he was wiser and braver and stronger than his companions. Therefore he had the responsibility of all their lives upon him and must consider whether there was no way to save them. So he kept himself awake and paced to and fro across the gloomy dungeon in which they were shut up.

Just before midnight the door was softly unbarred, and the gentle Ariadne showed herself, with a torch in her hand.

---

damsels (dam′zəlz) *n., pl.* young girls; maidens.
peril (per′əl) *n.* danger; a chance or risk of injury, loss, or destruction.

"Are you awake, Theseus?" she whispered.

"Yes," answered Theseus. "With so little time to live, I do not choose to waste any of it in sleep."

"Then follow me," said Ariadne.

Ariadne opened all the doors and led him forth from the darksome prison into the pleasant moonlight.

"Theseus," said the maiden, "you can now get on board your vessel and sail away for Athens."

"No," answered the young man. "I will never leave Crete unless I can first slay the Minotaur and save my poor companions and deliver Athens from this cruel tribute."

"I knew that this would be your resolution," said Ariadne. "Come then with me. Here is your own sword, which the guards deprived you of."

Then she led Theseus along until they came to a dark, shadowy grove, where the moonlight wasted itself on the tops of the trees without shedding so much as a glimmering beam upon their pathway. After going a good way, they reached a high marble wall which was overgrown with creeping plants. The wall seemed to have no door but rose up, lofty and massive and mysterious. Nevertheless, Ariadne pressed her finger against a particular block of marble, and it yielded, disclosing an entrance just wide enough to admit them. They crept through, and the marble stone swung back into place.

"We are now," said Ariadne, "in the famous labyrinth which Daedalus built. That Daedalus was a very cunning workman, but of all his artful contrivances, this labyrinth is the most wondrous. Were we to take but a few steps from the doorway, we might wander about all our lifetime and never find it again. In the center of this labyrinth is the Minotaur, and, Theseus, you must go to seek him."

Just then, they heard a rough and disagreeable roar, which greatly resembled the lowing of a fierce bull, but yet had some sort of sound like the human voice.

"That is the Minotaur's noise," whispered Ariadne. "You must follow that sound through the labyrinth and you will find him. Take the end of this silken string. I will hold the other end, and then if you win the victory, it will lead you again to this spot. Farewell, brave Theseus."

So the young man took the end of the silken string in his left hand and his gold-hilted sword in the

---

labyrinth (lab′ə rinth′) *n.* place with winding and connected passages or pathways in which it is easy to lose one's way; maze.

other and trod boldly into the labyrinth. Theseus had not taken five steps before he lost sight of Ariadne. But still he went on, now creeping through a low arch, now ascending a flight of steps, now in one crooked passage and now in another, with here a door opening before him, and there one banging behind, until it really seemed as if the walls spun round and whirled him round along with them. And all the while through these hollow avenues, now nearer, now farther off again, resounded the cry of the Minotaur, which now grew louder and louder and finally so loud that Theseus expected to come upon him at every new zigzag of the path. At last in an open space at the very center of the labyrinth, he did <u>discern</u> the hideous creature.

Ariadne and Theseus   Floor mosaic from a Roman villa in Austria last quarter of 3rd century A.D.

What an ugly monster it was! Only his horned head belonged to a bull, and yet somehow or other, he looked like a bull all over. He kept striding to and fro in a solitary frenzy of rage, continually emitting a hoarse roar. Now the Minotaur, turning suddenly about, caught sight of Theseus and instantly lowered his horribly sharp horns exactly as a mad bull does when he means to rush against an enemy. At the same time he belched forth a tremendous roar in which there was something like the words of human language, but all disjointed and shaken to pieces by passing through the gullet of a miserably enraged brute.

■
discern (di sûrn′) *v.t.* make out or recognize.

Theseus kills the Minotaur   Floor mosaic from a Roman villa in Austria   last quarter of 3rd century A.D.

head off. But Theseus leaped up and caught the monster off his guard. With all his force, he hit the Minotaur upon the neck and made his bull head skip from his human body, which fell down upon the ground.

So now the battle was ended. Immediately the moon shone out as brightly as if all the troubles of the world and all the wickedness and the ugliness that infest human life were past and gone forever. And Theseus, as he leaned on his sword, taking breath, felt a twitch of the silken cord. Eager to let Ariadne know of his success, he followed the guidance of the thread and soon found himself at the entrance of the labyrinth.

"Thou hast slain the monster," cried Ariadne, clasping her hands.

"Thanks to thee," answered Theseus, "I return victorious."

"Then," said Ariadne, "we must quickly summon thy friends and get them and thyself on board the vessel. If morning finds thee here, my father will <u>avenge</u> the Minotaur."

There ensued the most awful fight that ever happened beneath the sun or moon. The monster, in his first headlong rush against Theseus, missed him by a hair's breadth and broke one of his horns short off against the stone wall. After this, the two antagonists fought sword to horn for a long while. At last the Minotaur made a run at Theseus, grazed his left side, and flung him down. He opened his bull mouth from ear to ear and prepared to snap the young man's

---

avenge (ə venj′) *v.t.* get revenge for.

228

The captives were awakened and were told of what Theseus had done. Hastening down to the vessel, they all clambered on board except Theseus, who lingered behind, holding Ariadne's hand clasped in his own.

"Thou wilt surely go with us," said he. "Thou art too gentle and sweet for such an iron-hearted father as King Minos. Come with us, then, for he will be very angry when he knows what thou hast done."

"No, Theseus," the maiden said, "I cannot go with you. My father is old and has nobody but myself to love him. At first King Minos will be angry, but he will soon forgive his only child. Farewell!"

Nothing remained for Theseus, therefore, but to bid Ariadne an affectionate farewell and go on board the vessel and set sail. In a few moments the white foam was boiling up before their prow as Prince Theseus and his companions sailed out of the harbor with a whistling breeze behind them. In due season they came within sight of the coast of Attica, which was their native country. But here happened a sad misfortune.

King Aegeus had asked Theseus to hoist sunshine sails instead of black ones in case he should overcome the Minotaur and return victorious. In the joy of their success, however, these young people never once thought whether their sails were black, white, or rainbow colored. Thus the vessel returned, like a raven, with the same sable wings that had wafted her away. But poor King Aegeus, day after day, <u>infirm</u> as he was, had clambered to the summit of a cliff that overhung the sea and there sat watching for Theseus, homeward bound. No sooner did he behold the fatal blackness of the sails than he concluded that his dear son whom he loved so much and felt so proud of had been eaten by the Minotaur. He could not bear the thought of living any longer, so King Aegeus stooped forward and fell headlong over the cliff and was drowned in the waves that foamed at its base.

This was melancholy news for Prince Theseus, who when he stepped ashore found himself king of all the country. However, he sent for his mother to Athens and, by taking her advice in matters of state, became a very excellent <u>monarch</u> and was greatly beloved by his people.

---

infirm (in fûrm´) *adj.* physically weak, as from old age.
monarch (mon´ərk) *n.* hereditary ruler of a state or country, such as a king or queen.

229

Meet Nathaniel Hawthorne

Descended from Puritan immigrants, Nathaniel Hawthorne (1804–1864) was born on Independence Day in Salem, Massachusetts.

After graduating from Bowdoin College in 1825, Hawthorne devoted himself to writing and editing. Although dedicated to his craft, he was unable to make enough money to support himself and his family. To make ends meet, Hawthorne worked at various jobs. Then, in 1850, he published *The Scarlet Letter,* a novel that made him famous in both the United States and Great Britain. The next year he published *The House of the Seven Gables.*

Hawthorne is also known for his short stories, such as "Young Goodman Brown." *A Wonder Book* (1852), based on Greek mythology, has become a classic of juvenile literature.

More Myths from Around the World

- *The Children of Odin: The Book of Northern Myths* by Padraic Colum (Macmillan, 1984, originally published in 1920). The renowned Irish poet, playwright, and storyteller offers his adventure-packed version of the Norse sagas.

- *The Children's Homer: The Adventures of Odysseus and the Fall of Troy* by Padraic Colum (Collier Books, 1982, originally published in 1918). This exciting and very readable retelling of the *Iliad* and the *Odyssey* introduces readers to these classic tales of heroism and vengeance, glory and adventure.

- *In the Beginning* by Virginia Hamilton (Harcourt, 1988). Creation myths from around the world are retold in this splendidly illustrated, award-winning book.

RESPONDING TO *Literature*

THINK • TALK • WRITE

1 How would you describe the myth of Theseus to a friend? Jot down some ideas in your journal.

2 Why does Theseus's mother tell him about his father? How do you think she feels about telling him? Why does Theseus have to move the rock before starting his journey?

3 Why does Medea plot against Theseus? Why do you think Theseus's father is so happy to see his son? How do you think Theseus feels about meeting him?

4 What does Theseus fail to remember? Why does he forget? How do you think he feels when he learns of his father's death?

5 What could you learn about the ancient Greeks from this story? Use details to support your ideas.

ACTIVITIES

- **Write About Character: Motivation** Write a letter from Ariadne to her father explaining why she helped Theseus and asking for her father's forgiveness. The letter might also explain why she chose to remain with her father.

- **Put on a Play!** Work with a small group to write a script based on one of the scenes in the story. Be sure that you show your characters' motivations in how they speak and act. Assign parts and perform your play.

VOCABULARY PRACTICE

On a separate sheet of paper, write the word or term that best completes each sentence.

1 The old and **infirm** king was
a. powerful **b.** weak **c.** happy

2 A **venerable** scholar is very
a. foolish **b.** respected **c.** attractive

3 If a sailor can **discern** land, he can
a. see it **b.** dock there
c. get supplies

4 The **tremulous** voice of the patient sounded
a. strong **b.** shaky **c.** high

5 The **valiant** knight was full of
a. courage **b.** boasts **c.** anger

6 The liar's **pretense** at honesty can't fool us because we know it is
a. sincere **b.** faked **c.** temporary

7 One **peril** ships face is
a. sunshine **b.** icebergs **c.** fish

8 Theseus wanted to **avenge** himself on
a. the Minotaur **b.** his father
c. Ariadne

9 A **desolate** person is
a. wealthy **b.** without friends
c. sickly

10 Aegeus's **grievous** feelings made him
a. kill himself **b.** welcome Theseus
c. build palaces

WRITING

Folk tales, fables, and legends have captured people's imaginations for generations. These stories, often filled with extraordinary events and characters, are so appealing because they reflect basic human desires, hopes, and fears. Try writing a tale of your own.

PREWRITE

What's the purpose of your tale? Will your audience be entertained? Will they learn a lesson? What's your tale about? A problem solved? A villain punished or a hero rewarded? Jot down some notes.

To help readers understand your tale, you will have to show how certain events and conditions caused others to happen. This writer planned his tale using an organizer like the one here.

It's time to gather your notes. You might want to use an organizer similar to this one to put into order the causes and effects of the events in your tale.

DRAFT

Read the beginning of the draft of this writer's tale.

CHARACTERS:
traveler, innkeeper, guardian

PLOT EVENTS:

Cause: Traveler is tired and enters room.
Effect: Meets Guardian of the Jewels.

Cause: Guardian is angry at being disturbed.
Effect: Commands traveler to leave.

Cause: Guardian and traveler argue.
Effect: Innkeeper comes to room to settle things.

The writer began the story with dialog. Using dialog brings your characters alive for your readers.

The Jeweled Room

"I've voyaged far and I am weary, said the lonley traveler. The innkeeper looked at him. He decided to give the traveler the most beautifel room in the inn, which was a room filled with jewels.

Use your prewriting notes to write a draft of your tale. Remember to link clearly the causes and effects of the events you describe.

FOLKLORE

REVISE

After putting aside the draft, the writer went back and reread it. He decided to make some changes. What do you think of the revisions?

How do the changes in this sentence give you a clearer picture of the innkeeper?

"I've voyaged far and I am weary, said the lonley traveler. The innkeeper *stared* looked at him *with piercing eyes*. He decided to give the traveler the most beautifel room in the inn, which was a room filled with jewels.

Revise your draft. Fix any images, dialog, or description that feels clumsy or lifeless.

PROOFREAD

This writer consulted a proofreading checklist in his journal. He proofread several times.

Is your dialog punctuated correctly?

"I've voyaged far and I am weary," said the *lonely* (lonley) traveler. The innkeeper *stared* looked at him *with piercing eyes*, He decided to give the traveler the most *beautiful* (beautifel) room in the inn, which was a room filled with jewels.

Proofread your work. If there is any word that doesn't look right, check it in the dictionary. Check punctuation, capitalization, and grammar, too.

PUBLISH

How would you like to share your writing? You might want to get together with some classmates to compile your work in a book of folk tales.

233

WRITING

USING SPECIFIC NOUNS

ENRICH YOUR WRITING OF **FOLKLORE.**

Using specific nouns is one way to make your writing clearer and more impressive. Specific nouns paint precise pictures and help convey your ideas. Using specific nouns will save on the number of words you need to express a complete thought.

Read each paragraph below. Which one conveys ideas more clearly?

Paragraph 1

After gnawing a hole, the little animal crept inside. He scurried along. The other mouse was somewhere inside, and he called out for her with sounds.

Paragraph 2

After gnawing a hole in the gate, the little mouse crept inside. He scurried through the darkness. His mate was somewhere in the castle, and he called out for her with tiny squeaks.

PRACTICE 1 Respond on a separate sheet of paper.

1 What words in the second paragraph help create a precise picture of what is happening?

2 Change the details in the second paragraph by rewriting it using specific nouns other than the ones that are there.

& LANGUAGE

POSSESSIVE NOUNS

REMEMBER THESE RULES ABOUT POSSESSIVE NOUNS WHEN YOU ARE WRITING **FOLKLORE.**

- Possessive nouns are used to indicate who or what owns or has something. Add 's to form the possessive of a singular noun.

- Add an apostrophe (') to form the possessive of a plural noun ending in s.

- Add 's to form the possessive of a plural noun that does not end in s.

PRACTICE 2 Change the underlined nouns to their possessive form where necessary. Write your answers on a separate sheet of paper.

1 The <u>miller</u> son heard the mouse squeaking.

2 The mouse quickly left the <u>children</u> room.

3 Then the mouse heard his <u>beloved</u> voice.

4 The mouse headed for the <u>servants</u> quarters.

PRONOUN-ANTECEDENT AGREEMENT

USE THESE RULES ABOUT PRONOUNS AND THEIR ANTECEDENTS WHEN YOU ARE WRITING **FOLKORE.**

- A word or group of words that a pronoun replaces or refers to is called the antecedent.

- Pronouns and antecedents must agree in person, number, and gender.

PRACTICE 3 Rewrite these sentences on a separate sheet of paper, substituting pronouns for the underlined words.

1 When the miller lay down again, the mouse ran over <u>the miller</u>.

2 The cat darted forward, and the mouse ran away from <u>the cat</u>.

3 The miller's children began to gather up <u>the children's</u> toys.

4 Since the mice were safe, <u>the mice</u> were filled with happiness.

WRITING AN EDITORIAL

You know what you believe, but how good are you at convincing others of your ideas? Do you feel you know the answers to any of today's problems? Write an editorial that explains your solution to a problem.

PREWRITE

What's the purpose of your editorial? Who are you trying to convince? Once you've decided, jot down why you believe your solution would work. You can organize your ideas in a chart like this one:

> **PROBLEM:** Noise from new superhighway
>
> **SOLUTION:** Build soundproof fencing
>
> > **Reason:** Complaints
> > **Explanation:** Lots of people living near the highway have complained.
> >
> > **Reason:** Noise pollution
> > **Explanation:** Noise pollution causes unhealthy stress.
> >
> > **Reason:** Cost effective
> > **Explanation:** Soundproofing is cheaper than rebuilding the highway to bypass these homes.

DRAFT Keep your purpose in mind as you write. Think about this sentence: When my readers finish my editorial, they'll think that _____.

REVISE Put your draft aside for a while and then reread it. Are there weak points in your argument? Have you left anything out?

PROOFREAD Ask a friend to read your editorial and check for mistakes.

PUBLISH Send your editorial to a local newspaper or read it to friends.

▶ *Proofreading Alert!*

Use commas to set off appositives. Check page 205 in *Writing and Language Handbook*.

PROJECTS

CREATE A PUZZLE FOR FRIENDS TO SOLVE

REMEMBER TO: • PREWRITE • DRAFT • REVISE • PROOFREAD • PUBLISH

Create a puzzle to entertain friends. Your puzzle can be a crossword, a secret message, or some other kind of word puzzle.

Choose a topic. Then use a diagram like this one to note the words or phrases your topic brings to mind. These words and phrases might be the basis for your crossword. Or you could write a message with the words and phrases and then create a system to scramble them. Challenge your friends to decode the message.

MAKE A BULLETIN BOARD ABOUT PROBLEMS AND SOLUTIONS

REMEMBER TO: • PREWRITE • DRAFT • REVISE • PROOFREAD • PUBLISH

"5 W'S AND H" QUESTIONS

Why?
Who?
Where?
How?
What?
When?

Make a bulletin board that shows a problem and how it was solved. Talk with a few classmates to get ideas for a problem you might depict. The problem you choose might relate to history, technology, science, the environment, or another area that interests you.

Cut out pictures from magazines and newspapers or draw your own. Then write captions using the "5 W's and H" questions as your guide: What was the problem? Why did the problem occur? Where did the problem occur? When did the problem arise? Who solved the problem? How was it solved?

FINDING SOLUTIONS

Finding the best solution for a problem affecting your school or community takes hard work, cooperation, and the willingness to speak out about the issue. Sometimes people work quietly and effectively behind the scenes, trying to encourage support for their cause. At other times they take a more active stand by organizing rallies where speakers present their points of view in a public forum. Which approach is more effective? Should your collective voice be a shout or a whisper?

CONSIDER THIS ISSUE: There have been several serious traffic accidents at an intersection near your school. Students, parents, and teachers want the city to install a traffic light. Some people want to hold a demonstration in front of city hall. Others think a letter-writing campaign would be better. Which do you think is the more effective approach? Consider the issue.

- Would a public protest embarrass the people you need on your side?
- Isn't it better to get as much media coverage of your cause as possible?
- By working quietly behind the scenes, don't you involve people who are really committed to your cause?
- Is it worth the risk that a public demonstration can get out of hand?

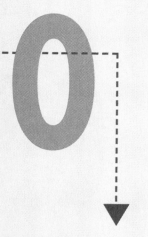

OINTS

Read the following viewpoints about the most effective way of getting something done. Decide which one is closest to your own opinion. Think of some arguments of your own to support the position you choose.

VIEWPOINT 1

I think the best way to solve the problem is by working quietly behind the scenes.

- Some people who are in favor of installing the traffic light might be turned off by a rally.
- Contacting people directly makes your appeal more personal.
- Writing or calling people keeps you better informed about their opinions on the issue.

VIEWPOINT 2

I think the best way to solve the problem is by speaking out at a rally.

- If you come out in numbers, you make a bigger impact.
- The more visible you become, the more likely you are to get media attention.
- Taking a more active, public approach can pressure your opponents into meeting with you.

VIEWPOINT 3

I think the best way to solve the problem is by encouraging petitions. If that doesn't work, then you should try a more visible approach.

- By campaigning quietly at first, you give the other side a chance to change their minds.
- It's good to have the option of making a more public protest at a later time.

WHAT DO YOU THINK?

Spend some time thinking about the issue. Do you share one of the viewpoints above, or do you have another? Discuss your ideas with a partner. Then decide which approach you would use to solve a particular community problem.

real life CONNECT

SOLUTIONS: It takes motivation, persistence, and ingenuity to find the solutions to problems.

Solutions are the answers to the problems that challenge us. The right solution can involve talking to someone, as Amanda does in "Amanda and the Wounded Birds." Or it can mean overcoming obstacles to help others, as Dr. Mary Joan Willard does in "Helping Hands." Whether the problem is personal or involves other people, it takes determination and inner strength to find the best solution.

There is more than one solution to many problems. Often the first step is to ask others what they think of various solutions. One way to learn how people feel about an issue is to conduct an opinion poll.

An **opinion poll** is a survey of public opinion on any topic. Polls are based on asking the same questions of a large number of people. The best opinion polls ask questions that are carefully phrased to avoid influencing the answers. The larger the number of people asked, the more accurate the poll is considered to be.

How To Conduct An
OPINION POLL

1 Decide what you want to find out by formulating a question or questions. It's a good idea to word the question or questions so that they can be answered "yes" or "no."

2 Decide on whom you will question—that is, select a **sample.** You may decide on a **random sample** (the persons to be questioned are selected by chance) or on a **quota sample** (the persons to be questioned belong to a particular group).

3 Question your sample, either in person or by telephone. Record the number of "yes" and "no" answers to your question(s). Also keep track of the number of people you question. The number of "yes" and "no" responses should equal the number of people questioned.

4 Tabulate the answers to your question(s) and express the results as percentages. Write a short sentence expressing the results of your poll.

EXAMPLE: *You want to find out how students in your school feel about having an arts club. Your question is: If an arts club were started, would you join?*

EXAMPLE: *You decide on a quota sample. You will question one fourth of the students in each of the grades (sixth, seventh, eighth) in your school.*

EXAMPLE: *You question your sample directly, keeping a record of the number of people sampled as well as a record of the number of "yes" and "no" responses. You interview 100 students.*

EXAMPLE: *You tabulate the number of "yes" and "no" responses. You find that 30 students responded "yes" and 70 students responded "no." You convert these numbers to percents by dividing each by 100 (the total number of interviews). You find that 30% of the sample responded "yes" to the question, and 70% responded "no." You summarize the results of your poll in this sentence: A survey of 100 students in our school showed that only 30% would join an arts club if one were started.*

IONS

THINK • TALK • WRITE

Here are three activities that involve opinion polls. Think of other situations in which an opinion poll might be useful. Then choose an activity below or one of your own and talk or write about it.

PROJECT 1

CONDUCT AN OPINION POLL Opinion polls can determine how groups of people feel about any issue or topic. Work with a partner to conduct an opinion poll about an issue affecting students in your school. First write the question or questions. Then conduct the poll, either in person or by telephone. Tabulate the student responses and write a one-sentence summary of your findings. Discuss the results of your poll in class.

PROJECT 2

SUMMARIZE A POLL Opinion polls are conducted by periodicals and television stations to learn how people feel about important issues. Find the results of an opinion poll reported in a local newspaper or on local television. Read a news article about the issue in the poll. Then write a paragraph summarizing the issue and the results of the opinion poll.

PROJECT 3

COMPARE THE POLLS Often opinion polls ask a variety of questions about the same topic. Work with other students in a small group to find the results of different opinion polls about the same issue. Try to find polls taken by both national and local periodicals or television stations. Compare the questions asked in each poll and the responses given. Discuss the results of these polls in class.

JUSTICE
JUSTICE
JUSTICE
JUSTICE

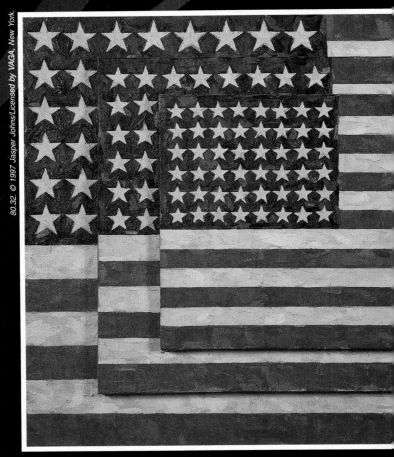

Three Flags 1958 Jasper Johns Whitney Museum of American Art, New York Encaustic on canvas. 30⅞ × 45½ × 5 in. (78.4 × 115.6 × 12.7 cm.) Collection of the Whitney Museum of American Art. 50th Anniversary Gift of the Gilman Foundation, Inc., The Lauder Foundation, A. Alfred Taubman, an anonymous donor, and purchase.

WORDS LIKE FREEDOM
by Langston Hughes

There are words like *Freedom*
Sweet and wonderful to say.
On my heartstrings freedom sings
All day everyday.

There are words like *Liberty*
That almost make me cry.
If you had known what I know
You would know why.

Justice

BEFORE READING

....

THE MAN WITHOUT A COUNTRY

CONNECT TO LITERATURE

Have you ever made a statement that you didn't expect people to take seriously, but that they did? In your journal, make some notes about what happened. As you read "The Man Without a Country," look for the similarities and differences between your experience and that of Philip Nolan.

Detail of *The U.S.S.* Constitution *and H.M.S. Guerriere, The Engagement.*

THINKING ABOUT THEME

The *theme* of a story is the most important idea an author wants to convey to a reader. This idea is usually about life or human nature and often cannot be expressed in a single sentence.

Although authors sometimes state their themes directly, more often you must think about the other elements of the story—the plot, characters, and setting, for example—to figure out the story's theme.

DID YOU KNOW?

The War of 1812, which is mentioned in this story, began on June 18, 1812, when the United States declared war on Great Britain. At the time, Great Britain was at war with France, and each country tried to restrict American trade with the other. While the British blockade of French ports annoyed Americans, what was even worse to their minds was the British seizure of American sailors whom the British believed to be deserters from their navy.

The United States tried to get the British to change their policies toward shipping and sailors, but it failed. The result was a war that lasted until December 24, 1814, when the Treaty of Ghent was signed in Belgium.

THE MAN
WITHOUT
A COUNTRY

BY EDWARD EVERETT HALE

Introductory

I suppose that very few casual readers of the *New York Herald* of August 13, 1863, observed in an obscure corner, among the "Deaths," the announcement:

> "NOLAN. Died on board U. S. Corvette *Levant,* Lat. 2° 11′ S., Long. 131° W., on the 11th of May, PHILIP NOLAN."

I happened to observe it, because I was stranded at the old Mission House in Mackinaw, waiting for a Lake Superior steamer which did not choose to come, and I was devouring to the very stubble all the current literature I could get hold of, even down to the deaths and marriages in the *Herald.* My memory for names and people is good, and the reader will see, as he goes on, that I had reason enough to remember Philip Nolan. There are hundreds of readers who would have paused at that announcement, if the officer of the *Levant* who reported it had chosen to make it thus: "Died, May 11, THE MAN WITHOUT A COUNTRY." For it was as "The Man Without a Country" that poor Philip Nolan had generally been known by the officers who had him in charge during some fifty years, as, indeed, by all the men who sailed under them.

There can now be no possible harm in telling this poor creature's story. Reason enough there has been till now, ever since Madison's administration went out in 1817, for very strict secrecy, the secrecy of honor itself, among the gentlemen of the navy who have had Nolan in successive charge. And certainly it speaks well for the profession, and the personal honor of its members, that to the press this man's story has been wholly unknown,—and, I think, to the country at large also.

But, as I say, there is no need for secrecy any longer. And now the poor creature is dead, it seems to me worth while to tell a little of his story, by way of showing young Americans of today what it is to be A MAN WITHOUT A COUNTRY.

1 Nolan Makes a Fatal Error

Philip Nolan was as fine a young officer as there was in the "Legion of the West," as the Western division of our army was then called. When Aaron Burr[1] made his first dashing expedition down to New Orleans in 1805, at Fort Massac, or somewhere above on the river, he met this gay, dashing, bright young fellow; at some dinner party, I think. Burr marked him, talked to him, walked with him, took him a day or two's voyage in his flatboat, and, in short, fascinated him. For the next year, barrack life was very tame to poor Nolan. He occasionally availed himself of the permission the great man had given him to write to him. Long, high-worded, stilted letters the poor boy wrote and rewrote and copied. But never a line did he have in reply from the deceiver. The other boys in the garrison[2] sneered at him, because he lost the fun which they found in shooting or rowing while he was working away on these grand letters to his grand friend. They could not understand why Nolan kept by himself. But before long the young fellow had his revenge. For this time His Excellency, Honorable Aaron Burr, appeared again under a very different aspect. There were rumors that he had an army behind him and everybody supposed that he had an empire before him. At that time the youngsters all envied him. Burr had not been talking twenty minutes with the commander before he asked him to send for Lieutenant Nolan. Then after a little talk he asked Nolan if he could show him something of the great river and the plans for the new post. He asked Nolan to take him out in his skiff to show him a cane-brake,[3] or a cottonwood tree, as he said,—really to win him over; and by the time the sail was over, Nolan was enlisted body and soul. From that time, though he did not yet know it, he lived as a man without a country.

What Burr meant to do I know no more than you, dear reader. It is none of our business just now. Only, when the grand catastrophe of Burr's trial came at Richmond, Fort Adams[4] got up a string of courts-martial[5] on the officers there. One and another of the colonels and majors were tried, and, to fill out the list, little Nolan, against whom there was evidence enough that he was sick of the service, had been willing to be false to it, and would have obeyed any order to march anywhere with any one who would follow him had the order been signed, "By command of His Exc. A. Burr." The courts dragged on. The big flies[6] escaped,—

~

1. **Aaron Burr** (1756–1836): famous historical figure who had ambitions of creating a new empire in the Southwest. Burr served as Vice President of the United States from 1801 to 1805. He may be most famous for the duel in which he killed Alexander Hamilton.
2. **garrison** (gar′ə sən) n. military post.
3. **canebrake** (kān′brāk′) n. dense growth of sugar cane.
4. **Fort Adams:** fort at which Nolan was stationed.
5. **courts-martial** (kôrts′mär′shəl) n., pl. trials in the army for offenses against military law.
6. **big flies:** Burr and the other high-ranking officers who plotted with him.

Engraving Special Collections Division Nimitz Library, United States Naval Academy, Annapolis, Maryland

rightly for all I know. Nolan was proved guilty enough, as I say; yet you and I would never have heard of him, reader, but that, when the president of the court asked him at the close whether he wished to say anything to show that he had always been faithful to the United States, he cried out, in a fit of frenzy—

"Damn the United States! I wish I may never hear of the United States again!"

2 Nolan Receives Punishment

I suppose he did not know how the words shocked old Colonel Morgan, who was holding the court. Half the officers who sat in it had served through the Revolution, and their lives, not to say their necks, had been risked for the very idea which he cursed in his madness. He, on his part, had grown up in the West of those days, in the midst of "Spanish plot," "Orleans plot,"[7] and all the rest. He had been educated on a plantation where the finest company was a Spanish officer or a French merchant from Orleans. His education, such as it was, had been perfected in commercial expeditions to Vera Cruz, and I think he told me his father once hired an Englishman to be a private tutor for a winter on the plantation. He had spent half his youth with an older brother, hunting horses in Texas; and, in a word, to him "United States" was scarcely a reality. Yet he had been fed by "United States" for all the years since he had been in the army. He had sworn to be true to "United States." It was "United States" which gave him the uniform he wore, and the sword by his side. Nay, my poor Nolan, it was only because "United States" had picked you out first as one of her own confidential men of honor that

7. **Spanish plot; Orleans plot:** schemes to seize territory from Spain which, at the time, owned all the land west of the Mississippi River.

"A. Burr" cared for you a straw more than for the flatboat men who sailed his ark for him. I do not excuse Nolan; I only explain to the reader why he damned his country, and wished he might never hear her name again.

From that moment, Sept. 23, 1807, till the day he died, May 11, 1863, he never heard her name again. For that half-century and more he was a man without a country.

Old Morgan, as I said, was terribly shocked. If Nolan had compared George Washington to Benedict Arnold,[8] or had cried, "God save King George,"[9] Morgan would not have felt worse. He called the court into his private room, and returned in fifteen minutes, with a face like a sheet, to say: "Prisoner, hear the sentence of the Court! The Court decides, subject to the approval of the President, that you never hear the name of the United States again."

Nolan laughed. But nobody else laughed. Old Morgan was too solemn, and the whole room was hushed dead as night for a minute. Even Nolan lost his swagger in a moment. Then Morgan added: "Mr. Marshal, take the prisoner to Orleans, in an armed boat, and deliver him to the Naval Commander there."

The Marshal gave his orders and the prisoner was taken out of court.

"Mr. Marshal," continued old Morgan, "see that no one mentions the United States to the prisoner. Mr. Marshal, make my respects to Lieutenant Mitchell at Orleans, and request him to order that no one shall mention the United States to the prisoner while he is on board ship. You will receive your written orders from the officer on duty here this evening. The Court is adjourned."

I have always supposed that Colonel Morgan himself took proceedings of the court to Washington city, and explained them to Mr. Jefferson.[10] Certain it is that the President approved them,—certain, that is, if I may believe the men who say they have seen his signature. Before the *Nautilus* got round from New Orleans to the Northern Atlantic coast with the prisoner on board, the sentence had been approved, and he was a man without a country.

The plan then adopted was substantially the same which was necessarily followed ever after. Perhaps it was suggested by the necessity of sending him by water from Fort Adams and Orleans. The Secretary of the Navy was requested to put Nolan on board a government vessel bound on a long cruise, and to direct that he should be only so far confined there as to make it certain that he never saw or heard of the country. We had few long cruises then, and I do not know certainly what his first cruise was. But the commander to whom he was intrusted,—perhaps it was Tingey or Shaw[11] regulated the etiquette and the precautions of the affair,

8. **Benedict Arnold** (1741–1801): traitor in the American Revolution.

9. **King George III:** king of England.

10. **Mr. Jefferson:** Thomas Jefferson (1743–1826), was the third President of the United States.

11. **Tingey or Shaw:** two men who had actually been in the naval service around that period.

---

adjourned (ə jûrnd´) *adj.* ended for the time being.

and according to his scheme they were carried out, I suppose, till Nolan died.

When I was second officer of the *Intrepid,* some thirty years after, I saw the original paper of instructions. I have been sorry ever since that I did not copy the whole of it. It ran, however, much in this way:

WASHINGTON [with a date, which must have been late in 1807].

Sir,—You will receive from Lieutenant Neale the person of Philip Nolan, late a lieutenant in the United States army.

This person on trial by court-martial expressed, with an oath, the wish that he might "never hear of the United States again."

The Court sentenced him to have his wish fulfilled.

For the present, the execution of the order is intrusted by the President to this Department.

You will take the prisoner on board your ship, and keep him there with such precautions as shall prevent his escape.

You will provide him with such quarters, rations, and clothing as would be proper for an officer of his late rank, if he were a passenger on your vessel on the business of his Government.

The gentlemen on board will make any arrangements agreeable to themselves regarding his society. He is to be exposed to no indignity of any kind, nor is he ever unnecessarily to be reminded that he is a prisoner.

But under no circumstances is he ever to hear of his country or to see any information regarding it; and you will especially caution all the officers under your command to take care, that, in the various <u>indulgences</u> *which may be granted, this rule, in which his punishment is involved, shall not be broken.*

It is the intention of the Government that he shall never again see the country which he has disowned. Before the end of your cruise you will receive orders which will give effect to this intention.

Respectfully yours,
W. SOUTHARD, for the
Secretary of the Navy.

If I had only preserved the whole of this paper, there would be no break in the beginning of my sketch of this story. For Captain Shaw, if it were he, handed it to his successor in the charge, and he to his, and I suppose the commander of the *Levant* has it today as his authority for keeping this man in this mild custody.

The rule adopted on board the ships on which I have met "The Man Without a Country" was, I think, <u>transmitted</u> from the beginning. No mess[12] liked to have him permanently, because his presence cut off all talk of home or of the prospect of return, of politics or letters, of peace or of war,— cut off more than half the talk men liked to have at sea. But it was always thought too

---

12. **mess** (mes) *n.* group of people who take meals together regularly, especially in the army or navy.

---

indulgences (in dul′jən səz) *n., pl.* favors, treats, or pardons allowed (to someone).
transmitted (trans′mi tid) *v.t.* communicated or conveyed from one person to another; handed down.

The U.S.S. Constitution **and H.M.S.** Guerriere, **The Engagement** *1812*
Michele Felice Corné   United States Naval Academy Museum, Annapolis, Maryland

hard that he should never meet the rest of us, except to touch hats, and we finally sank into one system. He was not permitted to talk with the men, unless an officer was by. With officers he had unrestrained intercourse, as far as they and he chose. But he grew shy, though he had favorites: I was one. Then the captain always asked him to dinner on Monday. Every mess in succession took up the invitation in its turn. According to the size of the ship, you had him at your mess more or less often at dinner. His breakfast he ate in his own stateroom— he always had a stateroom,—which was where a sentinel or somebody on the watch could see the door. And whatever else he ate or drank, he ate or drank alone. Sometimes, when the marines or sailors had any special jollification, they were permitted to invite "Plain-Buttons," as they called him. Then Nolan was sent with some officer, and the men were forbidden to speak of home while he was there. I believe the theory was that the sight of his punishment did them good. They called him "Plain-Buttons," because, while he always chose to wear a regulation army uniform, he was not permitted to wear the army button, for the reason that it bore either the initials or the insignia[13] of the country he had disowned.

13. **insignia** (in sig′nē ə) *n.* emblem of office.

3 Nolan Reads Aloud

I remember, soon after I joined the navy, I was on shore with some of the older officers from our ship and from the *Brandywine*. We fell to talking about Nolan, and some one told the system which was adopted from the first about his books and other reading. As he was almost never permitted to go on shore, even though the vessel lay in port for months, his time at the best hung heavy; and everybody was permitted to lend him books, if they were not published in America and made no allusion to it. These were common enough in the old days, when people in the other hemisphere talked of the United States as little as we do of Paraguay. He had almost all the foreign papers that came into the ship, sooner or later; only somebody must go over them first, and cut out any advertisement or stray paragraph that alluded to America. This was a little cruel sometimes, when the back of what was cut out might be innocent. Right in the midst of one of Napoleon's[14] battles, poor Nolan would find a great hole, because on the back of the page of that paper there had been an advertisement of a packet[15] for New York, or a scrap from the President's message. I say this was the first time I ever heard of this plan, which afterwards I had enough and more than enough to do with. I remember it, because poor Phillips, who was of the party, as soon as the allusion to reading was made, told a story of something which happened at the Cape of Good Hope on Nolan's first voyage; and it is the only thing I ever knew of that voyage. They had touched at the Cape, and had done the civil thing with the English Admiral and the fleet, and then, leaving for a long cruise up the Indian Ocean, Phillips had borrowed a lot of English books from an officer, which, in those days, as indeed in these, was quite a windfall. Among them was *The Lay of the Last Minstrel,*[16] which they had all of them heard of, but which most of them had never seen. I think it could not have been published long. Well, nobody thought there could be any risk of anything national in that though Phillips swore old Shaw had cut out *The Tempest* from Shakespeare before he let Nolan have it, because he said "the Bermudas[17] ought to be ours, and, by Jove, should be one day." So Nolan was permitted to join the circle one afternoon when a lot of them sat on deck reading aloud. People do not do such things so often now; but when I was young we got rid of a great deal of time so. Well, so it happened that in his turn Nolan took the book and read to the others; and he read very well, as I know.

14. **Napoleon:** French general who, at the time, was conquering Europe.
15. **packet** (pak'it) *n.* boat that carries mail, passengers, or freight.
16. ***The Lay of the Last Minstrel:*** poem written by Sir Walter Scott in 1805.
17. **Bermudas:** group of islands located in the northern Atlantic Ocean.

---

allusion (ə lü'zhən) *n.* mention made in passing.
windfall (wind'fôl') *n.* unexpected advantage or gain.

Nobody in the circle knew a line of the poem. Poor Nolan read steadily through the fifth canto, stopped a minute and drank something, and then began, without a thought of what was coming—

> Breathes there a man with soul so dead,
> Who never to himself hath said—

It seems impossible to us that anybody ever heard this for the first time; but all these fellows did then, and poor Nolan himself went on, still unconsciously or mechanically—

> This is my own, my native land!

Then they all saw that something was to pay; but he expected to get through, I suppose, turned a little pale, but plunged on—

> Whose heart hath ne'er within him burned,
> As home his footsteps he hath turned
> From wandering on a foreign strand?—
> If such there breathe, go mark him well—

By this time the men were all beside themselves, wishing there was any way to make him turn over two pages; but he had not quite presence of mind for that; he gagged a little, colored crimson, and staggered on—

> For him no minstrel raptures swell;
> High though his titles, proud his name,
> Boundless his wealth as wish can claim,
> Despite these titles, power, and pelf,
> The wretch, concentered all in self—

and here the poor fellow choked, could not go on, but started up, swung the book into the sea, vanished into his stateroom, "And by Jove," said Phillips, "we did not see him for two months again. And I had to make up some beggarly story to that English surgeon why I did not return his Walter Scott to him."

That story shows about the time when Nolan's braggadocio[18] must have broken down. At first, they said, he took a very high tone, considered his imprisonment a mere farce, affected to enjoy the voyage, and all that; but Phillips said that after he came out of his stateroom he never was the same man again. He never read aloud again, unless it was the Bible or Shakespeare, or something else he was sure of. But it was not that merely. He never entered in with the other young men exactly as a companion again. He was always shy afterwards, when I knew him,—very seldom spoke unless he was spoken to, except to a very few friends. He lighted up occasionally,—but generally he had the nervous, tired look of a heart-wounded man.

~

18. **braggadocio** (brag′ə dō′shē ō′) *n.* empty boasting or bragging.

4 Nolan Attends a Ball

When Captain Shaw was coming home,—if, as I say, it was Shaw,—rather to the surprise of everybody they made one of the Windward Islands,[19] and lay off and on for nearly a week. The boys said the officers were sick of salt-junk, and meant to have turtle soup before they came home. But after several days the *Warren* came to the same rendezvous;[20] they exchanged signals; she sent to Phillips and these homeward-bound men letters and papers, and told them she was outward-bound, perhaps to the Mediterranean, and took poor Nolan and his traps on the boat back to try his second cruise. He looked very blank when he was told to get ready to join her. He had known enough of the signs of the sky to know that till that moment he was going "home." But this was a distinct evidence of something he had not thought of, perhaps,—that there was no going home for him, even to a prison. And this was the first of some twenty such transfers, which brought him sooner or later into half our best vessels, but which kept him all his life at least some hundred miles from the country he had hoped he might never hear of again.

It may have been on that second cruise,—it was once when he was up the Mediterranean,—that Mrs. Graff, the celebrated Southern beauty of those days, danced with him. They had been lying a long time in the Bay of Naples, and the officers were very intimate in the English fleet, and there had been great festivities, and our men thought they must give a great ball on board the ship. How on board the *Warren* they ever did it I am sure I do not know. They wanted to use Nolan's stateroom for something, and they hated to do it without asking him to the ball; so the captain said they might ask him, if they would be responsible that he did not talk with the wrong people, "who would give him intelligence."[21] So the dance went on, the finest party that had ever been known, I dare say; for I never heard of a man-of-war ball that was not. For ladies they had the family of the American consul,[22] one or two travelers who had adventured so far, and a nice bevy of English girls and matrons.

Well, different officers relieved each other in standing and talking with Nolan in a friendly way, so as to be sure that nobody else spoke to him. The dancing went on with spirit, and after a while even the fellows who took this honorary guard of Nolan ceased to fear any trouble. Only when some English lady called for a set of "American dances," an odd thing happened. Everybody then danced line-dances. The band conferred as to what

~

19. **Windward Islands:** islands in the West Indies.
20. **rendezvous** (rän′də vü′) *n.* prearranged meeting place.
21. **who would give him intelligence:** who would give him news or information about the United States.
22. **consul** (kon′səl) *n.* offical appointed by a nation to live in a foreign city for the purpose of protecting that nation's interests there.

"American dances" were, and started off with "Virginia Reel," which they followed with "Money-Musk," which, in its turn in those days, should have been followed by "The Old Thirteen." But just as Dick, the leader, tapped for his fiddles to begin, and bent forward, about to say "'The Old Thirteen,' gentlemen and ladies!" as he had said "'Virginny Reel,' if you please!" and "'Money Musk,' if you please!" the captain's boy tapped him on the shoulder, whispered to him, and he did not announce the name of the dance; he merely bowed, began on the air, and they all fell to,—the officers teaching the English girls the figure, but not telling them why it had no name.

But that is not the story I started to tell. As the dancing went on, Nolan and our fellows all got at ease, as I said,—so much so, that it seemed quite natural for him to bow to that splendid Mrs. Graff, and say: "I hope you have not forgotten me, Miss Rutledge. Shall I have the honor of dancing?"

He did it so quickly, that Fellows, who was with him, could not hinder him. She laughed and said: "I am not Miss Rutledge any longer, Mr. Nolan; but I will dance all the same," just nodded to Fellows, as if to say he must leave Mr. Nolan to her, and led him off to the place where the dance was forming.

Nolan thought he had got his chance. He had known her at Philadelphia, and at other places had met her. You could not talk in line-dances, as you do in cotillions, or even in the pauses of waltzing; but there were chances for tongues and sounds, as well as for eyes and blushes. He began with her travels, and Europe and the French; and then, when they had worked down, and had that long talking time at the bottom of the set, he said boldly,—a little pale, she said, as she told me the story years after—

"And what do you hear from home, Mrs. Graff?"

And that splendid creature looked *through* him. Jove! how she *must* have looked through him!

"Home!! Mr. Nolan!!! I thought you were the man who never wanted to hear of home again"—and she walked directly up the deck to her husband, and left poor Nolan alone, as he always was. He did not dance again. I cannot give any history of him in order; nobody can now; and, indeed, I am not trying to.

These are the traditions which I sort out, as I believe them, from the myths which have been told about this man for forty years. The lies that have been told about him are legion.

5 Nolan Mans a Gun

A happier story than either of these I have told is of the war.[23] That came along soon after. I have heard this affair told in three or four ways,—and, indeed, it may

---

23. **the war:** War of 1812, fought between the United States and Great Britain.

have happened more than once. But which ship it was on I cannot tell. However, in one, at least, of the great frigate[24] duels with the English, in which the navy was really baptized, it happened that a round shot[25] from the enemy entered one of our ports[26] square, and took right down the officer of the gun himself, and almost every man of the gun's crew. Now you may say what you choose about courage, but that is not a nice thing to see. But, as the men who were not killed picked themselves up, and as they and the surgeon's people were carrying off the bodies, there appeared Nolan, in his shirt-sleeves, with the rammer in his hand, and, just as if he had been the officer, told them off with authority,—who should go to the cock-pit with the wounded men, who should stay with him—perfectly cheery, and with that way which makes men feel sure all is right and is going to be right. And he finished loading the gun with his own hands, aimed it, and bade the men fire. And there he stayed, captain of that gun, keeping those fellows in spirits, till the enemy struck,[27]—sitting on the carriage while the gun was cooling, though he was exposed all the time,—showing them easier ways to handle heavy shot,—making the raw hands laugh at their own blunders,—and when the gun cooled again, getting it loaded and fired twice as often as any other gun on the ship. The captain walked forward by way of encouraging the men, and Nolan touched his hat and said: "I am showing them how we do this in the artillery, sir."

And this is the part of the story where all the legends agree; the commodore said: "I see you are, and I thank you, sir; and I shall never forget this day, sir, and you never shall, sir."

And after the whole thing was over, and he had the Englishman's sword,[28] in the midst of the state and ceremony of the quarter-deck, he said: "Where is Mr. Nolan? Ask Mr. Nolan to come here."

And when Nolan came, he said: "Mr. Nolan, we are all very grateful to you today; you are one of us today; you will be named in the dispatches."[29]

And then the old man took off his own sword of ceremony, and gave it to Nolan and made him put it on. The man told me this who saw it. Nolan cried like a baby, and well he might. He had not worn a sword since that <u>infernal</u> day at Fort Adams. But always afterwards on occasions of ceremony, he wore that quaint old French sword of the commodore.

The captain did mention him in the dispatches. It was always said he asked that he might be pardoned. He wrote a special letter to the Secretary of War. But

24. **frigate** (frig'it) *n.* warship used for escort and patrol duties.
25. **round shot** (round shot) *n.* cannonball.
26. **ports** (pôrts) *n., pl.* openings in the side of a ship.
27. **the enemy struck:** lowered their flags in order to admit defeat.
28. **had the Englishman's sword:** as an act of surrender, the conquered gives his sword to the victor.
29. **dispatches** (di spach'əz) *n., pl.* written messages, especially having to do with military or governmental matters.

---

infernal (in fûr'nəl) *adj.* hateful; of, relating to, or characteristic of hell.

Boarding of the Chesapeake   *late 19th century   Thomas M. Hemy   Collection of Lady Liewellyn*

nothing ever came of it. As I said, that was about the time when they began to ignore the whole transaction at Washington, and when Nolan's imprisonment began to carry itself on because there was nobody to stop it without any new orders from home.

All that was near fifty years ago. If Nolan was thirty then, he must have been near eighty when he died. He looked sixty when he was forty. But he never seemed to me to change a hair afterwards. As I imagine his life, from what I have seen and heard of it, he must have been in every sea, and yet almost never on land. He must have known, in a formal way, more officers in our service than any man living knows. He told me once, with a grave smile, that no man in the world lived so methodical a life as he. He said it did not do for any one to try to read all the time; more than to do anything else all the time; and that he used to read just five hours a day. "Then," he said, "I keep up my notebooks, writing in them at such and such hours from what I have been reading; and I include these in my scrapbooks." These were very curious indeed. He had six or eight, of different subjects. There was one of History, one of Natural Science, one which he called "Odds and Ends." But they were not merely books of extracts from newspapers. They had bits of plants and ribbons, shells tied on, and carved scraps of bone and wood, which he had taught the men to cut for him, and they were beautifully illustrated. He drew admirably. He had some of the fun-

niest drawings there, and some of the most pathetic, that I have ever seen in my life. I wonder who will have Nolan's scrapbooks.

Well, he said his reading and his notes were his profession, and that they took five hours and two hours respectively of each day. "Then," said he, "every man should have a diversion as well as a profession. My Natural History is my diversion." That took two hours a day more. The men used to bring him birds and fish, but on a long cruise he had to satisfy himself with centipedes and cockroaches and such small game. He was the only naturalist I ever met who knew anything about the habits of the house-fly and the mosquito. These nine hours made Nolan's regular daily "occupation." The rest of the time he talked or walked. He always kept up his exercise; and I never heard that he was ill. If any other man was ill, he was the kindest nurse in the world; and he knew more than half the surgeons do. Then if anybody was sick or died, or if the captain wanted him to, on any other occasion, he was always ready to read prayers. I have said that he read beautifully.

6 Nolan Acts as Interpreter

My own acquaintance with Philip Nolan began six or eight years after the English war, on my first voyage after I was appointed a midshipman. From the time I joined, I believe I thought Nolan was a sort of lay chaplain,—a chaplain with a blue coat. I never asked about him. Everything in the ship was strange to me. I knew it was green to ask questions, and I suppose I thought there was a "Plain-Buttons" on every ship. We had him to dine in our mess once a week, and the caution was given that on that day nothing was to be said about home. But if they had told us not to say anything about the planet Mars or the Book of Deuteronomy,[30] I should not have asked why; there were a great many things which seemed to me to have as little reason. I first came to understand anything about "The Man Without a Country" one day when we overhauled a dirty little schooner which had slaves on board. An officer was sent to take charge of her, and, after a few minutes, he sent back his boat to ask that some one might be sent him who could speak Portuguese. We were all looking over the rail when the message came, and we all wished we could interpret, when the captain asked who spoke Portuguese. But none of the officers did; and just as the captain was sending forward to ask if any of the people could, Nolan stepped out and said he should be glad to interpret, if the captain wished, as he understood the language. The captain thanked him, fitted out another boat with him, and in this boat it was my luck to go.

When we got there, it was such a scene as you seldom see, and never want to. Nastiness beyond account, and chaos run loose in the midst of the nasti-ness. There were not a great many of the Negroes; but by way of making what there were understand that they were free, Vaughan had had their handcuffs and ankle-cuffs knocked off, and, for convenience's sake, was putting them upon the rascals of the schooner's crew. The Negroes were, most of them, out of the hold, and swarming all around the dirty deck, with a central throng surrounding Vaughan and addressing him in every dialect.

As we came on deck, Vaughan looked down from a hogshead, on which he had mounted in desperation, and said: "Is there anybody who can make these people understand something?"

Nolan said he could speak Portuguese, and one or two fine-looking Kroomen[31] were dragged out who had worked for the Portuguese on the coast at Fernando Po.

"Tell them they are free," said Vaughan.

Nolan explained it in such Portuguese as the Kroomen could understand, and they in turn to such of the Negroes as could understand them. Then there was such a yell of delight, clinching of fists, leaping and dancing, kissing of Nolan's feet, and a general rush made to the hogshead by way of spontaneous worship of Vaughan.

～

30. **Book of Deuteronomy:** fifth book of the Bible.
31. **Kroomen:** members of the Kruman tribe in northern Africa.

Naval Engagement between the U.S. Frigate Constitution **and H.M. Frigate** Java
(detail) 1815 Montardier Peabody Essex Museum, Salem, Massachusetts

"Tell them," said Vaughan, well pleased, "that I will take them all to Cape Palmas."

This did not answer so well. Cape Palmas was practically as far from the homes of most of them as New Orleans or Rio de Janeiro was; that is, they would be eternally separated from home there. And their interpreters, as we could understand, instantly said, *"Ah, non Palmas,"* and began to propose infinite other expedients in most <u>voluble</u> language. Vaughan was rather disappointed at this result of his liberality, and asked Nolan eagerly what they said. The drops stood on poor Nolan's white forehead, as he hushed the men down, and said, "He says, 'Not Palmas.' He says, 'Take us home, take us to our own country, take us to our own house, take us to our own children and our own women.' He says he has an old father and mother who will die if they do not see him. And this one says he left his people all sick, and paddled down to Fernando to beg the white doctor to come and help them, and that these slave traders caught him in the bay just in sight of home, and that he has never seen anybody from home since then. And this one says," choked out Nolan, "that he has not heard a word from his home in six months."

---

voluble (vol′yə bəl) *adj.* with a smooth, easy flow of words; talkative.

Vaughan always said Nolan grew gray himself while he struggled through this interpretation. I, who did not understand anything of the passion involved in it, saw that the very elements were melting with fervent heat, and that something was to pay somewhere. Even the Negroes themselves stopped howling, as they saw Nolan's agony, and Vaughan's almost equal agony of sympathy. As quick as Vaughan could get words, he said "Tell them yes, yes, yes, they shall go home!"

And after some fashion Nolan said so. And then they all fell to kissing him again.

But he could not stand it long; and getting Vaughan to say he might go back, he beckoned me down into our boat. He said to me: "Youngster, let that show you what it is to be without a family, without a home, and without a country. And if you are ever tempted to say a word or to do a thing that shall put a bar between you and your family, your home, and your country, pray God in His mercy to take you that instant home to His own heaven. Stick by your family, boy; forget you have a self, while you do everything for them. Think of your home, boy; write and send, and talk about it. Let it be nearer and nearer to your thought, the farther you have to travel from it; and rush back to it when you are free, as that poor slave is doing now. And for your country, boy," and the words rattled in his throat, "and for that flag," and he pointed to the ship, "never dream a dream but of serving her as she bids you, though the service carry you through a thousand hells. No matter what happens to you, no matter who flatters you or who abuses you, never look at another flag, never let a night pass but you pray God to bless the flag. Remember, boy, that behind all these men you have to do with, behind officers, and government, and people even, there is the Country herself, your Country, and that you belong to her as you belong to your own mother. Stand by her, boy, as you would stand by your mother!"

I was frightened to death by his calm, hard passion; but I blundered out that I would, by all that was holy, and that I had never thought of doing anything else. He hardly seemed to hear me; but he did, almost in a whisper, say: "O, if anybody had said so to me when I was of your age!"

I think it was this half-confidence of his, which I never abused, for I never told this story till now, which afterward made us great friends. He was very kind to me. Often he sat up, or even got up, at night to walk the deck with me, when it was my watch.[32] He explained to me a great deal of my mathematics, and I owe to him my taste for mathematics. He lent me books, and helped me about my reading. He never alluded so directly to his story again; but from one and another officer I have learned, in thirty years, what I am telling. When we parted from him in St. Thomas

32. **watch** (woch) *n.* time when a guard is on duty.

Engraving   Special Collections Division   Nimitz Library, United States Naval Academy, Annapolis, Maryland

harbor, at the end of our cruise, I was more sorry than I can tell. I was very glad to meet him again in 1830; and later in life, when I thought I had some influence in Washington, I moved heaven and earth to have him discharged. But it was like getting a ghost out of prison. They pretended there was no such man and never was such a man. Perhaps they do not know.

7 Nolan Inquires About Texas

There is a story that Nolan met Burr once on one of our vessels, when a party of Americans came on board in the Mediterranean. But this I believe to be a lie; or, rather, it is a myth involving a tremendous blowing-up with which he sunk Burr,—asking him how he liked to be "without a country." But it is clear from Burr's life, that nothing of the sort could have happened; and I mention this only as an illustration of the stories which get

a-going where there is the least mystery at bottom.

Philip Nolan, poor fellow, repented of his folly, and then, like a man, submitted to the fate he had asked for. He never intentionally added to the difficulty or delicacy of the charge of those who had him in hold. Accidents would happen; but never from his fault. Lieutenant Truxton told me that, when Texas was annexed there was a careful discussion among the officers, whether they should get hold of Nolan's handsome set of maps and cut Texas out of it—from the map of the world and the map of Mexico. The United States had been cut out when the atlas was bought for him. But it was voted, rightly enough, that to do this would be virtually to reveal to him what had happened. So it was from no fault of Nolan's that a great botch happened at my own table, when, for a short time, I was in command of the *George Washington* corvette, on the South

American station. We were lying in the La Plata,[33] and some of the officers, who had been on shore and had just joined again, were entertaining us with accounts of their misadventures in riding the half-wild horses of Buenos Aires. Nolan was at table, and was in an unusually bright and talkative mood. Some story of a tumble reminded him of an adventure of his own when he was catching wild horses in Texas with his adventurous cousin, at a time when he must have been quite a boy. He told the story with a good deal of spirit,—so much so, that the silence which often follows a good story hung over the table for an instant, to be broken by Nolan himself. For he asked perfectly unconsciously: "Pray, what has become of Texas? After the Mexicans got their independence, I thought that province of Texas would come forward very fast. It is really one of the finest regions on earth; it is the Italy of this continent. But I have not seen or heard a word of Texas for nearly twenty years."

There were two Texan officers at the table. The reason he had never heard of Texas was that Texas and her affairs had been painfully cut out of his newspapers. Waters and Williams, the two Texas men, looked grimly at each other and tried not to laugh. Edward Morris had his attention attracted by the third link in the chain of the captain's chandelier. Watrous was seized with a convulsion of sneezing. Nolan himself saw that something was to pay, he did not know what. And I, as master of the feast, had to say: "Texas is out of the map, Mr. Nolan."

After that cruise I never saw Nolan again. I wrote to him at least twice a year, for in that voyage we became even confidentially intimate; but he never wrote to me. The other men tell me that in those fifteen years he *aged* very fast, as well he might indeed, but that he was still the same gentle, uncomplaining, silent sufferer that he ever was, bearing as best he could his self-appointed punishment,—rather less social, perhaps, with new men whom he did not know, but more anxious, apparently, than ever to serve and befriend and teach the boys, some of whom fairly seemed to worship him. And now it seems the dear old fellow is dead. He has found a home at last, and a country.

Since writing this, and while considering whether or not I would print it, as a warning to the young Nolans of today of what it is to throw away a country, I have received from Danforth, who is on board the *Levant,* a letter which gives an account of Nolan's last hours. It removes all my doubts about telling this story.

The reader will understand Danforth's letter, or the beginning of it, if he will remember that after ten years of Nolan's <u>exile</u> every one who had him in charge was in a very delicate position. The Government had failed to renew the order of 1807 regarding him. What was a man to do? Should he let him go? What, then, if

33. **La Plata:** river in Argentina.

---

exile (eg′zīl) *n.* state of being sent away from one's country or home by law.

he were called to account by the Department for violating the order of 1807? Should he keep him? What, then, if Nolan should be liberated some day, and should bring an action for false imprisonment or kidnaping against every man who had had him in charge? I urged and pressed this upon Southard, and I have reason to think that other officers did the same thing. But the Secretary always said, as they so often do at Washington, that there were no special orders to give, and that we must act on our own judgment.

8 Nolan Proves His Loyalty

Here is the letter:

Levant, *2° 2'S. at 131° W.*

Dear Fred:—I try to find heart and life to tell you that it is all over with dear old Nolan. I have been with him on this voyage more than I ever was, and I can understand wholly now the way in which you used to speak of the dear old fellow. I could see that he was not strong, but I had no idea the end was so near. The doctor has been watching him very carefully, and yesterday morning came to me and told me that Nolan was not so well, and had not left his stateroom,—a thing I never remember before. He had let the doctor come and see him as he lay there,—the first time the doctor had been in the stateroom,—and he said he should like to see me. Oh, dear! do you remember the mysteries we boys used to invent about his room in the old Intrepid *days? Well, I went in, and there, to be sure, the poor fellow lay in his berth, smiling pleasantly as he gave me his hand, but looking very frail. I could not help a glance round, which showed me what a little shrine he had made of the box he was lying in. The stars and stripes were triced[34] up above and around a picture of Washington, and he had painted a majestic eagle, with lightnings blazing from his beak and his foot just clasping the whole globe, which his wings overshadowed. The dear old boy saw my glance, and said, with a sad smile, "Here, you see, I have a country!" And then he pointed to the foot of his bed, where I had not seen before a great map of the United States, as he had drawn it from memory, and which he had there to look upon as he lay. Quaint, queer old names were on it, in large letters: "Indiana Territory," "Mississippi Territory," and "Louisiana Territory," as I supposed our fathers learned such things: but the old fellow had patched in Texas, too; he had carried his western boundary all the way to the Pacific, but on that shore he had defined nothing.*

"O Captain," he said, "I know I am dying. I cannot get home. Surely you will tell me something now?—Stop! stop! Do not speak till I say what I am sure you know, that there is not in this ship, that there is not in America,—God bless her!—

34. **triced** (trīst) *v.t.* pulled up and secured with a rope.

_U.S.S._ Delaware _at sea off the coast of America_ (detail) 1836 J. G. Evans
Newport Historical Society, Newport, Rhode Island

a more loyal man than I. There cannot be a man who loves the old flag as I do, or prays for it as I do, or hopes for it as I do. There are thirty-four stars in it now, Danforth. I thank God for that, though I do not know what their names are. There has never been one taken away: I thank God for that. I know by that that there has never been any successful Burr. O Danforth, Danforth," he sighed out, "how like a wretched night's dream a boy's idea of personal fame or of separate sovereignty seems, when one looks back on it after such a life as mine! But tell me,—tell me something,—tell me everything, Danforth, before I die!"

Ingham, I swear to you that I felt like a monster, that I had not told him everything before. Danger or no danger, delicacy or no delicacy, who was I, that I should have been acting the tyrant all this time over this dear, sainted old man, who had years ago <u>expiated</u>, in his whole manhood's life, the madness of a boy's treason! "Mr. Nolan," said I, "I will tell you everything you ask about. Only, where shall I begin?"

Oh, the blessed smile that crept over his white face! and he pressed my hand and said, "God bless you! Tell me their names," he said, and he pointed to the stars on the flag. "The last I know is Ohio. My father lived in Kentucky. But I have guessed Michigan, and Indiana and Mississippi,—that was where Fort Adams is,—they make twenty. But where are your other fourteen? You have not cut up any of the old ones, I hope?"

Well, that was not a bad text, and I told him the names in as good order as I could, and he bade me take down his beautiful map and draw them in as I best could with my pencil. He was wild with delight about Texas, told me how his cousin died there; he had marked a gold cross near where he supposed his grave was; and he had guessed at Texas. Then he was delighted as he saw California and Oregon;—that, he said, he had suspected partly, because he had never been permitted to land on that shore, though the ships were there so much. "And the men," said he, laughing, "brought off a good deal besides furs." Then he went back—heavens, how far!—to ask about the Chesapeake, and what was done to Barron for surrendering her to the Leopard, and whether Burr ever tried again,—and he ground his teeth with the only passion he showed. But in a moment that was over, and he said, "God forgive me, for I am sure I forgive him." Then he asked about the old war,—told me the true story of his serving the gun the day we took the Java,—asked about dear old David Porter, as he called him. Then he settled down more quietly, and very happily, to hear me tell in an hour the history of fifty years.

How I wish it had been somebody who knew something! But I did as well as I could. I told him of the English war. I told him of Fulton[35] and the steamboat beginning. I told him about old Scott,[36] and Jackson;[37] told him all I could think of about the Mississippi, and New Orleans, and Texas, and his own old Kentucky. And, do you think, he asked who was in command of the "Legion of the West." I told him it was a very gallant officer named Grant,[38] and that, by our last news, he was about to establish his headquarters at

---

35. **Fulton:** Robert Fulton (1765–1815), inventor of the steamboat.

36. **Scott:** General Winfield Scott (1786–1866), general in the War of 1812 and in the Mexican War.

37. **Jackson:** Andrew Jackson (1767–1845), general in the War of 1812 and seventh President of the United States.

38. **Grant:** Ulysses S. Grant (1822–1885), general in the Civil War and eighteenth President of the United States.

---

expiated (ek′spē ā′tid) *v.t.* made amends for; atoned for.

Vicksburg.[39] Then, "Where was Vicksburg?" I worked that out on the map; it was about a hundred miles, more or less, above his old Fort Adams; and I thought Fort Adams must be a ruin now. "It must be at old Vick's plantation, at Walnut Hills," said he; "well, that is a change!"

I tell you, Ingham, it was a hard thing to condense the history of half a century into that talk with a sick man. And I do not know what I told him,—of *emigration*, and the means of it,—of steamboats, and railroads, and telegraphs,—of inventions, and books, and literature,—of the colleges, and West Point, and the Naval School, but with the queerest interruptions that ever you heard. You see it was Robinson Crusoe asking all the accumulated questions of fifty-six years!

I remember he asked, all of a sudden, who was President now; and when I told him, he asked if Old Abe[40] was General Benjamin Lincoln's son. He said he met old General Lincoln, when he was quite a boy himself, at some Indian treaty. I said no, that Old Abe was a Kentuckian like himself, but I could not tell him of what family; he had worked up from the ranks. "Good for him!" cried Nolan; "I am glad of that." Then I got talking about my visit to Washington. Ingham, I told him everything I could think of that would show the grandeur of his country and its prosperity.

And he drank it in and enjoyed it as I cannot tell you. He grew more and more silent, yet I never thought he was tired or faint. I gave him a glass of water, but he just wet his lips, and told me not to go away. Then he asked me to bring the Presbyterian Book of Public Prayer *which lay there, and said, with a smile, that it would open at the right place,—and so it did. There was his double red mark down the page; and I knelt down and read, and he repeated with me, "For ourselves and our country, 0 gracious God, we thank Thee, that, notwithstanding our manifold transgression of Thy Holy laws, Thou has continued to us Thy marvelous kindness,"—and so to the end of that thanksgiving. Then he turned to the end of the same book, and I read the words more familiar to me: "Most heartily we beseech Thee with Thy favor to behold and bless Thy servant, the President of the United States, and all others in authority." "Danforth," said he, "I have repeated those prayers night and morning, it is now fifty-five years." And then he said he would go to sleep. He bent me down over him and kissed me: and he said, "Look in my Bible, Captain, when I am gone." And I went away.*

But I had no thought it was the end. I thought he was tired and would sleep. I knew he was happy, and I wanted him to be alone.

But in an hour, when the doctor went in gently, he found Nolan had breathed his life away with a smile. He had something pressed close to his lips.

~

39. **Vicksburg:** fort on the Mississippi River, whose capture by Grant in 1863 marked the turning point in the Civil War.

40. **Old Abe:** Abraham Lincoln (1809–1865), sixteenth President of the United States.

---

emigration (em′i grā′shən) *n.* act or process of leaving one place to go live in another.

It was his father's badge of the Order of the Cincinnati.[41]

We looked in his Bible, and there was a slip of paper at the place where he had marked the text:

"They desire a country, even a heavenly: wherefore God is not ashamed to be called their God: for He hath prepared for them a city."

On this slip of paper he had written:

"Bury me in the sea; it has been my home, and I love it. But will not some one set up a stone for my memory at Fort Adams or at Orleans, that my disgrace may not be more than I ought to bear? Say on it:

In Memory of
PHILIP NOLAN
Lieutenant in the Army of the United States.
He loved his country as no other man has loved her; but no man deserved less at her hands."

41. **Order of the Cincinnati:** organization established by officers of the American Revolution and named for Cincinnatus, a Roman who left his plow to fight for his country.

MEET
EDWARD EVERETT HALE

Edward Everett Hale (1822–1909) was born into a well-known Boston family—among his ancestors was the Revolutionary war hero Nathan Hale. After graduating from Harvard at age seventeen, Hale worked as a teacher and a journalist before becoming a minister. He was also a popular author and lecturer, and eventually he became the chaplain for the U.S. Senate.

Hale devoted much of his time to humanitarian causes, but he may have done just as much good with his pen. In one of his short stories, a character proclaims, "Look up and not down; look forward and not back; look out and not in; and lend a hand." This story led to the creation of the Lend-A-Hand Societies, charity groups made up of young people.

RESPONDING TO *Literature*

THINK • TALK • WRITE

1 Which do you think Philip Nolan deserves more—pity or admiration? Explain in your journal.

2 At the end of his trial, how does Philip Nolan feel about his sentence? How does he come to feel later? Do you think his sentence is just? Tell why or why not.

3 When Philip Nolan helps tell the enslaved Africans that they are free, what is their greatest concern? Why do you think the captain agrees not to take them to Cape Palmas?

4 When Danforth visits Nolan for the last time, what does he discover about the way Nolan has decorated his stateroom? What are some other ways Nolan demonstrates that he loves his country and is deeply loyal?

5 Do you think the author of this selection places too much emphasis on the importance of home and homeland? Why or why not?

ACTIVITIES

- **Write About Theme** In your own words, state the theme of "The Man Without a Country." Compare your statement with a partner's.

- **Give a Speech** Imagine that you are Philip Nolan. Prepare and deliver a speech you would give to a group of fourth graders on the importance of patriotism.

VOCABULARY PRACTICE

Read each sentence. On a separate sheet of paper, write the vocabulary word from the list that best completes each sentence.

adjourned	infernal
indulgences	voluble
transmitted	exile
allusion	expiated
windfall	emigration

1 _____ is often the result of disease, starvation, or war in one's homeland.

2 The money the Brown family received for winning first prize was a _____.

3 Kate made an _____ to last year's school play.

4 This meeting is _____; we will meet again tomorrow at noon.

5 The man complained that the _____ noise was keeping him awake at night.

6 Because they had served three years in prison, the thieves felt they had _____ their crimes.

7 Mr. Rose allows his grandchildren many _____ because he loves them.

8 The officer _____ the message orally to her superior.

9 After having lived in _____ for over ten years, the family wanted to return to its homeland.

10 Her _____ words soothed the crowd's annoyance.

The Gettysburg Address

by Abraham Lincoln

Four score and seven years ago our fathers brought forth on this continent, a new nation, conceived in Liberty, and dedicated to the proposition that all men are created equal.

Now we are engaged in a great civil war, testing whether that nation, or any nation so conceived and so dedicated, can long endure. We are met on a great battlefield of that war. We have come to dedicate a portion of that field, as a final resting place for those who here gave their lives that that nation might live. It is altogether fitting and proper that we should do this.

But, in a larger sense, we can not dedicate—we can not consecrate—we can not hallow—this ground. The brave men, living and dead, who struggled here, have consecrated it, far above our poor power to add or detract. The world will little note, nor long remember what we say here, but it can never forget what they did here. It is for us the living, rather, to be dedicated here to the unfinished work which they who fought here have thus far so nobly advanced. It is rather for us to be here dedicated to the great task remaining before us—that from these honored dead we take increased devotion to that cause for which they gave the last full measure of devotion—that we here highly resolve that these dead shall not have died in vain—that this nation, under God, shall have a new birth of freedom—and that government of the people, by the people, for the people, shall not perish from the earth.

Tableau

LOCKED ARM IN ARM THEY CROSS THE WAY,

    THE BLACK BOY AND THE WHITE,

THE GOLDEN SPLENDOR OF THE DAY,

    THE SABLE PRIDE OF NIGHT.

FROM LOWERED BLINDS THE DARK FOLK STARE,

    AND HERE THE FAIR FOLK TALK,

INDIGNANT THAT THESE TWO SHOULD DARE

    IN UNISON TO WALK.

OBLIVIOUS TO LOOK AND WORD

    THEY PASS, AND SEE NO WONDER

THAT LIGHTNING BRILLIANT AS A SWORD

    SHOULD BLAZE THE PATH OF THUNDER.

— Countee Cullen

BEFORE READING

THE SCHOLARSHIP JACKET

CONNECT TO LITERATURE

Have you ever been denied something that you knew you had rightfully earned? How did you feel when this happened? In your journal, write about the incident. Then, as you read "The Scholarship Jacket," compare your own feelings and experiences with Martha's.

THINKING ABOUT PLOT AND CONFLICT

Every story has a *plot,* a series of events. Usually the plot is built around some form of *conflict,* or clash between opposing forces. The conflict might be between one character and another, or between a character and a force of nature; this is called an external conflict. Or the conflict might be internal—occurring within a character's mind, such as when the character is struggling over an important decision.

As you read "The Scholarship Jacket," think about the story's main conflict. Is it internal or external? Does it get resolved? How does the plot emerge out of that main conflict? Jot down some ideas in your journal.

DID YOU KNOW?

Originally Texas was a part of Mexico. Around 1820 the Mexican government began attracting settlers from the United States to Texas by providing cheap land and help with farming and ranching techniques.

American settlement led to a war after which Texas became an independent nation. In 1845 Texas joined the Union. Mexicans in Texas now became Mexican Americans and, in many cases, were treated as foreigners. Misunderstandings often separated Mexican Americans from the new settlers of the state. Today, a large percent of Texans are of Mexican American descent.

Meet
MARTA SALINAS

In a sense, Marta Salinas is an heiress. Although she was born and educated in the United States, she has inherited the rich culture and values of her Mexican ancestors. "The Scholarship Jacket" is part of a published collection of twenty-one short stories, *Cuentos Chicanos,* edited by Rudolfo A. Anaya and Antonio Márquez. The stories offer personalized literary accounts of what can happen when Anglo and Mexican cultural traditions meet.

THE
SCH

SCHOLARSHIP JACKET

BY MARTA SALINAS

ILLUSTRATED BY LISA PALOMBO
BORDERS BY JOSÉ ORTEGA

The small Texas school that I attended carried out a tradition every year during the eighth grade graduation; a beautiful gold and green jacket, the school colors, was awarded to the class valedictorian, the student who had maintained the highest grades for eight years. The scholarship jacket had a big gold S on the left front side and the winner's name was written in gold letters on the pocket.

My oldest sister Rosie had won the jacket a few years back and I fully expected to win also. I was fourteen and in the eighth grade. I had been a straight A student since the first grade, and the last year I had looked forward to owning that jacket. My father was a farm laborer who couldn't earn enough money to feed eight children, so when I was six I was given to my grandparents to raise. We couldn't participate in sports at school because there were registration fees, uniform costs, and trips out of town; so even though we were quite agile and athletic, there would never be a sports school jacket for us. This one, the scholarship jacket, was our only chance.

In May, close to graduation, spring fever struck, and no one paid any attention in class; instead we stared out the windows and at each other, wanting to speed up the last few weeks of school. I despaired every time I looked in the mirror. Pencil thin, not a curve anywhere, I was called "Beanpole" and "String Bean" and I knew that's what I looked like. A flat chest, no hips, and a brain, that's what I had. That really isn't much for a fourteen-year-old to work with, I thought, as I absent-mindedly wandered from my history class to the gym. Another hour of sweating in basketball and displaying my toothpick legs was coming up. Then I remembered my P.E. shorts were still in a bag under my desk where I'd forgotten them. I had to walk all the way back and get them. Coach Thompson was a real bear if anyone wasn't dressed for P.E. She had said I was a good forward and once she even tried to talk Grandma into letting me join the team. Grandma, of course, said no.

I was almost back at my classroom's door when I heard angry voices and arguing. I stopped. I didn't mean to eavesdrop; I just hesitated, not knowing what to do. I needed those shorts and I was going to be late, but I didn't want to interrupt an argument between my teachers. I recognized the voices: Mr. Schmidt, my history teacher, and Mr. Boone, my math teacher. They seemed to be arguing about me. I couldn't believe it. I still remember the shock that rooted me flat against the wall as if I were trying to blend in with the graffiti written there.

"I refuse to do it! I don't care who her father is, her grades don't even begin to compare to Martha's. I won't lie or falsify records. Martha has a straight A plus average and you know it." That was Mr. Schmidt and he sounded very angry. Mr. Boone's voice sounded calm and quiet.

"Look, Joann's father is not only on the Board, he owns the only store in town; we could say it was a close tie and—"

---

eavesdrop (ēvz′drop′) *v.i.* listen to the private conversation of others without their knowing it.

The pounding in my ears drowned out the rest of the words, only a word here and there filtered through. ". . . Martha is Mexican. . . . resign. . . . won't do it. . . ." Mr. Schmidt came rushing out, and luckily for me went down the opposite way toward the auditorium, so he didn't see me. Shaking, I waited a few minutes and then went in and grabbed my bag and fled from the room. Mr. Boone looked up when I came in but didn't say anything. To this day I don't remember if I got in trouble in P.E. for being late or how I made it through the rest of the afternoon. I went home very sad and cried into my pillow that night so grandmother wouldn't hear me. It seemed a cruel coincidence that I had overheard that conversation.

The next day when the principal called me into his office, I knew what it would be about. He looked uncomfortable and unhappy. I decided I wasn't going to make it any easier for him so I looked him straight in the eye. He looked away and fidgeted with the papers on his desk.

"Martha," he said, "there's been a change in policy this year regarding the scholarship jacket. As you know, it has always been free." He cleared his throat and continued. "This year the Board decided to charge fifteen dollars—which still won't cover the complete cost of the jacket."

I stared at him in shock and a small sound of <u>dismay</u> escaped my throat. I hadn't expected this. He still avoided looking in my eyes.

"So if you are unable to pay the fifteen dollars for the jacket, it will be given to the next one in line."

Standing with all the dignity I could muster, I said, "I'll speak to my grandfather about it, sir, and let you know tomorrow." I cried on the walk home from the bus stop. The dirt road was a quarter of a mile from the highway, so by the time I got home, my eyes were red and puffy.

"Where's Grandpa?" I asked Grandma, looking down at the floor so she wouldn't ask me why I'd been crying. She was sewing on a quilt and didn't look up.

"I think he's out back working in the bean field."

I went outside and looked out at the fields. There he was. I could see him walking between the rows, his body bent over the little plants, hoe in hand. I walked slowly out to him, trying to think how I could best ask him for the money. There was a cool breeze blowing and a sweet smell of <u>mesquite</u> in the air, but I didn't appreciate it. I kicked at a dirt clod. I wanted that jacket so much. It was more than just being a valedictorian and giving a little thank you speech for the jacket on graduation night. It represented eight years of hard work and expectation. I knew I had to be honest with Grandpa; it was my only chance. He saw me and looked up.

He waited for me to speak. I cleared my throat nervously and clasped my hands behind my back so he wouldn't see them shaking. "Grandpa, I have a big favor to ask you," I said

---

dismay (dis mā′) *n.* feeling of alarm or uneasiness; frightened amazement.

mesquite (mes kēt′) *n.* small, thorny tree or shrub that grows in desert regions from the southwestern United States to Chile.

in Spanish, the only language he knew. He still waited silently. I tried again. "Grandpa, this year the principal said the scholarship jacket is not going to be free. It's going to cost fifteen dollars and I have to take the money in tomorrow, otherwise it'll be given to someone else." The last words came out in an eager rush. Grandpa straightened up tiredly and leaned his chin on the hoe handle. He looked out over the field that was filled with the tiny green bean plants. I waited, desperately hoping he'd say I could have the money.

He turned to me and asked quietly, "What does a scholarship jacket mean?"

I answered quickly; maybe there was a chance. "It means you've earned it by having the highest grades for eight years and that's why they're giving it to you." Too late I realized the <u>significance</u> of my words. Grandpa knew that I understood it was not a matter of money. It wasn't that. He went back to hoeing the weeds that sprang up between the delicate little bean plants. It was a time consuming job; sometimes the small shoots were right next to each other. Finally he spoke again.

"Then if you pay for it, Marta, it's not a scholarship jacket, is it? Tell your principal I will not pay the fifteen dollars."

I walked back to the house and locked myself in the bathroom for a long time. I was angry with grandfather even though I knew he was right, and I was angry with the Board, whoever they were. Why did they have to change the rules just when it was my turn to win the jacket?

It was a very sad and withdrawn girl who dragged into the principal's office the next day. This time he did look me in the eyes.

"What did your grandfather say?"

I sat very straight in my chair.

"He said to tell you he won't pay the fifteen dollars."

The principal muttered something I couldn't understand under his breath, and walked over to the window. He stood looking out at something outside. He looked bigger than usual

---

significance (sig nif'i kəns) *n.* special value or importance.

when he stood up; he was a tall <u>gaunt</u> man with gray hair, and I watched the back of his head while I waited for him to speak.

"Why?" he finally asked. "Your grandfather has the money. Doesn't he own a small bean farm?"

I looked at him, forcing my eyes to stay dry. "He said if I had to pay for it, then it wouldn't be a scholarship jacket," I said and stood up to leave. "I guess you'll just have to give it to Joann." I hadn't meant to say that; it had just slipped out. I was almost to the door when he stopped me.

"Martha—wait."

I turned and looked at him, waiting. What did he want now? I could feel my heart pounding. Something bitter and <u>vile</u> tasting was coming up in my mouth; I was afraid I was going to be sick. I didn't need any sympathy speeches. He sighed loudly and went back to his big desk. He looked at me, biting his lip, as if thinking.

"Okay, damn it. We'll make an exception in your case. I'll tell the Board, you'll get your jacket."

I could hardly believe it. I spoke in a trembling rush. "Oh, thank you sir!" Suddenly I felt great. I didn't know about adrenalin in those days, but I knew something was pumping through me, making me feel as tall as the sky. I wanted to yell, jump, run the mile, do something. I ran out so I could cry in the hall where there was no one to see me. At the end of the day, Mr. Schmidt winked at me and said, "I hear you're getting a scholarship jacket this year."

His face looked as happy and innocent as a baby's, but I knew better. Without answering I gave him a quick hug and ran to the bus. I cried on the walk home again, but this time

---

gaunt (gônt) *adj.* extremely thin and with sunken eyes.
vile (vīl) *adj.* foul; disgusting; repulsive.

because I was so happy. I couldn't wait to tell Grandpa and ran straight to the field. I joined him in the row where he was working and without saying anything I crouched down and started pulling up the weeds with my hands. Grandpa worked alongside me for a few minutes, but he didn't ask what had happened. After I had a little pile of weeds between the rows, I stood up and faced him.

"The principal said he's making an exception for me, Grandpa, and I'm getting the jacket after all. That's after I told him what you said."

Grandpa didn't say anything, he just gave me a pat on the shoulder and a smile. He pulled out the crumpled red handkerchief that he always carried in his back pocket and wiped the sweat off his forehead.

"Better go see if your grandmother needs any help with supper."

I gave him a big grin. He didn't fool me. I skipped and ran back to the house whistling some silly tune.

RESPONDING TO *Literature*

THINK • TALK • WRITE

1 Do you think it is a good idea for a valedictorian to receive a prize? Why or why not? Jot down some ideas in your journal.

2 Why is Martha angry with her grandfather, even though she says she knows he was right? Do you think he was right to refuse to buy the jacket? Explain your opinion.

3 Why does the principal ask Martha to pay for the jacket? If you were in his place, how might you have handled the situation?

4 How would you answer the grandfather's question, "What does a scholarship jacket mean?" Try to think of as many different meanings as you can.

5 Do you think the scholarship jacket means more to Martha because she is a Mexican American? Why or why not?

ACTIVITIES

- **Write About Plot and Conflict** Imagine that Martha kept a diary. Write some diary entries for the time period covered by the story. Have Martha state her conflict and how it is resolved.

- **Create a Monologue** Imagine that you are Martha. Create a monologue, a one-person retelling of the story. Remember that Martha can only tell about the events she was involved in. You may want to perform your monologue for the class.

VOCABULARY PRACTICE

On a separate sheet of paper, write the letter of the phrase that is the best example of the word in color.

1 **gaunt**
   a. a lonely hiker sitting alone
   b. a thin and starved-looking person
   c. a horrible and frightening dream

2 **dismay**
   a. the winner of an Olympic gold medal
   b. a disco dancer
   c. the writer of a badly reviewed play

3 **vile**
   a. a treasure map
   b. a cheap and badly made toy
   c. a foul-smelling garbage can

4 **eavesdrop**
   a. to give away your last dollar
   b. to listen to a private conversation
   c. to snub someone you don't like

5 **significance**
   a. yesterday's newspaper
   b. a cruel coincidence
   c. a meaningful family picture

BEFORE READING

....

I DREAM A WORLD

CONNECT TO LITERATURE

What important lessons have you learned in your life? Which lessons would you like to share with others? Discuss your ideas with a classmate. As you read "I Dream a World," note in your journal the lessons that these women want to pass on to others.

THINKING ABOUT CHARACTER

All stories have *characters*—they're the people or animals who take part in the action of the story. The way a writer presents these characters is called characterization. Direct characterization is when a writer tells you how a character looks, behaves, and thinks. Indirect characterization is when you have to draw your own conclusions about a character from how the character speaks or acts, or how people react to the character.

In a sense, real people are characters, too—we all look, behave, and think in certain ways as we play out the story of our lives. As you read "I Dream a World," try to think of these three women as characters. What do they look like? What do their words reveal about them?

DID YOU KNOW?

If you had been born before 1964, you would have lived in a very different United States. In most Southern states, public facilities such as buses, restaurants, movie theaters, rest rooms, and swimming pools were segregated by race; many African Americans were also prevented from voting. Beginning with Rosa Parks's refusal to give up her bus seat in 1955, the civil rights movement led to the passage of the Civil Rights Act of 1964 and the Voting Rights Act of 1965, both of which outlawed racial discrimination. The outstanding leader of the movement was Dr. Martin Luther King, Jr., who won a Nobel Peace Prize in 1964 for his work.

I DREAM A WORLD

Portraits of Black Women Who Changed America

Civil rights activist Septima Poinsette Clark, born in 1898 in Charleston, South Carolina, died in 1987

As I think about the women I've met through this project, it strikes me how many of them grew up in strong, supportive families with the black church playing a major role. Though others outside their families or communities were quick to try to limit their world, their experiences inside the home instilled in them the conviction that they were not to be limited by anything. They were told they could do anything they chose if they only set their mind to it and worked hard. They were free to dream and were often driven to fulfill their dreams.

In fact, all of the women in this book have dreamed of a world not only better for themselves but for generations to come, a world where character and ability matter, not color or gender. As they dreamed that world, they acted on those dreams and they changed America.

This celebration of sisters is not an attempt to elevate or lower any segment of society, it is merely an opportunity to savor the triumphs of the human spirit, a spirit that does not speak only of black history. My greatest lesson was that this is my history, this is American history.

—Brian Lanker

Rosa Parks

Born February 4, 1913, in Tuskegee, Alabama

When Rosa Parks refused to give up her seat on a Montgomery, Alabama, bus in 1955, her silent defiance spoke for a whole people. Her arrest sparked a 381-day bus boycott, which ignited the civil rights movement and changed America. Fired from her tailoring job, she moved to Detroit, Michigan, where she was a special assistant to Congressman John Conyers for twenty-five years. She is the founder and president of the Rosa and Raymond Parks Institute for Self-Development, inaugurated in 1988.

As far back as I can remember, being black in Montgomery we were well aware of the inequality of our way of life. I hated it all the time. I didn't feel that, in order to have some freedom, I should have to leave one part of the United States to go to another part of the same country just because one was South and one was North.

My mother believed in freedom and equality even though we didn't know it for reality during our life in Alabama.

In some stores, if a woman wanted to go in to try a hat, they wouldn't be permitted to try it on unless they knew they were going to buy it, or they put a bag on the inside of it. In the shoe stores they had this long row of seats, and all of those in the front could be vacant, but if one of us would go in to buy, they'd always take you to the last one, to the back of the store. There were no black salespersons.

At the Montgomery Fair [a department store] I did men's alterations. Beginning in December coming up to the Christmas holiday, the work was a bit heavy. When I left the store that evening, I was tired, but I was tired every day. I had planned to get an electric heating pad so I could put some heat to my shoulder and my back and neck. After I stepped up on the bus, I noticed this driver as the same one who had evicted me from another bus way back in 1943.

Just back of the whites there was a black man next to one vacant seat. So I sat down with him. A few white people boarded the bus and they found seats except this one man. That is when

289

the bus driver looked at us and asked us to let him have those seats. After he saw we weren't moving immediately, he said, "Y'all make it light on yourselves and let me have those seats."

When he saw that I was still remaining in the seat, the driver said, "If you don't stand up, I'm going to call the police and have you arrested." I said, "You may do that."

Two policemen came and wanted to know what was the trouble. One said, "Why don't you stand up?" I said, "I don't think I should have to." At that point I asked the policemen, "Why do you push us around?" He said, "I don't know, but the law is the law and you're under arrest."

The decision was made by the three of us, my husband, my mother, and me, that I would go on and use my case as a test case challenging segregation on the buses.

When I woke up the next morning and realized I had to go to work and it was pouring down rain, the first thing I thought about was the fact that I never would ride a segregated bus again. That was my decision for me and not necessarily for anybody else.

People just stayed off the buses because I was arrested, not because I asked them. If everybody else had been happy and doing well, my arrest wouldn't have made any difference at all.

The one thing I appreciated was the fact that when so many others, by the hundreds and by the thousands, joined in, there was a kind of lifting of a burden from me individually. I could feel that whatever my individual desires were to be free, I was not alone. There were many others who felt the same way.

The first thing that happened after the people stayed off was the black cab companies were willing to just charge bus fare instead of charging cab fare. Others who had any kind of car at all would give people rides. They had quite a transportation system set up. Mass meetings were keeping the morale up. They were singing and praying and raising money in the collection to buy gasoline or tires.

> "The first thing I thought about was the fact that I never would ride a segregated bus again."

---

segregation (seg′ri gā′shən) *n.* practice of separating one racial group from another or from the rest of society.

There was a lot of humor in it, too. Somebody told a story about a [white] husband who had fired the family cook because she refused to ride the bus to work. When his wife came home, she said, "If you don't go get her, you better be on your way." Some white people who were not wanting to be deprived of their domestic help would just go themselves and pick up the people who were working for them.

The officials really became furious when they saw that the rain and bad weather or distance or any other problem didn't matter.

Many whites, even white Southerners, told me that even though it may have seemed like the blacks were being freed, they felt more free and at ease themselves. They thought that my action didn't just free blacks but them also.

Some have suffered much more than I did. Some have even lost their lives. I just escaped some of the physical—maybe not all—but some of the physical pain. And the pain still remains. From back as far as I can remember.

When people made up their minds that they wanted to be free and took action, then there was a change. But they couldn't rest on just that change. It has to continue.

It just doesn't seem that an older person like I am should still have to be in the struggle, but if I have to be in it then I have no choice but to keep on.

I've been dreaming, looking, for as far back as I had any thought, of what it should be like to be a human being. My desires were to be free as soon as I had learned that there had been slavery of human beings and that I was a descendant from them. If there was a proclamation setting those who were slaves free, I thought they should be indeed free and not have any type of slavery put upon us. ❖

"My desires were to be free as soon as I had learned that there had been slavery of human beings."

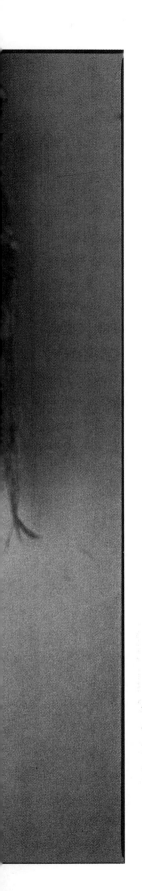

Charlayne Hunter-Gault

Born February 27, 1942, in Due West, South Carolina

Charlayne Hunter was one of two black students to desegregate the University of Georgia in Athens in 1961. She worked as a journalist for The New Yorker *and* The New York Times *before joining* The MacNeil/Lehrer NewsHour *as national correspondent in 1978. She has received two Emmy Awards, and in 1986 was the recipient of the George Foster Peabody Award for Excellence in Broadcast Journalism for "Apartheid's People," a report on South Africa.*

If you've ever been in the middle of a riot or the eye of a hurricane, you know it's very calm. It is. That is exactly how I felt the night of the riot. . . .

White students had been out there the night before yelling, and it was part of the resistance ritual, "Two, four, six, eight, we don't want to integrate." It sounded almost playful and then it got louder and louder and louder. And that's when the brick came through the window. I realized what had happened and it was like, "Wow! There is a riot in my room."

I probably didn't get frightened about it until ten or fifteen years later.

I think maybe that is part of what helps me in my journalism. I have a tremendous capacity to be detached but at the same time to be engaged.

Even in the best high school in Atlanta, we had hand-me-down textbooks and our labs were certainly not as well equipped. So the fact that we were prepared to compete in the way that we did was a minor miracle that the black schools accomplished.

That was the critical difference. We didn't want to go to school with white people—that wasn't it. It was those facilities they had.

There were real conflicts between Hamilton [Holmes, the other "first" black student] and me over our approach to the whole situation. I was really much more interested in integrating the place and Hamp was much more interested in desegregation.

It got to be bigger than I ever thought it would be. I didn't expect that. People wanted us to be perfect, I guess. And I wanted to be me, which was an imperfect person.

There was conflict and there was pain. There was crisis and there was ignorance and all of that. But I emerged as a whole person and the university came out the better for it.

The university itself has a lot of unfinished business. The young people have a lot of complaints and knowing how far they've come should not <u>mitigate</u> their demands for a more <u>equitable</u> piece of the state pie.

I was able to advance at *The New Yorker* because I could write. And so, like everybody else, when I wasn't licking envelopes and stuffing rejection letters and typing schedules, I was working on some little piece at lunchtime at my desk. I had some wonderful opportunities and I am not ungrateful, but I would still be there licking envelopes if I hadn't had some kind of talent that I was willing to work hard at and get people to help me develop.

You have to <u>assess</u> every situation that you're in and you have to decide, is this happening because I'm black? Is this happening because I'm a woman? Or is this happening because this is how it happens?

Whatever I have faced as a woman is probably a lot more subtle than what I have faced as a black person. We did find out, for example, at *The New York Times*, that women across the board were making less money than most men. And there was a successful lawsuit. But the same thing happened with blacks. And there was also a successful lawsuit.

I have never looked on being black or being a woman as a handicap and, honestly, I have used those things to my advantage, in the workplace particularly.

"You have to decide, is this happening because I'm black? Is this happening because I'm a woman? Or is this happening because this is how it happens?"

---

mitigate (mit′i gāt′) *v.t.* make milder or less severe.

equitable (ek′wi tə bəl) *adj.* fair or just.

assess (ə ses′) *v.t.* evaluate.

I have never apologized for doing black stories, being interested in black stories, and insisting that every institution that I work for report black stories.

I think the South has a much greater opportunity than the North to right some of the historic wrongs.

People have been lying in the North about race relations as long as I've been here. I haven't seen that many integrated schools, and yet I have seen a lot that are as segregated as the one I went to.

Integration has some negative by-products as well. It has helped to dilute some of the institutions where we have had this tremendous reservoir of confidence-building and strength—the black colleges, the churches, the family.

So there is good news and bad news. The good news is that you do begin to see some commitment to change. The bad news is that you've got to chip away at the concrete of institutional racism.

"If people are informed they will do the right thing. It's when they are not informed that they become hostages to prejudice."

South Africa is one of the greatest challenges that we in the media face. We are being manipulated by the South African government. Just beginning to contemplate what could happen in South Africa if the world can't watch is an awesome proposition. This is not a totally appropriate analogy, but if television had been there, could the Holocaust have happened?

Whatever you say about this country, we do have a Constitution where equality of opportunity is a basic principle. We have problems living up to it, but it is there in the Constitution, which isn't the case in South Africa.

If people are informed they will do the right thing. It's when they are not informed that they become hostages to prejudice. ❖

analogy (ə nal′ə jē) *n.* comparison or parallel.

Barbara Jordan

Born February 21, 1936, in Houston, Texas

When Barbara Jordan was elected to the Texas Senate in 1966, she became the first black senator to sit in that body since 1883. She was elected to the United States House of Representatives in 1972 and served for three highly visible terms. Since 1979, she has been a professor at the Lyndon Baines Johnson School of Public Affairs at the University of Texas in Austin.

When I was a student at Texas Southern University in Houston, I had to ride the bus from my house to school across town. There was a little plaque on the bus near the back that said "Colored" and when I'd get on I'd have to go all the way back to that little plaque and I was passing empty seats all the time.

In 1962, I lost a contest for the state House of Representatives. And some of the people were saying that I probably lost the race because people are just not accustomed to voting for a woman. And I just said, "Well, now, that is totally ridiculous and I'll just have to try to alter that."

All my growth and development led me to believe that if you really do the right thing, and if you play by the rules, and if you got enough good, solid judgment and common sense, that you're going to be able to do whatever you want to do with your life. My father taught me that.

The civil rights movement called America to put a giant mirror before it and look at itself. I believe that the movement said to America, "Look at what you have been saying to us black people all of these years. Look what you have been trying to sell us as the bill of goods for America. Look at that and then ask yourselves, have you really done it? Do the black people who were born on this soil, who are American citizens, do they really feel this is the land of opportunity, the land of the free, the home of the brave, all that great stuff?"

And when America looked into that giant mirror and heard these questions, the drumbeat—that's what the movement was, this drumbeat of questions—America had to say, "No, I really haven't, as a country, lived up to what I've said this country would be for you." And so the civil rights movement was a time of requiring that America be honest in its promises. And that was the goodness of the movement.

I am telling the young people that if you're dissatisfied—and I don't think they can be students in a school of public affairs and not be dissatisfied—if you are dissatisfied with the way things are, then you have got to resolve to change them. I am telling them to get out there and occupy these positions in government and make the decisions, do the job and make it work for you.

There seems to be a chilling of opportunity rather than an enlivening and enhancing of opportunity. But to me, that should just be the spark that energizes you to get out there and do things.

How do you communicate to young people that you do better, your opportunity is expanded and enhanced if you're educated? That's the message I know many teachers out there are trying to deliver now, but it's a drumbeat which must continue. The drop-out rate is criminal.

We've got to bring a new kind of literacy and it's not going to be easy and it is going to cost money. But I say that we need first to develop the will to try to do something. Can we afford it? We have to.

Things which matter cost money, and we've got to spend the money if we do not want to have generations of parasites rather than generations of productive citizens.

"If you are dissatisfied with the way things are, then you have got to resolve to change them."

It is the linkage of humanity which has to solve the problem. Yes, these kids are perhaps <u>predominantly</u> black or brown or whatever, but they are human. And I say to the whites that you are being very shortsighted to say they're not your kids. They are your kids because we are all representative of everybody else. That is the human linkage.

It is a burden of black people that we have to do more than talk. We have somehow got to sacrifice our lives as an example to move young people along so that they will understand that it is a long, slow, tough road to really make it so that it lasts. I have got

---

predominantly (pri dom′ə nənt lē) *adv.* more frequently, commonly, or noticeably.

to offer myself as a role model to others so that perhaps something in my life will help move a young black person who might otherwise drop out to stay in school. That is part of my mission.

I define morality as <u>adherence</u> to the Golden Rule, "Do unto others as you would have them do unto you." If that is one's code of behavior, in my opinion, that person is moral. That is my code.

Texas is more than a place. It is a frame of mind. A Texan believes that the individual is powerful. Texas has that rugged individualism. It may not be polished, may not be smooth, and it may not be silky, but it is there. I believe that I get from the soil and the spirit of Texas the feeling that I, as an individual, can accomplish whatever I want to and that there are no limits, that you can just keep going, just keep soaring. I like that spirit.

❖ ❖ ❖

adherence (ad hîr′əns) *n.* firm attachment; faithful support.

Meet Brian Lanker

D*uring his childhood, Brian Lanker was unaware that bigotry was a problem in America. He thought "that Abraham Lincoln had made everyone equal." He first learned about the civil rights movement from television. He was shocked when he saw pictures of African Americans being attacked by dogs, clubs, and fire hoses.*

Lanker continued to be impressed by the power of pictures. In college he studied photography. He remembers that one particular photography instructor helped him to get in touch with the deeper emotions in himself and in his photographic subjects. The instructor taught him to use the camera as a probe and encouraged him to strive to reveal "the inner essence of the individual."

Lanker's interest and skill led to photography jobs for publications such as Life *and* Sports Illustrated. *In 1973, he was awarded the Pulitzer Prize for feature photography.*

Because he was deeply affected by the civil rights movement and the women's movement, Brian Lanker decided to create a book to celebrate the accomplishments of African-American women.

RESPONDING TO *Literature*

THINK • TALK • WRITE

1 Do you admire the women interviewed in this selection? Are you sympathetic to their views? Jot down some thoughts in your journal to explain your opinion.

2 Why did Rosa Parks refuse to give up her bus seat? Do you think there would have been a civil rights movement if she hadn't refused?

3 What do you think Barbara Jordan means when she says ". . . we are all representative of everybody else"? Do you agree with her? Explain your opinion.

4 What characteristics did the three women share? How did these characteristics help them succeed in their lives?

5 What did you learn about the lives of African Americans in the South before the civil rights movement? How are things different today? How are they similar?

ACTIVITIES

- **Write About Character** Choose someone you think deserves recognition. Write a description of the person's life. Use details to reveal the character of the person you select.

- **Take Portrait Photographs** Using your own or a borrowed camera, take photographs of people you know. Try to create photos that reveal your subjects' characters. You might want to share your portrait photographs with the class.

VOCABULARY PRACTICE

On a separate sheet of paper, write a word from the list to fill in each blank and complete the paragraph.

equitable   predominantly

assess   adherence

analogy

   Although years have passed, it is still difficult to ___**1**___ the civil rights movement. Many people joined protests and sit-ins, but the participants were ___**2**___ African Americans. Their ___**3**___ to nonviolent protest finally succeeded. They demanded ___**4**___ treatment for African Americans. Today, some people see an ___**5**___ in the women's movement and other movements for equality.

BEFORE READING

"AM I AN AMERICAN?"

CONNECT TO LITERATURE

Have you ever been accused of something you didn't do? What were your feelings about the people who accused you? Did you prove that you were innocent? Discuss your experience with a classmate. As you read "Am I an American?" note in your journal all the ways that Gordon Hirabayashi fought what he thought was an unfair accusation.

THINKING ABOUT PERSUASION AND PROPAGANDA

Every author has a purpose for writing. It might be to entertain or to educate, or, in some cases, to *persuade*—to make the reader agree with the author's ideas. Persuasive writing uses logic to sway readers' thinking; it builds a case by amassing facts and examples to lead to a particular conclusion. Sometimes persuasive writing uses emotional language to appeal to people's fears or hopes or prejudices. This is called *propaganda.* Because propaganda does not depend on logic, it is less likely to stand up to rational investigation.

There is nothing wrong with persuasion. However, you should be aware when an author is using techniques of persuasion. This knowledge will help you to evaluate the author's arguments.

DID YOU KNOW?

In 1942 the U.S. government forced many Japanese Americans out of their homes and into large prison camps, because war hysteria had convinced many Americans that these people would aid Japan in the war.

By 1944 the U.S. Army had begun drafting inmates of the camps. One regiment made up entirely of Japanese Americans received more than 18,000 decorations for combat duty. However, it was not until 1990 that the government finally apologized for its wartime treatment of these Americans and paid them reparations.

"AM I AN AMERICAN?"

★ ★ ★ BY PETER IRONS ★ ★ ★

Collage by Steve Karchin

On December 7, 1941, Japan bombed Pearl Harbor, an American naval base in Hawaii, and the United States of America entered World War II. On that fateful day, the life of Gordon Hirabayashi, a Japanese-American college student living in Seattle, changed forever. Fearful that all persons of Japanese ancestry in this country, citizen and noncitizen alike, would support Japan's war effort, the United States government issued two orders. The first was a curfew, which required that Japanese and Japanese-Americans be off the streets by eight o'clock each night. The second, the exclusion order, demanded that all persons of Japanese heritage be moved from the West Coast to internment camps in which they would remain, behind barbed wire, for the duration of the war. Although Gordon's parents, who had immigrated to the United States more than twenty years earlier, were not permitted by law to become citizens, Gordon, born in this country, was a citizen. He resented the fact that his constitutional rights were being violated. Gordon and another Japanese-American student, Bill Makino, made a conscious decision to defy the laws, which they believed were a violation of the freedom guaranteed by the Constitution.

I had no plans to bring a test case. Today, if I violate anything on the grounds of principle, I would spend some time thinking about the legal aspects, the court battles and so on. But at that time, I was just a student. I had read of World War I and constitutional cases, but I didn't give it very much thought. I did anticipate that I would be apprehended, but I didn't know very much about the legal procedures in these things. I just felt that something was going to happen to curtail my freedom.

I had met a lawyer named Arthur Barnett at the Friends Meeting. Bill and I met with Art and asked him some questions about the legal implications of the position we were contemplating. But there was no, Should we, or shouldn't we? Some people knew what I was thinking, but they didn't know what I was going to do.

Eventually, I wrote out a statement explaining the reasons I was refusing evacuation, and I planned to give it to the FBI when I turned myself in. By that time my roommate, Bill Makino, had to cope with his parents' request that he stick with them and go along to the camp. Bill was the only son of parents who were at least ten years older than my parents and the pressure was very strong on him. I didn't want to have someone who would be having remorse all the way through, because I figured that we'll run into serious problems. In the course of our discussions, I said, You should think this through carefully

and, if there's any way you could persuade yourself to go with your family, you should do that. You should come with me *only* if you just can't go and you have to object. Then I welcome you. He thought about it and decided he'd have to stick with his family.

I didn't have the same moral pressure. Dad was physically able, so I didn't have that worry. My mother said that she gave me moral support but she wanted me to come with the family to the camp. I know you're right and I admire this stand of yours, she said, but we don't know if we'll ever see each other again. In that period, I didn't know what was going to happen to me, and I didn't know what was going to happen to them, where they were going, how far away and for how long. Everything was just a total blank, full of anxiety. So she said, It's a matter of life and death. Why stick to a principle? Stick with us. She used everything—tears and everything. And I couldn't do it.

So when I wrote my statement it was only me. When this got around, Mary Farquharson came to see me. Mary was the state senator for the University district and she was a regular resource person for the student Y. She said, I'm checking on a rumor that you are intending to defy the exclusion order. Is that true? And I said, Yes, I've already made a stand and written a statement. She said, Are you planning to make a test case of this? I said, I know that's a possibility, but I don't know very much about law and I don't

---

violate (vī′ə lāt′) *v.t.* fail to obey or keep; break.

implications (im′pli kā′shənz) *n., pl.* indirect suggestions.

remorse (ri môrs′) *n.* deep, painful feeling of guilt or sorrow for wrongdoing.

have any money. I haven't talked to anybody about this. I don't know what's going to happen as a result of it and I've made no plans. And she said, Well, if you've made no plans, there's a group here that is very upset about what's happening to our liberties, the status of citizenship, and we'd like to battle it, but we haven't been able to find anyone yet. Do you have any objection to our group using your case as a vehicle to fight for citizens' rights?

Mary's group included some people I knew and respected—some Quakers, ministers, professors, businessmen in the University district. Our plan was to hire a constitutional lawyer, get the case started, and then the American Civil Liberties Union would take over. But we had to change these plans. Roger Baldwin, the national ACLU director, regretfully informed Mary that his national board had failed to back him. So Mary and the Seattle group organized a Gordon Hirabayashi Defense Committee and continued the fight.

The day after the University district deadline for evacuation, Art took me to the FBI office to turn myself in. At first, I was only charged with violating the exclusion order. They threw in the curfew count afterward. One of the FBI agents who interrogated me regarding the exclusion order refusal stopped at one point and said, Well, gee, if you feel this

A girl wearing a family detention tag being taken by truck to a detention camp

way about it, what would you do about curfew? And I said, Well, what were *you* doing the past few nights? Were you out after eight o'clock? He said, Yeah. And I said, So was I. Other Americans were ignoring it, and so did I. When they confiscated my journal from my briefcase, I had some events listed of violating the curfew, and they picked one of those and added it to the counts against me.

Shortly, Art left the FBI office and I was in their hands for most of that day. There was an initial attempt to get me to register for evacuation, and they drove me to the registration center in a Catholic church. But when I found there were no changes in the regulations from the time I had previously found it impossible to register, I refused their offer. They took me back to the car and I'm sitting there while they must have been mulling over what to do with me. And then they took me back to headquarters and promised to drop the charges and give me a ride to the fairgrounds in Puyallup, if I would just go in without registering. I told them that not only would I refuse that offer, but they were proposing to do something illegal.

At the end of the day I was checked into the federal tank of the King County jail in downtown Seattle. I had no notion of anything. I was so naive, I'd never even *seen* a jail. I was a sociology student but my class had

never taken a field trip. After I was put in jail, within a couple of days I was brought into court for arraignment, and I was represented by a lawyer named John Geisness, with Art Barnett as advisor. We made a plea of not guilty to both counts and then they set bail. The original amount was five hundred dollars.

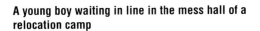

A young boy waiting in line in the mess hall of a relocation camp

---

curfew (kûr'fū) *n.* order or rule requiring certain persons to be indoors or at home before a fixed time, especially at night.
arraignment (ə rān'mənt) *n.* appearance before a judge in which charges are formally made.

Interned Japanese aliens line up for inspection outside their tents.

So I said to Geisness, What if I put up that five hundred? Can I just walk out like anybody else? He raised this question and the judge, after consulting for a while, said, No, if he puts up bail he'll have to go to camp at Puyallup. Things would have been better physically in the camp. Emotionally, it would have been very difficult for me, because I had objected to the whole thing and then I'm there. I'd have to be subject to all sorts of regulations, many of which were objectionable. I just felt that I couldn't accept that, so I stayed on in jail.

In the course of my staying in jail from May to October, when my district court trial was set, there were two or three legal skirmishes during the summer. My lawyers filed motions requesting that the case be dropped because, as a citizen, I wasn't given due process and, in effect, I was subject to these orders only on the grounds of ancestry, which was outside of constitutional guarantees. Judge Black denied these challenges.

King County jail is a holding place, primarily for people to be arraigned or serve sentences of sixty days or less. So the stays are quite short, and when a guy like me is there for months, I'm the senior person. Eventually I became the 'mayor' of the tank and I was in that capacity when they brought my Dad in to testify at my trial.

My trial in October lasted just one day. It started in the morning and they took a noon recess and continued in the afternoon until my conviction. The government <u>subpoenaed</u> my parents and they put Dad on the stand. They only asked him a couple of questions, like, Were you born in Japan? Are you a Japanese citizen? The only point was to impress on the jury that this man was Japanese and didn't speak English well and that this defendant is his son.

---

subpoenaed (sə pē′nəd) *v.t.* summoned to a court of law by virtue of having a subpoena, or legal document.

Camp detainees were forced to share overcrowded barracks.

I really objected to the government putting my parents in jail for ten days before my trial. They were brought up from the Tule Lake Concentration Camp in California and my Dad was placed in the federal tank with me. Mother was put in the only tank for women, with street walkers, petty thieves, <u>embezzlers</u>. The tank was cockroachy and the food was greasy. On the day of my trial, we had to wait ten minutes for her to come down. Six of the women had been working on her hair and fingernails. She came out looking like a queen. She told me that whatever the women were charged with, she had never met such warmhearted people. But I'll *never* forgive the government for putting my parents in jail like that, just to prejudice the jury against me.

Judge Black's instructions to the jury before they retired were very <u>succinct</u>. You can forget all those legal arguments, he said. Here are the only questions that you must determine. I am instructing you that the curfew and exclusion orders of the Army are valid. You are to determine whether the defendant is of Japanese ancestry, and if he is, he's subject to this regulation. Then you are to determine whether he <u>complied</u> with it. Gee, there's no question! They go in and they were back in ten minutes. I was guilty on both counts. You could have a whole bunch of civil-liberties people on the jury and

embezzlers (em bez′lərz) *n., pl.* people who steal or have stolen money entrusted to their care.

succinct (sək singkt′) *adj.* expressed in few words; brief and concise.

complied (kəm plīd′) *v.t.* acted in agreement, as with a rule.

Two brothers await the train that will transport them to an evacuation relocation center.

they are subject to the judge's instructions. They *had* to vote against me. It was cut and dried.

Judge Black sentenced me the next day. He said, Taking into consideration that you have already been five months in jail on a conviction with a maximum of twelve months, I'm going to sentence you to thirty days for the exclusion order conviction and thirty days for curfew order violation, to be served consecutively, or sixty days. Then he asked if the prisoner had anything to say, and I asked if he could add fifteen days to each count so that it would total ninety days. I'd been told by jailhouse friends that if my sentence was ninety days or longer, I could serve on a work camp and be outdoors instead of in jail behind bars. When Judge Black heard this he smiled and said, I could

accommodate that. Why don't we make it three months on each count, to be served <u>concurrently</u>. Nobody saw any objection to that, and nobody realized that the Supreme Court would use that to avoid ruling on the exclusion order conviction.

Two days after I was sentenced, we appealed, and I continued to remain in jail because the judge and I couldn't agree on bail conditions. He said that if my backers put up the bail he would release me to one of the barbed-wire internment camps. And I said, If my backers put up the bail, I should be released out the front door like anybody else. He said, There's a law that says you're not allowed out in the streets, so I can't do that.

With that <u>stalemate</u>, I remained in jail until the end of the ninth month, four months into the appeal period. Then we worked out a compromise with Judge

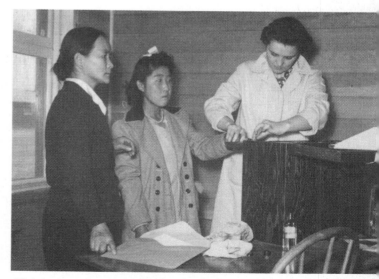

All detention camp inmates 12 years of age and older were photographed and fingerprinted.

---

concurrently (kən kûr′ənt lē) *adv.* at the same time.
stalemate (stāl′māt′) *n.* any position or situation in which no further action is possible; deadlock; standstill.

Black. By that time he was willing to get me out of jail. We'd become sort of like old friends in terms of his knowledge of me, and he said, We ought to get him out. We worked out a compromise that I would go to Spokane, which was outside the restricted area for Japanese. The American Friends Service Committee was setting up a branch in Spokane to work on the relocation of Japanese who might be able to come out of the camps if they had a place to live and a job. And my assignment would have been like a field officer working up places to stay and lining up jobs. Judge Black said, I want the prisoner's promise that he will not return to the restricted area for the duration of the appeal. That sounded acceptable to me, so I went out to the Spokane post.

When the Supreme Court decision in my case came down in June 1943, I expected I would have to serve my sentence. Around the middle of July a couple of FBI agents came after me in Spokane. I was living with a Japanese doctor at the time, and I was mowing the lawn when they came. What kept you so long? I said. I've been waiting for you. Can I go in and get my things? They took me to the federal attorney's office and booked me into custody. His name was Connolly and he said, Well, I guess you'll have to serve your sentence in the federal tank of the Spokane county jail. I said, Wait a minute! I've got ninety days to serve and that's too long for the county jail. So he said, The only federal work camp I can send you to is in Tucson, Arizona. But we don't

Inmates at the Manzanar detention camp in California

have any money to send you there. You'll have to serve your time here.

I was wracking my brain. I said, What if I go on my own to Tucson? And Connolly said, If you want to do that, it's okay with me. In fact, I'll write a letter for you, in case somebody gives you problems. It was against my principles to pay my way to prison, so I hitch-hiked. This is 1,600 miles away, down the middle of the mountain states, during gas <u>rationing</u>, so there's not many cars on the road, and traffic is slow. I stopped in Idaho to visit with my parents for a few days and then I stopped at Salt Lake City to visit friends, and finally got to Tucson after two weeks.

I went to the U.S. marshal's office and told them I was reporting to serve my sentence. This marshal looked in his

A truckload of evacuees arriving at a detention camp

papers and said, We don't have any record for you here. You might as well turn around and go back. You're free to go. I said, Look around, there must be something. If I go, someday you're going to find those papers and I'll have to interrupt what I'm doing and come back. So I might as well get this over with. It was a hot day, and he said, Why don't you go to an air-conditioned movie and come back tonight. Well, they found my papers at the bottom of the pile. So they took me to the work camp, which was like a CCC camp up in the mountains, and I did my sentence there. Most of the prisoners were there for selling liquor to Indians or as wetbacks, illegal aliens. It was actually a good experience, getting to know these people and working in the woods on conservation projects. The ironic thing was that the work camp was in the restricted area that I wasn't sup-posed to enter.

After my time was up, they gave me a bus ticket back to Spokane. I continued my work where I left off, with

---

rationing (rash′ən ing) *n.* government limits on portions or shares.

This photograph by Dorothea Lange shows a sandstorm at the Manzanar camp in July 1942.

a feeling that I might as well settle in for the duration now. After one month, I got a special questionnaire from my draft board, which they had <u>concocted</u> for persons of Japanese ancestry. This one had the usual Selective Service questions that I had filled in already, plus these additional questions that demanded that you agree to serve in the military and <u>renounce</u> any loyalty to the emperor of Japan. This was like, Have you stopped beating your wife? If you never had a loyalty to Japan, how could you renounce it? So I wrote to my draft board and asked if they were sending this to all sorts of Americans of various ancestries, or only to those of Japanese ancestry. I never got a response, and I waited for a reasonable time and put my response in. I told them the questions were a form of racial discrimina-

tion and that as an American citizen I can't support that. So I'm returning this unfilled.

Then I got an order to report for a physical. I ignored it, and then I got another order to report for induction in Oregon. When that date came, I didn't show up. Later on, when I went to prison for this for a year, I met some guys who had walked out of the CO camps. They said, When we were in the army base in Oregon we saw your name on the list of those who were reporting for induction. So we went down to the station that morning to welcome you, and when the train came in and you didn't get off, we let out a great cheer! I could have fought that case on appeal, because I was subject to the draft on the basis of ancestry, but by that time I was tired of court cases.

---

concocted (kon kok′tid) *v.t.* put together; devised.
312   **renounce** (ri nouns′) *v.t.* give up or abandon, especially by formal declaration.

When I came out of prison, the war had just finished, and so I was released to Seattle. I had been married just before I went in, and my wife and twin daughters in their little baskets were waiting for me at the dock from McNeil Island, where the prison was. Although I had four mouths to feed by then, I thought I should first complete my bachelor's degree at the University of Washington, feeling that whatever I went into, a degree would come in handy. I completed my degree that year, and then I went on to graduate school in sociology and I finished my Ph.D. in 1952.

As my first appointment, I accepted an assistant professorship at the American University of Beirut in Lebanon. I had a strong feeling of wanting international experience and that was the first teaching job I could find. I was there for three years, and then I taught in Cairo until 1959, about four years. So for most of the 1950s I was in the Arab Middle East. I came back to North America for family reasons, primarily. My kids were getting to junior-high age, and I felt they should have continuity in high school, although we all appreciated the international schooling background for the early years. I finally accepted an offer at the University of Alberta, in Canada, since it was the most attractive offer. I have been there ever since, so I guess we have liked it personally and as a family. In 1983, the

Upon arrival at the detention camps, detainees were lined up and searched.

year during which I became 65, I retired at the end of the academic year and took an emeritus position.

After the Supreme Court decided my case in 1943, there was always a continuous hope and interest on my part that the case could be reviewed at some point. Not being a lawyer, I didn't know exactly what my options were. During the time I was overseas I didn't spend much time looking into that possibility, but during the latter part of the sixties and beginning of the seventies I had discussions with law professors at the University of California, but they couldn't find anything promising. And later I talked with a judge who suggested that I move to quash the charges in my case. The courts would have to look at that motion and in that process we might get a kind of hearing.

I shared that idea with a few others, but nothing came of it. I had certain feelings of finality about my case. You know, while I'm hoping as a layman that something can be done, well, the Supreme Court is the Supreme Court. That's the end, and when they have made a decision, there aren't many ways open to reverse it. It wasn't until Peter Irons called me from Boston in 1981, saying that he had discovered some documents that might present an opportunity under a rarely used legal device to petition for a rehearing, that I felt there was a chance. I said to him, I've been waiting over forty years for this kind of a phone call. So he arranged to fly out to Edmonton, and

eventually we got a legal team organized that filed a petition in the federal court in Seattle to vacate my conviction.

My petition was filed in January 1983 and we had a two-week evidentiary hearing in June 1985. Judge Donald Voorhees, who presided over the case, impressed me as a very fair judge. He was obviously interested in the case and well-informed about the evidence. Naturally, I was delighted that he ruled that my exclusion order conviction had been <u>tainted</u> by government misconduct. But I was disappointed that he upheld the curfew conviction, and we appealed that. The government also appealed on the exclusion order. We had arguments before the <u>appellate</u> judges in March 1987, and they handed down a unanimous opinion in September, upholding Judge Voorhees on the exclusion order and also striking down the curfew conviction. So I finally got the <u>vindication</u> that I had wanted for forty years, although I'm a little disappointed that the Supreme Court didn't have a chance to overrule the decision they made in 1943.

When my case was before the Supreme Court in 1943, I fully expected that as a citizen the Constitution would protect me. Surprisingly, even though I lost, I did not abandon my beliefs and values. And I never look at my case as just my own, or just as a Japanese American case. It is an *American* case, with principles that affect the fundamental human rights of all Americans.

---

tainted (tān′tid) *v.i.* spoiled, blemished, or damaged.

appellate (ə pel′it) *adj.* having the power to hear and rule on legal appeals and to review the decisions of lower courts.

vindication (vin′di kā′shən) *n.* state of being cleared of charges of wrongdoing.

MEET PETER IRONS

Would you be willing to go to jail for your beliefs? As a young man, Peter Irons did. Because he refused, for religious reasons, to carry a draft card and would not apply for conscientious objector status, he was sentenced to three years in a federal penitentiary. After appealing his case and losing, he accepted his jail term.

Irons served more than two years of his sentence, and the experience left him angry with the judge who had dismissed his legal arguments. But he decided to turn his anger toward a positive end.

After his release from prison, he earned a Ph.D. in Political Science and went on to attend Harvard Law School. During his law training, the Supreme Court ruled that the reasons for his jail sentence had, in fact, been unlawful. His conviction was erased, but by that time, Irons had become devoted to helping others achieve their constitutional rights.

"Am I an American?" is an excerpt from Peter Irons's *The Courage of Their Convictions*, a collection of sixteen true stories about a diverse group of American men and women who courageously took their fight for constitutional liberties all the way to the Supreme Court.

The background photograph is of the Supreme Court Building in Washington, D.C.

RESPONDING TO *Literature*

THINK • TALK • WRITE

1 Did you admire Gordon Hirabayashi? Explain why you did or did not. Jot down some thoughts in your journal.

2 Hirabayashi says, "I wrote out a statement explaining the reasons I was refusing evacuation." What might have been some of these reasons? Be as specific as possible.

3 How do Hirabayashi's parents feel about his decision to resist? How might you have felt if you were in their position?

4 Why did Hirabayashi not fill out the special questionnaire the draft board mailed to him? How do you think he would have responded to the draft if there had been no questionnaire? Give details from the story to support your opinion.

5 The events of this story occur because of ignorance about a minority's culture. Do you think this is an unusual situation? Can you name other real-life examples? Describe them.

ACTIVITIES

• **Write About Persuasion** Write a persuasive essay supporting or opposing Gordon Hirabayashi's position on the exclusion order. Remember to support your position with logic and examples.

• **Make a Poster** Choose a cause you really believe in. Make a poster that will convince others to share your opinion. Display your work.

VOCABULARY PRACTICE

On a separate sheet of paper, write the word that is *least* like the other words in each row.

violate   complied
implications   concurrently
remorse   concocted
curfew   renounce
subpoenaed   tainted

1 complied   agreed   argued
2 tainted   pure   clean
3 violate   disobey   welcome
4 subpoenaed   ordered   suggested
5 renounce   abandon   seize
6 implications   suggestions   failures
7 remorse   anger   regret
8 concocted   revealed   planned
9 concurrently   together   alone
10 curfew   regulation   acceptance

IN RESPONSE TO EXECUTIVE ORDER 9066: All Americans of Japanese Descent Must Report to Relocation Centers

Dear Sirs:
Of course I'll come. I've packed my galoshes
and three packets of tomato seeds. Denise calls them
love apples. My father says where we're going
they won't grow.

I am a fourteen-year-old girl with bad spelling
and a messy room. If it helps any, I will tell you
I have always felt funny using chopsticks
and my favorite food is hot dogs.
My best friend is a white girl named Denise—
we look at boys together. She sat in front of me
all through grade school because of our names:
O'Connor, Ozawa. I know the back of Denise's head very well.

I tell her she's going bald. She tells me I copy on tests.
We're best friends.

I saw Denise today in Geography class.   ■ by Dwight Okita ■
She was sitting on the other side of the room.
"You're trying to start a war," she said, "giving secrets
away to the Enemy. Why can't you keep your big
mouth shut?"

I didn't know what to say.
I gave her a packet of tomato seeds
and asked her to plant them for me, told her
when the first tomato ripened
she'd miss me.

Barracks   1944   Taneyuki Dan Harada   The Michael Brown Collection

S P on O T

BIOGRAPHY

Portrait photographer Yousuf Karsh once said, "There is a brief moment when all that there is in a man's mind and soul and spirit may be reflected through his eyes, his hands, his attitude. This is the moment to record. This is the elusive 'moment of truth.'" How do these words apply to the subject of the portrait below?

Martin Luther King, Jr. Thomas Blackshear Smithsonian Institution

What do you know about the person depicted above? What can you guess about him based on what you see?

Think about other portraits you have seen. How did the artists reveal their subjects? Now think about biographies you have read. How did the writers reveal their subjects? What do portraits and biographies have in common?

LIGHT

ELEMENTS OF A BIOGRAPHY

A biography is the true story of a real person's life written by someone else. Here are some important parts of a biography.

SUBJECT is the person whose life a biography presents. The subject of a biography may be famous or little known and alive or dead, but he or she is always someone who has actually lived.

CHARACTERIZATION is the way the writer brings the subject to life.

- *Direct characterization* takes place when the writer describes how the subject looks, acts, and thinks.
- *Indirect characterization* takes place when the writer lets you draw your own conclusions about a subject. For example, he or she may show you other people's reactions to the subject.

CONFLICT in literature is a clash between opposing forces. The biographer often describes how the subject deals with a conflict, which may be internal or external.

- *Internal conflict* exists within the subject's mind, like the struggle to make a hard decision.
- *External conflict* occurs between the subject and another person or a force of nature.

CHRONOLOGICAL ORDER is the order in which events in a biography usually unfold. Typically the biographer traces the subject's life from beginning to end.

SOURCES OF INFORMATION are the materials from which the biographer obtains details about the subject's life. These sources often include letters, diaries, books by and about the subject, and interviews.

AUTHOR'S POINT OF VIEW is the biographer's attitude toward the subject. For example, this point of view can be admiring or critical and is usually conveyed by the writer's choice of words and presentation of details.

In the selections that follow, you will read about the lives of some famous people. What you learn will help you to understand and enjoy this important type of literature and to write a biography yourself.

BIOGRAPHY

ELEANOR ROOSEVELT: ON HER OWN

CONNECT TO LITERATURE

Have you ever seen a person being treated unfairly? Did you decide to do something about it? Was it difficult? What were your feelings? Write in your journal about what happened. Then, as you read "Eleanor Roosevelt: On Her Own," compare your experience with Eleanor Roosevelt's as she fights for human rights.

INTRODUCTION TO THE MODEL BIOGRAPHY

When you read the biographies in this unit, you will find that they have several things in common. For one thing, they are the stories of real people's lives as told by others. In addition, each biography has informational sources, an author's point of view, and events presented in chronological order.

As you read "Eleanor Roosevelt: On Her Own," use the notes in the margin. The notes will help you to see the structure of a biography and show you how the basic elements of the biography are connected to each other.

DID YOU KNOW?

Eleanor Roosevelt was a very unusual First Lady. In addition to performing the usual White House social duties, she found time to write extensively and work for legislation that would improve living conditions for many Americans. Mrs. Roosevelt also lectured widely and traveled on many humanitarian missions.

After President Roosevelt's death in 1945, Mrs. Roosevelt served as a delegate to the United Nations until 1951; she returned to the United Nations in 1961 at the request of President Kennedy.

Eleanor Roosevelt died in 1962 and was buried in Hyde Park, New York, next to her husband.

Eleanor Roosevelt
On Her Own

by Russell Freedman

"Life has got to be lived—that's all there is to it."

"The story is over," Eleanor Roosevelt told a reporter shortly after her husband's death. With FDR gone, she doubted that she could play much of a role in the postwar world.

It was hard to accept Franklin's absence after a forty-year marriage. Writing to Joseph Lash, her friend and biographer, she said, "I want to cling to those I love because I find that mentally I counted so much on Franklin I feel a bit bereft."

She was sixty years old and on her own. As she came to terms with her loss, she realized that the world was watching. The story was far from over. "I did not want to cease trying to be useful in some way," she wrote. "I did not want to feel old. . . ."

The new president came to Eleanor Roosevelt for advice. Harry Truman valued her insider's knowledge of Washington and was mindful of her influence. He wanted her on his side as he tried to fill FDR's gigantic shoes.

When Japan surrendered on August 14, 1945, ending World War II, Truman personally called Mrs. Roosevelt in Hyde Park to give her the news. Later he asked her to serve as one of five American delegates to the first meeting of the United Nations General Assembly, to be held in London that winter. Eleanor hesitated. She told the president that she had no real experience in foreign affairs and knew little about parliamentary procedure. But her friends urged her to accept, and finally she did, beginning "one of the most wonderful and worthwhile experiences in my life." She believed that the United Nations was FDR's most important legacy. Her appointment as a delegate was a tribute to him, she said.

The other American delegates were men: Secretary of State James F. Byrnes; Senator Tom Connally of Texas; Senator Arthur H. Vandenberg of Michigan; and Edward R. Stettinius, Jr., who was the

---

bereft (bi reft´) *adj.* deprived.

legacy (leg´ə sē) *n.* something handed down from the past.

appointment (ə point´mənt) *n.* act of naming someone to an office or position, or the state of having been named.

tribute (trib´ūt) *n.* anything done, given, or observed as a sign of devotion.

Eleanor Roosevelt with her "crowning achievement," the Universal Declaration of Human Rights

United States representative on the United Nations Security Council. They were not especially happy with their female colleague, dismissing her as an emotional, rattlebrained woman. Without her knowledge, these four gentlemen met and assigned Mrs. Roosevelt to Committee Three, which would deal with <u>humanitarian</u>, educational, and cultural questions. She imagined them saying, "Ah, here's the safe spot for her—Committee Three. She can't do much harm there!" She assumed that they wanted to keep her away from committees dealing with political and economic matters simply because she was a woman. "I kept my thoughts to myself and humbly agreed to serve where I was asked to serve," she wrote.

When the London session got under way, Eleanor Roosevelt quickly became known as the hardest-working and best-informed member of the American delegation. Nothing could make her miss a meeting. When King George and Queen Elizabeth invited her to Buckingham Palace for lunch, she accepted gracefully. But she told them that she would have to leave early to attend a subcommittee meeting.

To everyone's surprise, Committee Three, Mrs. Roosevelt's "safe spot," turned out to be a hotbed of

The attitude toward their subjects, which authors convey through their writing, is called the author's **point of view.**

■

humanitarian (hū man'i târ'ē ən) *adj.* concerned with or promoting the general welfare of humanity.

controversy. The end of the war in Europe had left more than a million <u>refugees</u> stranded in displaced person's camps. The Soviet Union insisted on forced repatriation—all displaced persons must be returned to their homelands. Yet many of the refugees from eastern Europe were opponents of the Communist regimes that were seizing power in their countries. They feared that forced repatriation would mean imprisonment or death. The United States and other Western nations supported the right of political asylum—allowing refugees to choose their own homes. The issue of refugee repatriation landed in the lap of Committee Three.

Since that was Mrs. Roosevelt's committee, it was up to her to speak for the United States. Her opponent in the General Assembly debate would be Andrei Vishinsky, the head of the Soviet delegation, one of Russia's great legal minds, and a powerful <u>orator</u>. "I was badly frightened," Eleanor recalled. "I trembled at the thought of speaking against the famous Mr. Vishinsky."

By quoting her directly, Freedman reveals Eleanor Roosevelt's personality in a way that makes her seem more "real."

As she had done so many times before at lectures and press conferences, Mrs. Roosevelt spoke without notes when she addressed the delegates of the UN's original fifty-one member nations. Afterward Andrei Vishinsky delivered a fiery speech that lasted late into the night. Finally the General Assembly voted against forced repatriation. The refugees were free to choose their own homes.

The vote was a political triumph for the United States and a personal victory for Eleanor Roosevelt. The tall lady in the flowered hat had <u>emerged</u> as the world's foremost spokesperson for human rights. Her fellow American delegates, who had opposed her appointment, now had to eat their words. As Senator Vandenberg put it: "I want to say that I take back everything I ever said about her, and believe me it's been plenty."

Mrs. Roosevelt had helped determine the fate of thousands of displaced persons, yet she had never

---

refugees (ref'yủ jēz') *n., pl.* people who flee to safety or refuge, especially those who leave home or homeland because of persecution, war, or danger and seek safety in another place.

orator (ôr'ə tər) *n.* skilled public speaker.

emerged (i mûrjd') *v.i.* came into being or notice.

Eleanor Roosevelt listening at the UN

seen a refugee camp. When her fellow delegates returned home at the end of the UN session, she flew to
Germany on an Air Force plane and visited several
camps. One of them was Zilcheim, where Jewish sur-
vivors of Nazi death camps had built a stone monument inscribed "To the Memory of All Jews Who Died
in Germany."

    As she toured the camp, a ragged boy about
twelve years old approached with his little brother,
who was about six. He did not know his own name,
where his home was, or what had happened to his
parents. He wanted to sing for her, he said, so Eleanor
and her guides stopped to listen. Standing in the mud,
gripping his brother's hand, the youngster lifted his
head and sang "A Song of Freedom."

rs. Roosevelt served as a UN delegate throughout Truman's two terms as president. During those years of Cold War suspicion and hostility, she held firm to her belief that a strong United Nations was the best hope for a lasting peace.

In 1946, she was elected chair of the United Nations' eighteen-member Human Rights Commission, which had been instructed to draft an international bill of rights. The commission's task was to define the basic rights of people all over the world, such as the right to free speech and a fair trial, or the right to an education and a decent standard of living. During the next two years Mrs. Roosevelt proved herself a skillful diplomat as she <u>mediated</u> among the clashing views of delegates from different nations and cultures, each with its own ideas about the meaning of "human rights."

Details such as these are the methods of **characterization** authors use to reveal their subjects.

When the commission fell behind in its work, she drove her colleagues mercilessly, insisting on fourteen- and sixteen-hour days. The delegate from Panama begged Mrs. Roosevelt to remember that UN delegates have human rights, too. She replied that their sessions would be shorter if their speeches weren't so long-winded.

It was in 1945 that Truman appointed Mrs. Roosevelt to serve as a delegate to the UN. Biographies often present events in the order in which they happened in time. This method of organizing material is called **chronological order.**

On December 10, 1948, at three A.M., the Universal Declaration of Human Rights finally came to a vote and was overwhelmingly approved by the United Nations General Assembly. Then something happened that never happened at the UN before or since. The delegates rose to give a standing <u>ovation</u> to a single delegate—a moving tribute to Eleanor Roosevelt's leadership.

Expressed as Mrs. Roosevelt wanted, in simple and <u>eloquent</u> <u>prose</u>, the Universal Declaration has now been published in the native languages of all countries. To this day, it stands as the most widely recognized statement of the rights to which every person on this planet is entitled.

---

mediated (mē′dē ā′tid) *v.t.* settled (differences or disputes) by coming between and working with disagreeing or opposing parties.
ovation (ō vā′shən) *n.* enthusiastic burst of applause.
eloquent (el′ə kwənt) *adj.* having or showing the ability to use language effectively.
prose (prōz) *n.* everyday written or spoken language that is not like poetry.

Meet
RUSSELL FREEDMAN

After growing up in San Francisco and graduating from the University of California at Berkeley, Russell Freedman (born 1929) served in the Korean War. Upon discharge from the service, he worked as a reporter and writer for the Associated Press and then as a television publicist. In 1961 Freedman published his first book and since then has been a full-time writer. The author of over thirty-nine books on a variety of subjects, Freedman won the Newbery Medal in 1988 for *Lincoln: A Photobiography*; in 1992 *The Wright Brothers: How They Invented the Airplane* was named a Newbery Honor Book. *Eleanor Roosevelt: A Life of Discovery*, from which this excerpt is taken, received a 1994 Boston Globe–Horn Book Award for Nonfiction.

More Biographies by Russell Freedman

- *Lincoln: A Photobiography* (Clarion, 1987). Using photographs and prints from the period and a sampler of Lincoln's own words, Freedman has created a moving portrait of the man who presided over a divided nation and led it to "form a more perfect union."

- *Kids at Work: Lewis Hines and the Crusade Against Child Labor* (Clarion, 1994). Before the child-labor laws were enacted, many children—some as young as five—worked twelve-hour shifts, six days a week. Hines, a photographer, set out to document their plight and to bring the issue to the public's attention. Many of his powerful photographs have been used to illustrate this book.

- *The Wright Brothers: How They Invented the Airplane* (Holiday House, 1991). Wilbur and Orville Wright photographed each step of the process as they built the first airplane. These photos are included in the biography and add a special note of authenticity to their story.

RESPONDING TO Literature

THINK • TALK • WRITE

1 What do you most admire about Eleanor Roosevelt? Jot down your opinion and some supporting details in your journal.

2 How do the other members of the U.S. delegation to the United Nations feel about Mrs. Roosevelt at first? Why does Senator Vandenberg say later, "I take back everything I ever said about her, and believe me it's been plenty"?

3 Eleanor Roosevelt helped many people through her work at the United Nations. How do you think her time there might have helped her personally?

4 Why do you think the author might have chosen to include the incident with the boy in the refugee camp?

5 Eleanor Roosevelt was very concerned about the refugees from World War II. Use a newspaper to find stories about refugees in the world today. What impact has war had on the cultures of these countries?

ACTIVITY

• **Write About Biography** Copy and complete the time line below. Fill it in with events from "Eleanor Roosevelt: On Her Own."

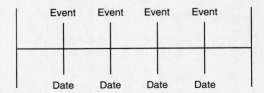

VOCABULARY PRACTICE

On a separate sheet of paper, write the vocabulary word that is closest in meaning to each italicized word.

bereft	refugees
legacy	mediated
appointment	ovation
tribute	eloquent
humanitarian	prose

1 Eleanor's *bequest* was to those who are *deprived* of hope.

2 Her *naming* was a *compliment* to her *kindly* instincts.

3 She *negotiated* the argument about war's *victims*.

4 Her declaration is written in *beautiful writing*.

5 The *applause* recognized her accomplishment.

328

BIOGRAPHY

·······································

CRISPUS ATTUCKS

CONNECT TO LITERATURE

Can one person really make a difference in history? What does a person have to do in order to be remembered? Share your ideas with a classmate. As you read "Crispus Attucks," note in your journal how Crispus Attucks made a difference in American history.

THINKING ABOUT SETTING

"Crispus Attucks" takes place in Boston in the eighteenth century. Visualizing this *setting* is important to understanding fully the events described in the selection. In those days, Boston was not a large, modern city; it was a town of wooden houses and narrow, unlit streets. Most communication happened by word of mouth, which made it easy for rumors to spread and grow.

The Boston Massacre happened at night. In the darkness and confusion, some people probably became frightened. As you read, picture the setting and think about how it affected the events of the story.

DID YOU KNOW?

The first slaves were brought to Britain's North American colonies in 1619. For the next two hundred years, slaves worked in northern factories just as they did on southern plantations. At the beginning of the eighteenth century, one in every five slaves worked in the North. Except in Massachusetts, where slaves possessed certain legal protections, the slave codes in the northern colonies were much like those of the South. Several major slave rebellions took place in the northern colonies.

In the late eighteenth century, after the American Revolution, the North began to abolish slavery, until by 1820 all slaves living in the northern states were free. Slavery now existed only in the South, setting the stage for the Civil War some four decades later.

Crispus Attucks

by Jim Haskins

"**R**AN-away from his master *William Brown* of *Framingham*, on the 30th of Sept. last, a Molatto Fellow, about 27 Years of Age, named *Crispas*, 6 Feet two Inches high, short curl'd Hair, his Knees nearer together than common; had on a light colour'd Bearskin Coat, plain brown Fustian Jacket, or Brown all-Wool one, new Buckskin Breeches, blue YarnStockings, and a check'd woollenShirt.

Whoever shall take up said Runaway, and convey him to his abovesaid Master, shall have *ten Pounds*, old TenorReward, and all necessary Charges paid. And allMasters of Vessels and others, are hereby caution'd against concealing or carrying off saidServant on Penalty of the Law."

Boston Gazette, October 2, 1750

IN 1770 CRISPUS ATTUCKS, a black man born a slave, was the first American to die in the cause of the American Revolution. As the advertisement shows, he had already declared his own independence twenty years earlier.

Little is known about Crispus's early life. He was born into slavery, probably in the colony of Massachusetts. It is said that his father was African, and if so then his father was brought to the colonies on a slave ship. Crispus's mother was said to be an Indian and was probably a descendant of John Attucks.

John Attucks was a member of the Natick Indian tribe, and the word *attuck* in the language of the Naticks means "deer." John Attucks lived in the 1600s and converted to Christianity. But during an Indian uprising that came to be known as King Philip's War, he sided with his own people. He was executed by New England colonists for treason in 1676.

Crispus was born some fifty years after that. We do not know anything about his upbringing, only that by 1750 he was a slave who belonged to a William Brown of Framingham.

According to local legend in Framingham, Attucks was an expert trader of horses and cattle, and dealt with free white men all the time. He kept the money he made for himself and probably tried to buy his freedom from William Brown. But Brown would not sell him his freedom, perhaps because Crispus was too valuable to him. So Crispus ran away.

In spite of the ad, Crispus was never caught and sent back to his master. No one knows what he did for the next twenty years. More than likely, he spent those years as a sailor, working on cargo ships that sailed to and from the West Indies, and on whaling ships off the New England coast.

During those same twenty years, trouble had arisen between England and her far-off colonies on the eastern coast of North America. Citizens of the colonies resented having to buy nearly everything they needed from England and complained about the lack of free trade. The colonies also complained of having to pay taxes to the king when they had no say in their own government.

Citizens of the colony of Massachusetts, especially in Boston, the capital of the colony, were the most outspoken in their complaints about British tyranny. So restive was that colony that in 1768 the British king, George III, decided to send in troops to occupy Boston. The king's hope was that the troops would calm down Boston and also serve as a warning to other colonies not to make trouble.

Two regiments, totaling about 1,000 soldiers, from British posts in Canada sailed into Boston Harbor on six warships in the late fall of 1769. The first ever sent to the colonies in peacetime, the troops marched ashore and took over the Customs House on King Street (now State Street). They set up tents on Boston Common and proceeded to anger the local citizens by stopping and searching innocent people. What made the citizens even angrier was that the city of Boston and the colony of Massachusetts were ordered to pay for the board and lodging of the very troops that had been sent to occupy their city.

As word spread outside Boston that 1,000 British troops were occupying the city of about 15,000 people, men and boys from the surrounding countryside began to make their way to the city. They were not an organized opposition, but they were united in their anger.

MEANWHILE, THE PEOPLE OF BOSTON were equally upset. There were minor incidents between the soldiers and the citizens. Snowballs with stones in the centers were thrown at the soldiers, but the soldiers were under orders not to fire their guns. In fact, most of the guns were not even loaded. But they used their bayonets to beat whoever attacked them, and sometimes to beat innocent bystanders.

Two incidents occurred in early 1770 that increased tensions in Boston. In early February a large crowd attacked a Boston man who was known to be friendly to the British. They chased him into his house, and then began to batter down his door with sticks and clubs. The man grabbed his musket and shot into the crowd, killing a twelve-year-old boy named Christopher Snider. The crowd tried to kill the man, but soldiers intervened and took him to jail.

About a month later, on March 2, a British soldier named Killroy walked into a rope maker's shop and asked for a part-time job. The owner wasn't there, but a rope maker named Samuel Gray was. To a

---

tyranny (tir'ə nē) *n.* cruel and unjust use of force, power, or authority.
restive (res'tiv) *adj.* stubborn and difficult to manage; unruly.
board (bôrd) *n.* meals provided regularly for pay.
lodging (loj'ing) *n.* rented room or rooms.

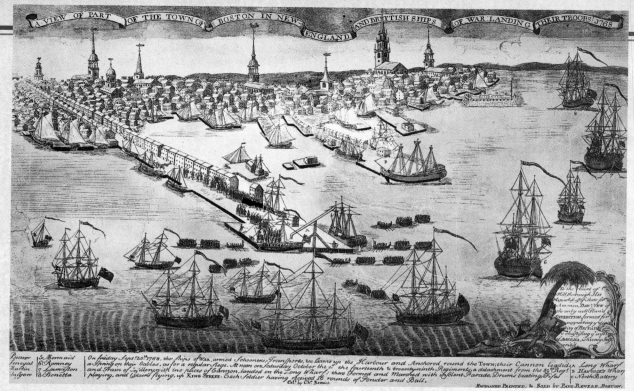

Landing of British Troops at Boston, Massachusetts, October 1, 1768 to enforce Writs of Assistance *1770 Paul Revere Granger Collection*

man, the rope makers of Boston hated the British soldiers, and Killroy and Gray got into a fight. Other rope makers joined in the beating of Killroy.

When Killroy returned to his barracks, he told his fellow soldiers what had happened. They grabbed sticks and swords and went out after the rope makers, who fought back with iron bars, lengths of rope, and sticks. The wild fight was finally broken up by Boston police and ordinary citizens.

Crispus Attucks was in Boston at that time. A slave named Andrew later said that Attucks had been living in New Providence, in the British colony of the Bahamas, and was in Boston "in order to go [to] North Carolina." The slave Andrew described Attucks as "stout," and since he was over six feet tall he must have been a commanding presence. According to some reports, he was eating supper at a local inn the night of Monday, March 5, when he heard fire alarms and rushed into the street to see what was happening.

Clashes between soldiers and citizens were occurring in several areas that night. A crowd of young men and boys were battling with soldiers on Brattle Street. Around the same time, on King Street, a

---

barracks (bar′əks) *n.* building or set of buildings for housing soldiers or other military personnel.

The BLOODY MASSACRE perpetrated in King—t Street BOSTON on March 5th 1770 by a party of the 29th REGt.

BUTCHER'S HALL

Engrav'd Printed & Sold by PAUL REVERE BOSTON

Unhappy Boston! see thy Sons deplore,
Thy hallow'd Walks besmear'd with guiltless Gore,
While faithless P——n and his savage Bands,
With murdrous Rancour stretch their bloody Hands,
Like fierce Barbarians grinning o'er their Prey,
Approve the Carnage and enjoy the Day.

If scalding drops from Rage from Anguish Wrung,
If speechless Sorrows lab'ring for a Tongue,
Or if a weeping World can ought appease
The plaintive Ghosts of Victims such as these;
The Patriot's copious Tears for each are shed,
A glorious Tribute which embalms the Dead.

But know, Fate summons to that awful Goal,
Where Justice strips the Murd'rer of his Soul;
Should venal C——ts the scandal of the Land,
Snatch the relentless Villain from her Hand,
Keen Execrations on this Plate inscrib'd,
Shall reach a Judge who never can be brib'd.

The unhappy Sufferers were Messrs. Saml. GRAY, Saml. MAVERICK, Jams. CALDWELL, CRISPUS ATTUCKS & Patk. CARR
Killed. Six wounded; two of them (CHRISTr. MONK & JOHN CLARK) Mortally

Boston Massacre, March 5, 1770 *1770 Paul Revere Granger Collection*

British private named Hugh Montgomery hit a barber's <u>apprentice</u> in the face after the boy had insulted a British captain. The boy ran through the streets shouting that he had been "killed."

Someone set fire bells ringing, and Crispus Attucks left his supper to investigate.

He made his way to Dock Square, where a large crowd had gathered. Seeing that the people were <u>milling about</u> aimlessly, he picked up a large stick and shouted to the people to follow him to King Street, where the main guard of the British army was stationed. The crowd followed him to the Customs House, where Private Hugh Montgomery had taken up his post as guard.

Some of the boys in the crowd began to taunt Montgomery, whose musket wasn't loaded. The frightened private called for reinforcements, yelling, "Turn out, main guard!" Captain Preston, who

---

apprentice (ə pren′tis) *n.* person who works for a skilled worker in order to learn a trade or art.
milling about moving in an aimless or confused manner.

was in charge of the guardhouse that day, ordered seven soldiers to go out and help Montgomery. One of them was Private Killroy, who had been beaten by the rope makers. The soldiers used their bayonets as clubs to cut through the crowd and drive it back. Seeing that the crowd was in no mood to retreat, the soldiers loaded their muskets.

The crowd had swelled, as nearly everyone in Boston heard that something was happening on King Street. Samuel Gray, the rope maker, was among those who joined the increasingly unruly mob.

Standing at the front of the crowd was Crispus Attucks. According to the slave named Andrew, who was at the scene, the crowd was crying, "They dare not fire, we are not afraid of them." Attucks threw himself into the group of soldiers, said Andrew, and struck at Captain Preston. A group of men followed him, yelling, "Kill the dogs, knock them over."

The soldiers fired. Crispus Attucks was the first to fall, hit by two musket balls. Four other men died: Samuel Gray, the rope maker; James Caldwell, a ship's mate; Samuel Maverick, an apprentice joiner (furniture maker); and Patrick Carr, identified only as an Irishman. Six others in the crowd were wounded, but later recovered.

The next day, the bodies of Attucks and Caldwell were taken to Faneuil Hall, because neither man had a home in Boston. Two days after that, all the shops in the city were closed for the public funeral for the five victims. Thousands of people flocked in from the countryside, and the *Boston Gazette* reported that the funeral was attended by the largest crowd ever assembled in North America.

The coffins of Attucks and Caldwell were carried to meet the hearses with the other coffins on King Street. All the bells in the city tolled in the dead men's honor. There was a long procession to the cemetery, where they were all buried together in one grave.

While some called Attucks and the others heroes, others called them villains. But everyone agreed that Crispus Attucks was the main actor in the event, a stranger who had stepped forward to lead the attack on the soldiers.

The soldiers were placed on trial for the murders of the five citizens. In the bill of indictment that the court brought against the soldiers, the main section was devoted to Attucks, presenting his name first and separately from those of the other victims and charging

---

hearses (hûr′sɘz) *n., pl.* vehicles for carrying dead people from one place to another before or after a funeral service.

that he had been assaulted "with force and arms, <u>feloniously</u>, willfully, and of <u>malice</u> aforethought."

John Adams was one of the lawyers for the defense. He would become the second president of the United States, but at the time he was loyal to the king of England. He, too, focused on Attucks, saying that it was to his "mad behavior [that], in all probability, the dreadful <u>carnage</u> of that night is chiefly <u>ascribed</u>." Adams claimed that the soldiers had every right to fear the "stout mulatto fellow, whose very looks was enough to terrify any person."

John Adams

Captain Preston was found not guilty, since the court ruled that he had acted to protect his troops. Two soldiers were found guilty. As punishment, they were branded in the hand with a hot iron. Those who were against the British did not believe that justice had been done.

Clashes between British soldiers and colonists continued. King George III kept <u>levying</u> taxes upon the colonies without giving them a voice in their own government. Within three years, John Adams had changed his mind and no longer supported the king. He had also changed his mind about Crispus Attucks and the event he called the Boston Massacre.

On a Monday in July 1773, Adams wrote in his diary a letter to Governor Thomas Hutchinson of Massachusetts. He may have intended to publish it. He wrote it as if it had come from Crispus Attucks:

> *You will hear from Us with Astonishment. You ought to hear from Us with Horror. You are chargeable before God and Man, with our Blood. The Soldiers were but passive Instruments, were Machines, neither moral nor voluntary Agents in our Destruction more than the leaden Pelletts, with which we were wounded.—You was a free Agent. You acted, coolly, deliberately, with all that premeditated Malice, not against Us in Particular but against the People in general, which in the sight of the law is an ingredient in the Composition of Murder. You will hear from Us hereafter.*

Adams signed the letter "Crispus Attucks."

---

feloniously (fə lo′nē əs lē) *adv.* in a manner of, relating to, or classified as a criminal act, designated by law to be more serious than a misdemeanor.

malice (mal′is) *n.* wish to cause harm, injury, or pain to another; spite.

carnage (kär′nij) *n.* great and bloody slaughter, as in battle.

ascribed (ə skrībd′) *v.t.* regarded (something) as coming from a particular source.

levying (lev′ē ing) *v.t.* imposing or collecting by force or authority.

Crispus Attucks

FIVE YEARS AFTER ATTUCKS'S DEATH, the battle of Lexington, with its "shot heard 'round the world," began the War of Independence. But even earlier Attucks's willingness to take a stand for liberty spurred the slaves of Massachusetts to petition for their freedom. Five separate petitions were presented to the governor, the House of Representatives, and the general court in 1773 and 1774. Unfortunately, none of these petitions was acted upon.

When colonial patriots gathered at Lexington and Concord, Massachusetts, to confront the redcoats from Boston in April 1775, black minutemen were among them. A slave from Lexington named Prince Easterbrooks was one of the first to be wounded at Lexington. Perhaps even more than the white patriots, these black patriots knew what the word *liberty* meant.

Crispus Attucks knew what liberty meant. In 1750 he had seized his own freedom by running away. Twenty years later, he had died fighting for a larger freedom—for himself and for others.

Blacks have honored Crispus Attucks ever since. After the Revolutionary War, black military companies took the name of Attucks Guards. From 1858 to 1870 blacks in Boston held annual Crispus Attucks Days. In 1888 they managed to get the city and state authorities to erect a Crispus Attucks monument on Boston Common. It was the earliest American public monument to a black man.

■
---
petition (pə tish′ən) *v.t.* make a formal request to a person in a position of authority.
confront (kən frunt′) *v.t.* face boldly or with defiance.

MEET Jim Haskins

Jim Haskins (born 1941) has written numerous books for young people. Among them are *The Story of Stevie Wonder,* which won the 1976 Coretta Scott King Award; *Black Dance in America: A History Through Its People,* which was named a Coretta Scott King Award Honor Book for Nonfiction; and *Black Music in America,* which won the Carter G. Woodson Award. A professor of English at the University of Florida at Gainesville, Haskins divides his time between New York City and Gainesville.

More Biographies About Freedom Fighters

- *Anthony Burns: The Defeat and Triumph of a Fugitive Slave* by Virginia Hamilton (Knopf, 1988). Anthony Burns was born a slave but died a free man—an achievement that cost him greatly both physically and emotionally. This is his triumphant story and the story of those who rallied to his cause.

- *Corazon Aquino* by Howard Chua-Eoan (Chelsea House, 1988). She never dreamed she would be president! Here are the fascinating facts behind the battle to restore democracy to the Philippines.

- *Brave Are My People: Indian Heroes Not Forgotten* by Frank Waters (Clear Light, 1993). Included in this collection are the biographies of Native American chiefs who made the difficult decision to lead their people into battle in order to preserve their historic hunting lands.

RESPONDING TO *Literature*

THINK • TALK • WRITE

1 What questions would you like to ask Crispus Attucks? Jot down some ideas in your journal.

2 Why did British soldiers fire at Crispus Attucks and the others on King Street? Do you sympathize with the soldiers? Can you understand why they reacted as they did? Explain your answers.

3 What do you think John Adams meant when he wrote that the British soldiers who killed Attucks were "but passive Instruments . . . neither moral nor voluntary Agents in our Destruction"? Do you agree? Why or why not?

4 What were some of the long-term effects of Attucks's death? How did his death influence other Americans?

5 What can you learn from this selection about the life of African Americans in the American colonies? Use story details to explain your answer.

ACTIVITIES

- **Write About Setting** Imagine you are writing a letter to a friend in Philadelphia right after the Boston Massacre. Use descriptive words to help your friend picture the scene.

- **Picture the Setting** Paul Revere made a famous drawing of the Boston Massacre. His picture isn't very accurate because he wanted to excite public opinion. Reread the selection carefully. Try to draw a more accurate picture of the events of the Boston Massacre.

VOCABULARY PRACTICE

On a separate sheet of paper, recopy the paragraph below. Replace the italicized words with synonyms from the vocabulary list.

tyranny	carnage
restive	ascribed
board	levying
lodging	petition
malice	confront

Many colonists hated British *domination*. Parliament was *ordering* new taxes, and would not accept a *request* from Boston citizens. In addition, Boston had to give *housing* and *meals* to British soldiers. The people of Boston were *uneasy*. They *attributed* terrible *spite* to the British. In the end, they felt they had to *face* the troops. Terrible *slaughter* was the result.

BIOGRAPHY

THE UNITED STATES VS. SUSAN B. ANTHONY

CONNECT TO LITERATURE

Have you ever wanted to do something you knew was right, but someone else wouldn't let you do it? How did you feel? What did you decide to do about the situation? In your journal, write about what happened. As you read this selection, compare your own reactions with Susan B. Anthony's as she fights an injustice.

THINKING ABOUT CHRONOLOGICAL ORDER

Chronological order means that events in a story are told in the same order in which they occurred in real life—the earliest events are described before the later ones. Most biographies are arranged in chronological order, because this makes it easier for readers to understand how one event led to another, and how the various events influenced the subject of the biography.

HAVE YOU EVER?

Have you ever wondered how American women won the right to vote? It began in 1848 with a convention held in Seneca Falls, New York, which called for equal rights for women, including suffrage—the right to vote. Led by women like Susan B. Anthony and Lucy Stone, a national movement spent decades fighting for women's suffrage. From 1878 on, a suffrage amendment was introduced into the U.S. Congress every year. The House of Representatives finally passed the amendment in 1918; the Senate passed it the following year. By 1920, enough states had approved the amendment for it to become law. The Nineteenth Amendment to the Constitution states: "The rights of citizens of the United States to vote shall not be denied or abridged by the United States or by any other state on account of sex."

THE UNITED STATES vs. SUSAN B. ANTHONY

BY MARGARET TRUMAN

Susan B. Anthony was a stern and single-minded woman. Like most crusaders for causes — especially unpopular causes — she had little time for fun and games. But I have a sneaky feeling that behind her severe manner and unremitting devotion to duty, she may actually have had a sense of humor. Let me tell you about my favorite episode in Susan B. Anthony's career, and perhaps you'll agree.

It began on Friday morning, November 1, 1872. Susan was reading the morning paper at her home in Rochester. There, at the top of the editorial page of the *Democrat and Chronicle*, was an <u>exhortation</u> to the city's residents:

Now register! Today and tomorrow are the only remaining opportunities. If you were not permitted to vote, you would fight for the right, undergo all privations for it, face death for it. You have it now at the cost of five minutes' time to be spent in seeking your place of registration and having your name entered. And yet, on election day, less than a week hence, hundreds of you are likely to lose your votes because you have not thought it worth while to give the five minutes. Today and tomorrow are your only opportunities. Register now!

Susan B. Anthony read the editorial again. Just as she thought, it said nothing about being addressed to men only. With a gleam in her eye, she put down the paper and summoned her sister Guelma, with whom she lived. The two women donned their hats and cloaks and went off to call on two other Anthony sisters who lived nearby. Together, the four women headed for the barber shop on West Street, where voters from the Eighth Ward were being registered.

For some time, Susan B. Anthony had been looking for an opportunity to test the Fourteenth Amendment to the Constitution as a weapon to win the vote for women. Adopted in 1870, the Amendment had been designed to protect the civil rights—especially the voting rights—of recently freed slaves. It stated that:

All persons born or naturalized in the United States, and subject to the jurisdiction thereof, are citizens of the United States and of the State wherein they reside. No State shall make or enforce any law which shall <u>abridge</u> the privileges or immunities of citizens of the United States, nor shall any State deprive any person of life, liberty, or property without due process of law, nor deny to any person within its jurisdiction the equal protection of the laws.

The Amendment did not say that "persons" meant only males, nor did it spell out "the privileges and immunities of citizens." Susan B. Anthony felt perfectly justified in concluding that the right to vote was among the privileges of citizenship and that it extended to women as well as men. I'm sure she must have also seen the humor of outwitting the supposedly superior males who wrote the Amendment.

It was bad enough for a bunch of women to barge into one sacred male precinct—the barber shop—but to insist on being admitted to another holy of holies—the voting booth—was absolutely outrageous. Moustaches twitched, throats were cleared, a whispered conference was held in the corner.

Susan had brought along a copy of the Fourteenth Amendment. She read it aloud, carefully pointing out to the men in charge of registration that the document failed to state that the privilege of voting extended only to males.

---

exhortation (eg′zôr tā′shən) *n.* act of trying to persuade by appeal, argument, or warning.
abridge (ə brij′) *v.t.* make less; lessen; restrict.

Only one man in the barber shop had the nerve to refuse the Anthony sisters the right to register. The rest buckled under Susan's determined oratory and allowed them to sign the huge, leather-bound voter registration book. If the men in the barber shop thought they were getting rid of a little band of crackpots the easy way, they were wrong. Susan urged all her followers in Rochester to register. The next day, a dozen women invaded the Eighth Ward barber shop, and another thirty-five appeared at registration sites elsewhere in the city. The *Democrat and Chronicle,* which had <u>inadvertently</u> prompted the registrations, expressed no editorial opinion on the phenomenon, but its rival, the *Union and Advertiser,* denounced the women. If they were allowed to vote, the paper declared, the poll inspectors "should be prosecuted to the full extent of the law."

The following Tuesday, November 5, was Election Day. Most of the poll inspectors in Rochester had read the editorial in the *Union and Advertiser* and were too intimidated to allow any of the women who had registered to vote. Only in the Eighth Ward did the males weaken. Maybe the inspectors were *Democrat and Chronicle* readers, or perhaps they were more afraid of Susan B. Anthony than they were of the law. Whatever the reason, when Susan and her sisters showed up at the polls shortly after 7 A.M., there was only a minimum of fuss. A couple of inspectors were hesitant about letting the women vote, but when Susan assured them that she would pay all their legal expenses if they were prosecuted, the men relented, and one by one,

the women took their ballots and stepped into the voting booth. There were no insults or sneers, no rude remarks. They marked their ballots, dropped them into the ballot box, and returned to their homes.

Susan B. Anthony's feat quickly became the talk of the country. She was applauded in some circles, <u>vilified</u> in others. But the day of reckoning was not long in arriving. On November 28, Deputy U.S. Marshal E. J. Keeney appeared at her door with a warrant for her arrest. She had violated Section 19 of the Enforcement Act of the Fourteenth Amendment, which held that anyone who voted illegally was to be arrested and tried on criminal charges.

Susan B. Anthony was a great believer in planning ahead. The day after she registered, she decided to get a legal opinion on whether or not she should attempt to vote. A number of lawyers turned her away, but she finally found one who agreed to consider the case. He was Henry R. Selden, a former judge of the Court of Appeals, now a partner in one of Rochester's most <u>prestigious</u> law firms.

On the Monday before Election Day, Henry Selden informed his new client that he agreed with her interpretation of the Fourteenth Amendment and that in his opinion, she had every right to cast her ballot. The U.S. Commissioner of Elections in Rochester, William C. Storrs, did not concur.

---

inadvertently (in′əd vûr′tənt lē) *adv.* in an accidental or unintended manner.
vilified (vil′ə fīd′) *v.t.* spoke or wrote evil of; slandered.
prestigious (pre stij′əs) *adj.* having or giving prestige; highly honored or respected.

The Apotheosis of Liberty *late 19th century Elizabeth Cady Stanton and Susan B. Anthony flank George Washington*

E. J. Keeney, the marshal <u>dispatched</u> to arrest Susan B. Anthony, was not at all happy with his assignment. He nervously twirled his tall felt hat while waiting for her to come to the front door. When she finally appeared, he blushed and stammered, shifted uncomfortably from one foot to another, and finally blurted out, "The Commissioner wishes to arrest you."

Susan couldn't help being amused at Keeney's embarrassment. "Is this your usual method of serving a warrant?" she asked calmly. With that, the marshal recovered his official dignity, presented her with the warrant, and told her that he had come to escort her to the office of the Commissioner of Elections.

When Susan asked if she could change into a more suitable dress, the marshal saw his opportunity to escape. "Of course," he said, turning to leave. "Just come down to the Commissioner's office whenever you're ready."

"I'll do no such thing," Susan informed him <u>curtly</u>. "You were sent here to arrest me and take me to court. It's your duty to do so."

Keeney had no choice but to wait while his prisoner went upstairs and put on a more appropriate outfit. When she returned, she thrust out her wrists and said, "Don't you want to handcuff me, too?"

"I assure you, madam," Marshal Keeney stuttered, "it isn't at all necessary."

With the U.S. Marshal at her side, Susan was brought before the Federal Commissioner of Elections, William C. Storrs. Her arrest was recorded, and she was ordered to appear the next day for a hearing. It was conducted by U.S. District Attorney Richard Crowley and his assistant, John E. Pound.

Susan answered District Attorney Crowley's questions politely. She said that she thought the Fourteenth Amendment gave her the right to vote. She admitted that she had consulted an attorney on the question but said that she would have voted even if he had not advised her to do so. When Crowley asked if she had voted deliberately to test the law, she said, "Yes, sir. I have been determined for three years to vote the first time I happened to be at home for the required thirty days before an election."

The District Attorney's next step was to <u>convene</u> a grand jury to draw up a bill of indictment. He and his assistant fell to wrangling over a suitable trial date. Susan interrupted them. "I have lecture dates that will take me to central Ohio," she said. "I won't be available until December 10."

---

dispatched (di spacht′) *v.t.* sent off quickly to a certain place or for a certain purpose.
curtly (kûrt′lē) *adv.* in a rudely brief or abrupt manner.
convene (kən vēn′) *v.t.* cause to assemble.

"But you're supposed to be in custody until the hearing," Crowley informed her.

"Is that so?" said Susan coolly. "I didn't know that."

The District Attorney backed down without an argument and scheduled the grand jury session for December 23.

Sixteen women had voted in Rochester. All sixteen were arrested and taken before the grand jury, but Susan alone was brought to trial. The District Attorney had decided to single her out as a test case. The three poll inspectors who had allowed the women to vote were also arrested. The grand jury indicted them too, set bail at five hundred dollars each, and ordered their trial set for the summer term of the U.S. District Court.

Susan Anthony's case now involved nineteen other men and women. All of them—including Susan—were liable to go to prison if they were found guilty and the judge was in a sentencing mood. Prison in the 1870s was a very unpleasant place. There were no minimum security setups where a benevolent government allowed corrupt politicians, crooked labor leaders, and political agitators to rest and rehabilitate, as we do today. Prison meant a cold cell, wretched food, the company of thieves and murderers.

For a while it looked as if Susan might be behind bars even before her trial. She refused to post a bond for her five-hundred-dollar bail. Henry Selden paid the money for her. "I could not see a lady I respected put in jail," he said.

It must be agonizing to sweat out the weeks before a trial. There is time to look ahead and brood about the possibility of an unfavorable verdict and time to look back, perhaps with regret, at the decision that placed you in the hands of the law. But Susan B. Anthony had no regrets. Nor did she appear to have any anxieties about her trial. She had already proven her fortitude by devoting twenty years of her life to fighting for the right to vote. If she won her case, the struggle would be over. But even if she lost, Susan was not ready to give up the fight.

Some prospective defendants are too demoralized to do anything but sit around and worry. Not Susan B. Anthony. In the course of the next few months, she attended woman's rights conventions in Ohio, Illinois, and Indiana. She appeared before a session that was meeting in Albany to revise the New York State Constitution and tried to persuade them to include equal suffrage among its provisions. Then she went back to Rochester to cast her ballot again in the city elections on March 4, 1873.

Deputy Marshal Keeney appeared at the railroad every time she left Rochester. He reminded her that she was not supposed to leave the city while she was out on bail. Susan would smile, nod, and get on the train. Keeney never tried to stop her.

The summer term of the District Court opened in May. In mid-March, Susan launched a new lecture tour. Her topic: Is it a crime for a citizen of the United States to vote? The lecture

---

benevolent (bə nev'ə lənt) *adj.* doing or desiring to do good; kindly; generous.
corrupt (kə rupt') *adj.* influenced by bribery; dishonest.
fortitude (fôr'ti tüd') *n.* courage or strength in the face of pain, danger, or misfortune.

centered on the U.S. Constitution, particularly the Fourteenth Amendment.

She spoke in every town in New York's Monroe County and drew surprisingly large audiences. When she polled the crowd at the end of each lecture, the majority <u>invariably</u> supported her. Even those who had been skeptics when they entered the hall usually changed their minds when they heard her arguments.

District Attorney Crowley soon decided that Susan was making it difficult for him to find an unprejudiced jury anywhere in the <u>vicinity</u> of Rochester. When he voiced his concern to Susan, she replied by asking him if he honestly believed that a jury could be prejudiced by having the Constitution of the United States read and explained to them.

Crowley became so exasperated that when the District Court opened on May 13, he requested a change of venue from Rochester to Canandaigua in adjacent Ontario County. The change forced a postponement of the trial until June 17. Susan promptly launched a whirlwind lecture tour of the villages around Canandaigua. She managed to cover twenty-one postal districts on her own, while her good friend and supporter, Matilda Joslyn Gage, covered the remaining sixteen.

The trial of *The United States* vs. *Susan B. Anthony* opened on the afternoon of June 17, 1873, with the tolling of the Canandaigua Courthouse bell. The presiding justice was Ward Hunt, a prim, pale man, who owed his judgeship to the good offices of Senator Roscoe Conkling, the Republican boss of New York State. Conkling was a fierce foe of woman suffrage, and Hunt, who had no wish to offend his powerful patron, had written his decision before the trial started.

District Attorney Crowley opened the arguments for the prosecution. They didn't make much sense at the time, and in retrospect, they sound nothing short of ridiculous. The District Attorney mentioned that Susan B. Anthony was a woman and therefore she had no right to vote. His principal witness was an inspector of elections for the Eighth Ward, who swore that on November 5 he had seen Miss Anthony put her ballot in the ballot box. To back up his testimony, the inspector produced the voter registration book with Susan B. Anthony's signature in it.

Henry Selden's reply for the defense was equally simple. He <u>contended</u> that Susan Anthony had registered and voted in good faith, believing that it was her constitutional right to do so. When he attempted to call his client to the stand, however, District Attorney Crowley announced that she was not competent to testify in her own behalf. Judge Hunt agreed, and the only thing Henry Selden could do was read excerpts from the testimony Susan had given at her previous hearings when presumably she was no less incompetent than she was right now.

---

invariably (in vâr′ē ə blē) *adv.* in an unchanging or unchangeable manner.

vicinity (və sin′i tē) *n.* area near or surrounding a particular place.

contended (kən ten′dəd) *v.t.* argued.

Henry Selden tried to make up for this gross injustice by making his closing argument a dramatic, three-hour speech on behalf of woman suffrage. District Attorney Crowley replied with a two-hour rehash of the original charge.

By the afternoon of June 18, the case of *The United States* vs. *Susan B. Anthony* was ready to go to the jury. It was impossible to predict what their verdict might be, so Judge Hunt, determined to make it the verdict he and Roscoe Conkling wanted, took matters into his own hands. "Gentlemen of the jury," he said, "I direct that you find the defendant guilty."

Henry Selden leaped to his feet. "I object, your honor," he thundered. "The court has no power to direct the jury in a criminal case."

Judge Hunt ignored him. "Take the verdict, Mr. Clerk," he said.

The clerk of the court must have been another Conkling man. "Gentlemen of the jury," he intoned as if the whole proceeding was perfectly normal, "hearken to the verdict as the court hath recorded it. You say you find the defendant guilty of the offense charged. So say you all."

The twelve jurymen looked stunned. They had not even met to discuss the case, much less agree on a verdict. When Henry Selden asked if the clerk could at least poll the jury, Judge Hunt rapped his gavel sharply and declared, "That cannot be allowed. Gentlemen of the jury, you are discharged."

An enraged Henry Selden lost no time in introducing a motion for a new trial on the grounds that his client had been denied the right to a jury verdict.

Judge Hunt denied the motion. He turned to Susan B. Anthony and said, "The prisoner will stand up. Has the prisoner anything to say why sentence shall not be pronounced?"

Thus far in the trial, Susan B. Anthony had remained silent. Now, she rose to her feet and said slowly, "Yes, your honor, I have many things to say."

Without further preliminaries, she launched into a <u>scathing</u> <u>denunciation</u> of Judge Hunt's conduct of her trial. ". . . In your ordered verdict of guilty," she said, "you have trampled underfoot every <u>vital</u> principle of our government. My natural rights, my civil rights, my political rights, are all alike ignored. Robbed of the fundamental privilege of citizenship, I am degraded from the <u>status</u> of a citizen to that of a subject; and not only myself individually, but all of my sex, are, by your honor's verdict, doomed to political subjection under this so-called Republican government."

Judge Hunt reached for his gavel, but Susan B. Anthony refused to be silenced.

"May it please your honor," she continued. "Your denial of my citizen's right to vote is the denial of my right to a trial by a jury of my peers as an offender against law, therefore, the denial of my sacred rights to life, liberty, property, and—"

"The court cannot allow the prisoner to go on," Judge Hunt cried out.

■

scathing (skā′<u>th</u>ing) *adj.* very severe or harsh.
denunciation (di nun′sē ā′shən) *n.* public expression of disapproval; open condemnation.
vital (vī′təl) *adj.* of greatest importance; essential.
status (stā′təs) *n.* relative place or rank, especially social or professional standing.

347

SUSAN B. ANTHONY'S VOTE.

MISS SUSAN B. ANTHONY, the redoubtable champion and exponent of the political rights of women, has at length come to grief at the hands of the law. Not satisfied with promulgating her "peculiar" views from the platform and through the press, she determined to make a test of the matter at the ballot-box, and the result must be discouraging in the extreme. In the last November election, it will be remembered, Miss ANTHONY voted, in the city of Rochester, New York, the Congressional, State, and Assembly tickets. This she did in the belief that the right of suffrage was conveyed to her sex under the Fourteenth Amendment of the Constitution of the United States, which defines citizens as "*all persons* born or naturalized in the United States, and subject to the jurisdiction thereof." The authorities, however, took quite a different view of the matter, and Miss ANTHONY was arrested and indicted for illegal voting.

The trial of the case was held on the 17th June, in the Circuit Court of the United States sitting at Canandaigua, Judge HUNT presiding. Mr. RICHARD CROWLEY, the District Attorney, conducted the prosecution, and Judge HENRY R. SELDEN and Mr. JOHN VAN VOORHIS appeared for the defense. The judge directed the jury to find the defendant "guilty," and a fine of $100 and costs was imposed. The inspectors who received the vote were also convicted, and fined $25 each, with costs.

Newspaper report from Harper's Weekly *about Susan B. Anthony's illegal voting 1873*

Susan ignored him and continued her impassioned tirade against the court. Hunt frantically rapped his gavel and ordered her to sit down and be quiet. But Susan, who must have been taking delight

in his consternation, kept on talking. She deplored the fact that she had been denied the right to a fair trial. Even if she had been given such a trial, she insisted, it would not have been by her peers. Jury, judges, and lawyers were not her equals, but her superiors, because they could vote and she could not. Susan was adamant about the fact that she had been denied the justice guaranteed in the Constitution to every citizen of the United States.

Judge Hunt was sufficiently cowed by now to try to defend himself. "The prisoner has been tried according to the established forms of law," he sputtered.

"Yes, your honor," retorted Susan, overlooking his blatant lie, "but by forms of law all made by men, interpreted by men, administered by men, in favor of men, and against women; and hence your honor's ordered verdict of guilty, against a United States citizen for the exercise of that citizen's right to vote, simply because that citizen was a woman and not a man. But yesterday, the same manmade forms of law declared it a crime punishable with a one-thousand-dollar fine and six months imprisonment, for you, or me, or any of us, to give a cup of cold water, a crust of bread, or a night's shelter to a panting fugitive while he was tracking his way to Canada. And every man or woman in whose veins coursed a drop of human

---

impassioned (im pash′ənd) *adj.* filled with passion or strong feeling; fiery; ardent.

deplored (di plôrd′) *v.t.* disapproved of strongly.

adamant (ad′ə mənt) *adj.* not changing position at all; totally unyielding.

blatant (blā′tənt) *adj.* impossible to overlook; very obvious; conspicuous.

sympathy violated that wicked law, reckless of consequences, and was justified in so doing. As, then, the slaves who got their freedom must take it over, or under, or through the unjust forms of law, precisely so now must women, to get their right to a voice in this government, take it, and I have taken mine, and mean to take it at every opportunity."

Judge Hunt flailed his gavel and gave the by now futile order for the prisoner to sit down and be quiet. Susan kept right on talking.

"When I was brought before your honor for trial," she said, "I hoped for a broad and liberal interpretation of the Constitution and its recent Amendments. One that would declare all United States citizens under its protection. But failing to get this justice—failing, even, to get a trial by a jury not of my peers—I ask not leniency at your hands—but to take the full rigors of the law."

With that Susan finally obeyed Judge Hunt's orders and sat down. Now he had to reverse himself and order her to stand up so he could impose sentence. As soon as he pronounced the sentence— a fine of one hundred dollars plus the costs of prosecuting the trial—Susan spoke up again. "May it please your honor," she said, "I shall never pay a dollar of your unjust penalty. All the stock in trade I possess is a ten-thousand-dollar debt, incurred by publishing my paper—*The Revolution*—four years ago, the sole object of which was to educate all women to do precisely as I have done, rebel against your manmade, unjust, unconstitutional forms of law, that tax,

fine, imprison, and hang women, while they deny them the right of representation in the government; and I shall work on with might and main to pay every dollar of that honest debt, but not a penny shall go to this unjust claim. And I shall earnestly and persistently continue to urge all women to the practical recognition of the old Revolutionary maxim, that 'Resistance to tyranny is obedience to God.' "

Judge Hunt must have had strict orders not only to see that the defendant was convicted, but to do everything he could to prevent the case from going on to a higher court. He allowed Susan to walk out of the courtroom without imposing a prison sentence in lieu of her unpaid fine. If he had sent her to prison, she could have been released on a writ of habeas corpus and would have had the right to appeal. As it was, the case was closed.

Although she was disappointed that her case would not go to the Supreme Court as she had originally hoped, Susan knew that she had struck an important blow for woman's suffrage. Henry Selden's arguments and her own speech at the end of the trial were widely publicized, and Judge Hunt's conduct of the trial stood as proof that women were treated unjustly before the law.

---

futile (fū′təl) *adj.* useless or hopeless; ineffective.
leniency (lē′nē ən sē) *n.* state or quality of being merciful, tolerant, not severe or harsh.
stock in trade: person's resources for any purpose.
incurred (in kûrd′) *v.t.* brought something on oneself by one's own actions.
might and main: all one's strength.

usan did not forget the election inspectors who had allowed her to cast her ballot. The men were fined twenty-five dollars each and sent to jail when they refused to pay. In all, they spent about a week behind bars before Susan, through the influence of friends in Washington, obtained presidential pardons for each of them. In the meantime, her followers, who included some of the best cooks in Rochester, saw to it that the men were supplied with delicious hot meals and home-baked pies.

True to her promise, Susan paid the legal expenses for the three inspectors. With the help of contributions from sympathetic admirers, she paid the costs of her own trial. But she never paid that one-hundred-dollar fine. Susan B. Anthony was a woman of her word as well as a woman of courage.

MEET MARGARET TRUMAN

Margaret Truman (born 1924) comes from Independence, Missouri, and is a graduate of George Washington University. A person of many talents, Truman has been a concert singer, an actress, and a broadcaster. However, she is probably best known for her work as an author. Prior to writing *Women of Courage,* from which this excerpt is taken, Truman wrote *Harry S. Truman,* a best-selling biography about her father, the thirty-third President of the United States.

More Biographies of Courageous Women

- *Susan B. Anthony: Woman Suffragist* by Barbara Weisberg (Chelsea House, 1988). Read more about this determined woman who believed in the right of every woman and man to vote.

- *Indira Gandhi* by Francella Butler (Chelsea House, 1986). After fighting all her life for the civil rights of her people, Indian prime minister Indira Gandhi suspended these rights in 1975. This is the story of a remarkable woman who governed during a complex time in her nation's history.

- *Dreams into Deeds: Nine Women Who Dared* by Linda Peavy and Ursula Smith (Scribner's, 1985). This collection of short biographies contains the stories of nine courageous women who dared to dream the impossible and then worked to make those dreams come true.

RESPONDING TO Literature

THINK • TALK • WRITE

1 What quality do you find most admirable about Susan B. Anthony? Jot down some thoughts in your journal.

2 Why do you think Susan B. Anthony and other women's suffragists fought so hard for the right to vote? Why might they have chosen to focus on this issue?

3 In her statement to the court, why did Anthony contend that she was not being tried before a jury of her peers?

4 Why do you think Anthony mentioned the earlier laws against helping runaway slaves? Do you think this was an appropriate analogy? Explain your opinion.

5 Susan B. Anthony challenged the culture of nineteenth-century America. What story clues can you find that will help you to describe that culture? Support your ideas with story details.

ACTIVITIES

- **Write About Chronological Order**
Select four events that happened to you this past week. Then write a paragraph describing them in chronological order. See if you can show how each event led to the next.

- **Make a Comparative Time Line**
Do some research about Susan B. Anthony. Make a time line of her life. Mark the important events of her life below the time line. Then research events from American history during the same period. Include these events in the appropriate places above your time line.

VOCABULARY PRACTICE

On a separate sheet of paper, write whether the words in each pair are *synonyms* (words with the same meaning) or *antonyms* (words with opposite meanings).

1 convene—assemble

2 vilified—criticized

3 adamant—unsure

4 vicinity—neighborhood

5 prestigious—unknown

6 vital—crucial

7 denunciation—praise

8 status—position

9 contended—argued

10 fortitude—weakness

WRITING

BIOGRAPHICAL SKETCH

Taking a stand on an important issue often requires courage and determination. Write a biographical sketch about someone who demonstrated this. The person can be a friend, a relative, or a famous person.

PREWRITE

List some people whose courage and determination you admire. Jot down their accomplishments.

This writer chose to write about an environmental activist in her community. She used a time line to organize her thoughts.

❶	**❷**	**❸**	**❹**	**❺**	**❻**
Shari was upset about chemical dumping in Mirror Lake.	She tried to speak to the factory owners, but they wouldn't listen.	She wrote a letter to the chamber of commerce but got no answer.	She protested at the lake.	The local paper covered the protest.	The town council stopped the dumping.

Now it's time to organize your notes. Try using a time line.

DRAFT

Here's the first paragraph of the draft about Shari. Has the writer considered her audience? If so, Shari should seem interesting to you.

This writer decides to let her readers see Shari as she sees her. - - - - - - - - →

> <u>The Girl Who Fought City Hall</u>
>
> I never bothered to talk to Shari, she was the quite type. I thought she wasn't very interesting. Then I found out what I was missing.

Use your notes to begin your draft. Visualize your subject as you write.

BIOGRAPHY

REVISE

This writer asked a friend how she might improve the first paragraph.
The friend suggested she work on the tone.

How has the tone changed as a
result of this revision? Does it
make the writing more effective? ----

> I never bothered to talk to Shari, she
> was the quite type. I thought she wasn't
> "cool.
> very interesting. Then I found out what I
> was missing.

Now revise your draft. Do you think
readers would like to meet Shari? Talk with a partner
about details you might add to make Shari seem more interesting.

PROOFREAD

The writer proofread and made a few corrections. She discovered an
error that she had made during the revising stage.

The writer realizes that the --------------
opening sentence is actually
two complete sentences.
Here, the writer notices an --------------
error she made while revising.

> I never bothered to talk to Shari, she
> quiet
> was the (quite) type. I thought she wasn't
> "cool.
> very interesting. Then I found out what I
> was missing.

Now proofread your work carefully. It's a good idea to ask someone
else to check it as well.

PUBLISH

The author decided that her story would work well if read aloud, so she
read it to the entire class.

How will you share your writing? Ask a few classmates for some ideas.

WRITING

VIVID VERBS

ENRICH YOUR WRITING OF **BIOGRAPHICAL SKETCHES.**

Vivid verbs will add color, personality, and action to your writing. They will help you convey your ideas with accuracy and precision.

Read the two paragraphs below. How effectively does each of these paragraphs describe the action?

The Granger Collection

Paragraph 1

Paul Revere was one of the people who climbed onto an English ship and put its tea into Boston Harbor. According to legend, at midnight on April 18, 1775, Revere came into the town of Concord, Massachusetts. His voice called out the news about the British soldiers who were approaching the town.

Paragraph 2

Paul Revere was one of the people who stormed onto an English ship and dumped its tea into Boston Harbor. According to legend, at midnight on April 18, 1775, Revere galloped into the town of Concord, Massachusetts. His voice boomed out the news about the British soldiers who were approaching the town.

PRACTICE 1 Respond on a separate sheet of paper.

1 Which words in the second paragraph make the action seem more exciting and easier to visualize?

2 Rewrite the first paragraph, replacing the verbs with more vivid ones.

& LANGUAGE

SUBJECT-VERB AGREEMENT

REMEMBER THESE RULES ABOUT VERBS WHEN YOU ARE WRITING **BIOGRAPHICAL SKETCHES.**

- Identify the subject of the sentence. Then make sure the verb agrees with it. A singular subject takes a singular verb. A plural subject takes a plural verb.

- When a compound subject is joined by *and,* use a plural verb. When a compound subject is joined by *or, either . . . or,* or *neither . . . nor,* the verb agrees with the subject that is closest to it.

PRACTICE 2 Choose the correct form of the verb for each of these sentences. Write your answers on a separate sheet of paper.

1 Mr. Foster (tells, tell) the class to work in pairs on a project about a famous person in American history.

2 Neither Luisa nor her classmates (is, are) sure how to begin.

3 Luisa and Martin (decides, decide) to write about Paul Revere.

4 They (agrees, agree) to meet at the library on Saturday to begin work.

PRESENT, PAST, AND FUTURE TENSES

USE THESE RULES ABOUT TENSES WHEN YOU ARE WRITING **BIOGRAPHICAL SKETCHES.**

- Use the present tense to indicate an action that is happening now or that happens repeatedly.

- Use the past tense to indicate an action that was completed at a time in the past.

- Use the future tense to indicate an action that will take place in the future.

PRACTICE 3 Change the verb to the tense that matches the time of the action being described. Write your answers on a separate sheet of paper.

1 Last week Luisa (decide) to write about Paul Revere.

2 Now Martin (wish) he had chosen an easier subject.

3 Next time Martin (write) about the Boston Tea Party.

4 The teacher (return) our graded papers tomorrow.

WRITING A SOCIAL STUDIES REPORT

The struggle for justice has produced dramatic events in history. Write a social studies report about one of those events.

PREWRITE

How will you decide on a topic? Brainstorm with a partner. Think about an event that really interests you. Try to pinpoint the key incidents in the struggle for justice and the people who were involved in them. What were the causes and effects of those incidents? A chart can help you organize your information. If you were writing about the French Revolution, your chart might look like this:

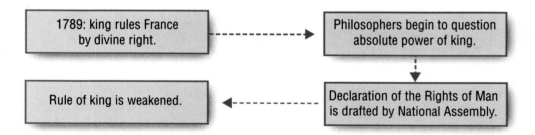

1789: king rules France by divine right. ----> Philosophers begin to question absolute power of king.

Rule of king is weakened. <---- Declaration of the Rights of Man is drafted by National Assembly.

DRAFT Start writing your draft. Express your main idea clearly and grab your reader's interest in the first paragraph.

REVISE Take a break and then reread your report. How objective is it? Are the facts correct?

PROOFREAD Correctly spelled names and accurate dates are crucial to a social studies report. Recheck them if you feel uncertain.

PUBLISH Find out what topics other classmates have written about for their reports. Collect a few pieces that go together well and combine them into a collection of writings about the struggle for justice.

----▶ *Proofreading Alert!* ----

Use irregular verbs correctly. Check page 173 in *Writing and Language Handbook.*

PROJECTS

CREATE A MOCK COURT OF JUSTICE

REMEMBER TO: • PREWRITE • DRAFT • REVISE • PROOFREAD • PUBLISH

Organize your own court of law in the classroom.

First take nominations for judge. Have the judge appoint a committee to draft a case for consideration. Let lawyers appointed by the committee argue each side of the case. The rest of the class can act as a jury. Use the "5 W's and H" focus questions to outline the case: What's the issue at hand? When and where did it happen? Who was involved in it? Why has it come to court? How should it be argued?

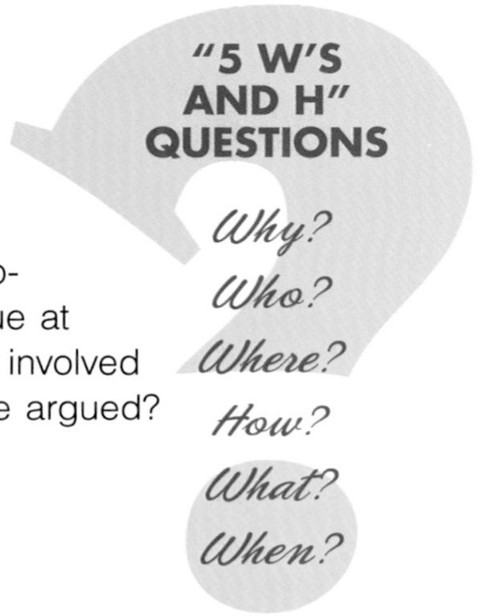

"5 W'S AND H" QUESTIONS

Why?
Who?
Where?
How?
What?
When?

MAKE A SCRAPBOOK

REMEMBER TO: • PREWRITE • DRAFT • REVISE • PROOFREAD • PUBLISH

Think about issues of justice that you have read about, have seen on TV, or are aware of because they arose in your community. Choose one of these issues and make a scrapbook of words and pictures about it.

What will you use to make your scrapbook? You could cut out photos from magazines or newspapers, or you could make your own drawings. Then write captions to tell what happened. Use a chart like this one to plan your ideas.

Issue	Who Was Involved	Events	Outcome
Use of empty land near center of city	City planners; local botanical society	Protest; debate; small group meetings	Compromise reached to divide land

STUDENT COURTS

Students who break a school rule are usually disciplined by adults—either their teachers or other school authorities. That means students have no say in dealing with problems that affect them most directly. But is there another way? After all, adults are judged by their peers—in courts of law. Why shouldn't teenagers have the same right to settle their disputes themselves in student courts? Of course, pleading your case before your peers is one thing; abiding by their decision is something else.

CONSIDER THIS ISSUE: Is it a good idea to start a student court system in your school? Students would have the opportunity to plead their cases before their peers. But would they accept the court's rulings? What do you think?

- Wouldn't students be better off learning to settle their disputes by themselves, instead of always relying on adults?
- Are students responsible enough to judge their peers?
- Is it fair to make students agree to follow the court's rulings?
- Would student defendants be more honest with their peers than they are with school authorities?

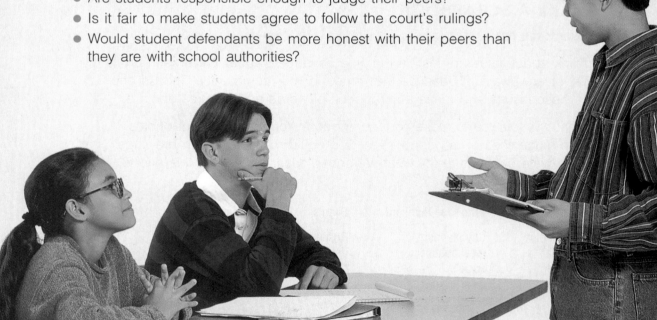

O I N T S

Read the following viewpoints about the issue of student courts. Decide which one is closest to your own opinion. Think of some arguments of your own to support the position you choose.

VIEWPOINT 1

I think a student court system should be instituted in our school.
- Students should have the right to plead their cases before other students, instead of always being judged by adults.
- Other students who have been in similar situations would be more understanding and fairer than teachers would be.
- A student court system would give the students who participate in it a sense of responsibility.

VIEWPOINT 2

I think a student court system should not be instituted in our school.
- Most students aren't responsible enough to judge their peers.
- Some students would take advantage of the court system to get back at those against whom they had a grudge.
- A student court system would weaken the authority of teachers and other school personnel.

VIEWPOINT 3

I think students should have the option of pleading their cases before a student court, but the court's ruling shouldn't be binding.
- If students want to be judged by their peers instead of by adults, they should have that choice.
- Explaining their actions in a student court would be a good learning experience for both student defendants and judges.
- Students shouldn't have to abide by decisions of the court unless the decisions are fair.

WHAT DO YOU THINK?

Consider this issue. Do you share one of the viewpoints above, or do you have another? Discuss your views with a group of students. Then role-play several scenes involving students pleading their cases before a court of their peers.

real life
CONNECT

JUSTICE: It's the pursuit of fairness, of treating all people equally. In this pursuit, many people have taken a risk.

The struggle for justice has changed lives. Everyone wants to be treated fairly, and most people believe that others should be treated fairly as well. "Crispus Attucks" tells the true-life story of an African American who risked his life to gain freedom from slavery. Later he died, still seeking justice, in a struggle that finally led to the American Revolution.

When we argue for justice, we want our voices to be heard. Susan B. Anthony's powerful speech, quoted in "The United States *vs.* Susan B. Anthony," was probably an interesting newspaper story in 1873. In the same way, the front page of any modern newspaper will usually include a news article or feature about people struggling for justice. Look at the front page of this newspaper.

A **newspaper's front page** includes the major news stories of each day. Usually photographs will accompany the most important stories. Often there is also an index, which lists the page numbers of other news stories and sections of the paper.

Center City Times

Monday, September 6, 1993   Center City, Idaho   2 Sections   22 pages   Delivered 25¢   Newsstand 35¢

Children Found After Two-Day Search
by PAUL METZ
Times Reporter

Today may be Labor Day, but for one local family it feels more like Christmas Day.

After an intense two-day search through the Wilderness Mountain Wildlife Refuge, Mark and Becky Liff were found safe and sound late last night.

The two children had been missing since Friday night, after being separated from their family at a picnic area in the state park. The two were found by Wallace Higgins, a local pharmacist. Higgins was the unofficial leader of a search team that included local townspeople, state park rangers, the local national guard, and city police rescue.

Mark and Becky Liff with Wallace Higgins, the Center City pharmacist who led local residents in assisting the rescue effort.

LABOR DAY WEEKEND – SAFE SO FAR HERE
BY JILL HENDRON
Times Reporter

So far across the nation, Labor Day weekend has taken its predictable toll in accidents. But it's been a safe holiday in Center City.

While many families took advantage of this late summer holiday for excursions to nearby parks, lakes, and mountains, others stayed at home to take part in some of the activities planned and sponsored by local service clubs.

The "Sportorama" sponsored by the local sports by Climpton R

State Lottery Experiments with Vending Machines

Capital City (AP)—The State lottery has begun to add vending machines to its marketing schemes. The lottery commission has been experimenting for several months with machines that automatically dispense tickets. So far, the results are promising.

The lottery commission placed machines in three Capital City businesses in June, July, and August. It has also installed four machines at the state fairgrounds. Sales Director Jordan Garcia said officials wanted to determine whether machines would increase ticket sales. Merchants who have tried the machines

---

MONDAY
AND THE WEEK AHEAD

Bus Fares – Starting tomorrow, it will cost more to ride the Center City buses. Fares increase from 50 cents to 75 cents for adults, and from 30 cents to 50 cents for children. Fares for the elderly and handicapped will remain at 25 cents. For the time being, shuttle service will continue to be free.

Radio – The state's first statewide public affairs radio series—"Status of the State"—will debut at 7:00 p.m. today on KZCX-FM/90.3.

Holiday – Today is Labor Day. Government agencies, business offices, schools, and other institutions will be closed, and there will be no mail service. Most malls will be open for business.

Sports – The fall high school sports season begins Friday night when Center City High meets East Linville High at 7:00 p.m. on the Center City Field. The Cross Country Invitational will take place Saturday, beginning at 10:00 a.m. at Center City Track.

Chili Feed and Contest – The tenth annual Chili Festival will be held Saturday at the Savemore Stores parking lot, Carter and 10th Streets, beginning at 10 a.m. The event features food, entertainment, a chili-eating contest, and a street dance. Admission is free until 6 p.m., when a $5 cover will be charged for the dance.

Local Youth Wins Grand Championship in Lamb Division

Capital City (UPI)—Sara Renton of Center City walked off as Grand Champion in the Lamb Division at the State Fair on Saturday. Her market lamb was rated as the best in the field of about 500 by show judge Larry Major.

It was the biggest prize ever won by Sara, the daughter of Kathleen and Thomas Renton. Sara's lamb had earlier won grand champion at the Center County Fair. "It was great winning at the county fair," said Sara, "but I really didn't expect to come in very well at the State Fair."

Sara, who is a senior at Center City High, has three more years of eligibility in 4-H. "I had planned to go out seriously for volleyball this year," she commented, "but now I'm going to have to think about it. I'm not so sure I shouldn't spend more time with 4-H projects, including raising more lambs."

Judge Major said that Sara's lamb had a lot of "eye appeal." "Of course," he said, "the bottom line is meat production." The lamb was purchased by Creighton Industries of Center City.

Sara has been a member of the Happy Valley 4-H Club for eight years. During that time she has shown lambs, calves, and turkeys. She has seven grand championship ribbons from county fair judges.

STATE FAIR
Winners, Page 10

INDEX

Classifieds	16
Comics	20, 21
Dear Andy	4
Deaths	15
Events	4
Life Styles	4
Movies	14
Opinion	9
Puzzles	14
Sports	11
State & Local News	6
TV Programs	14
Weather	15
World News	2, 3

For Home Delivery
CALL 555-3232

I O N S

THINK • TALK • WRITE

Here are three activities in which you have to read the front page of a newspaper. Think of other situations in which reading the front page is important. Then choose an activity below or one of your own and talk or write about it.

PROJECT 1

THE FRONT PAGE Read the front page of your local newspaper for a week. What news stories are featured? What can you learn from the headlines? Do any articles focus on a particular subject (crime, unemployment) or a person rather than an event? Did a story on the same subject appear on more than one day? How had the story changed each day? Discuss these questions in a small group.

PROJECT 2

A NEWS SUMMARY Most news stories print the most important details in the first paragraph. Write the five *W*s: *Who, What, Where, When, Why.* Read the first paragraph of a front-page news story. Can you answer each *W* question from the information in this paragraph? Write a news summary based on the answers to your questions. Did you include the most important facts and summarize them accurately?

PROJECT 3

STORY SEQUENCE Photocopy a news story from the front page. Cut the story apart paragraph by paragraph. Scramble the paragraphs. Trade your story with a partner. Try to assemble each other's news stories in the correct order. Remember that the first paragraph will contain a basic summary of the story. Check your story against the original. Discuss how the paragraph orders are alike and different.

Landscape at Collioure/Study for "Le bonheur de vivre" 1905
Henri Matisse   Statens Museum for Kunst, Copenhagen, Denmark

ING points

The Road Not Taken
by Robert Frost

Two roads diverged in a yellow wood,
And sorry I could not travel both
And be one traveler, long I stood
And looked down one as far as I could
To where it bent in the undergrowth;

Then took the other, as just as fair,
And having perhaps the better claim,
Because it was grassy and wanted wear;
Though as for that, the passing there
Had worn them really about the same,

And both that morning equally lay
In leaves no step had trodden black.
Oh, I kept the first for another day!
Yet knowing how way leads on to way,
I doubted if I should ever come back.

I shall be telling this with a sigh
Somewhere ages and ages hence:
Two roads diverged in a wood, and I—
I took the one less traveled by,
And that has made all the difference.

turning points

BEFORE READING

AT LAST I KILL A BUFFALO

CONNECT TO LITERATURE

How will you know when you are an adult? What will you be able to do that you cannot do now? Share your ideas with a classmate. As you read "At Last I Kill a Buffalo," note in your journal the skills Luther Standing Bear needed to learn to be considered an adult among his people.

Detail of **Buffalo,** Oscar Howe.

THINKING ABOUT NARRATION

Narration is any type of writing that tells a story. That story can be either fiction or nonfiction, depending on whether or not it describes real events. Nonfiction narrative writing can take many forms: it can be an autobiography, a biography, or a narrative essay.

Authors of nonfiction must make choices about what events to include in their writing. The events they finally decide upon are the ones they believe will best illustrate the main ideas they want to convey or those that most clearly reveal the personalities of the subjects. As you read, ask yourself why an author chose to include a set of particular events and not others.

DID YOU KNOW?

The buffalo was extremely important to the Native Americans of the plains. They used every part of the buffalo for food, clothing, and shelter. However, when migrating herds started creating problems for railroad construction in the West, buffalo were slaughtered in almost unimaginable numbers: between 1850 and 1890 white hunters shot about *20 million* buffalo. By 1900 only 300 buffalo were left in the United States. Fortunately, conservation techniques managed to save the species, and today there are about 15,000 buffalo in this country, mostly on fenced-in game preserves.

Onkto' Mi Dreaming   *1976   Oscar Howe   Collection of the University of South Dakota*

AT
LAST
I KILL
A BUFFALO

▲ ▲ ▲ ▲ ▲

BY LUTHER STANDING BEAR

At last the day came when my father allowed me to go on a buffalo hunt with him. And what a proud boy I was!

Ever since I could remember my father had been teaching me the things that I should know and preparing me to be a good hunter. I had learned to make bows and to string them; and to make arrows and tip them with feathers. I knew how to ride my pony no matter how fast he would go, and I felt that I was brave and did not fear danger. All these things I had learned for just this day when father would allow me to go with him on a buffalo hunt. It was the event for which every Sioux boy eagerly waited. To ride side by side with the best hunters of the tribe, to hear the terrible noise of the great herds as they ran, and then to help to bring home the kill was the most thrilling day of any Indian boy's life. The only other event which could equal it would be the day I went for the first time on the warpath to meet the enemy and protect my tribe.

On the following early morning we were to start, so the evening was spent in preparation. Although the tipis were full of activity, there was no noise nor confusion outside. Always the evening before a buffalo hunt and when every

367

one was usually in his tipi, an old man went around the circle of tipis calling, "I-ni-la," "I-ni-la," not loudly, but so every one could hear. The old man was saying, "Keep quiet," "Keep quiet." We all knew that the scouts had come in and reported buffalo near and that we must all keep the camp in stillness. It was not necessary for the old man to go into each tipi and explain to the men that tomorrow there would be a big hunt, as the buffalo were coming. He did not order the men to prepare their weapons and neither did he order the mothers to keep children from crying. The one word, "I-ni-la," was sufficient to bring quiet to the whole camp. That night there would be no calling or shouting from tipi to tipi and no child would cry aloud. Even the horses and dogs obeyed the command for quiet, and all night not a horse neighed and not a dog barked. The very presence of quiet was everywhere. Such is the orderliness of a Sioux camp that men, women, children, and animals seem to have a common understanding and sympathy. It is no mystery but natural that the Indian and his animals understand each other very well both with words and without words. There are words, however, that the Indian uses that are understood by both his horses and dogs. When on a hunt, if one of the warriors speaks the word "A-a-ah" rather quickly and sharply, every man, horse, and dog will stop instantly and listen. Not a move will be made by an animal until the men move or speak further. As long as the hunters listen, the animals will listen also.

The night preceding a buffalo hunt was always an exciting night, even though it was quiet in camp. There would be much talk in the tipis around the fires. There would be sharpening of arrows and of knives. New bow-strings would be made and quivers would be filled with arrows.

It was in the fall of the year and the evenings were cool as father and I sat by the fire and talked over the hunt. I was only eight years of age, and I know that father did not expect me to get a buffalo at all, but only to try perhaps for a small calf should I be able to get close enough to one. Nevertheless, I was greatly excited as I sat and watched father working in his easy, firm way.

I was wearing my buffalo-skin robe, the hair next to my body. Mother had made me a rawhide belt and this, wrapped around my waist, held my blanket on when I threw it off my shoulders. In the early morning I would wear it, for it would be cold. When it came time to shoot, I should not want my blanket but the belt would hold it in place.

You can picture me, I think, as I sat in the glow of the campfire, my little brown body bare to the waist, watching and listening intently to my father. My hair hung down my back and I wore moccasins and breech-cloth of buckskin. To my belt was fastened a rawhide holster for my knife, for when I was eight years of age we had plenty of knives. I

---

preceding (pri sē′ding) *adj.* going or coming before.
quivers (kwiv′ərz) *n., pl.* cases for holding arrows.

was proud to own a knife, and this night I remember I kept it on all night. Neither did I lay aside my bow, but went to sleep with it in my hand, thinking, I suppose, to be all the nearer ready in the morning when the start was made.

Father sharpened my steel points for me and also sharpened my knife. The whetstone was a long stone which was kept in a buckskin bag, and sometimes this stone went all over the camp; every tipi did not have one, so we shared this commodity with one another. I had as I remember about ten arrows, so when father was through sharpening them I put them in my rawhide quiver. I had a rawhide quirt, too, which I would wear fastened to my waist. As father worked, he knew I was watching him closely and listening whenever he spoke. By the time all preparations had been made, he had told me just how I was to act when I started out in the morning with the hunters.

We went to bed, my father hoping that tomorrow would be successful for him so that he could bring home some nice meat for the family and a hide for my mother to tan. I went to bed, but could not go to sleep at once, so filled was I with the wonderment and excitement of it all. The next day was to be a test for me. I was to prove to my father whether he was or was not justified in his pride in me. What would be the result of my training? Would I be brave if I faced danger and would father be proud of me? Though I did not know it that night I was to be tried for the strength of my manhood and my honesty in this hunt.

Something happened that day which I remember above all things. It was a test of my real character and I am proud to say that I did not find myself weak, but made a decision that has been all these years a gratification to me.

The next morning the hunters were catching their horses about daybreak. I arose with my father and went out and caught my pony. I wanted to do whatever he did and show him that he did not have to tell me what to do. We brought our animals to the tipi and got our bows and arrows and mounted. From over the village came the hunters. Most of them were leading their running horses. These running horses were anxious for the hunt and came prancing, their ears straight up and their tails waving in the air. We were joined with perhaps a hundred or more riders, some of whom carried bows and arrows and some armed with guns.

The buffalo were reported to be about five or six miles away as we should count distance now. At that time we did not measure distance in miles. One camping distance was about ten miles, and these buffalo were said to be about one half camping distance away.

Some of the horses were to be left at a stopping-place just before the herd was reached. These horses were pack-animals which were taken along to carry extra blankets or weapons. They were trained to remain there until the hunters came for them. Though they were neither

---

quirt (kwûrt) *n.* riding whip made of knotted rawhide.

Buffalo   *1970   Oscar Howe   Federal Reserve Bank of Minneapolis, Minneapolis, Minnesota*

hobbled nor tied, they stood still during the shooting and noise of the chase.

My pony was a black one and a good runner. I felt very important as I rode along with the hunters and my father, the chief. I kept as close to him as I could.

Two men had been chosen to scout or to lead the party. These two men were in a sense policemen whose work it was to keep order. They carried large sticks of ash wood, something like a policeman's <u>billy</u>, though longer. They rode ahead of the party while the rest of us kept in a group close together. The leaders went ahead until they sighted the herd of grazing buffalo. Then they stopped and waited for the rest of us to ride up. We all rode slowly toward the herd, which on sight of us had come together, although they had been scattered here and there over the plain. When they saw us, they all ran close together as if at the command of a leader. We continued riding slowly toward the herd until one of the leaders shouted, "Ho-ka-he!" which means, "Ready, Go!" At that command every man started for the herd. I had been listening, too, and the minute the hunters started, I started also.

Away I went, my little pony putting all he had into the race. It was not long before I lost sight of father, but I kept going just the same. I threw my blanket

---

billy (bil′ē) *n.* short, heavy club or stick.

370

back and the chill of the autumn morning struck my body, but I did not mind. On I went. It was wonderful to race over the ground with all these horsemen about me. There was no shouting, no noise of any kind except the pounding of the horses' feet. The herd was now running and had raised a cloud of dust. I felt no fear until we had entered this cloud of dust and I could see nothing about me—only hear the sound of feet. Where was father? Where was I going? On I rode through the cloud, for I knew I must keep going.

Then all at once I realized that I was in the midst of the buffalo, their dark bodies rushing all about me and their great heads moving up and down to the sound of their hoofs beating upon the earth. Then it was that fear overcame me and I leaned close down upon my little pony's body and clutched him tightly. I can never tell you how I felt toward my pony at that moment. All thought of shooting had left my mind. I was seized by blank fear. In a moment or so, however, my senses became clearer, and I could distinguish other sounds beside the clatter of feet. I could hear a shot now and then and I could see the buffalo beginning to break up into small bunches. I could not see father nor any of my companions yet, but my fear was vanishing and I was safe. I let my pony run. The buffalo looked too large for me to tackle, anyway, so I just kept going. The buffalo became more and more scattered. Pretty soon I saw a young calf that looked about my size. I remembered now what father had told me the night before as we sat about the fire. Those instructions were important for me now to follow.

I was still in back of the calf, being unable to get alongside of him. I was anxious to get a shot, yet afraid to try, as I was still very nervous. While my pony was making all speed to come alongside, I chanced a shot and to my surprise my arrow landed. My second arrow glanced along the back of the animal and sped on between the horns, making only a slight wound. My third arrow hit a spot that made the running beast slow up in his gait. I shot a fourth arrow, and though it, too, landed it was not a <u>fatal</u> wound. It seemed to me that it was taking a lot of shots, and I was not proud of my <u>marksmanship</u>. I was glad, however, to see the animal going slower and I knew that one more shot would make me a hunter. My horse seemed to know his own importance. His two ears stood straight forward and it was not necessary for me to urge him to get closer to the buffalo. I was soon by the side of the buffalo and one more shot brought the chase to a close. I jumped from my pony, and as I stood by my fallen game, I looked all around wishing that the world could see. But I was alone. In my determination to stay by until I had won my buffalo, I had not noticed that I was far from everyone else. No admiring friends were about, and as far as I could see I

fatal (fā′təl) *adj.* causing death.
marksmanship (märks′mən ship′) *n.* skill in shooting a gun or other weapon.

was on the plain alone. The herd of buffalo had completely disappeared. And as for father, much as I wished for him, he was out of sight and I had no idea where he was.

I stood and looked at the animal on the ground. I was happy. Everyone must know that I, Ota K'te, had killed a buffalo. But it looked as if no one knew where I was, so no one was coming my way. I must then take something from this animal to show that I had killed it. I took all the arrows one by one from the body. As I took them out, it occurred to me that I had used five arrows. If I had been a skillful hunter, one arrow would have been sufficient, but I had used five. Here it was that temptation came to me. Why could I not take out two of the arrows and throw them away? No one would know, and then I should be more greatly admired and praised as a hunter. As it was, I knew that I should be praised by father and mother, but I wanted more. And so I was tempted to lie.

I was planning this as I took out my skinning knife that father had sharpened for me the night before. I skinned one side of the animal, but when it came to turning it over, I was too small. I was wondering what to do when I heard my father's voice calling, "To-ki-i-la-la-hu-wo," "Where are you?" I quickly jumped on my pony and rode to the top of a little hill near by. Father saw me and came to me at once. He was so pleased to see me and glad to know that I was safe. I knew that I could never lie to my father. He was too fond of me and I too

proud of him. He had always told me to tell the truth. He wanted me to be an honest man, so I resolved then to tell the truth even if it took from me a little glory. He rode up to me with a glad expression on his face, expecting me to go back with him to his kill. As he came up, I said as calmly as I could, "Father, I have killed a buffalo." His smile changed to surprise and he asked me where my buffalo was. I pointed to it and we rode over to where it lay, partly skinned.

Father set to work to skin it for me. I had watched him do this many times and knew perfectly well how to do it myself, but I could not turn the animal over. There was a way to turn the head of the animal so that the body would be balanced on the back while being skinned. Father did this for me, while I helped all I could. When the hide was off, father put it on the pony's back with the hair side next to the pony. On this he arranged the meat so it would balance. Then he covered the meat carefully with the rest of the hide, so no dust would reach it while we traveled home. I rode home on top of the load.

I showed my father the arrows that I had used and just where the animal had been hit. He was very pleased and praised me over and over again. I felt more glad than ever that I had told the truth and I have never regretted it. I am more proud now that I told the truth than I am of killing the buffalo.

---

resolved (ri zolvd′) *v.* decided (to do something); determined.

We then rode to where my father had killed a buffalo. There we stopped and prepared it for taking home. It was late afternoon when we got back to camp. No king ever rode in state who was more proud than I that day as I came into the village sitting high up on my load of buffalo meat. Mother had now two hunters in the family and I knew how she was going to make a fuss over me. It is not customary for Indian men to brag about their exploits and I had been taught that bragging was not nice. So I was very quiet, although I was bursting with pride. Always when arriving home I would run out to play, for I loved to be with the other boys, but this day I lingered about close to the tipi so I could hear the nice things that were said about me. It was soon all over camp that Ota K'te had killed a buffalo.

My father was so proud that he gave away a fine horse. He called an old man to our tipi to cry out the news to the rest of the people in camp. The old man stood at the door of our tipi and sang a song of praise to my father. The horse had been led up and I stood holding it by a rope. The old man who was doing the singing called the other old man who was to receive the horse as a present. He accepted the horse by coming up to me, holding out his hands to me, and saying, "Ha-ye," which means "Thank you." The old man went away very grateful for the horse.

That ended my first and last buffalo hunt. It lives only in my memory, for the days of the buffalo are over.

---

exploits (ek′sploits) *n., pl.* heroic deeds or acts.
lingered (ling′gərd) *v.i.* stayed on as if reluctant to leave.

MEET
LUTHER STANDING BEAR

Luther Standing Bear, a member of the Lakota/Sioux tribe, was born in the 1860s in the area that is present-day North and South Dakota. In his memoir entitled *My Indian Boyhood,* from which the selection "At Last I Kill a Buffalo" is taken, Standing Bear describes in detail the home life and education of Lakota/Sioux children. In addition to *My Indian Boyhood,* Luther Standing Bear has written *My People the Sioux, Land of the Spotted Eagle,* and *Stories of the Sioux.*

RESPONDING TO *Literature*

THINK • TALK • WRITE

1 What did you think of Luther Standing Bear? Does he have qualities you admire? Write a few lines in your journal to express your opinions.

2 To what is Luther Standing Bear referring when he says, "Something happened that day which I remember above all things"? Why does he consider it a test of his "real character"? Why does he remember it so well?

3 What are the different emotions that Luther Standing Bear experiences from the beginning to the end of the hunt? How do you think he is changed by the events of the day?

4 Do you think Luther Standing Bear's father would have been proud of him if he had not killed a buffalo? Why or why not? Explain your answer.

5 What did reading this story teach you about the way of life of Luther Standing Bear's people? Use story details to write a brief description of the life of a Sioux Indian camp.

ACTIVITIES

• **Write About Narration** Recall an incident from your life in which you accomplished something you had never been able to before. Write a brief narration of that incident, including all the important events. Make sure to keep the events in chronological order.

• **Make a Picture Story** Some Native American tribes used pictures to narrate stories about important events. Make a picture story of Luther Standing Bear's hunt. Be sure to include all the important details of the hunt in your picture.

VOCABULARY PRACTICE

On a separate sheet of paper, write the letter of the word that is the best substitute for the colored word in each sentence.

1 My grandfather always told me that it is not appropriate to brag about one's **exploits.**
   a. relatives   **b.** accomplishments
   c. grades   **d.** talents

2 Unfortunately, I turned on the radio too late to hear the title of the **preceding** song.
   a. previous   **b.** prize-winning
   c. later   **d.** catchy

3 The rebel soldiers **resolved** to capture the capital city.
   a. prepared   **b.** gathered
   c. determined   **d.** compromised

4 The motorcycle rider's injuries were not **fatal.**
   a. extensive   **b.** fortunate
   c. deadly   **d.** expected

5 Many of the students **lingered** after the dance was over.
   a. applauded   **b.** complained
   c. ate   **d.** stayed

New Mexico Sunset *1978 Linda Lomahaftewa The Heard Museum*

UNDER ONE SUN

by Neal Beaumont

The early morning, overcast and quiet,
found me walking alone on a side of a ridge.
I stopped to gaze
over the valleys and canyons.
As I looked, I wondered how my ancestors lived.
The wind that blew around me sounded like drums
beating at a powwow.
I started to realize the meaning of this series of beats.
After a while, I started to hum
to the beats. Then all of a sudden
it went away.
While walking home, I realized
how much I needed to hold on to
my culture.

PROSPECTIVE IMMIGRANTS PLEASE NOTE

Either you will
go through this door
or you will not go through.

If you go through
there is always the risk
of remembering your name.

Things look at you doubly
and you must look back
and let them happen.

If you do not go through
it is possible
to live worthily

to maintain your attitudes
to hold your position
to die bravely

but much will blind you,
much will evade you,
at what cost who knows?

The door itself
makes no promises.
It is only a door.

—Adrienne Rich

BEFORE READING

LITTLE BY LITTLE

CONNECT TO LITERATURE

Did you ever feel like an outsider? Did you act differently because you hoped to be accepted? Write about the experience in your journal. Then, as you read "Little by Little," note the things Jean Little does to feel accepted by her class.

THINKING ABOUT ANECDOTE

Any good biography or autobiography will contain *anecdotes,* brief and entertaining accounts of true events. Authors use anecdotes to amuse, to help illustrate a main idea, or to reveal an aspect of a character's personality.

As you read the following anecdote from the autobiography *Little by Little,* ask yourself why the author chose to include it.

DID YOU KNOW?

In this autobiographical excerpt, author Jean Little describes an incident in which a classmate makes fun of her for being cross-eyed. Cross-eye is actually one form of a condition that doctors call *strabismus.* Strabismus means that one of the eyes does not look straight ahead. If the eye looks inward toward the nose, the person is said to have cross-eye; if the eye looks outward to the side, the person is said to have wall-eye.

Strabismus is most common in young children. It can often be corrected by means of glasses or eye drops, or occasionally by surgery. Sometimes, a patch is placed over one eye for a period of time. When treated early, strabismus usually does not cause any permanent vision problems.

from Little by Little

by Jean Little

I was eating my porridge when Hugh, hurrying too fast, fell down the back stairs. Before Mother could get up, he limped in, sniffling slightly, and displayed a bumped elbow for her inspection. Mother examined it gravely.

"A slight <u>haematoma</u>," she said in a serious voice. "And an abrasion almost invisible to the naked eye. You'll live."

Hugh, who always recovered with the speed of light and who won Mother's admiration with his bravery, chuckled at the impressive words.

"What does that mean?" he asked.

"A little bruise and a scrape I can hardly see."

I glowered at my oatmeal. Why did she have to smile at him like that? He was not so special. I searched my mind for something terrible he had done that I could tell her about.

---

haematoma (hē′mə tō′mə) *n.* tumor or swelling containing blood.

378

Jean Little as a young girl

"Jean, hurry up or you'll be late," Grandma said.

I did not want to go to school. We were going to have another mental arithmetic test, and I still did not know my times tables. If only I could fall down and break my leg . . .

Four-year-old Pat grinned at me.

"Huwwy up, Jean," she parroted. "You'll be late."

I wanted to slap the wide smile off her silly little face. Instead I scooped up a few drops of milk on the tip of my spoon and let fly. The tiny bit of milk splashed her on the nose. I laughed. Before anyone could stop her, Pat grabbed up her mug filled to the brim with milk and sent its entire contents sloshing over me, soaking me to the skin.

The next thing I knew, I was back upstairs changing out of my wet serge dress, cotton petticoat, long brown stockings and underwear into clean dry clothes. Not only was this going to make me really late, but Mother handed me the knitted suit Aunt Gretta had made for my tenth birthday. The ribbed blue skirt was sewn onto a sleeveless cotton vest. Over it went a horizontally striped blue and pink sweater with short sleeves. Nobody else in Miss Marr's class had a homemade knitted suit anything like it.

"I can't wear it," I said in anguished tones.

"It's lovely," my mother said calmly. "Gretta worked hard to make it for you. Don't be ridiculous. Of course you will wear it."

In ten minutes I was gobbling toast and honey, gulping down milk and hating my cheerful little sister who was the cause of all the trouble and who got to stay home and be spoiled by everybody.

When I reached the street, it was <u>ominously</u> quiet. I really was going to be late, and it was all Pat's fault. I ran the first three blocks, but slowed down when I got a stitch in my side. There was still not a single child in sight.

As I passed St. John's School, I could hear the grade four class singing "God Save the King." I sent the small building a look of longing. Mr. Johnston had not had these horrid mental arithmetic tests.

Then I stood stock still. When I got to school, Miss Marr would tell me to put my name on the board to stay after four. I didn't mind staying late—lots of the others got detentions—I wasn't sure what to write, though I had a strong suspicion that you did not write out your

---

ominously (om′ə nəs lē) *adv.* in a manner suggesting misfortune.

whole name. Did you just write your initials? Or one initial and your surname? Or your first name and your last initial?

I had to get it right. The others still called me names when no teacher was near enough to hear. The only game I had ever been invited to play was Crack the Whip, and they always made me go on the end. Then, when the big girl at the front swung everybody around in a long *Crack!,* I ended up flying through the air and landing with a jarring crash on my hands and knees. As I picked myself up, I'd try to look as though I thought crash-landings were fun. Nobody was fooled.

If I wrote my name up there differently than the others did, they would have a new thing to tease me about. I could hear the jeering voices already.

"You're not just cross-eyed, you're so *dumb* you don't even know how to write your name on the board!"

I stood there, thinking hard. How could I save myself? Once in a while, when a child brought a note from home, he got out of putting his name on the board. Well, my mother would not write me a note.

Perhaps, if your parents were not at home, and some emergency cropped up and you had to deal with it, Miss Marr just might let you sit down without asking for a note. It would have to be a desperate emergency . . .

I began to walk again, taking my time. I had to invent the most convincing lie of my life. Bit by bit, I worked it out. As I imagined how it must have happened, it grew so real that I began to believe it myself. I had every detail ready as I turned the last corner. Then I began to run.

I knew it was essential that I be out of breath when I arrived.

I dashed up the stairs, puffing hard. I opened the door, said a private prayer for help, and entered the grade five classroom. Miss Marr was at her desk. Out of the corner of my eye, I could see monitors collecting the test papers. So far so good.

"Jean," said my teacher, "you're late."

"Yes," I panted, facing her and opening my eyes wide so that I would look innocent and pitiful. "I know. I couldn't help it."

"Why are you late?" she asked.

I took a deep breath.

"Well, I was all ready in plenty of time. But just as I was going out the door, the telephone rang. I knew I should not go back to answer

---

jeering (jîr'ing) *adj.* scornful; mocking.

it, but you know my mother and father are both doctors and I was afraid it might be an emergency."

Miss Marr opened her mouth to ask a question, but I rushed on, not giving her time to get a word in edgewise.

"The trouble was, you see, that nobody was home but me. So I took the receiver off the hook and I said, 'Dr. Littles' residence.' "

Everybody was listening now, even the boys who never paid attention. I kept going.

"MY DAUGHTER IS DYING! MY DAUGHTER IS DYING!"

I saw my teacher jump as I shrieked the words at the top of my lungs. Her eyes were wide with shock. The class gasped. I did not stop for effect. I could not give the teacher time to interrupt.

"It was a man's voice. He sounded frantic with worry. 'I'm sorry,' I told him, 'my parents are out. If you call back, they should be home in one hour.' 'No! Please, don't hang up,' he begged. 'You must come and save her life. If I wait for your parents, she will surely die.' 'Well, I guess if she is dying, I'd better come. Where do you live?' I asked him. '111 King Street,' he told me."

Miss Marr did not even try to ask a question as I paused to catch my breath. The entire class was sitting <u>spellbound</u>. The silence was absolute. Not a desk seat squeaked. Not a giggle broke the hush.

"I hurried in and got the right medicine from the office and then I ran out the door. I didn't go the long way around by the Norwich Street bridge. I was afraid it would take too long. I went down London Road and across some stepping stones down there. When I got to King Street, there was the house. It was a log cabin with wind whistling through the cracks. And as I came up to it, I saw the door was standing open and there were a bunch of people in the doorway and they were all crying. 'What's wrong?' I asked them. 'You are too late,' they sobbed. 'She's dead already.' "

This time, as I snatched a breath, Miss Marr choked back a small sound. She made no attempt to <u>stem</u> the flood of my story. I pressed on.

" 'Oh, I am so sorry,' I told them. 'Take me to see her.' So they took me into the cabin and there lay the girl on a <u>trundle bed</u>. Her face was blue and her eyes had rolled up till you could just see white and her teeth were clenched. And her fingers and toes all curled over backwards."

■

spellbound (spel'bound') *adj.* held as if by a magic spell; entranced.

stem (stem) *v.t.* stop or restrain as if by damming.

trundle bed: *n.* low, movable bed that may be pushed under another bed for storage.

I watched Miss Marr carefully at this point, because I was not absolutely sure what a dead person looked like. The last bit worried me especially. I had heard someone say that when people died, they turned their toes up. That could only mean that their toes curled over backwards, but I was not sure about the fingers.

Miss Marr's face quivered a little and her mouth twitched, but she did not speak. I hurried, eager to finish. It would be a relief to sit down. Even so, in spite of myself, I kept putting in extra bits as they occurred to me.

" 'She's not quite dead,' I cried. 'She's just on the point of death. I think I can save her.' I hit her chin and her mouth opened. I poured in the medicine. She fluttered her lashes and turned a normal colour and said weakly, 'Where am I?' I turned and hurried toward the door. But before I could escape, all the weeping people went down on their knees and grabbed hold of my skirt and they said, 'You saved her life! We want to give you a reward. Gold, silver, a bag of emeralds, a horse that will come when you whistle . . . tell us the one thing you want more than anything else in the world and you can have it.' "

I paused for effect this time. I knew no one would break the hush. I wanted my teacher to take in the next bit.

" 'The one thing I want more than anything else in the world,' I told them, 'is to be on time for school.' So they let me go and I ran down the hill and across the stepping stones. When I got to the third last stone, though, I slipped and fell in the river and cut my knee. I had to get to shore, go home and bandage my knee and put on dry clothes. Then I hurried here as fast as I could. And that is why I am late."

There was a stunned silence in the classroom. Miss Marr and I stared at each other for a long, long minute. I waited for her to tell me to write my name on the board. Instead she pointed her finger at my desk. Speaking extremely slowly and wearily, she said, "Take . . . your . . . seat. Just . . . take . . . your . . . seat."

I tried to keep a <u>solemn</u> expression on my face. But it was hard not to grin. I sat down and did not turn my head as a buzz of whispers broke out behind me. I had missed the mental arithmetic test. I had not had to write my name on the board. And I had kept every single person <u>transfixed</u> with my exciting story.

At least three <u>blissful</u> minutes went by before I realized I had no cut on my knee and no bandage, either. Not only that, but I could not

---

solemn (sol'əm) *adj.* serious and earnest; grave; sober.
transfixed (trans fikst') *adj.* motionless as from awe or fear.
blissful (blis'fəl) *adj.* full of great happiness.

remember whether I had told her which knee I was supposed to have cut.

She had believed me. I was sure of that. Yet any second she was going to discover that I had told her a stupendous lie.

I hooked one knee over the other and clasped my hands around the knee on top. I spent the entire morning that way. When I was required to write, I used only one hand. Miss Marr did not ask me a direct question. When recess time came and she said, "Class, stand," I stayed where I was.

"Jean, aren't you going out for recess?" she asked when the others had marched out and there I still sat.

"Oh, Miss Marr," I said in my smallest, most <u>pathetic</u> voice, "I am so tired from saving that girl's life that I have to stay in and have a rest."

Still clutching my knee with both hands, I laid my head down on my desk and shut my eyes.

She did not say a word.

At noon, when she had her back turned, I ran out of the classroom, dashed home, sneaked bandaids from my parents' office and plastered them over both knees, to be on the safe side. When I returned to school, Miss Marr smiled and did not ask why both my knees were bandaged.

I sat through the afternoon thinking over what had happened. Did she really guess? The other kids did not seem to have figured out that I had lied. One girl had even smiled at me, as though she might be my friend. Nobody in my class had called me cross-eyed. A boy in grade seven had, though. If only I could shut him up the way I had hushed everybody that morning.

Then I remembered Hugh's knee. That night I asked Mother, "What are the long words for what's wrong with my eyes?"

I was standing beside her chair. She looked up at me.

"Why?" she asked.

"I want to know, that's all. They call me cross-eyed. I want to know the long words, the ones doctors use."

She rhymed off a whole list.

"Say it again. Slowly."

"Strabismus, nystagmus, corneal opacities and eccentric pupils."

I practised.

The next day I was late coming out of school. The same grade-seven boy was waiting for me. He had his first snowball ready.

---

pathetic (pə thet′ik) *adj.* arousing pity, sadness, or sympathy.

"Cross-eyed, cross-eyed," he chanted and waited for me to start running so that he could chase me, pelting me with hard-packed snowballs.

I turned on him instead.

"I am not cross-eyed," I said in a strong, clear voice. "I have corneal opacities and eccentric pupils."

I glared at him as I spoke, and my eyes were as crossed as ever. But he was so surprised that he stood there, his mouth gaping open like a fish's.

Then I turned my back and walked away. Perhaps his aim was off because he was so used to firing his missiles at a running target. But the first snowball flew past me harmlessly. The second exploded with a smack against a nearby tree.

I kept walking, chin in the air.

In the last two days, I had learned a lot about the power of words. Snowballs would hit me again and I would run away and cry. I would be late and, eventually, I would even have to write my name on the board.

But I had found out what mere words could do. I would not forget.

meet Jean Little

Canadian author Jean Little (born 1932) is known throughout North America for her sensitive portrayals of adolescent life. Only partially sighted herself, Little often writes about characters with physical disabilities.

Her first published book, *Mine for Keeps,* was about a girl with cerebral palsy. The novel won the Canadian Children's Book Award. She wrote the book for the disabled children she was teaching at the time—not because they needed a book to help them adjust, but because "crippled children had a right to find themselves represented in fiction."

Little has published eighteen books, including two autobiographies, *Little by Little* and *Stars Come Out Within.* Her novel *Mama's Going to Buy You a Mockingbird* was made into a television movie.

RESPONDING TO Literature

THINK • TALK • WRITE

1 What did you think of Jean Little? Have you ever known anyone like her? Jot down some thoughts in your journal.

2 Jean thinks the teacher believes her story. What do *you* think? Explain your opinion.

3 Why do you think Little includes the anecdote about the boy with the snowball? What does it help reveal about her character?

4 At the end of the selection, Little writes, "I had learned a lot about the power of words." What do you think she had learned?

5 The setting for this selection is Canada during the early 1940s. What details can you find that seem fitting to that time and place?

ACTIVITIES

- **Write About Anecdote** Suppose you want to illustrate one of your own personal characteristics. Write an anecdote from your life that reveals the characteristic you want to illustrate.

- **Musical Anecdotes** Many country, folk, rock, or rap songs tell an anecdote from the singer's life. With a classmate, find an example of a song that contains an anecdote. You might want to play it for the class, and then describe what idea or characteristic the anecdote reveals.

VOCABULARY PRACTICE

On a separate sheet of paper, write the vocabulary word that best describes each of the situations below.

ominously   transfixed
jeering   pathetic
solemn

1 The cold and hungry child clutched at his ragged coat and shivered.

2 After striking out, the ballplayer heard the boos of the angry fans.

3 The deer stared into my headlights and froze, unable to move.

4 People placed photographs and flowers on the war memorial.

5 With the rain pouring down, I heard a groan as a crack appeared in the dam.

I STEPPED FROM PLANK TO PLANK

by Emily Dickinson

I stepped from plank to plank
  So slow and cautiously;
The stars about my head I felt,
  About my feet the sea.

I knew not but the next
  Would be my final inch,—
This gave me that precarious gait
  Some call experience.

SPOT on

SHORT STORY

Many artists would tell you that a painting is a statement without words. If this is true, then the painting below can probably tell you something. What do you think that something is? What is the "story" behind the painting?

Waiting for Dad *1873   Winslow Homer   Collection of Mr. and Mrs. Paul Mellon*

Take a close look at the people in this painting. What can you tell about them? What kinds of details has the artist given?

Where and when do you think this scene is taking place? Which of the details make you think this?

What do you think is happening in this scene? Why do you think this is happening?

Think about stories you have read or heard. What elements in those stories also appear in this painting?

LIGHT

ELEMENTS OF A SHORT STORY

CHARACTERS are the people or animals that take part in the action of a story. Characterization is used by a writer to present characters.

- *Direct characterization* is used when the writer tells you how a character looks, behaves, and thinks.
- *Indirect characterization* is used when the writer lets you draw your own conclusions about a character from the way the character speaks or acts or how other people react to the character.

SETTING is the place and time in which the story unfolds.

PLOT is the series of events in a story. Usually the plot is built around a conflict, or clash between opposing forces.

- *External conflicts* occur between a character and another person or a force of nature.
- *Internal conflicts* occur within a character's mind. For example, a character may struggle over an important decision or problem.

Most plots involve five stages.

- *Exposition* introduces the characters, setting, and conflict.
- *Rising action* builds suspense as the conflict becomes clear.
- *Climax* is the point of greatest suspense and the point at which the conflict is resolved.
- *Falling action* shows the effects of the climax and describes what happens to the characters next.
- *Resolution* answers any remaining questions related to the plot.

POINT OF VIEW is the standpoint from which a story is told. In the *first-person point of view,* the narrator is a character in the story. In the *third-person point of view,* the narrator is outside the story.

THEME is the author's message about life. Themes can be stated directly or suggested indirectly through the plot, characters, and setting.

In the selections that follow, you will learn more about short stories. Your discoveries will add to your understanding and enjoyment of short stories and will help you in writing your own.

SHORT STORY

A RETRIEVED REFORMATION

CONNECT TO LITERATURE

Have you ever done something you didn't want to do to help someone in trouble? Was it a difficult decision? In your journal, write about what happened. Then as you read "A Retrieved Reformation," compare your experience with the decision that Jimmy Valentine has to make.

INTRODUCTION TO THE MODEL SHORT STORY

When you read the short stories in this unit, you will find that they are made up of similar elements. For example, each story has a main character, a plot, a setting, a theme, and is told from a particular point of view.

As you read "A Retrieved Reformation," use the notes in the margin. The notes will help you see the structure of the story and show you how the basic elements of the story are connected to each other. As you read the story, you might like to note your own thoughts and impressions in your journal.

HAVE YOU EVER?

Have you ever moved to a new town far away? If you have, you already know how difficult it can be. It sometimes takes a long time to feel comfortable in your new surroundings, especially when it comes to making new friends.

On the other hand, some people *like* to move every once in a while. They think that it's exciting to live in a new place and learn all about it, especially if it's very different from the place they lived before. And for some people—like the character in the story you're about to read—moving is a chance to begin over again, to start living a new kind of life.

A Retrieved Reformation

BY O. HENRY

A guard came to the prison shoe-shop, where Jimmy Valentine was <u>assiduously</u> stitching uppers, and escorted him to the front office. There the warden handed Jimmy his pardon, which had been signed that morning by the governor. Jimmy took it in a tired kind of way. He had served nearly ten months of a four-year sentence. He had expected to stay only about three months, at the longest. When a man with as many friends on the outside as Jimmy Valentine had is received in the "stir" it is hardly worthwhile to cut his hair.

"Now, Valentine," said the warden, "you'll go out in the morning. Brace up, and make a man of yourself. You're not a bad fellow at heart. Stop cracking safes, and live straight."

"Me?" said Jimmy, in surprise. "Why, I never cracked a safe in my life."

"Oh, no," laughed the warden. "Of course not. Let's see, now. How was it you happened to get sent up on that Springfield job? Was it because you wouldn't prove an alibi for fear of compromising somebody in extremely high-toned society? Or was it simply a case of a mean old jury that had it in for you? It's always one or the other with you innocent victims."

"Me?" said Jimmy, still blankly virtuous. "Why, warden, I never was in Springfield in my life!"

"Take him back, Cronin," smiled the warden, "and fix him up with outgoing clothes. Unlock him at seven in the morning, and let him come to the bull-pen. Better think over my advice, Valentine."

At a quarter past seven on the next morning Jimmy stood in the warden's outer office. He had on a suit of the villainously fitting, ready-made clothes and a pair of the stiff, squeaky shoes that the state furnishes to its discharged <u>compulsory</u> guests.

The clerk handed him a railroad ticket and the five-dollar bill with which the law expected him to rehabilitate himself into good citizenship and prosperity. The warden gave him a cigar, and shook hands. Valentine, 9762, was chronicled on the books "Pardoned by Governor," and Mr. James Valentine walked out into the sunshine.

---

assiduously (ə sij′ü əs lē) *adv.* attentively, diligently.
compulsory (kəm pul′sə rē) *adj.* required.

Jimmy headed straight for a restaurant. There he tasted the first sweet joys of liberty in the shape of a broiled chicken and a bottle of white wine—followed by a cigar a grade better than the one the warden had given him. From there he proceeded leisurely to the depot. He tossed a quarter into the hat of a blind man sitting by the door, and boarded his train. Three hours set him down in a little town near the state line. He went to the café of one Mike Dolan and shook hands with Mike, who was alone behind the bar.

Telling about the actions of their characters is one way authors give them personality. Methods of revealing characters is called **characterization.**

"Sorry we couldn't make it sooner, Jimmy, me boy," said Mike. "But we had that protest from Springfield to buck against, and the governor nearly balked. Feeling all right?"

"Fine," said Jimmy. "Got my key?"

He got his key and went upstairs, unlocking the door of a room at the rear. Everything was just as he had left it. There on the floor was still Ben Price's collar-button that had been torn from that <u>eminent</u> detective's shirt-band when they had overpowered Jimmy to arrest him.

When authors use pronouns like *he* and *him,* it means that the person telling the story is outside the story. This is called the **third-person point of view.**

Pulling out from the wall a folding-bed, Jimmy slid back a panel in the wall and dragged out a dust-covered suitcase. He opened this and gazed fondly at the finest set of burglar's tools in the East. It was a complete set, made of specially tempered steel, the latest designs in drills, punches, braces and bits, jimmies, clamps, and augers, with two or three novelties invented by Jimmy himself, in which he took pride. Over nine hundred dollars they had cost him to have made at——, a place where they make such things for the profession.

In half an hour Jimmy went downstairs and through the café. He was now dressed in tasteful and well-fitting clothes, and carried his dusted and cleaned suitcase in his hand.

"Got anything on?" asked Mike Dolan, genially.

"Me?" said Jimmy, in a puzzled tone. "I don't understand. I'm representing the New York Amalgamated Short Snap Biscuit Cracker and Frazzled Wheat Company."

This statement delighted Mike to such an extent that Jimmy had to take a seltzer-and-milk on the spot. He never touched "hard" drinks.

---

eminent (em'ə nənt) *adj.* distinguished.

A week after the release of Valentine, 9762, there was a neat job of safeburglary done in Richmond, Indiana, with no clue to the author. A scant eight hundred dollars was all that was secured. Two weeks after that a patented, improved, burglar-proof safe in Logansport was opened like a cheese to the tune of fifteen hundred dollars, currency; securities and silver untouched. That began to interest the rogue-catchers. Then an old-fashioned bank-safe in Jefferson City became active and threw out of its crater an eruption of bank-notes amounting to five thousand dollars. The losses were now high enough to bring the matter up into Ben Price's class of work. By comparing notes, a remarkable similarity in the methods of the burglaries was noticed. Ben Price investigated the scenes of the robberies, and was heard to remark:

"That's Dandy Jim Valentine's autograph. He's resumed business. Look at that combination knob—jerked out as easy as pulling up a radish in wet weather. He's got the only clamps that can do it. And look how clean those tumblers were punched out! Jimmy never has to drill but one hole. Yes, I guess I want Mr. Valentine. He'll do his bit next time without any short-time or clemency foolishness."

Ben Price knew Jimmy's habits. He had learned them while working up the Springfield case. Long jumps, quick get-aways, no confederates, and a taste for good society—these ways had helped Mr. Valentine to become noted as a successful dodger of retribution. It was given out that Ben Price had taken up the trail of the elusive cracksman, and other people with burglar-proof safes felt more at ease.

One afternoon Jimmy Valentine and his suitcase climbed out of the mail-hack in Elmore, a little town five miles off the railroad down in the black-jack country of Arkansas. Jimmy, looking like an athletic young senior just home from college, went down the board sidewalk toward the hotel.

The place and time in which a story happens is the **setting** of the story.

A young lady crossed the street, passed him at the corner and entered a door over which was the sign "The Elmore Bank." Jimmy Valentine looked into her eyes, forgot

---

currency (kûr′ən sē) *n.* money that is used in a country.
securities (si kyúr′i tēz) *n., pl.* stock or bond certificates.
clemency (klem′ən sē) *n.* mercy in punishing or judging.

what he was, and became another man. She lowered her eyes and colored slightly. Young men of Jimmy's style and looks were scarce in Elmore.

Jimmy collared a boy that was loafing on the steps of the bank as if he were one of the stock-holders, and began to ask him questions about the town, feeding him dimes at intervals. By and by the young lady came out, looking royally unconscious of the young man with the suitcase, and went her way.

"Isn't that young lady Miss Polly Simpson?" asked Jimmy, with <u>specious</u> guile.

"Naw," said the boy. "She's Annabel Adams. Her pa owns this bank. What'd you come to Elmore for? Is that a gold watch-chain? I'm going to get a bulldog. Got any more dimes?"

Jimmy went to the Planters' Hotel, registered as Ralph D. Spencer, and engaged a room. He leaned on the desk and declared his platform to the clerk. He said he had come to Elmore to look for a location to go into business. How was the shoe business, now, in the town? He had thought of the shoe business. Was there an opening?

The clerk was impressed by the clothes and manner of Jimmy. He, himself, was something of a pattern of fashion to the thinly <u>gilded</u> youth of Elmore, but he now perceived his shortcomings. While trying to figure out Jimmy's manner of tying his four-in-hand he cordially gave information.

Yes, there ought to be a good opening in the shoe line. There wasn't an exclusive shoe-store in the place. The dry-goods and general stores handled them. Business in all lines was fairly good. Hoped Mr. Spencer would decide to locate in Elmore. He would find it a pleasant town to live in, and the people very sociable.

Mr. Spencer thought he would stop over in the town a few days and look over the situation. No, the clerk needn't call the boy. He would carry up his suitcase, himself; it was rather heavy.

---

specious (spē′shəs) *adj.* seemingly true or reasonable, but actually false.
gilded (gild′əd) *adj.* covered with a thin layer of gold; sparkling as if covered with a thin layer of gold.

Mr. Ralph Spencer, the phoenix that arose from Jimmy Valentine's ashes—ashes left by the flame of a sudden and alternative attack of love—remained in Elmore, and prospered. He opened a shoe-store and secured a good run of trade.

Socially he was also a success, and made many friends. And he accomplished the wish of his heart. He met Miss Annabel Adams, and became more and more captivated by her charms.

At the end of a year the situation of Mr. Ralph Spencer was this: he had won the respect of the community, his shoe-store was flourishing, and he and Annabel were engaged to be married in two weeks. Mr. Adams, the typical, plodding, country banker, approved of Spencer. Annabel's pride in him almost equalled her affection. He was as much at home in the family of Mr. Adams and that of Annabel's married sister as if he were already a member.

One day Jimmy sat down in his room and wrote this letter, which he mailed to the safe address of one of his old friends in St. Louis:

Dear Old Pal:

I want you to be at Sullivan's place, in Little Rock, next Wednesday night at nine o'clock. I want you to wind up some little matters for me. And, also, I want to make you a present of my kit of tools. I know you'll be glad to get them—you couldn't duplicate the lot for a thousand dollars. Say, Billy, I've quit the old business—a year ago. I've got a nice store. I'm making an honest living, and I'm going to marry the finest girl on earth two weeks from now. It's the only life, Billy—the straight one. I wouldn't touch a dollar of another man's money now for a million. After I get married I'm going to sell out and go West, where there won't be so much danger of having old scores brought up against me. I tell you, Billy, she's an angel. She believes in me; and I wouldn't do another crooked thing for the whole world. Be sure to be at Sully's, for I must see you. I'll bring along the tools with me.

Your old friend,
Jimmy

Through his own words, Jimmy reveals the kind of person he has become. Learning about characters through their own words is another method of **characterization.**

n the Monday night after Jimmy wrote this letter, Ben Price jogged <u>unobtrusively</u> into Elmore in a livery buggy. He lounged about town in his quiet way until he found out what he wanted to know. From the drug-store across the street from Spencer's shoe-store he got a good look at Ralph D. Spencer.

"Going to marry the banker's daughter are you, Jimmy?" said Ben to himself, softly. "Well, I don't know!" .

The next morning Jimmy took breakfast at the Adamses. He was going to Little Rock that day to order his wedding-suit and buy something nice for Annabel. That would be the first time he had left town since he came to Elmore. It had been more than a year now since those last professional "jobs," and he thought he could safely venture out.

After breakfast quite a family party went downtown together—Mr. Adams, Annabel, Jimmy, and Annabel's married sister with her two little girls, aged five and nine. They came by the hotel where Jimmy still boarded, and he ran up to his room and brought along his suitcase. Then they went on to the bank. There stood Jimmy's horse and buggy and Dolph Gibson, who was going to drive him over to the railroad station.

All went inside the high, carved oak railings into the banking-room—Jimmy included, for Mr. Adams's future son-in-law was welcome anywhere. The clerks were pleased to be greeted by the good-looking, agreeable young man who was going to marry Miss Annabel. Jimmy set his suitcase down. Annabel, whose heart was bubbling with happiness and lively youth, put on Jimmy's hat and picked up the suitcase. "Wouldn't I make a nice drummer?" said Annabel. "My! Ralph, how heavy it is! Feels like it was full of gold bricks."

"Lot of nickel-plated shoe-horns in there," said Jimmy, coolly, "that I'm going to return. Thought I'd save express charges by taking them up. I'm getting awfully economical."

Authors describe characters to make them come alive. This is yet another method of **characterization.**

---

unobtrusively (un′əb trü′siv lē) *adv.* in a way that does not cause notice or disturbance; inconspicuously.

The Elmore Bank had just put in a new safe and vault. Mr. Adams was very proud of it, and insisted on an inspection by every one. The vault was a small one, but it had a new, patented door. It fastened with three solid steel bolts thrown simultaneously with a single handle, and had a time-lock. Mr. Adams beamingly explained its workings to Mr. Spencer, who showed a courteous but not too intelligent interest. The two children, May and Agatha, were delighted by the shining metal and funny clock and knobs.

While they were thus engaged Ben Price <u>sauntered</u> in and leaned on his elbow, looking casually inside between the railings. He told the teller that he didn't want anything; he was just waiting for a man he knew.

Suddenly there was a scream or two from the women, and a commotion. Unperceived by the elders, May, the nine-year-old girl, in a spirit of play, had shut Agatha in the vault. She had then shot the bolts and turned the knob of the combination as she had seen Mr. Adams do.

The old banker sprang to the handle and tugged at it for a moment. "The door can't be opened," he groaned. "The clock hasn't been wound nor the combination set."

Agatha's mother screamed again, hysterically.

"Hush!" said Mr. Adams, raising his trembling hand. "All be quiet for a moment, Agatha!" he called as loudly as he could. "Listen to me." During the following silence they could just hear the faint sound of the child wildly shrieking in the dark vault in a panic of terror.

"My precious darling!" wailed the mother. "She will die of fright! Open the door! Oh, break it open! Can't you men do something?"

"There isn't a man nearer than Little Rock who can open that door," said Mr. Adams, in a shaky voice. "My God! Spencer, what shall we do? That child—she can't stand it long in there. There isn't enough air, and, besides, she'll go into convulsions from fright."

Agatha's mother, frantic now, beat the door of the vault with her hands. Somebody wildly suggested dynamite. Annabel turned to Jimmy, her large eyes full of anguish, but not yet despairing. To a woman nothing seems quite impossible to the powers of the man she worships.

"Can't you do something, Ralph—*try,* won't you?"

He looked at her with a queer, soft smile on his lips and in his keen eyes.

"Annabel," he said, "give me that rose you are wearing, will you?"

Hardly believing that she heard him right, she unpinned the bud from the bosom of her dress, and placed

Authors create **suspense** in stories so you will want to continue reading to discover how things turn out.

Jimmy has to make a decision. The struggle that takes place inside a character's mind is called an **internal conflict.**

---

saintered (sôn'tərd) *v.i.* walked in a slow, relaxed way; strolled.

Jimmy resolves his conflict. The point in a story at which the conflict is resolved is called the **climax** of the story.

it in his hand. Jimmy stuffed it into his vest-pocket, threw off his coat and pulled up his shirtsleeves. With that act Ralph D. Spencer passed away and Jimmy Valentine took his place.

"Get away from the door, all of you," he commanded, shortly.

He set his suitcase on the table, and opened it out flat. From that time on he seemed to be unconscious of the presence of any one else. He laid out the shining, queer implements swiftly and orderly, whistling softly to himself as he always did when at work. In a deep silence and immovable, the others watched him as if under a spell.

In a minute Jimmy's pet drill was biting smoothly into the steel door. In ten minutes—breaking his own burglarious record—he threw back the bolts and opened the door.

Agatha, almost collapsed, but safe, was gathered into her mother's arms.

Jimmy Valentine put on his coat, and walked outside the railings toward the front door. As he went he thought he heard a far-away voice that he once knew call "Ralph!" But he never hesitated.

At the door a big man stood somewhat in his way.

"Hello, Ben!" said Jimmy, still with his strange smile. "Got around at last, have you? Well, let's go. I don't know that it makes much difference, now."

And then Ben Price acted rather strangely.

"Guess you're mistaken, Mr. Spencer," he said. "Don't believe I recognize you. Your buggy's waiting for you, ain't it?"

And Ben Price turned and strolled down the street.

In this story, O. Henry makes the point that people can change themselves for the better. This observation about life is the central message of the story and is called the story's **theme.**

O. Henry

O. Henry (1862–1910), whose real name was William Sydney Porter, was born in Greensboro, North Carolina. When he was nineteen, O. Henry moved to Texas, where he held many jobs, including one in a bank. Accused of embezzling funds from the bank, O. Henry fled to Central America to avoid arrest by federal authorities. However, when he returned to the United States to be with his dying wife, O. Henry was arrested, tried, and convicted for embezzlement. After serving over three years in an Ohio prison, O. Henry was released from jail and moved to New York City.

Although O. Henry published his first story in 1899, it wasn't until 1906 that he gained wide popularity. Perhaps best known for his short stories with surprise endings, such as "The Gift of the Magi" and "After Twenty Years," O. Henry died in New York City in 1910.

More Short Stories

• *Collected Stories* by O. Henry (Bantam Books, 1991). This collection contains some of the most famous and best-loved short stories by the master of the surprise ending.

• *Eight Plus One: Stories* by Robert Cormier (Dell, 1991). Here is a collection of nine short stories that will appeal to you because they portray characters dealing with issues that concern young people today.

• *America Street: A Multicultural Anthology of Stories* edited by Anne Mazer (Persea Books, 1993). In this collection of fourteen short stories, you will meet young people from various ethnic and cultural backgrounds who must cope with the challenges of growing up in America.

RESPONDING TO *Literature*

THINK • TALK • WRITE

1 Was the ending of this story a surprise to you? What had you thought was going to happen? Write a few lines in your journal.

2 How would you describe Jimmy Valentine? Do you think he really undergoes a change of character? What story details lead you to believe this?

3 Why do you think O. Henry might have chosen the name "Jimmy Valentine"? Does this seem an appropriate name for the character?

4 Why do you think Ben Price decides not to arrest Jimmy Valentine? Do you agree with his decision? Why or why not?

5 Should Jimmy have told Annabel that he used to be a safecracker? Why does he give away his secret? What would you have done if you were him?

ACTIVITY

- **Write About Short Story** Copy and complete this character-change story map for "A Retrieved Reformation."

Character at Beginning of Story	Events that Caused Change	Character at End of Story

VOCABULARY PRACTICE

On a separate sheet of paper, write the vocabulary word closest in meaning to each given word.

assiduously   clemency

compulsory   specious

eminent   gilded

currency   unobtrusively

securities   sauntered

1 money

2 false

3 stocks

4 attentively

5 decorated

6 mercy

7 required

8 distinguished

9 strolled

10 inconspicuously

SHORT STORY

....

THE MOUSTACHE

CONNECT TO LITERATURE

Do you know older people who like to tell stories about the past? What would you most like to know about their lives? Jot down some questions in your journal. As you read "The Moustache," think about how Mike learns about his grandmother's life, and what it teaches him about his own.

THINKING ABOUT THEME

The *theme* is the main idea or central message of a story. Sometimes the author will state the theme directly; other times, readers must analyze the story's events and characters to figure out the theme for themselves.

DID YOU KNOW?

Due to the efforts of such groups as the American Association of Retired Persons and the Gray Panthers, the way that Americans regard the elderly is slowly changing. Congress has passed laws prohibiting discrimination against the elderly in housing. The government has also prohibited compulsory retirement ages in the workplace; still, many older workers are passed over for promotions or retraining because their employers believe that "you can't teach an old dog new tricks." Studies have shown, though, that older workers are able to perform as well as—or better than—younger workers. They also miss fewer work days each year!

Meet Robert Cormier

"The question I hear most often when the subject of writing comes up is 'Where do you get your ideas?'" says award-winning author Robert Cormier. "I tell people that my ideas usually grow out of an emotion—something I have experienced, observed, or felt. The emotion sparks my impulse to . . . get the emotion and its impact down on paper. Out of that comes a character and then a plot."

Cormier began to develop ideas for "The Moustache" when his teenage son Peter returned from visiting his grandmother in a nursing home. Peter was saddened because his grandmother hadn't recognized him.

Cormier explains that he had once experienced a similar sadness about his own grandmother. "Now, almost thirty years later, Peter's emotion had merged with mine," says Cormier, "and I found myself struggling to express it at the typewriter. . . . In effect, I have used real emotions but the people are real only on the printed page—the boy in the story is not Peter and the woman is not his grandmother."

Robert Cormier's first novel about teenagers, *The Chocolate War*, won many awards and established him as a major author for young adults.

The Moustache

by Robert Cormier

illustrated by Tom Bookwalter

At the last minute Annie couldn't go. She was invaded by one of those twenty-four-hour flu bugs that sent her to bed with a fever, moaning about the fact that she'd also have to break her date with Handsome Harry Arnold that night. We call him Handsome Harry because he's actually handsome, but he's also a nice guy, cool, and he doesn't treat me like Annie's kid brother, which I am, but like a regular person. Anyway, I had to go to Lawnrest alone that afternoon. But first of all I had to stand inspection. My mother lined me up against the wall. She stood there like a one-man firing squad, which is kind of funny because she's not like a man at all, she's very feminine, and we have this great relationship—I mean, I feel as if she really likes me. I realize that sounds strange, but I know guys whose mothers love them and cook special stuff for them and worry about them and all but there's something missing in their relationship.

Anyway. She frowned and started the routine.

"That hair," she said. Then admitted: "Well, at least you combed it."

I sighed. I have discovered that it's better to sigh than argue.

"And that moustache." She shook her head. "I still say a seventeen-year-old has no business wearing a moustache."

"It's an experiment," I said. "I just wanted to see if I could grow one." To tell the truth, I had proved my point about being able to grow a decent moustache, but I also had learned to like it.

"It's costing you money, Mike," she said.

"I know, I know."

The money was a reference to the movies. The Downtown Cinema has a special Friday night offer—half-price admission for high school couples, seventeen or younger. But the woman in the box office took one look at my moustache and charged me full price. Even when I showed her my driver's license. She charged full admission for Cindy's ticket, too, which left me practically broke and unable to take Cindy out for a hamburger with the crowd afterward. That didn't help matters, because Cindy has been getting impatient recently about things like the fact that I don't own my own car and have to concentrate on my studies if I want to win that college scholarship, for instance. Cindy wasn't exactly crazy about the moustache, either.

Now it was my mother's turn to sigh.

"Look," I said, to cheer her up. "I'm thinking about shaving it off." Even though I wasn't. Another discovery: You can build a way of life on postponement.

"Your grandmother probably won't even recognize you," she said. And I saw the shadow fall across her face.

Let me tell you what the visit to Lawnrest was all about. My grandmother is seventy-three years old. She is a resident—which is supposed to be a better word than *patient*—at the Lawnrest Nursing Home. She used to make the greatest turkey dressing in the world and was a nut about baseball and could even quote batting averages, for crying out loud. She always rooted for the losers. She was in love with the Mets until they started to win. Now she has arteriosclerosis, which the dictionary says is "a chronic disease characterized by abnormal thickening and hardening of the arterial walls." Which really means that she can't live at home anymore or even with us, and her memory has betrayed her as well as her body. She used to wander off and sometimes didn't recognize people. My mother visits her all the time, driving the thirty miles to Lawnrest almost every day. Because Annie was home for a semester break from college, we had decided to make a special Saturday visit. Now Annie was in bed, groaning theatrically—she's a drama major—but I told my mother I'd go, anyway. I hadn't seen my grandmother since she'd been admitted to Lawnrest. Besides, the place is located on the Southwest Turnpike, which meant I could barrel along in my father's new Le Mans. My <u>ambition</u> was to see the speedometer hit seventy-five. Ordinarily, I used the old station wagon, which can barely stagger up to fifty.

Frankly, I wasn't too crazy about visiting a nursing home. They reminded me of hospitals and hospitals turn me off. I mean, the smell of ether makes me nauseous, and I feel faint at the sight of blood. And as I approached Lawnrest—which is a terrible cemetery kind of name, to begin with—I was sorry I hadn't avoided the trip. Then I felt guilty about it. I'm loaded with guilt complexes. Like driving like a madman after promising my father to be careful. Like sitting in the parking lot, looking at the nursing home with dread and thinking how I'd rather be with Cindy. Then I thought of all the Christmas and birthday gifts my

---

ambition (am bish′ən) *n.* strongly desired goal.

grandmother had given me and I got out of the car, guilty, as usual.

Inside, I was surprised by the lack of hospital smell, although there was another odor or maybe the absence of an odor. The air was <u>antiseptic</u>, sterile. As if there was no atmosphere at all or I'd caught a cold suddenly and couldn't taste or smell.

A nurse at the reception desk gave me directions— my grandmother was in East Three. I made my way down the tiled corridor and was glad to see that the walls were painted with cheerful colors like yellow and pink. A wheelchair suddenly shot around a corner, self-propelled by an old man, white-haired and toothless, who cackled merrily as he barely missed me. I jumped aside—here I was, almost getting wiped out by a two-mile-an-hour wheelchair after doing seventy-five on the pike. As I walked through the corridor seeking East Three, I couldn't help glancing into the rooms, and it was like some kind of wax museum—all these figures in various <u>stances</u> and attitudes, sitting in beds or chairs, standing at windows, as if they were frozen for-ever in these postures. To tell the truth, I began to hurry because I was getting depressed. Finally, I saw a beautiful girl approaching, dressed in white, a nurse or an attendant, and I was so happy to see someone young, someone walking and acting normally, that I gave her a wide smile and a big hello and I must have looked like a kind of nut. Anyway, she looked right through me as if I were a window, which is about par for the course whenever I meet beautiful girls.

I finally found the room and saw my grand-mother in bed. My grandmother looks like Ethel Barrymore. I never knew who Ethel Barrymore was until I saw a terrific movie, *None But the Lonely Heart,* on TV, starring Ethel Barrymore and Cary Grant. Both my grandmother and Ethel Barrymore have these great craggy faces like the side of a mountain and

---

antiseptic (an'ti sep'tik) *adj.* free from germs.
stances (stan'səz) *n., pl.* manners of standing.

wonderful voices like syrup being poured. Slowly. She was propped up in bed, pillows puffed behind her. Her hair had been combed out and fell upon her shoulders. For some reason, this flowing hair gave her an almost girlish appearance, despite its whiteness.

She saw me and smiled. Her eyes lit up and her eyebrows arched and she reached out her hands to me in greeting. "Mike, Mike," she said. And I breathed a sigh of relief. This was one of her good days. My mother had warned me that she might not know who I was at first.

I took her hands in mine. They were fragile. I could actually feel her bones, and it seemed as if they would

J. BOOKWALTER.

411

break if I pressed too hard. Her skin was smooth, almost slippery, as if the years had worn away all the roughness the way the wind wears away the surfaces of stones.

"Mike, Mike, I didn't think you'd come," she said, so happy, and she was still Ethel Barrymore, that voice like a caress. "I've been waiting all this time." Before I could reply, she looked away, out the window. "See the birds? I've been watching them at the feeder. I love to see them come. Even the blue jays. The blue jays are like hawks—they take the food that the small birds should have. But the small birds, the chickadees, watch the blue jays and at least learn where the feeder is."

She lapsed into silence, and I looked out the window. There was no feeder. No birds. There was only the parking lot and the sun glinting on car windshields.

She turned to me again, eyes bright. Radiant, really. Or was it a medicine brightness? "Ah, Mike. You look so grand, so grand. Is that a new coat?"

"Not really," I said. I'd been wearing my Uncle Jerry's old army-fatigue jacket for months, practically living in it, my mother said. But she insisted that I wear my raincoat for the visit. It was about a year old but looked new because I didn't wear it much. Nobody was wearing raincoats lately.

"You always loved clothes, didn't you, Mike?" she said.

I was beginning to feel uneasy because she regarded me with such intensity. Those bright eyes. I wondered—are old people in places like this so lonesome, so abandoned that they go wild when someone visits? Or was she so happy because she was suddenly lucid and everything was sharp and clear? My mother had described those moments when my grandmother suddenly emerged from the fog that so often obscured her mind. I didn't know the answers, but it felt kind of spooky, getting such an emotional welcome from her.

---

caress (kə res′) *n.* light, soothing touch.

412

"I remember the time you bought the new coat—the Chesterfield," she said, looking away again, as if watching the birds that weren't there. "That lovely coat with the velvet collar. Black, it was. Stylish. Remember that, Mike? It was hard times, but you could never resist the glitter."

I was about to protest—I had never heard of a Chesterfield, for crying out loud. But I stopped. Be patient with her, my mother had said. Humor her. Be gentle.

*W*e were interrupted by an attendant who pushed a wheeled cart into the room. "Time for juices, dear," the woman said. She was the standard forty- or fifty-year-old woman: glasses, nothing hair, plump cheeks. Her manner was cheerful but a businesslike kind of cheerfulness. I'd hate to be called "dear" by someone getting paid to do it. "Orange or grape or cranberry, dear? Cranberry is good for the bones, you know."

My grandmother ignored the interruption. She didn't even bother to answer, having turned away at the woman's arrival, as if angry about her appearance.

The woman looked at me and winked. A conspiratorial kind of wink. It was kind of horrible. I didn't think people winked like that anymore. In fact, I hadn't seen a wink in years.

"She doesn't care much for juices," the woman said, talking to me as if my grandmother weren't even there. "But she loves her coffee. With lots of cream and two lumps of sugar. But this is juice time, not coffee time." Addressing my grandmother again, she said, "Orange or grape or cranberry, dear?"

"Tell her I want no juices, Mike," my grandmother commanded regally, her eyes still watching invisible birds.

The woman smiled, patience like a label on her face. "That's all right, dear. I'll just leave some cranberry for you. Drink it at your leisure. It's good for the bones."

---

conspiratorial (kən spir′ə tôr′ē əl) *adj.* secretive, as if planned together.

She wheeled herself out of the room. My grandmother was still absorbed in the view. Somewhere a toilet flushed. A wheelchair passed the doorway—probably that same old driver fleeing a hit-run accident. A television set exploded with sound somewhere, soap-opera voices filling the air. You can always tell soap-opera voices.

I turned back to find my grandmother staring at me. Her hands cupped her face, her index fingers curled around her cheeks like parenthesis marks.

"But you know, Mike, looking back, I think you were right," she said, continuing our conversation as if there

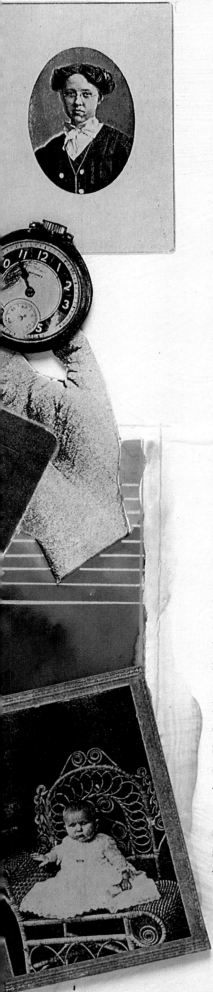

had been no interruption. "You always said, 'It's the things of the spirit that count, Meg.' The spirit! And so you bought the baby-grand piano—a baby grand in the middle of the Depression. A knock came on the door and it was the deliveryman. It took five of them to get it into the house." She leaned back, closing her eyes. "How I loved that piano, Mike. I was never that fine a player, but you loved to sit there in the parlor, on Sunday evenings, Ellie on your lap, listening to me play and sing." She hummed a bit, a fragment of melody I didn't recognize. Then she drifted into silence. Maybe she'd fallen asleep. My mother's name is Ellen, but everyone always calls her Ellie. "Take my hand, Mike," my grandmother said suddenly. Then I remembered—my grandfather's name was Michael. I had been named for him.

"Ah, Mike," she said, pressing my hands with all her feeble strength. "I thought I'd lost you forever. And here you are, back with me again. . . ."

Her expression scared me. I don't mean scared as if I were in danger but scared because of what could happen to her when she realized the mistake she had made. My mother always said I favored her side of the family. Thinking back to the pictures in the old family albums, I recalled my grandfather as tall and thin. Like me. But the resemblance ended there. He was thirty-five when he died, almost forty years ago. And he wore a moustache. I brought my hand to my face. I also wore a moustache now, of course.

"I sit here these days, Mike," she said, her voice a lullaby, her hand still holding mine, "and I drift and dream. The days are fuzzy sometimes, merging together. Sometimes it's like I'm not here at all but somewhere else altogether. And I always think of you. Those years we had. Not enough years, Mike, not enough. . . ."

Her voice was so sad, so mournful that I made sounds of sympathy, not words exactly but the kind of soothings that mothers murmur to their children when they awaken from bad dreams.

"And I think of that terrible night, Mike, that terrible night. Have you ever really forgiven me for that night?"

"Listen . . ." I began. I wanted to say: "Nana, this is Mike your grandson, not Mike your husband."

"Sh . . . sh . . ." she whispered, placing a finger as long and cold as a candle against my lips. "Don't say anything. I've waited so long for this moment. To be here. With you. I wondered what I would say if suddenly you walked in that door like other people have done. I've thought and thought about it. And I finally made up my mind—I'd ask you to forgive me. I was too proud to ask before." Her fingers tried to mask her face. "But I'm not proud anymore, Mike." That great voice quivered and then grew strong again. "I hate you to see me this way—you always said I was beautiful. I didn't believe it. The Charity Ball when we led the grand march and you said I was the most beautiful girl there . . ."

"Nana," I said. I couldn't keep up the pretense any longer, adding one more burden to my load of guilt, leading her on this way, playing a pathetic game of make-believe with an old woman clinging to memories. She didn't seem to hear me.

"But that other night, Mike. The terrible one. The terrible accusations I made. Even Ellie woke up and began to cry. I went to her and rocked her in my arms and you came into the room and said I was wrong. You were whispering, an awful whisper, not wanting to upset little Ellie but wanting to make me see the truth. And I didn't answer you, Mike. I was too proud. I've even forgotten the name of the girl. I sit here, wondering now—was it Laura or Evelyn? I can't remember. Later, I learned that you were telling the truth all the time, Mike. That I'd been wrong . . ." Her eyes were brighter than ever as she looked at me now, but tear-bright, the tears gathering. "It was never the same after that night, was it, Mike? The glitter was gone. From you. From us. And then the accident . . . and I never had the chance to ask you to forgive me . . ."

*M*y grandmother. My poor, poor grandmother. Old people aren't supposed to have those kinds of memories. You see their pictures in the family albums and that's what they are: pictures. They're not supposed to come to life. You drive out in your father's Le Mans doing seventy-five on the pike and all you're doing is visiting an old lady in a nursing home. A duty call. And then you find out that she's a person. She's *somebody.* She's my grandmother, all right, but she's also herself. Like my own mother and father. They exist outside of their relationship to me. I was scared again. I wanted to get out of there.

"Mike, Mike," my grandmother said. "Say it, Mike."

I felt as if my cheeks would crack if I uttered a word.

"Say you forgive me, Mike. I've waited all these years . . ."

I was surprised at how strong her fingers were.

"Say, *'I forgive you, Meg.'*"

I said it. My voice sounded funny, as if I were talking in a huge tunnel. "I forgive you, Meg."

Her eyes studied me. Her hands pressed mine. For the first time in my life, I saw love at work. Not movie love. Not Cindy's sparkling eyes when I tell her that we're going to the beach on a Sunday afternoon. But love like something alive and tender, asking nothing in return. She raised her face, and I knew what she wanted me to do. I bent and brushed my lips against her cheek. Her flesh was like a leaf in autumn, crisp and dry.

She closed her eyes and I stood up. The sun wasn't glinting on the cars any longer. Somebody had turned on another television set, and the voices were the show-off voices of the panel shows. At the same time you could still hear the soap-opera dialogue on the other television set.

I waited awhile. She seemed to be sleeping, her breathing serene and regular. I buttoned my raincoat.

Suddenly she opened her eyes again and looked at me. Her eyes were still bright, but they merely stared at me. Without recognition or curiosity. Empty eyes. I smiled at her, but she didn't smile back. She made a kind of moaning sound and turned away on the bed, pulling the blankets around her.

I counted to twenty-five and then to fifty and did it all over again. I cleared my throat and coughed <u>tentatively</u>. She didn't move; she didn't respond. I wanted to say, "Nana, it's me." But I didn't. I thought of saying, "Meg, it's me." But I couldn't.

*F*inally I left. Just like that. I didn't say goodbye or anything. I stalked through the corridors, looking neither to the right nor the left, not caring whether that wild old man with the wheelchair ran me down or not.

On the Southwest Turnpike I did seventy-five—no, eighty—most of the way. I turned the radio up as loud as it could go. Rock music—anything to fill the air. When I got home, my mother was vacuuming the living-room rug. She shut off the cleaner, and the silence was deafening. "Well, how was your grandmother?" she asked.

I told her she was fine. I told her a lot of things. How great Nana looked and how she seemed happy and had called me Mike. I wanted to ask her—hey, Mom, you and Dad really love each other, don't you? I mean—there's nothing to forgive between you, is there? But I didn't.

Instead I went upstairs and took out the electric razor Annie had given me for Christmas and shaved off my moustache.

---

tentatively (ten′tə tiv lē) *adv.* with hesitation or uncertainty.

RESPONDING TO
Literature

THINK • TALK • WRITE

1 How would you feel if you were in Mike's place, visiting someone in a nursing home? Write down some thoughts in your journal.

2 What do you think Mike means by his statement, "You can build a way of life on postponement"?

3 What event in the past does Mike's grandmother still regret? Why does she ask for forgiveness?

4 What do you think is the meaning of Mike's realization that his parents "exist outside of their relationship to me"?

5 How has Mike changed as a result of visiting his grandmother? What has he learned? Why does he go home and shave off his moustache?

ACTIVITIES

• **Write About Theme** Write a sentence summing up the theme of this selection. Then make an outline for a short story of your own that can be summed up by the same theme.

• **Make a Photo Essay** Find out when and where an older relative or friend lived as a teenager. Try to get photos, cartoons, and headlines that illustrate that time and place. Make a photo essay that shows the events this person experienced.

VOCABULARY PRACTICE

Read each book title below. Then on a separate sheet of paper, write the vocabulary word that is most likely to appear in that book.

ambition   conspiratorial

stances   tentatively

caress

1 *Spies in World History*

2 *Positions and Postures in Karate*

3 *How to Be Successful in Politics*

4 *Techniques of Gentle Massage*

5 *The Social Life of Shy People*

SHORT STORY

THE TREASURE OF LEMON BROWN

CONNECT TO LITERATURE

Do you have a favorite musician or singer? What would you want to ask this performer if you met him or her? List some ideas in your journal. Then, as you read "The Treasure of Lemon Brown," jot down some questions you might want to ask Lemon Brown, a once famous blues singer.

Detail of **Boy with Tire,** Hughie Lee-Smith.

THINKING ABOUT DIALOG

Most stories contain *dialog,* which is conversation between characters. In stories, dialog is usually set off by quotation marks. Dialog shows the exact words characters speak; therefore, dialog can include slang, contractions, and sentence fragments.

DID YOU KNOW?

Blues, a completely American musical form, originated over a century ago. It was created as vocal music by African-American field workers on plantations in the South, who used the blues to express feelings from loneliness and despair to amusement and defiance. Soon musicians began adding inexpensive, portable instruments like the guitar and the harmonica. By the early 1900s the music was spreading across the country. Since then, blues musicians like Robert Johnson, Leadbelly, B. B. King, and Muddy Waters have become legends. The flexibility of the blues form also led to the creation of many other musical styles. Rhythm and blues, soul, rock, and rap all descend from the blues.

THE Treasure of LEMON BROWN

by Walter Dean Myers

The dark sky, filled with angry, swirling clouds, reflected Greg Ridley's mood as he sat on the stoop of his building. His father's voice came to him again, first reading the letter the principal had sent to the house, then lecturing endlessly about his poor efforts in math.

"I had to leave school when I was 13," his father had said, "that's a year younger than you are now. If I'd had half the chances that you have, I'd . . ."

Greg had sat in the small, pale green kitchen listening, knowing the lecture would end with his father saying he couldn't play ball with the Scorpions. He had asked his father the week before, and his father had said it depended on his next report card. It wasn't often the Scorpions took on new players, especially 14-year-olds, and this was a chance of a lifetime for Greg. He hadn't been allowed to play high school ball, which he had really wanted to do, but playing for the Community Center team was the next best thing. Report cards were due in a week, and Greg had been hoping for the best. But the principal had ended the suspense early when she sent that letter saying Greg would probably fail math if he didn't spend more time studying.

"And you want to play *basketball?*" His father's brows knitted over deep brown eyes. "That must be some kind of a joke. Now you just get into your room and hit those books."

Boy with Tire   1952   Hughie Lee-Smith   Detroit Institute of Arts

That had been two nights before. His father's words, like the distant thunder that now echoed through the streets of Harlem, still rumbled softly in his ears.

I t was beginning to cool. Gusts of wind made bits of paper dance between the parked cars. There was a flash of nearby lightning, and soon large drops of rain splashed onto his jeans. He stood to go upstairs, thought of the lecture that probably awaited him if he did anything except shut himself in his room with his math book, and started walking down the street instead. Down the block there was an old tenement that had been abandoned for some months. Some of the guys had held an <u>impromptu</u> checker tournament there the week before, and Greg had noticed that the door, once boarded over, had been slightly ajar.

Pulling his collar up as high as he could, he checked for traffic and made a dash across the street. He reached the house just as another flash of lightning changed the night to day for an instant, then returned the graffiti-scarred building to the grim shadows. He vaulted over the outer stairs and pushed tentatively on the door. It was open, and he let himself in.

---

impromptu (im promp′tü) *adj.* done on the spur of the moment.

The inside of the building was dark except for the dim light that filtered through the dirty windows from the streetlamps. There was a room a few feet from the door, and from where he stood at the entrance, Greg could see a squarish patch of light on the floor. He entered the room, frowning at the <u>musty</u> smell. It was a large room that might have been someone's parlor at one time. Squinting, Greg could see an old table on its side against one wall, what looked like a pile of rags or a torn mattress in the corner, and a couch, with one side broken, in front of the window.

He went to the couch. The side that wasn't broken was comfortable enough, though a little creaky. From this spot he could see the blinking neon sign over the bodega on the corner. He sat a while, watching the sign blink first green then red, allowing his mind to drift to the Scorpions, then to his father. His father had been a postal worker for all Greg's life, and was proud of it, often telling Greg how hard he had worked to pass the test. Greg had heard the story too many times to be interested now.

For a moment Greg thought he heard something that sounded like a scraping against the wall. He listened carefully, but it was gone.

Outside the wind had picked up, sending the rain against the window with a force that shook the glass in its frame. A car passed, its tires hissing over the wet street and its red tail lights glowing in the darkness.

Greg thought he heard the noise again. His stomach tightened as he held himself still and listened intently. There weren't any more scraping noises, but he was sure he had heard something in the darkness—something breathing!

He tried to figure out just where the breathing was coming from; he knew it was in the room with him. Slowly he stood, tensing. As he turned, a flash of lightning lit up the room, frightening him with its sudden brilliance. He saw nothing, just the overturned table, the pile of rags and an old newspaper on the floor. Could he have been imagining the sounds? He continued listening, but heard nothing and thought that it might have just been rats. Still, he thought, as soon as the rain let up he would leave. He went to the window and was about to look out when he heard a voice behind him.

musty (mus′tē) *adj.* stale or moldy.

"Don't try nothin' 'cause I got a razor here sharp enough to cut a week into nine days!"

Greg, except for an involuntary <u>tremor</u> in his knees, stood stock still. The voice was high and brittle, like dry twigs being broken, surely not one he had ever heard before. There was a shuffling sound as the person who had been speaking moved a step closer. Greg turned, holding his breath, his eyes straining to see in the dark room.

The upper part of the figure before him was still in darkness. The lower half was in the dim rectangle of light that fell unevenly from the window. There were two feet, in cracked, dirty shoes from which rose legs that were wrapped in rags.

"Who are you?" Greg hardly recognized his own voice.

"I'm Lemon Brown," came the answer. "Who're you?"

"Greg Ridley."

"What you doing here?" The figure shuffled forward again, and Greg took a small step backward.

"It's raining," Greg said.

"I can see that," the figure said.

The person who called himself Lemon Brown peered forward, and Greg could see him clearly. He was an old man. His black, heavily wrinkled face was surrounded by a halo of crinkly white hair and whiskers that seemed to separate his head from the layers of dirty coats piled on his smallish frame. His pants were bagged to the knee, where they were met with rags that went down to the old shoes. The rags were held on with strings, and there was a rope around his middle. Greg relaxed. He had seen the man before, picking through the trash on the corner and pulling clothes out of a Salvation Army box. There was no sign of the razor that could "cut a week into nine days."

"What are you doing here?" Greg asked.

"This is where I'm staying," Lemon Brown said. "What you here for?"

"Told you it was raining out," Greg said, leaning against the back of the couch until he felt it give slightly.

"Ain't you got no home?"

---

tremor (trem'ər) *n.* shaking; trembling.

"I got a home," Greg answered.

"You ain't one of them bad boys looking for my treasure, is you?" Lemon Brown cocked his head to one side and squinted one eye. "Because I told you I got me a razor."

"I'm not looking for your treasure," Greg answered, smiling. "*If* you have one."

"What you mean, *if* I have one," Lemon Brown said. "Every man got a treasure. You don't know that, you must be a fool!"

"Sure," Greg said as he sat on the sofa and put one leg over the back. "What do you have, gold coins?"

"Don't worry none about what I got," Lemon Brown said. "You know who I am?"

"You told me your name was orange or lemon or something like that."

"Lemon Brown," the old man said, pulling back his shoulders as he did so, "they used to call me Sweet Lemon Brown."

"Sweet Lemon?" Greg asked.

"Yessir. Sweet Lemon Brown. They used to say I sung the blues so sweet that if I sang at a funeral, the dead would commence to rocking with the beat. Used to travel all over Mississippi and as far as Monroe, Louisiana, and east on over to Macon, Georgia. You mean you ain't never heard of Sweet Lemon Brown?"

"Afraid not," Greg said. "What . . . what happened to you?"

"Hard times, boy. Hard times always after a

Gamin 1929 Augusta Savage Schomburg Center for Research in Black Culture

426

poor man. One day I got tired, sat down to rest a spell and felt a tap on my shoulder. Hard times caught up with me."

"Sorry about that."

"What you doing here? How come you didn't go on home when the rain come? Rain don't bother you young folks none."

"Just didn't." Greg looked away.

"I used to have a knotty-headed boy just like you." Lemon Brown had half walked, half shuffled back to the corner and sat down against the wall. "Had them big eyes like you got. I used to call them moon eyes. Look into them moon eyes and see anything you want."

"How come you gave up singing the blues?" Greg asked.

"Didn't give it up," Lemon Brown said. "You don't give up the blues; they give you up. After a while you do good for yourself, and it ain't nothing but foolishness singing about how hard you got it. Ain't that right?"

"I guess so."

"What's that noise?" Lemon Brown asked, suddenly sitting upright.

Greg listened, and he heard a noise outside. He looked at Lemon Brown and saw the old man was pointing toward the window.

Greg went to the window and saw three men, neighborhood thugs, on the stoop. One was carrying a length of pipe. Greg looked back toward Lemon Brown, who moved quietly across the room to the window. The old man looked out, then <u>beckoned</u> frantically for Greg to follow him. For a moment Greg couldn't move. Then he found himself following Lemon Brown into the hallway and up darkened stairs. Greg followed as closely as he could. They reached the top of the stairs, and Greg felt Lemon Brown's hand first lying on his shoulder, then probing down his arm until he finally took Greg's hand into his own as they crouched in the darkness.

"They's bad men," Lemon Brown whispered. His breath was warm against Greg's skin.

"Hey! Rag man!" A voice called. "We know you in here. What you got up under them rags? You got any money?"

---

beckoned (bek′ənd) *v.t.* signaled or summoned (someone) by a sign or gesture.

Silence.

"We don't want to have to come in and hurt you, old man, but we don't mind if we have to."

Lemon Brown squeezed Greg's hand in his own hard, gnarled fist.

There was a banging downstairs and a light as the men entered. They banged around noisily, calling for the rag man.

"We heard you talking about your treasure." The voice was slurred. "We just want to see it, that's all."

"You sure he's here?" One voice seemed to come from the room with the sofa.

"Yeah, he stays here every night."

"There's another room over there; I'm going to take a look. You got that flashlight?"

"Yeah, here, take the pipe too."

Greg opened his mouth to quiet the sound of his breath as he sucked it in uneasily. A beam of light hit the wall a few feet opposite him, then went out.

"Ain't nobody in that room," a voice said. "You think he gone or something?"

"I don't know," came the answer. "All I know is that I heard him talking about some kind of treasure. You know they found that shopping bag lady with that money in her bags."

"Yeah. You think he's upstairs?"

"HEY, OLD MAN, ARE YOU UP THERE?"

Silence.

"Watch my back, I'm going up."

There was a footstep on the stairs, and the beam from the flashlight danced crazily along the peeling wallpaper. Greg held his breath. There was another step and a loud crashing noise as the man banged the pipe against the wooden banister. Greg could feel his temples throb as the man slowly neared them. Greg thought about the pipe, wondering what he would do when the man reached them—what he *could* do.

Then Lemon Brown released his hand and moved toward the top of the stairs. Greg looked around and saw stairs going up to the next floor. He tried waving to Lemon Brown, hoping

---

gnarled (närld) *adj.* rough or rugged in appearance.

the old man would see him in the dim light and follow him to the next floor. Maybe, Greg thought, the man wouldn't follow them up there. Suddenly, though, Lemon Brown stood at the top of the stairs, both arms raised high above his head.

"There he is!" A voice cried from below.

"Throw down your money, old man, so I won't have to bash your head in!"

Lemon Brown didn't move. Greg felt himself near panic. The steps came closer, and still Lemon Brown didn't move. He was an eerie sight, a bundle of rags standing at the top of the stairs, his shadow on the wall looming over him. Maybe, the thought came to Greg, the scene could be even eerier.

Greg wet his lips, put his hands to his mouth and tried to make a sound. Nothing came out. He swallowed hard, wet his lips once more and howled as evenly as he could.

"What's that?"

As Greg howled, the light moved away from Lemon Brown, but not before Greg saw him hurl his body down the stairs at the men who had come to take his treasure. There was a crashing noise, and then footsteps. A rush of warm air came in as the downstairs door opened, then there was only an ominous silence.

Greg stood on the landing. He listened, and after a while there was another sound on the staircase.

"Mr. Brown?" he called.

"Yeah, it's me," came the answer. "I got their flashlight."

Greg exhaled in relief as Lemon Brown made his way slowly back up the stairs.

"You OK?"

"Few bumps and bruises," Lemon Brown said.

"I think I'd better be going," Greg said, his breath returning to normal. "You'd better leave, too, before they come back."

"They may hang around outside for a while," Lemon Brown said, "but they ain't getting their nerve up to come in here again. Not with crazy old rag men and howling spooks. Best you stay a while till the coast is clear. I'm heading out west tomorrow, out to east St. Louis."

"They were talking about treasures," Greg said. "You *really* have a treasure?"

Harmonica Blues   1940   *Dox Thrash   Free Library of Philadelphia*

"What I tell you? Didn't I tell you every man got a treasure?" Lemon Brown said. "You want to see mine?"

"If you want to show it to me," Greg shrugged.

"Let's look out the window first, see what them scoundrels be doing," Lemon Brown said.

They followed the oval beam of the flashlight into one of the rooms and looked out the window. They saw the men who had tried to take the treasure sitting on the curb near the corner. One of them had his pants leg up, looking at his knee.

"You sure you're not hurt?" Greg asked Lemon Brown.

"Nothing that ain't been hurt before," Lemon Brown said. "When you get as old as me all you say when something hurts is, 'Howdy, Mr. Pain, sees you back again.' Then when Mr. Pain see he can't worry you none, he go on mess with somebody else."

Greg smiled.

"Here, you hold this." Lemon Brown gave Greg the flashlight.

He sat on the floor near Greg and carefully untied the strings that held the rags on his right leg. When he took the rags away, Greg saw a piece of plastic. The old man carefully took off the plastic and unfolded it. He revealed some yellowed newspaper clippings and a battered harmonica.

"There it be," he said, nodding his head. "There it be."

Greg looked at the old man, saw the distant look in his eye, then turned to the clippings. They told of Sweet Lemon Brown, a blues singer and harmonica player who was appearing at different theaters in the South. One of the clippings said he had been the hit of the show, although not the headliner. All of the clippings were reviews of shows Lemon Brown had been in more than 50 years ago. Greg looked at the harmonica. It was dented badly on one side, with the reed holes on one end nearly closed.

"I used to travel around and make money for to feed my wife and Jesse—that's my boy's name. Used to feed them good, too. Then his mama died, and he stayed with his mama's sister. He growed up to be a man, and when the war come he saw fit to go off and fight in it. I didn't have nothing to give him except these things that told him who I was, and what he come from. If you know your pappy did something, you know you can do something too.

"Anyway, he went off to war, and I went off still playing and singing. 'Course by then I wasn't as much as I used to be, not without somebody to make it worth the while. You know what I mean?"

"Yeah," Greg nodded, not quite really knowing.

"I traveled around, and one time I come home, and there was this letter saying Jesse got killed in the war. Broke my heart, it truly did.

"They sent back what he had with him over there, and what it was is this old mouth fiddle and these clippings. Him carrying it around with him like that told me it meant something to him. That was my treasure, and when I give it to him he treated it just like that, a treasure. Ain't that something?"

"Yeah, I guess so," Greg said.

"You *guess* so?" Lemon Brown's voice rose an octave as he started to put his treasure back into the plastic. "Well, you got to guess 'cause you sure don't know nothing. Don't know enough to get home when it's raining."

"I guess . . . I mean, you're right."

"You OK for a youngster," the old man said as he tied the strings around his leg, "better than those scalawags what come here looking for my treasure. That's for sure."

"You really think that treasure of yours was worth fighting for?" Greg asked. "Against a pipe?"

"What else a man got 'cepting what he can pass on to his son, or his daughter, if she be his oldest?" Lemon Brown said. "For a big-headed boy you sure do ask the foolishest questions."

Lemon Brown got up after patting his rags in place and looked out the window again.

"Looks like they're gone. You get on out of here and get yourself home. I'll be watching from the window so you'll be all right."

Lemon Brown went down the stairs behind Greg. When they reached the front door the old man looked out first, saw the street was clear and told Greg to scoot on home.

"You sure you'll be OK?" Greg asked.

"Now didn't I tell you I was going to east St. Louis in the morning?" Lemon Brown asked. "Don't that sound OK to you?"

"Sure it does," Greg said. "Sure it does. And you take care of that treasure of yours."

"That I'll do," Lemon said, the wrinkles about his eyes suggesting a smile. "That I'll do."

The night had warmed and the rain had stopped, leaving puddles at the curbs. Greg didn't even want to think how late it was. He thought ahead of what his father would say and wondered if he should tell him about Lemon Brown. He thought about it until he reached his stoop, and decided against it. Lemon Brown would be OK, Greg thought, with his memories and his treasure.

Greg pushed the button over the bell marked Ridley, thought of the lecture he knew his father would give him, and smiled.

Meet WALTER DEAN MYERS

In a roundabout way, reading aloud in class might be said to have helped Walter Dean Myers win a Newbery Award. "As a kid," he recalls, "I had a severe speech problem. It was a real trauma for me when we all had to stand up in class and read aloud. . . . It was frustrating not to be able to say what I wanted to say, or say it quickly enough." To solve the problem, Myers decided to act on the advice of a teacher and write something of his own to read to the class. "Hey," he thought, "this is great. If I do the writing I can leave out all of the hard words." The strategy worked perfectly, and by the time Myers conquered his speech problem, he had discovered that he loved to write.

Earning a living as a writer isn't easy. Until he became established, Myers worked at a variety of jobs: Postal worker, interoffice messenger, clerk/interviewer in a factory, and editor. Although he continued to write, ten years of his adult life passed before he sold a book. Since that first book, Myers has had many young adult novels published. These include his Newbery Honor novel *Scorpions* and two Coretta Scott King Award winners, *Fallen Angels* and *Motown and Didi*. "Ultimately," Myers admits, "what I want to do with my writing is make the connection—reach out and touch the lives of my characters and share them with a reader."

RESPONDING TO *Literature*

THINK • TALK • WRITE

1 Which character did you like best in this story? Explain your answer.

2 What does Lemon Brown mean by his statement, "You don't give up the blues; they give you up"?

3 Lemon Brown says, "Every man got a treasure. You don't know that, you must be a fool!" What kind of treasure is he referring to? What is his "treasure"?

4 Why do you think the author included the information about Greg's father? How might Greg's relationship with his father be changed by meeting Lemon Brown?

5 In this story, you learned about an old-time blues musician from the American South. What story details can you find that describe the life of such performers?

ACTIVITIES

- **Write About Dialog** Write the scene in which Lemon Brown gives his "treasures" to his son. Make sure to include dialog that reveals the personalities of Brown and his son.

- **A Blues Show** With a classmate, research a blues musician. In the library, find books or articles with information about this musician. Make a brief presentation to the class about your subject's life, then play them one of his or her songs.

VOCABULARY PRACTICE

On a separate sheet of paper, write the vocabulary word that best completes each sentence.

impromptu   beckoned

musty   gnarled

tremor

1 His hands were _____ and twisted with age and disease.

2 The closed-up rooms smelled _____ and dank.

3 She _____ to me; she wanted me to follow her.

4 Without rehearsal, she played an _____ concert for me.

5 The newspaper clippings rustled as a _____ shook his hands.

SHORT STORY

LATHER AND NOTHING ELSE

CONNECT TO LITERATURE

Have you ever felt torn between two choices and just didn't know the right thing to do? How did you finally decide? Talk it over with a classmate. Then as you read "Lather and Nothing Else," note in your journal some of the thoughts that occur to the narrator as he tries to make a difficult choice.

THINKING ABOUT SUSPENSE

Sometimes while reading a story, you feel a growing excitement as you wait to find out what's going to happen. This feeling of tension is called *suspense*. One way writers build suspense is by suggesting more than one possible ending to a story. As you read you become more and more curious about the story's outcome.

As you read "Lather and Nothing Else," try to figure out how the author builds suspense. Does he suggest more than one possible ending?

DID YOU KNOW?

The author of the next story, Hernando Téllez, lived through some of the most troubled years in the history of his country, Colombia. In 1948 the popular leader of one political party was assassinated in Bogotá, the capital city. Violent rioting left the city in ruins, and some 2,000 people died. Declaring a national emergency, the country's president began to rule as a dictator, disbanding the Congress and ending freedom of the press, the courts, and religion. A civil war between the government and revolutionaries spread across the country; many rural areas swarmed with bandits. The fighting, called *La Violencia* by Colombians, killed about 250,000 people over the next twenty years, until peace was finally restored.

LATHER
AND NOTHING ELSE

BY HERNANDO TÉLLEZ

He came in without a word. I was <u>stropping</u> my best razor. And when I recognized him, I started to shake. But he did not notice. To cover my nervousness, I went on <u>honing</u> the razor. I tried the edge with the tip of my thumb and took another look at it against the light.

Meanwhile, he was taking off his cartridge-studded belt with the pistol holster suspended from it. He put it on a hook in the wardrobe and hung his cap above it. Then he turned full around toward me and,

---

stropping (strŏ′ping) *v.t.* sharpening on a flexible leather strip.
honing (hō′ning) *v.t.* sharpening the edge of.

loosening his tie, remarked, "It's hot as the devil. I want a shave." With that he took his seat.

I estimated he had a four-days' growth of beard, the four days he had been gone on the last foray after our men. His face looked burnt, tanned by the sun.

I started to work carefully on the shaving soap. I scraped some slices from the cake, dropped them into the mug, then added a little lukewarm water, and stirred with the brush. The lather soon began to rise.

"The fellows in the troop must have just about as much beard as I." I went on stirring up lather.

"But we did very well, you know. We caught the leaders. Some of them we brought back dead; others are still alive. But they'll all be dead soon."

"How many did you take?" I asked.

"Fourteen. We had to go pretty far in to find them. But now they're paying for it. And not one will escape; not a single one."

He leaned back in the chair when he saw the brush in my hand, full of lather. I had not yet put the sheet on him. I was certainly flustered. Taking a sheet from the drawer, I tied it around my customer's neck.

He went on talking. He evidently took it for granted that I was on the side of the existing <u>regime</u>.

"The people must have gotten a scare with what happened the other day," he said.

"Yes," I replied, as I finished tying the knot against his nape, which smelt of sweat.

"Good show, wasn't it?"

"Very good," I answered, turning my attention now to the brush. The man closed his eyes wearily and awaited the cool caress of the lather.

I had never had him so close before. The day he ordered the people to file through the schoolyard to look upon the four rebels hanging there, my path had crossed his briefly. But the sight of those <u>mutilated</u> bodies kept me from paying attention to the face of the man who had been directing it all and whom I now had in my hands.

It was not a disagreeable face, certainly. And the beard, which aged him a bit, was not unbecoming. His name was Torres. Captain Torres.

I started to lay on the first coat of lather. He kept his eyes closed.

---

regime (rə zhēm') *n.* government.
mutilated (mū′tə lā′tid) *adj.* very damaged or disfigured.

"I would love to catch a nap," he said, "but there's a lot to be done this evening."

I lifted the brush and asked, with pretended indifference: "A firing party?"

"Something of the sort," he replied, "but slower."

"All of them?"

"No, just a few."

I went on lathering his face. My hands began to tremble again. The man could not be aware of this, which was lucky for me. But I wished he had not come in. Probably many of our men had seen him enter the shop. And with the enemy in my house I felt a certain responsibility.

I would have to shave his beard just like any other, carefully, neatly, just as though he were a good customer, taking heed that not a single pore should emit a drop of blood. Seeing to it that the blade did not slip in the small <u>whorls</u>. Taking care that the skin was left clean, soft, shining, so that when I passed the back of my hand over it not a single hair should be felt. Yes. I was secretly a revolutionary, but at the same time I was a <u>conscientious</u> barber, proud of the way I did my job. And that four-day beard presented a challenge.

I took up the razor, opened the handle wide, releasing the blade, and started to work, downward from one sideburn. The blade responded to perfection. The hair was tough and hard; not very long, but thick. Little by little the skin began to show through. The razor gave out its usual sound as it gathered up layers of soap mixed with bits of hair. I paused to wipe it clean, and taking up the strop once more went about improving its edge, for I am a painstaking barber.

The man, who had kept his eyes closed, now opened them, put a hand out from under the sheet, felt of the part of his face that was emerging from the lather, and said to me, "Come at six o'clock this evening to the school."

"Will it be like the other day?" I asked, stiff with horror.

"It may be even better," he replied.

"What are you planning to do?"

"I'm not sure yet. But we'll have a good time."

Once more he leaned back and shut his eyes. I came closer, the razor on high.

"Are you going to punish all of them?" I timidly <u>ventured</u>.

"Yes, all of them."

---

whorls (hwûrlz) *n., pl.* patterns resembling coils or spirals.

conscientious (kon'shē en'shəs) *adj.* guided by a sense of right and wrong.

ventured (ven'chərd) *v.i.* expressed at the risk of objection.

The lather was drying on his face. I must hurry. Through the mirror, I took a look at the street. It appeared about as usual; there was the grocery shop with two or three customers. Then I glanced at the clock, two-thirty.

The razor kept descending. Now from the other sideburn downward. It was a blue beard, a thick one. He should let it grow like some poets, or some priests. It would suit him well. Many people would not recognize him. And that would be a good thing for him, I thought, as I went gently over all the throat line. At this point you really had to handle your blade skillfully, because the hair, while <u>scantier</u>, tended to fall into small whorls. It was a curly beard. The pores might open, minutely, in this area and let out a tiny drop of blood. A good barber like myself stakes his reputation on not permitting that to happen to any of his customers.

And this was indeed a special customer. How many of ours had he sent to their death? How many had he mutilated? It was best not to think about it. Torres did not know I was his enemy. Neither he nor the others knew it. It was a secret shared by very few, just because that made it possible for me to inform the revolutionaries about Torres's activities in the town and what he planned to do every time he went on one of his raids to hunt down rebels. So it was going to be very difficult to explain how it was that I had him in my hands and then let him go in peace, alive, clean-shaven.

His beard had now almost entirely disappeared. He looked younger, several years younger than when he had come in. I suppose that always happens to men who enter and leave barbershops. Under the strokes of my razor, Torres was <u>rejuvenated</u>; yes, because I am a good barber, the best in this town, and I say this in all modesty.

A little more lather here under the chin, on the Adam's apple, right near the great vein. How hot it is! Torres must be sweating just as I am. But he is not afraid. He is a tranquil man, who is not even giving thought to what he will do to his prisoners this evening. I, on the other hand, polishing his skin with this razor but avoiding the drawing of blood, careful with every stroke—I cannot keep my thoughts in order.

Confound the hour he entered my shop! I am a revolutionary but not a murderer. And it would be so easy to kill him. He deserves it. Or

---

scantier (skan′tē ər) *adj.* skimpier; thinner.
rejuvenated (ri jü′və nā′tid) *adj.* young again.

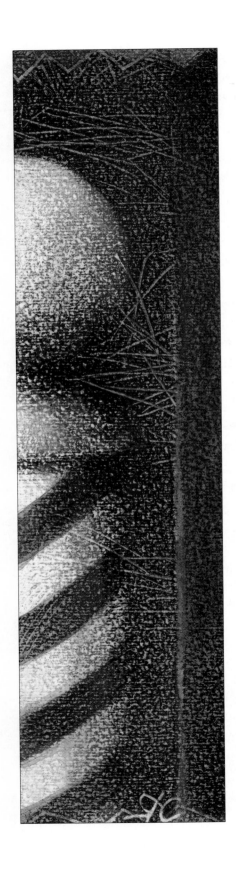

does he? No! No one deserves the sacrifice others make in becoming assassins. What is to be gained by it? Nothing. Others and still others keep coming, and the first kill the second, and then these kill the next, and so on until everything becomes a sea of blood. I could cut his throat, so, swish, swish! He would not even have time to moan, and with his eyes shut he would not even see the shine of the razor or the gleam in my eye.

But I'm shaking like a regular murderer. From his throat a stream of blood would flow on the sheet, over the chair, down on my hands, onto the floor. I would have to close the door. But the blood would go flowing, along the floor, warm, indelible, not to be <u>stanched</u>, until it reached the street like a small scarlet river.

I'm sure that with a good strong blow, a deep cut, he would feel no pain. He would not suffer at all. And what would I do then with the body? Where would I hide it? I would have to flee, leave all this behind, take shelter far away, very far away. But they would follow until they caught up with me. "The murderer of Captain Torres. He slit his throat while he was shaving him. What a cowardly thing to do."

And others would say, "The avenger of our people. A name to remember"—my name here. "He was the town barber. No one knew he was fighting for our cause."

And so, which will it be? Murderer or hero? My fate hangs on the edge of this razor blade. I can turn my wrist slightly, put a bit more pressure on the blade, let it

---

stanched (stôncht) *v.t.* brought the flow of blood to a stop.

sink in. The skin will yield like silk, like rubber, like the strop. There is nothing more tender than a man's skin, and the blood is always there, ready to burst forth. A razor like this cannot fail. It is the best one I have.

But I don't want to be a murderer. No, sir. You came in to be shaved. And I do my work honorably. I don't want to stain my hands with blood. Just with lather, and nothing else. You are an executioner; I am only a barber. Each one to his job. That's it. Each one to his job.

The chin was now clean, polished, soft. The man got up and looked at himself in the glass. He ran his hand over the skin and felt its freshness, its newness.

"Thanks," he said. He walked to the wardrobe for his belt, his pistol, and his cap. I must have been very pale, and I felt my shirt soaked with sweat. Torres finished adjusting his belt buckle, straightened his gun in its holster, and, smoothing his hair mechanically, put on his cap. From his trousers pocket he took some coins to pay for the shave. And he started toward the door. On the threshold he stopped for a moment, and turning toward me he said,

"They told me you would kill me. I came to find out if it was true. But it's not easy to kill. I know what I'm talking about."

MEET

HERNANDO TÉLLEZ

Throughout his life, Hernando Téllez (1908–1966) was no stranger to political violence. Colombia, his South American homeland, had been shaken by conflict and civil war since it became an independent republic in 1819.

As a well-known journalist and as a Colombian senator, Téllez observed and wrote about the unrest in his country. He is best remembered for his collection of short stories, Ashes for the Wind and Other Tales, *in which "Lather and Nothing Else" first appeared.*

RESPONDING TO *Literature*

THINK • TALK • WRITE

1 The barber wonders, if he were to kill Torres, whether he would be called murderer or hero. Which would you call him? Write a few lines in your journal to explain your opinions.

2 How would you describe the character of the barber? Why is he torn about whether to kill Torres?

3 What do you think the barber would say to the statement, "The end justifies the means"? Explain your ideas.

4 Why do you think the author chose to call this story "Lather and Nothing Else"?

5 Some Hispanic Americans have come to the United States to escape civil wars in their homelands. What does this story tell you about dangers they might have faced?

ACTIVITIES

• **Write About Suspense** Imagine that the rebels have won the war and Torres is on trial for his crimes. Outline a short story about the trial. List the ways in which you would build suspense.

• **A Radio News Flash** In small groups, write a brief news flash for "Rebel Radio" describing the resistance of the people to an attack by the government army. Then deliver your news flash to the class.

VOCABULARY PRACTICE

Read each question. On a separate sheet of paper, write the vocabulary word that answers each question.

regime   scantier

conscientious   rejuvenated

ventured

1 Which word tells how Captain Torres looked after his shave?

2 Which word describes how the barber asked Torres a question?

3 Which word would the narrator use to describe himself as a barber?

4 Which word would the barber use to compare the hair on the throat to the hair on the cheeks?

5 Which word would the barber use to talk about the body of people that makes laws for his country?

SHORT STORY

THE NECKLACE

CONNECT TO LITERATURE

Have you ever heard the expression "Pride goeth before a fall"? What does it mean? Discuss your ideas with a classmate. As you read "The Necklace," note in your journal how Madame Loisel's pride leads to her downfall.

THINKING ABOUT IRONY

Sometimes an event seems to have an odd twist. Imagine a fistfight breaking out at a peace rally! Or a millionaires' club going bankrupt! This kind of surprising, contradictory, or amusing twist—when things are actually very different than you would expect them to be—is called *irony*. Many writers use irony to give their stories a surprise ending: the reader is led to expect one result and then is surprised when the opposite occurs.

DID YOU KNOW?

If you had lived in Paris in the 1880s—the setting of "The Necklace"—you would have been living in the most exciting and beautiful city in Europe. Under the Emperor Napoleon III, Paris had been transformed into a city of broad boulevards and magnificent parks. The upper classes led a glittering life of balls, art exhibitions, and performances at the opera.

However, two-and-a-quarter million people lived in the French capital, and most of them were not wealthy. For those not in the privileged class, life was difficult and often frustrating. They were locked out of the glamorous life that went on in their city—and probably many of them, like the character in the next story, wished desperately to become part of it.

Lady Sewing 1879 *Pierre-Auguste Renoir* Collection of The Art Institute of Chicago

The Necklace

BY GUY DE MAUPASSANT

She was one of those pretty, charming young ladies, born, as if through an error of destiny, into a family of clerks. She had no dowry, no hopes, no means of becoming known, appreciated, loved, and married by a man either rich or distinguished; and she allowed herself to marry a petty clerk in the office of the Board of Education.

She was simple, not being able to adorn herself; but she was unhappy, as one out of her class; for women belong to no caste, no race; their grace, their beauty, and their charm serving them in the place of birth and family. Their inborn <u>finesse</u>, their instinctive elegance, their <u>suppleness</u> of wit are their only aristocracy, making some daughters of the people the equal of great ladies.

---

finesse (fi nes′) *n.* refinement or skill in doing something.
suppleness (sup′əl nes) *n.* flexibility; adaptability.

The Conversation *c.1878 Pierre-Auguste Renoir*
Collection of the Statens Konstmuseer, Stockholm

She suffered <u>incessantly</u>, feeling herself born for all delicacies and luxuries. She suffered from the poverty of her apartment, the shabby walls, the worn chair, and the faded stuffs. All these things, which another woman of her station would not have noticed, tortured and angered her. The sight of the little Breton, who made this humble home, awoke in her sad regrets and desperate dreams. She thought of quiet antechambers, with their Oriental hangings, lighted by high, bronze torches, and of the two great footmen in short trousers who sleep in the large armchairs, made sleepy by the heavy air from the heating <u>apparatus</u>. She thought of large drawing-rooms, hung in old silks, of graceful pieces of furniture carrying bric-a-brac of inestimable value, and of the little perfumed coquettish apartments, made for five o'clock chats with most intimate friends, men known and sought after, whose attention all women envied and desired.

When she seated herself for dinner, before the round table where the tablecloth had been used three days, opposite her husband, who uncovered the tureen with a delighted air, saying: "Oh! the good potpie! I know nothing better than that—" she would think of elegant dinners, of the shining silver, of the tapestries peopling the walls with ancient personages and rare birds in the midst of fairy forests; she thought of the exquisite food served on marvelous dishes, of the whispered gallantries, listened to with the smile of the sphinx, while eating the rose-colored flesh of the trout or a chicken's wing.

She had neither frocks nor jewels, nothing. And she loved only those things. She felt that she was made for them. She had such a desire to please, to be sought after, to be clever, and courted.

She had a rich friend, a schoolmate at the convent, whom she did not like to visit, she suffered so much when she returned. And she wept for whole days from chagrin, from regret, from despair, and disappointment.

---

incessantly (in ses′ənt lē) *adv.* continuously; unceasingly.
apparatus (ap′ə rat′əs) *n.* device or mechanism used for a particular purpose.

*O*ne evening her husband returned <u>elated</u>, bearing in his hand a large envelope.

"Here," he said, "here is something for you."

She quickly tore open the wrapper and drew out a printed card on which were inscribed these words:

The Minister of Public Instruction and
Madame George Ramponneau ask the honor of
Monsieur and Madame Loisel's company
Monday evening, January 18,
at the Minister's residence.

Instead of being delighted, as her husband had hoped, she threw the invitation spitefully upon the table murmuring:

"What do you suppose I want with that?"

"But, my dearie, I thought it would make you happy. You never go out, and this is an occasion, and a fine one! I had a great deal of trouble to get it. Everybody wishes one, and it is very select; not many are given to employees. You will see the whole official world there."

She looked at him with an irritated eye and declared impatiently:

"What do you suppose I have to wear to such a thing as that?"

He had not thought of that; he stammered:

"Why, the dress you wear when we go to the theater. It seems very pretty to me—"

He was silent, <u>stupefied</u>, in dismay, at the sight of his wife weeping. Two great tears fell slowly from the corners of her eyes toward the corners of her mouth; he stammered:

"What is the matter? What is the matter?"

By a violent effort, she had controlled her <u>vexation</u> and responded in a calm voice, wiping her moist cheeks:

"Nothing. Only I have no dress and consequently I cannot go to this affair. Give your card to some <u>colleague</u> whose wife is better fitted out than I."

He was grieved, but answered:

"Let us see, Matilda. How much would a suitable costume cost, something that would serve for other occasions, something very simple?"

---

elated (i lā′tid) *adj.* in high spirits.

stupefied (stü′pə fīd′) *adj.* amazed; overwhelmed.

vexation (vek sā′shən) *n.* annoyance.

colleague (kol′ēg) *n.* fellow member of a profession or other group.

She reflected for some seconds, making estimates and thinking of a sum that she could ask for without bringing with it an immediate refusal and a frightened exclamation from the economical clerk.

Finally she said, in a hesitating voice:

"I cannot tell exactly, but it seems to me that four hundred francs ought to cover it."

He turned a little pale, for he had saved just this sum to buy a gun that he might be able to join some hunting parties the next summer, on the plains of Nanterre, with some friends who went to shoot larks up there on Sunday. Nevertheless, he answered:

"Very well. I will give you four hundred francs. But try to have a pretty dress."

*T*he day of the ball approached and Madame Loisel seemed sad, disturbed, anxious. Nevertheless, her dress was nearly ready. Her husband said to her one evening:

"What is the matter with you? You have acted strangely for two or three days."

And she responded: "I am vexed not to have a jewel, not one stone, nothing to adorn myself with. I shall have such a poverty-laden look. I would prefer not to go to this party."

He replied: "You can wear some natural flowers. At this season they look very *chic*. For ten francs you can have two or three magnificent roses."

She was not convinced. "No," she replied, "there is nothing more humiliating than to have a shabby air in the midst of rich women."

Then her husband cried out: "How stupid we are! Go and find your friend Madame Forestier and ask her to lend you her jewels. You are well enough acquainted with her to do this."

She uttered a cry of joy: "It is true!" she said. "I had not thought of that."

The next day she took herself to her friend's house and related her story of distress. Madame Forestier went to her closet with the glass doors, took out a large jewel-case, brought it, opened it, and said: "Choose, my dear."

She saw at first some bracelets, then a collar of pearls, then a Venetian cross of gold and jewels and of admirable workmanship. She tried the jewels before the glass, hesitated, but could neither decide to take them nor leave them. Then she asked:

"Have you nothing more?"

"Why, yes. Look for yourself. I do not know what will please you."

Suddenly she discovered, in a black satin box, a superb necklace of diamonds, and her heart beat fast with an immoderate desire. Her hands trembled as she took them up. She placed them about her throat against her dress, and remained in ecstasy before them. Then she asked, in a hesitating voice, full of anxiety:

"Could you lend me this? Only this?"

"Why, yes, certainly."

She fell upon the neck of her friend, embraced her with passion, then went away with her treasure.

*T*he day of the ball arrived. Madame Loisel was a great success. She was the prettiest of all, elegant, gracious, smiling, and full of joy. All the men noticed her, asked her name, and wanted to be presented. All the members of the Cabinet wished to waltz with her. The Minister of Education paid her some attention.

She danced with enthusiasm, with passion, <u>intoxicated</u> with pleasure, thinking of nothing, in the triumph of her beauty, in the glory of her success, in a kind of cloud of happiness that came of all this homage, and all this admiration, of all these awakened desires, and this victory so complete and sweet to the heart of woman.

She went home toward four o'clock in the morning. Her husband had been half asleep in one of the little salons since midnight, with three other gentlemen whose wives were enjoying themselves very much.

He threw around her shoulders the wraps they had carried for the coming home, modest garments of everyday wear, whose poverty clashed with the elegance of the ball costume. She felt this and wished to hurry away in order not to be noticed by the other women who were wrapping themselves in rich furs.

---

intoxicated (in tok′si kā′tid) *adj.* greatly excited.

450   **Dance in the City** *c.1883* *Pierre-Auguste Renoir* *Collection of the Musee d'Orsay, Paris*

Loisel retained her: "Wait," said he. "You will catch cold out there. I am going to call a cab."

But she would not listen and descended the steps rapidly. When they were in the street, they found no carriage; and they began to seek for one, hailing the coachmen whom they saw at a distance.

They walked along toward the Seine, hopeless and shivering. Finally they found on the dock one of those old nocturnal coupés that one sees in Paris after nightfall, as if they were ashamed of their misery by day.

It took them as far as their door in Martyr Street, and they went wearily up to their apartment. It was all over for her. And on his part, he remembered that he would have to be at the office by ten o'clock.

She removed the wraps from her shoulders before the glass, for a final view of herself in her glory. Suddenly she uttered a cry. Her necklace was not around her neck.

Her husband, already half undressed, asked: "What is the matter?"

She turned toward him excitedly:

"I have—I have—I no longer have Madame Forestier's necklace."

He arose in dismay: "What! How is that? It is not possible."

And they looked in the folds of the dress, in the folds of the mantle, in the pockets, everywhere. They could not find it.

He asked: "You are sure you still had it when we left the house?"

"Yes, I felt it in the vestibule as we came out."

"But if you had lost it in the street, we should have heard it fall. It must be in the cab."

"Yes. It is probably. Did you take the number?"

"No. And you, did you notice what it was?"

"No."

They looked at each other utterly cast down. Finally, Loisel dressed himself again.

"I am going," said he, "over the track where we went on foot, to see if I can find it."

And he went. She remained in her evening gown, not having the force to go to bed, stretched upon a chair, without ambition or thoughts.

Toward seven o'clock her husband returned. He had found nothing.

He went to the police and to the cab offices, and put an advertisement in the newspapers, offering a reward; he did everything that afforded them a suspicion of hope.

---

retained (ri tānd′) *v.t.* continued to have or hold.

vestibule (ves′tə būl′) *n.* entrance hall or passage between the outer door and the interior of a building.

She waited all day in a state of bewilderment before this frightful disaster. Loisel returned at evening with his face harrowed and pale; and had discovered nothing.

"It will be necessary," said he, "to write to your friend that you have broken the clasp of the necklace and that you will have it repaired. That will give us time to turn around."

She wrote as he dictated.

*A*t the end of a week, they had lost all hope. And Loisel, older by five years, declared:

"We must take measures to replace this jewel."

The next day they took the box which had inclosed it, to the jeweler whose name was on the inside. He consulted his books:

"It is not I, Madame," said he, "who sold this necklace; I only furnished the casket."

Then they went from jeweler to jeweler seeking a necklace like the other one, consulting their memories, and ill, both of them, with chagrin and anxiety.

In a shop of the Palais-Royal, they found a chaplet of diamonds which seemed to them exactly like the one they had lost. It was valued at forty thousand francs. They could get it for thirty-six thousand.

They begged the jeweler not to sell it for three days. And they made an arrangement by which they might return it for thirty-four thousand francs if they found the other one before the end of February.

Loisel possessed eighteen thousand francs which his father had left him. He borrowed the rest.

He borrowed it, asking for a thousand francs of one, five hundred of another, five louis of this one, and three louis of that one. He gave notes, made ruinous promises, took money of usurers and the whole race of lenders. He compromised his whole existence, in fact, risked his signature, without even knowing whether he could make it good or not, and, harassed by anxiety for the future, by the black misery which surrounded him, and by the prospect of all physical privations and moral torture, he went to get the new necklace, depositing on the merchant's counter thirty-six thousand francs.

■

harrowed (har′ōd) *adj.* frightened, distressed.
privations (prī vā′shənz) *n., pl.* lacks in the comforts or necessities of life.

When Madame Loisel took back the jewels to Madame Forestier, the latter said to her in a frigid tone:

"You should have returned them to me sooner, for I might have needed them."

She did not open the jewel-box as her friend feared she would. If she should perceive the substitution, what would she think? What should she say? Would she take her for a robber?

*M*adame Loisel now knew the horrible life of necessity. She did her part, however, completely, heroically. It was necessary to pay this frightful debt. She would pay it. They sent away the maid; they changed their lodgings; they rented some rooms under a mansard roof.

She learned the heavy cares of a household, the odious work of a kitchen. She washed the dishes, using her rosy nails upon the greasy pots and the bottoms of the stewpans. She washed the soiled linen, the chemises and dishcloths, which she hung on the line to dry; she took down the refuse to the street each morning and brought up the water, stopping at each landing to breathe. And, clothed like a woman of the people, she went to the grocer's, the butcher's, and the fruiterer's, with her basket on her arm, shopping, haggling over the last sou of her miserable money.

Every month it was necessary to renew some notes, thus obtaining time, and to pay others.

The husband worked evenings, putting the books of some merchants in order, and nights he often did copying at five sous a page.

And this life lasted for ten years.

At the end of ten years, they had restored all, all, with interest of the usurer, and accumulated interest besides.

Madame Loisel seemed old now. She had become a strong, hard woman, the crude woman of the poor household. Her hair badly dressed, her skirts awry, her hands red, she spoke in a loud tone, and washed the floors with large pails of water. But sometimes, when her husband was at the office, she would seat herself before the window and think of that evening party of former times, of that ball where she was so beautiful and so flattered.

---

mansard (man′särd) *adj.* having two slopes on all sides, with the lower slopes almost vertical.
chemises (shə mē′zəz) *n., pl.* loose, shirtlike undergarments worn by women.

How would it have been if she had not lost that necklace? Who knows? Who knows? How singular is life, and how full of changes! How small a thing will ruin or save one!

One Sunday, as she was taking a walk in the Champs-Elysées, to rid herself of the cares of the week, she suddenly perceived a woman walking with a child. It was Madame Forestier, still young, still pretty, still attractive. Madame Loisel was affected. Should she speak to her? Yes, certainly. And now that she had paid, she would tell her all. Why not?

She approached her. "Good morning, Jeanne."

Her friend did not recognize her and was astonished to be so familiarly addressed by this common personage. She stammered:

"But, Madame—I do not know—You must be mistaken—"

"No, I am Matilda Loisel."

Her friend uttered a cry of astonishment: "Oh! my poor Matilda! How you have changed—"

"Yes, I have had some hard days since I saw you; and some miserable ones—and all because of you—"

"Because of me? How is that?"

"You recall the diamond necklace that you loaned me to wear to the Commissioner's ball?"

"Yes, very well."

"Well, I lost it."

"How is that, since you returned it to me?"

"I returned another to you exactly like it. And it has taken us ten years to pay for it. You can understand that it was not easy for us who have nothing. But it is finished and I am decently content."

Madame Forestier stopped short. She said:

"You say that you bought a diamond necklace to replace mine?"

"Yes. You did not perceive it then? They were just alike."

And she smiled with a proud and simple joy. Madame Forestier was touched and took both her hands as she replied:

"Oh! my poor Matilda! Mine were false. They were not worth over five hundred francs!"

The Umbrellas   *1881   Pierre-Auguste Renoir   Collection of the National Gallery, London*

MEET *Guy de Maupassant*

For years, Guy de Maupassant worked at a job he found boring. All the while, this French author longed to be a famous writer and a part of the glamorous world of the rich. In 1882, his efforts paid off; one of his stories was an enormous success. De Maupassant was very productive for the next ten years. But eventually the strain of overwork and his wild lifestyle destroyed his health. He died at age forty-three.

In masterpieces such as "A Piece of String" and "The Umbrella," as well as "The Necklace," de Maupassant created unforgettable characters who long for a better life. To attain their dreams, they make decisions that have profound and, as Madame Loisel discovers, unexpected results.

More Short Stories

- *To Break the Silence*, edited by Peter A. Barrett (Dell, 1986). This collection of thirteen short stories by well-known British and American authors is one you're sure to enjoy because of the carefully drawn characters and entertaining plots.
- *Sixteen*, edited by Donald R. Gallo (Dell, 1984). In this compilation of short stories written especially for teenagers, you will meet a variety of characters who deal with issues that concern young people today.
- *Visions*, edited by Donald R. Gallo (Dell, 1987). Here is another collection of stories that will appeal to you because of their diversity, excitement, and relevancy.

RESPONDING TO
Literature

THINK • TALK • WRITE

1 Were you surprised by the ending of this story? Jot down your reactions in your journal.

2 What kind of person is Madame Loisel? How does her character lead to her downfall?

3 If she had to do it all over again, do you think Madame Loisel would go to the ball? Why or why not?

4 How do you suppose Madame Loisel feels at the end of the story? How do you think Madame Forestier feels?

5 How does the author describe the status of women in the Paris of the 1890s? Use story details in your response. Do you think things are different for women today? Why or why not?

ACTIVITIES

• **Write About Irony** Many newspapers use irony to grab attention. Think of the *Titanic* disaster. Headlines might have said, "Unsinkable Ship Lost at Sea." Choose three events. Use irony to write headlines that will grab a reader's attention.

• **A Dream of Luxury** Draw one of the luxurious rooms Madame Loisel dreams of having. Be sure to include story details in your drawing.

VOCABULARY PRACTICE

Read each sentence. On a separate sheet of paper, write the vocabulary word that best completes each sentence.

suppleness	vexation
incessantly	colleague
apparatus	intoxicated
elated	retained
stupefied	vestibule

1 The student was _____ by the difficulty of the math problems.

2 Burners, beakers, and tubes make up a laboratory's _____.

3 The worker decided to discuss the problem with her _____.

4 Suede leather is soft, with a special _____.

5 A frustrated listener is probably feeling great _____.

6 The tenant complained because the people upstairs were playing the radio _____.

7 The winner of a million-dollar lottery probably feels _____.

8 The champagne and excitement _____ Madame Loisel.

9 They stepped through the front door into a small painted _____.

10 She _____ her sense of humor even during the war.

WRITING

Life has many turning points. Often these moments are unpredictable, and once they happen, nothing seems the same. Write a short story about just such a turning point.

PREWRITE

How will you plan your story? Think about some of the turning points in your own life or in the life of a friend. Base your short story on one of these real-life experiences.

You can use a diagram like the one here to develop details for your story. Suppose your story describes a visit to Japan. Here's what one writer did.

Select the best ideas from your diagram and from any other notes you have written. Add other ideas that improve your story.

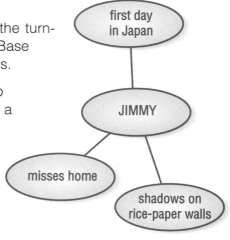

DRAFT

Read the beginning of this draft about a turning point. Would you have started with this moment in the story?

This writer begins by plunging right into a dramatic moment.

> ### A Fateful Trip
>
> Jimmy woke up suddenly. Shadows that looked like people were moving across the rice-paper screen. Jimmy's heart beet wildly. He had been away from the United States for only a day and he missed home alredy.

Now it's time to start your draft. Keep your audience in mind and don't forget your purpose for writing. It might help if you talk about your opening paragraph with a partner.

458

A SHORT STORY

REVISE

Sometimes taking a break before you revise helps. This writer waited a few hours and then made adjustments.

The writer decides to use a more vivid image of Jimmy waking up. ┄┄┄►

Does this change make it easier to picture the shadows on the screen? ┄┄┄►

> *shot up in bed*
> Jimmy ~~woke up suddenly~~. Shadows
> *creeping*
> that looked like people were moving
> across the rice-paper screen. Jimmy's
> heart beet wildly. He had been away from
> the United States for only a day and he
> missed home alredy.

Revise your own draft. Talk about your story with a partner. Have you used vivid language to make the action easier for readers to picture?

PROOFREAD

Study the writer's proofreading corrections. Do you agree with each of the changes?

A computer spelling check will help you, but it won't correct every ┄┄┄► error. This one is an example.

> *shot up in bed*
> Jimmy ~~woke up suddenly~~. Shadows
> *creeping*
> that looked like people were moving
> across the rice-paper screen. Jimmy's
> *beat*
> heart (beet) wildly. He had been away from
> the United States for only a day, and he
> *already*
> missed home (alredy.)

Errors in spelling, punctuation, or grammar can make readers lose interest. Make sure you correct all of these mistakes.

PUBLISH

Jot down some ideas for publishing your short story. Choose the one you like best. Ask friends what they think of your presentation idea.

WRITING

EFFECTIVE ADJECTIVES AND ADVERBS

ENRICH YOUR WRITING OF **SHORT STORIES.**

Adjectives and adverbs can add color and excitement to your writing. They can be used to create precise images, ideas, and feelings in the reader's mind.

Read the paragraphs below. Which makes you feel as if you can see, hear, feel, taste, or touch what is happening in the scene?

Paragraph 1

Marisol inched up the cliff. Above her she saw a shelf of rock. She fixed her eyes on it and continued to climb.

Paragraph 2

With legs trembling, Marisol cautiously inched up the steep, rocky cliff. Above her she saw a moss-covered shelf of rock. She fixed her frightened eyes on it and continued to climb.

PRACTICE 1 Respond on a separate sheet of paper.

1 Which words in the second paragraph bring the scene to life?

2 Rewrite the second paragraph using other adjectives and adverbs to bring a different feeling to the scene.

460

COMPARATIVE AND SUPERLATIVE ADJECTIVES

REMEMBER THESE RULES ABOUT ADJECTIVES WHEN YOU ARE WRITING **SHORT STORIES.**

- Add *-er* and *-est* to form the comparative and superlative forms of most one-syllable adjectives and some two-syllable adjectives. If *-er* and *-est* sound awkward, use *more* and *most.*

- Use *more* and *most* for the comparative and superlative of all adjectives of three or more syllables.

- A few adjectives, such as *good* and *bad,* have irregular forms of comparison. (*better, best; worse, worst*)

PRACTICE 2 Change each adjective into its comparative or superlative form as necessary. Write your answers on a separate sheet of paper.

1 The next cliff was even (high) than the previous one.

2 Of all the climbs this would be the (dangerous).

3 This rock shelf was (sunny) than the one below.

4 Marisol was the (good) climber in her school.

COMPARATIVE AND SUPERLATIVE ADVERBS

USE THESE RULES ABOUT ADVERBS WHEN YOU ARE WRITING **SHORT STORIES.**

- Add *-er* and *-est* to form the comparative and superlative forms of one-syllable adverbs and a few two-syllable adverbs. Use *more* and *most* to form the comparative and superlative of most other adverbs.

- A few adverbs, such as *well* and *little,* have irregular forms of comparison. (*better, best; less, least*)

- Use *less* and *least* for all negative comparisons.

PRACTICE 3 Change each adverb into its comparative or superlative form. Use a negative comparison for the last sentence.

1 We hiked up the hill (quickly) than the teacher.

2 All three of us came early, but Mike got there (early).

3 After the climb, I ate (little) than he did.

4 He climbed (high) than I did. (negative comparison)

PROJECT 1

WRITING A BUSINESS LETTER

Getting a job or taking a volunteer position can change your life. One step in getting such a job is to write a business letter to a prospective employer in which you portray yourself in the best possible light.

PREWRITE

How do you see yourself and your talents? Could you convince others of your worth? Make two lists in which you jot down your skills and best qualities. Then focus on those that match the job you want to get. Take a look at what one writer did.

Skills	Qualities
1. good at math	1. prompt
2. athletic	2. friendly
3. good with hands	3. sense of humor
	4. caring

DRAFT Think about your purpose and audience when you write your draft. Keep your letter formal and to the point.

REVISE Take some time out before you revise your letter so you can look at the draft with a fresh eye. Is there anything confusing or misleading in the letter? Is it well organized and in the correct form for a business letter?

PROOFREAD Read your letter for errors. Then ask a friend to check it for mistakes.

PUBLISH Send your letter to the right person if you are ready to apply for a position. Or save your letter for a future date.

> ▶ *Proofreading Alert!*
>
> Avoid double negatives by removing one of the negative words. Check page 187 in *Writing and Language Handbook*.

PROJECTS

PROJECT 2

DOCUMENT A TURNING POINT WITH PHOTOS

REMEMBER TO: • PREWRITE • DRAFT • REVISE • PROOFREAD • PUBLISH

Use photos and captions to tell about a real turning point you or someone else experienced. Borrow photos from a family album or cut them from newspapers or magazines. Before you begin, decide on what kind of images will most effectively convey the incident you want to describe.

You can use the "5 W's and H" questions, to get your ideas flowing: What happened? When did it happen? Where did it happen? Who was involved? Why did it happen? How was it a turning point?

Arrange your photos and captions and share your work with a friend.

"5 W'S AND H" QUESTIONS

Why?
Who?
Where?
How?
What?
When?

PROJECT 3

ROLE-PLAY A TURNING POINT

REMEMBER TO: • PREWRITE • DRAFT • REVISE • PROOFREAD • PUBLISH

Work with a few other classmates to act out an event that could change a person's life. You might use a diagram like this one to organize your ideas.

Characters and Setting	What's the Problem?	What's the Solution?
swimmer in ocean	swimmer struggling in water; calling for help	save swimmer
two or three teens on beach		
lifeguard		

V I E W P

IS SCHOOL IMPORTANT TO YOUR FUTURE?

How many times has someone said, "You can't get anywhere today without an education"? First you're expected to graduate from high school, then college. Some professions even require a postcollege degree. If you just spent a week studying for a math test and then flunked it anyway, you're probably wondering where it all ends. Or, if you're interested in work that doesn't require a college degree, you might think school isn't important to your future.

CONSIDER THIS ISSUE: You're interested in becoming a carpenter. That will mean getting a job as a carpenter's apprentice after high school. You start to question how important your classes are to your professional goal. Why should you bother to study if your school-work seems to have little to do with your career choice? Think about both sides of the issue before making up your mind.

- No matter what you make your life's work, isn't a good education valuable?
- Can school prepare you for a future in which the job market changes all the time?
- Isn't what you learn outside of school just as important to your future as what you learn in school?

464

Read the following viewpoints about the importance of school to your future. Then take some time to decide which one is closest to your own opinion. Think of some arguments of your own to support the position you choose.

VIEWPOINT 1

I think school is very important to my future.

- Your education *is* your future. No matter what occupation you choose, it's important to have a good education.
- In school you learn how to think and to apply what you've learned to your life in the outside world.
- School involves more than classes and homework; you also learn how to work with other people on a daily basis.

VIEWPOINT 2

I don't consider school to be important to my future.

- What you learn in school doesn't seem to have much to do with the outside world.
- There's no way that what you learn in school can prepare you for a specific job.
- Some people can learn more by working than they can by studying in a classroom.

VIEWPOINT 3

Since my ideas about my future change all the time, I'm not sure how relevant school is to my future plans.

- School isn't as important to me as being able to learn a specific job skill.
- What happens to me in the future will depend more on the person I become than on what I learn in school.
- There are so many different ways to "learn," including educational television and computers, that a traditional education doesn't seem so important.

WHAT DO YOU THINK?

Do you share one of the viewpoints above, or do you have another? Brainstorm other opinions. Then make up questions about this issue to ask in a student poll. Discuss the poll results in class.

real life
CONNECT

TURNING POINTS: They are dramatic and sometimes unexpected events, decisions, or insights that can change a life forever.

A turning point may be a great historical event or a moment of personal truth. But big or small, every turning point changes lives in unexpected ways. Jimmy Valentine discovers love and a turning point in O. Henry's "A Retrieved Reformation," and a career burglar becomes an honest man. In "Little by Little," Jean Little reaches a turning point when she discovers the power of words.

Personal turning points become part of us for the rest of our lives. Turning points can change a nation as well. Historic events leave their mark on a nation and the world. One way to highlight these key events is on a **time line,** such as the one below.

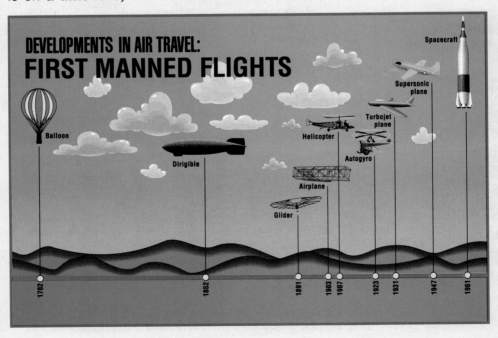

DEVELOPMENTS IN AIR TRAVEL:
FIRST MANNED FLIGHTS

Spacecraft

Supersonic plane

Turbojet plane

Helicopter

Autogyro

Balloon

Dirigible

Airplane

Glider

1782   1852   1891   1903   1907   1923   1931   1947   1961

I O N S

THINK • TALK • WRITE

Here are three activities in which you use time lines. Think of other situations which require creating or using time lines. Then choose an activity below or one of your own and talk or write about it.

PROJECT 1

STUDY A TIME LINE Time lines give us important information about historical or contemporary events. Find a time line in a national news magazine. Identify the title and subject. What is the time period covered by the time line? What are the beginning and end dates on the time line? What key information can you learn from the time line? Discuss the answers to these questions in small groups.

PROJECT 2

CREATE A TIME LINE Time lines are simple to make. Read several newspaper or magazine articles about a current event. Create a time line on posterboard highlighting key events from the news stories in chronological order. Write the date and a brief description of each event on the time line. Display your completed time line in class.

PROJECT 3

PERSONAL TIME LINES Time lines can help you keep track of ongoing events in your daily life, such as the record of a sports team. You can also use a personal time line to record important events in your own life. Make a time line to represent your school year. Write a summary of each event and the date on the time line. Continue your time line throughout the school year by adding important events to the time line.

THE NATURAL WORLD

CATERPILLAR

Brown and furry
  Caterpillar in a hurry,
   Take your walk
    To the shady leaf, or stalk,
  Or what not,
   Which may be the chosen spot.
  No toad spy you,
  Hovering bird of prey pass by you;
  Spin and die,
  To live again a butterfly.

—Christina Rossetti

Mountains in Four Seasons *1990   Fumiko Hori   The Sato Museum*

THE NATURAL WORLD

BEFORE READING

....

POLAR NIGHT

CONNECT TO LITERATURE

Does your year have a regular pattern?
Do you do the same things each fall,
each winter, each spring, each summer? Discuss your ideas with a
classmate. As you read "Polar Night,"
jot down in your journal all the things
the mother polar bear does at the
same time each year.

THINKING ABOUT SETTING

The time and place in which the main action of a story occurs is
called the *setting.* A story might be set in the past, present, or future,
or during a particular time of day or time of year—for example, during the winter of 1942 or at nine o'clock on a Friday evening. The
place where a story is set can be a planet, a country, a state, a
community, a neighborhood, a building, or even a room; it can also
be real or imaginary. A story's setting might be New York City, Mars,
or a teenager's bedroom.

HAVE YOU EVER?

Have you ever wished on a summer day that the sun would never
set? If you lived in the Arctic Circle, your wish would come true!
The Arctic Circle is an imaginary line across the northern regions of
Alaska, Russia, Scandinavia, and Canada, about 1,600 miles (2,600
km) from the North Pole. Inside the circle the sun does not set on
the longest day of summer; on the longest day of winter the sun
never rises.

The climate of this region is very harsh; winter temperatures average
−45˚F (−43˚C) and have gone as low as −93˚F (−69˚C). There are
no trees there, although some species of plants manage to survive.
The most common animals are reindeer and caribou, and the Inuit
people, who live in the Arctic Circle, hunt these animals for their meat.
They also hunt foxes, squirrels, and polar bears.

POLAR

NIGHT

By Norah Burke

As the hot arctic summer drew to a close, till the magenta sun only slid along the horizon to sink again at once, the polar bear knew that a hard time lay ahead for her.

During the months of night, fifty degrees below zero, her cubs would be born. The great task of motherhood was already begun, the time soon coming when she would bury herself deep down under the snow to give birth. From then until the day when she and the cubs burrowed up into daylight again, she would not eat. She and they must live on what she had stored in her body during the summer, and on what she could catch and eat now. She must finish fattening herself up for the ordeal, and there was not much time left.

At the moment she was hunting along the edge of the ice, because where there was water there were seals, also fish, and the chance of a porpoise or walrus. As winter closed the roots and berries and <u>lichen</u> and seaweed of the polar islands into glass, the bears moved to the ice-edge for their food.

This was the arctic region, the area north of the limit of tree-growth. The shores of Greenland, Siberia, Alaska, Canada bordered upon this <u>spectral</u> sea. It was a landscape of snow and old ice and new ice, of drifting pack ice, and berg ice from the glaciers, all in constant motion, lanes and pools of pure cobalt looking-glass opening and closing all the time in the pack. Where the old ice had been pushed up together in terraces, ice-eaves burned green and lilac underneath. In summer the skuas and ivory gulls and other birds made the air <u>raucous</u> with quarrels, but now all that the bear could hear was the wash of blue water against grinding ice.

Under the dark sky, on the white land, in the desolation of the arctic landscape, she was part of its white power, moving with a long swinging walk and huge flat yellow hairy snow-man footfalls. Strong and dangerous,

the largest of bears, able to swim forty miles out to sea if need be, she stalked her kingdom in which no natural enemy challenged her reign. Her feet, bristled underneath to give grip on the ice, carried her huge weight with a light and silent tread; while the low swinging head searched the ice all the time for food.

She was not clearly aware of what was happening in her body, but the instinct was there to love the unborn cubs, to prepare for them and protect them; she did not risk her body in careless adventures as she would at other times.

But food? Food—

Already the iron of winter was in the clean cold air, though she felt the cold only with her eyes and black nose and black lips, where the air stung her, and on the long pinkish gray tongue, moving all the time to prevent freezing, that slung in and out of her mouth among the large cruel teeth.

Suddenly, away down the ice-field, where a dark blue lead showed in the pack, she saw a blackish slug on the ice—a seal. It was essential to catch him. In a moment she had decided on her approach, and slipped silently into the water to cut off his

---

lichen (lī′kən) *n.* any of a large group of plantlike organisms found in all parts of the world, usually growing on tree trunks, rocks, or the ground. Lichens consist of a fungus and an algae growing together.
spectral (spek′trəl) *adj.* ghostly.
raucous (rô′kəs) *adj.* disorderly; rowdy.

line of retreat. The ice rocked as her great weight left it.

The bear was as much at home in the water as on land—buoyant, swimming like a dog, but on top or submerged—and the water much warmer than the air on her face. Not wet, either: inside the layer of fat and the shaggy oily watertight coat, she felt as dry as on land.

By a series of cunning dives and approaches, and keeping under the shoulder of ice, she got near to the seal. Breathing carefully, every nerve keyed to the task of silent approach, ready to spring—to dive—to slaughter, she slid nearer—nearer—

Suddenly the seal saw her. Terror convulsed his face. A moment of awful indecision—whether to plunge into the sea, his natural line of escape, and perhaps fall straight into her jaws, or to struggle across the ice to that other hole—

He swung away from her, humping madly along. The bear lunged up out of the water, on to the ice, on to the terrified seal.

The water slushed off her everywhere like a tidal wave. There was a flurry of snow and water and fighting seal. His quick struggling body flapped under her as she slew him. Blood spurted on to the snow.

When the seal was dead, the bear attended first to herself, getting rid of the wet from her coat before it could freeze, although oil had kept off the frost so far. She shook, and the drops flew off in rainbows in all directions. She rolled and nosed along in the snow, wiping her flanks, her chin, and soon all was dry. A few hairs crisped up and stuck to each other with frost.

Now for the seal. She ripped up the body, turning back the skin and blubber, letting out a cloud of steam, and ate greedily of the hot crimson meat. Seal meat was her favorite, full of flavor, a hot meal, not like the white icy flakes of cod.

Then, although the bear had no natural enemies, she stopped suddenly as she ate, lifted her head, looked, listened, scented. Blood dripped from her chin onto the snow.

There was nothing.

All the same she trusted her instinct and, leaving the rest of the meal, slipped into the water, where she could keep her cubs safe, where it was warmer, and easier to move.

Presently she saw upright seals coming along the shore. They were rather rare creatures, these, and dangerous for all they were so weak. The places where they lived had light and noise, and smelled full of good food. The she-bear often drew near the places, attracted by those smells. She hunted these land-seals too, and ate them when she could. They were not like the sea-seals, though. They wore seal fur, and

---

convulsed (kən vulsd´) *v.t.* shook or disturbed violently.

their skins were rubbed with seal blubber, but there was a different taste inside.

They in their turn hunted bear, as the she-bear knew well. She had sometimes found the place of the kill, and seen the white empty skins hanging up by the camps, smelled the dark red gamy flesh cooking.

Now as she watched the approaching men, she considered whether to kill them, but the unborn life in her said get away. So she dived and swam and melted out of their radius.

In the next few days the bear gorged on fish and seal. No longer the hot rocks and <u>scree</u> of summer gave forth good-tasting moss and lichens or the sharp-fleshed berries and sweet roots. She dived into the cold blue ocean for her food.

But now the arctic day was over. In the pink twilight a snowy owl was flitting silently across the waste, moving south and south as life was squeezed out of the arctic desert by the polar night.

Then came the freezing of the sea. Crystals formed below the surface and rose, and needles of ice shot across from one to another, joining them together, thickening, hardening, adding more ice to the <u>floes</u> already many years old. The ice talked, grinding its teeth, sending out every now and then a singing crack. Curtains of colored flame rippled in the sky. The polar night began.

Now the real cold came. Now the food disappeared, and old male bears grew lean and savage.

The she-bear chose her den.

There was a great raw range of decayed ice that had been pushed up into mountains whose hollows were

---

scree (skrē) *n.* pile of stones and debris from a landslide lying on a slope at the base of a cliff.
floes (flōz) *n., pl.* masses or sheets of floating ice.

packed with snow. Icicles yards long hung on the south side from the summer, and behind this curtain of ice she found a great purple cave, carved in diamond and full of snow.

This was the place.

Her body was ready now for the ordeal. Thick fat, gathered from seal and halibut, lined her skin.

She burrowed down into the violet snow on the floor of the cave. It was so light that the wind of moving blew it about like feathers, and she could breathe in it. She burrowed deeper and deeper, while the snow sifted and fell in soundlessly behind her, till presently she was deep enough.

She curled and rolled herself round and round, pushing the snow, packing it, shaping the den. All the sides of it melted with her heat, then froze again into slippery walls. And the hot breath passed up through the way she had dug, melting the sides of the channel which also froze again and left a tube which would supply her with air until she came up in the spring.

Inside the snow and ice—inside her thick oily fur and the layer of blubber, she was warm, full fed and sleepy. She slept and waited.

In the fullness of time, the first familiar pang of birth trembled in her stomach. Pain fluttered like a butterfly and was gone.

She stirred, lifted her head, rearranged herself.

It came again, stronger, longer.

She moved uneasily.

Then in long strong accomplishing strokes it was there—hard, forcing, contracting, out of her control. Moving to a crescendo. She grunted, tensed all her muscles, pressed and gasped. Another spasm, and on the smooth strong river of pain, she felt the first cub come out.

A wave of relief relaxed her.

There he lay mewing, so wet and tiny, hardly alive, and she nuzzled him delightedly, starting to clean him up.

But now another spasm—the same long final one as before, though easier—and the second cub was born.

It was over now. She felt the diminishing contractions, the subsidence of pain, pulsing quieter.

Now to clean them up. She licked and licked them, turning them over, rolling and caressing them; then life strengthened in them as they dried, as they fed. She lay in bliss, feeling her own life flowing from her heart.

Meanwhile in the world above, the sun had returned, first a green glow, then a rosy one, then touching the topmost peaks, days before the first sunrise.

Deep in the snow cave, the bear knew it as the snow grew luminous with the light pressing through.

One day she heard voices. The snow vibrated with footsteps, the ice ceiling cracked.

---

crescendo (kri shen′dō) *n.* gradual increase in loudness or force.
luminous (lü′mə nəs) *adj.* sending out light of its own; shining.

She rose, shook herself free of the cubs and stood ready in case the land-seals saw the warm yellow air hole that marked her den—in case one of them walked over her and fell in . . .

She stood fierce, lean, ready to defend her cubs, her heart pounding hot and loud as fever in her thin body.

Gradually the voices and the footsteps died away.

Presently it was time to come out into the world again. The cubs' eyes were open, their coats grown, they were walking, getting stronger every day. Now they must come out and face the world and swim and fight and catch seals. There was everything to teach them, and while they were still learning—still babies, they had got to be kept safe and fed. All this she had to do alone. Other years she'd had a mate to help her, but this time he was gone—lost—Those white skins hanging by the camps—

She began to tear her way out, the giant paws and black nails breaking open the ice walls of their den. The ice gave, snow fell in.

They climbed out.

Clean frozen air, dazzling with sun, hit them like the stroke of an axe. Light entered the brain in needles through the eyes. Only gradually, as the pupils contracted, did it become possible to see.

Under an iridescent sun-halo, the arctic landscape blazed white and navy blue. Everything hit them at

once—light, noise, wind—the blast of a new world.

Down there was the water—

The mother bear plunged joyfully into the buoyant cleanness. All the dirt and staleness of winter were washed away. It was like flight. She plunged and rose and shook and plunged again

---

iridescent (ir'i des'ənt) *adj.* displaying shimmering and changing colors, like those reflected by soap bubbles.

in sheer joy. So fresh, so clean, the salt cold water running through her teeth—

Then she resumed the heavy duties of parenthood, turned to the cubs. They were sitting on the edge, squeaking with fright, and she began urging them to come in. They kept feeling forward, then scrambling back. Suddenly one ventured too far down the ice, and slithered, shrieking, into the sea, where he bobbed up again like a cork.

His brother, seeing this, plucked up courage and plunged in too in one desperate baby-jump, landing with a painful *smack!* and blinking in the spray.

They found they could swim.

Presently she pushed them up on to the ice again where they shook and dried, and the next thing was food. She left them while she killed a seal, and the three of them ate it.

After that there were lessons, how to fish, how to kill. Living was thin at first, for three hunters cannot move as silently as one, but they got along.

Until the day when land-seals approached them unseen from behind an ice ridge. The first they knew of it was an explosion, and one cub gasped and doubled up as he was hit. The bears dived for the water, even the wounded little one. He managed to keep up with them, and his mother and brother would die rather than desert him.

They all swam on, but slowly—slowly. Both cubs were still so small and *slow,* and they must hurry—

Blood ran in the sapphire water.

Other shots spattered beside them.

Anxiety roared in the she-bear's blood. Her heart was bursting. She pushed the cubs on, and turned to meet her enemies. Reared up on to the ice and galloped towards them, a charge that nothing could stop—not even death—if they'd stayed to face it, but they broke and ran.

The bear returned to her cubs.

The wounded one was sinking lower and lower in the water, breathing waves, and she managed to push him out at last on to distant ice. Then she licked him as he lay suffering in the snow, and his brother licked him too, whimpering with distress as he worked.

So that presently the blood stopped, and after a long time the suffering too. The cub sniffed the air. In the first real moment of recovery he consented to take food.

Pain went away from her heart.

Before them lay all the arctic lands, the snow in retreat. The floes, soft and friable from solar radiation, were being broken up by the waves. Plant life teemed in the water, the more open sea colored bright green by diatoms. Millions of wild flowers studded the rocky scree. There was every-thing to eat at once—lichen and moss and roots and halibut and seals. Salmon swam the green water, and cod. Seaweed washed round the rocks. On the land there were hares and young birds.

The summer gathered to almost tropical heat. Snow water dribbled into pools. Icicles glistened with wet, dropped and broke like glass.

And the mother bear, in the snow, with her cubs did not know why she behaved as she did. There was pain and there was happiness, and these two things drove her according to unfathomable laws. When the summer ended, and the polar night began, she would do the same things over again, and her children after her.

---

diatoms (dī′ə tomz′) *n., pl.* any of a large group of microscopic, one-celled algae that live in fresh and salt water and have cell walls made up mostly of silica.
unfathomable (un fath′ə mə bəl) *adj.* that cannot be measured.

Meet NORAH BURKE

Norah Burke (born 1907), a native of Great Britain, spent her early childhood in India, where her father was stationed as an army officer. Like most British children living abroad, she was sent to boarding school in England to be educated. Burke told the story of her early life in her autobiography, *Jungle Child.* She has also published short stories and novels.

RESPONDING TO *Literature*

THINK • TALK • WRITE

1 What did you find most interesting or memorable about this selection? Jot down some thoughts in your journal.

2 Why do you think the author might have used the phrase "the iron of winter" to describe the oncoming cold weather?

3 Who are the "upright seals" that the polar bear sees? Why are they described in that way?

4 Why does the bear decide not to kill the land seals when she first encounters them? In what way is her motivation similar to her later motivation to attack them?

5 There are brief mentions of Inuit life in this selection. What facts could you gather about Inuit life from reading "Polar Night"?

ACTIVITIES

- **Write About Setting** Imagine it is the longest day of the year. What are you doing? Describe your activities, making sure to include details that vividly convey the setting you are in.

- **Create a Brochure** What did you learn about life in the frozen North? Make a brochure for travelers in the region, describing the weather and the animal and plant life they will encounter. Include maps, photos, and survival tips.

VOCABULARY PRACTICE

You would expect to see certain words in books about certain subjects. For example, you would expect to find the word *species* in a book about animals. Read each book title below. Choose the vocabulary word that is most likely to be found in each of the books. Write your answers on a separate sheet of paper.

raucous   iridescent

convulsed   unfathomable

luminous

1 *Shimmering Colors and Patterns*

2 *The Beauty of Moonlight*

3 *Remembering the San Francisco Earthquake*

4 *Unsolved Mysteries and Disappearances*

5 *Twist and Shout: A Study of Crowds at Rock Shows*

BEFORE READING

....

RAIN FORESTS

CONNECT TO LITERATURE

What do you know about rain forests? Where are they found? Why are they important? What might happen if they disappear? Discuss your ideas with a classmate. As you read "Rain Forests," note the answers to your questions in your journal.

THINKING ABOUT AUTHOR'S PURPOSE

Every author has a *purpose* for writing. The purpose might be to express an opinion, to entertain or inform readers, or to persuade them to believe something. Sometimes an author might have more than one purpose. For example, Norah Burke wrote "Polar Night" both to entertain readers and to inform them about the life of polar bears.

As you read the articles in "Rain Forests," think about why they were written. Jot down your ideas in your journal.

DID YOU KNOW?

About 25 percent of all Earth's forests are rain forests. A rain forest contains tall trees (as high as 200 feet) whose tops create a canopy that blocks out almost all sunlight from the forest floor. Rain forests are hot and humid places. The temperature there rarely rises above 93°F (34°C) or falls below 68°F (20°C); in fact, a rain forest's hottest month is usually only a few degrees warmer than its coldest month. At least 80 inches of rain falls annually in a rain forest, and much of that rain is produced by the trees themselves, which give off water through the pores of their leaves.

ORESTS

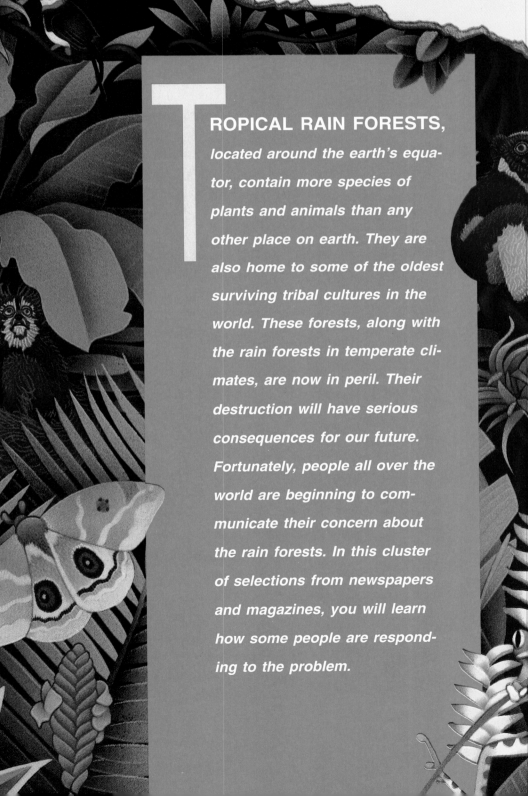

TROPICAL RAIN FORESTS, located around the earth's equator, contain more species of plants and animals than any other place on earth. They are also home to some of the oldest surviving tribal cultures in the world. These forests, along with the rain forests in temperate climates, are now in peril. Their destruction will have serious consequences for our future. Fortunately, people all over the world are beginning to communicate their concern about the rain forests. In this cluster of selections from newspapers and magazines, you will learn how some people are responding to the problem.

DESTRUCTION OF RAIN FORESTS, WARNS A CONSERVATIONIST, IS ENDANGERING MANY SPECIES— INCLUDING OUR OWN

from *People Weekly*
November 28, 1988

"Wonder, astonishment and sublime devotion fill and elevate the mind," the evolutionist Charles Darwin wrote in 1832 after a visit to a rain forest in Brazil. Today tropical rain forests around the world are under siege. Fifty acres are destroyed every minute. An area the size of the state of New York is burned or cleared every year. Within five to 10 years, Haiti and El Salvador will have virtually no forests left. Recent devastating floods in Bangladesh have been aggravated by deforestation.

This loss of tropical rain forests—jungle that receives at least 80 inches of rain a year—may have profound meaning for the future of mankind. Scientists generally agree that the burning of rain forests is contributing to the "greenhouse effect," in which increasing levels of carbon dioxide in the atmosphere trap the sun's heat, preventing it from radiating back into space. The result is a gradual warming of the atmosphere. Many scientists suspect that the greenhouse effect contributed to making this past summer the hottest in more than half a century.

One of the most energetic champions of rain forests is 38-year-old conservationist Dr. Russell Mittermeier. Trained as a primatologist at Harvard, Mittermeier is the vice-president for science of the World Wildlife Fund and an associate professor of anatomical sciences at the State University of New York at Stony Brook. As a child, Mittermeier wanted to be a jungle explorer. Today he spends more than a third of the year in the wild, tracking rare primates and overseeing conservation programs. He spoke with senior writer Harriet Shapiro.

Why are we losing so much rain forest?

There is a variety of factors, among them slash-and-burn agriculture, timber extraction, mining, hydroelectric projects, clearing for plantation agriculture and cattle ranching. And intimately linked with all of this is the ever-expanding human population, which is putting enormous pressure on the tropical forests.

What exactly do you mean by slash-and-burn agriculture?

This is a practice whereby trees are cut down by farmers and then burned where they lie. The problem is that most of the nutrients are in the living organisms, the trees, not in the topsoil. So if the forest is cut down and burned, there is a very thin layer of ash in which you can grow crops for a few years. But once the nutrients have been picked up by the crops that have been grown for food or been washed away by the warm rains, the land becomes virtually worthless, a wasteland.

How does burning rain forests contribute to the greenhouse effect?

It's kind of a double whammy. First, the burning itself releases huge amounts of carbon dioxide. Second, since trees absorb carbon dioxide, the loss of the rain forest destroys one of the great natural sinks for this gas. Together, the burning and the destruction have almost certainly contributed to an increased global warming or, as it is commonly called, the greenhouse effect.

In addition to combating the greenhouse effect, what other reasons are there for saving the rain forests?

The forests are critical to the conservation of biological diversity, that is, the vast wealth of species and ecosystems that makes our planet what it is. In the Amazon, a single pond the size of a tennis court contains more species of fish than all the rivers of Europe combined. Rain forests cover only 8 percent of the earth's land surface, yet at least 70 percent of the world's plants, insects and animals live within their boundaries. By protecting tropical forests, we're protecting most species on the planet.

What about plant life?

People often forget that not all valuable chemical compounds are invented in laboratories. Many are discovered in nature. In rain forests, the possibilities are limitless. So far we've looked at less than 2 percent of tropical forest plants to see what valuable compounds they might contain. Alkaloids from the rosy periwinkle, a small plant that originated in Madagascar, are very effective in treating Hodgkin's disease and childhood leukemia. Curare, an Indian arrow poison that is made from a plant that grows only

Among the plant and animal life threatened by tropical rain forest destruction are (left to right): the rosy periwinkle, aye-aye, masked puddle frog, jungle glory butterfly, and scarlet macaw.

in the Amazon, is used in heart operations as a muscle relaxant. For all we know, solutions to health problems like cancer and AIDS may well exist in tropical forests.

How do rain forests affect our everyday lives?

Think about what we eat. Some food, such as Brazil nuts, grows only in rain forests, while others—coffee, sugarcane and cocoa—originated in rain forests. They are now grown elsewhere, but many commercial crops have a very small genetic base. If a pest of one kind or another attacked, they could be wiped out. So we have to be able to go back to the rain forests in order to crossbreed commercial crops with their relatives from the wild.

How valuable is the rain forest in economic terms?

One study, done by Charles Peters, a scientist at the New York Botanical Garden,

stated that the fruit, latex and timber alone on an acre of Amazon rain forest in Peru is worth approximately $3,600. The same land would be worth only around $1,300 if used for cattle pasture or a wood-pulp plantation. And Peters was just examining fruits and a few other products, not the medicinal plants and the animals.

What is happening to the indigenous people living in the rain forests?

As soon as there is contact with the outside world, the process of cultural disintegration begins. And looking at it from a purely economic point of view, the knowledge these people have developed over thousands of years is tremendously valuable. Their shamans—or medicine men—discovered beneficial uses for quinine and curare long before the civilized world. The knowledge of how to utilize forest plants is disappearing much faster than the plants themselves.

What other effects might deforestation have?

The threat to some animals is severe. Ninety percent of all primates, for example, live in tropical forests, and their populations are rapidly declining around the world. Of the 227 species of primates on the planet today, 113 are currently considered either endangered, vulnerable or rare. Fifteen to 20 species could very well be extinct by the turn of the century if we don't take action now to reverse those trends.

What are some of these species?

In Madagascar, the mysterious aye-aye, a nocturnal lemur, and the spectacular indri, which looks like a cross between a giant panda and a teddy bear, are in danger of becoming extinct. In South America, the muriqui, the largest monkey on that continent; the golden lion tamarin, a squirrel-size monkey with brilliant golden fur and a

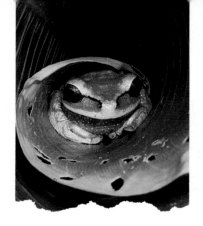

lionlike mane; and the grotesque white uakari are all down to just a few hundred individuals in the wild.

Why should anyone care about preserving rain forest animals?

We put millions of dollars into conserving the works of our own species in museums, but we are not very good at conserving nature's works of art. Even severe pollution is reversible, but species extinction is irreversible. Once a certain species is gone, it's gone forever. In the words of the naturalist William Beebe, "Another heaven and another earth must pass before such a one can be again."

How serious is the threat of extinction for rain forest species?

At this point all we can do is guess, but the crisis we're facing right now is comparable to the extinction of the dinosaurs. If some of the trends continue, we stand to lose thousands of species before the turn of the century. It's difficult to estimate extinction rates when perhaps 90 percent of certain groups in the tropics, like insects, have yet to be described by scientists.

> **❝❝…we stand to lose thousands of species before the turn of the century.❞❞**

How is the international community responding to the tropical forest crisis?

Over the past few years there has been an amazing growth of interest on the part of organizations like the World Bank and agencies like USAID and the Norwegian NORAD. There's a growing recognition that we can't have long-term sustainable development without conserving global biological resources, and that includes the rain forests.

What can be done to save rain forests?

Public awareness is part of the solution. We must greatly increase the interest in tropical-forest and species conservation and make it the truly global issue it deserves to be. We must also increase the political visibility of conservation worldwide. To some extent, this is already happening. Brazil, for instance, which is home to more species than any other country on earth, is now including a major section on conservation and the protection of its ecosystems in its constitution.

After all the talk about life in other solar systems, this is still the only place where we know for certain that life exists in the whole vast universe. So we should appreciate life in its many magnificent manifestations and do everything possible to ensure that the earth remains a living planet in the fullest sense of the word. ∎

Gold Monkeys Learn How to Live in Wild in Brazilian Preserve

Project is a model for saving threatened primates.

by James Brooke
from *The New York Times*

SILVA JARDIM, BRAZIL—In a flash of orange fur, a golden lion tamarin suddenly appeared, hopping and swinging easily through the green forest foliage. Nine others followed, browsing for fruit and insects, keeping balance with foot-long <u>prehensile</u> tails.

The monkey family that crossed a forest trail here in the 20-square-mile Poço das Antas Biological Reserve offered a scene that is increasingly rare in Brazil. Only 400 golden lion tamarins are known to survive in the wild, all of them in Brazil.

But the number of tamarins has started to grow in the reserve, and the project now serves as a model for programs to save other primates hemmed in by Brazilian development.

To save the tamarins, primatologists have used a three-pronged approach: research to improve breeding at zoos, introduction of captive-bred monkeys to the wild, and education of local residents to protect the monkeys. Researchers quickly learned that the residents were not the only ones who needed schooling; the zoo monkeys had to be shown such basic skills as how to peel a banana and how to avoid poisonous fruits.

With 51 different species, more than any African nation, Brazil is the country with the richest primate diversity on earth.

Unfortunately, with widespread destruction of tropical forests, Brazil also leads the list with the largest number of endangered monkey species, 19.

The largest number of threatened monkey species in Brazil is here in the Atlantic forest, a once-luxuriant strip of jungle that now bears the mark of almost 500 years of European colonization. Of an original expanse of 400,000 square miles, only 2 percent of the coastal forest remains.

With international assistance, Brazilian primatologists are also working to save three other primate species found only in the Atlantic forest: the black lion tamarin, the golden-headed lion tamarin and the woolly spider monkey, which can measure five feet long and is the largest wild primate in the New World.

For centuries, golden lion tamarins were common in Brazil, just as passenger pigeons once were in the United States. In 1519, a Jesuit historian voyaging with Fernando Magellan wrote of seeing dozens of monkeys "similar to little lions." Squirrel-size and weighing about a pound, the monkeys became favored pets in 18th century Europe. Madame Pompadour bought one for the French court.

In a more democratic era, they were exported by the dozen to zoos and pet shops around the world. "In the 1960's, the export of golden lion tamarins was entirely free: 100 were shipped out every week," Adelmar F. Coimbra-Filho, director of Rio de Janeiro's

---

prehensile (prē hen'sil) *adj.* adapted for grasping or holding, especially by wrapping around.

Primatology Center, said in an interview here. "Today, the United States has more lion tamarins than we do."

In a twist of biological fate, this golden lion diaspora may save the species from extinction.

By the time Brazil woke up to Mr. Coimbra-Filho's warnings, the wild tamarin population had dwindled to several hundred. In 1974, when the reserve was established here, about 100 survived in the area.

At about the same time there were only 70 golden lion tamarins in zoos worldwide. Reproduction was low and mortality was high. The problem, researchers discovered, was that zoo keepers were trying to maintain Brazilian monkeys with techniques that worked with African monkeys. Several recommendations were made: exposure to ultraviolet light to cure rickets, addition of crickets to diets to cure protein deficiencies, and housing in monogamous families to avoid single sex rivalries. By making these and other changes, zoo keepers increased the captive population to over 500 today.

The second step was to train animals born in captivity to live in the wild. The goal is not only to increase the wild population, but also to increase genetic diversity. "If you don't, the species will degenerate," said Dionizio M. Pessamilio, director of the reserve. "There will be more lame monkeys, more blind monkeys."

But the first attempt was a failure. Of 15 monkeys introduced in 1984, only 2 survived in the wild. Several are back in zoos. Others died.

"Zoo monkeys don't even know how to peel a banana; they have been served rations on plates all their lives," Mr. Pessamilio said.

---

diaspora (dī asʹpər ə) *n.* scattering.
mortality (môr talʹi tē) *n.* death rate.
degenerate (di jenʹə rāt') *v.i.* become worse in condition; deteriorate.

"They see a fruit. They don't know it's poisonous. They eat it and die."

Others were bitten by snakes and spiders, or died of exposure because they did not know how to nest in tree holes.

"It's a little scary," Suzanne Kolb, an American forestry researcher here, said of the socializing work. "There is not much of a margin of error with an endangered species."

'Zoo monkeys don't even know how to peel a banana.' They eat off plates.

Indeed, researchers found it a challenge to train monkeys to live like monkeys. Some monkeys distrusted branches that were of a different diameter than their cage bars.

"Zoo-born animals were very reluctant to use slender vegetation that bent and swayed," a Smithsonian Institution study found in 1987. "They also had considerable difficulty figuring how to get from one place to another. They did not seem able to plan out a complicated route."

After several experiments at the National Zoological Park in Washington, primatologists decided that the cheapest and most effective monkey wilderness training would take place here in their future habitat.

With food and nest boxes as lures, zoo monkeys now undergo training in a semifree setting. In the wild, golden lion tamarins use their long, slender fingers to probe small holes for grubs, lizards and baby birds. To encourage captive-born monkeys to do this, trainers built special feeders with crevices to hold hidden food. "Favorite foods were placed on thin branches to entice the animals onto swaying, unstable pathways," the Smithsonian report said.

Graduates of this new course have done well. Of 37 zoo monkeys introduced in the last two years, all but three are believed to survive. In October, a new group of 11 is to arrive here from American zoos.

There are several cases of matings between zoo-born monkeys and wild monkeys. The most stable couples seem to be between zoo males and wild females. "The wild-born babies are growing up and are indistinguishable from wild tamarins," the Smithsonian study concluded.

Parallel to this work, educators led by Lou Ann Dietz of the World Wildlife Fund started a program to teach local residents about the golden lion tamarins.

Today six local teachers give ecology classes in local schools and take children for nature walks. In late July, an environmental education center opened at the reserve. Built largely with aid from the Canadian Government, the structure offers exhibits on animals and plants of the reserve. Locally, the project has become so popular that about 40 local farmers have signed up to have golden lion tamarin families on their land.

"Only 20 years ago, people used to trap the monkeys with bananas and sell them by the side of the road," Antonio Carlos de Lacerda, Mayor of Silva Jardim, said in an interview. "Now, we are all in favor of the park."

On the national level, publicity has led Brazilians to call a hotline telephone number to denounce people who still keep golden lion tamarins in captivity. "We have received over 30 through denunciations," Mr. Pessamilio said. "We got one from a couple in a

---

reluctant (ri luk'tənt) *adj.* unwilling or hesitant.

Copacabana apartment. Apparently, it was living off cockroaches."

Indeed, modern Brazilians appear to be increasingly proud of their primates. At the most recent Brazilian Congress of Primatology, in 1987, attendance reached 3,000.

The upsurge in interest here and overseas has helped efforts to save three other species threatened by the destruction of the Atlantic forest.

In a step forward for the black lion tamarin, four Brazilian zoos have succeeded in persuading captive animals to procreate. "There are only 200 in the wild," said Claudio Padua, a Brazilian biologist, who is studying the community at Morro do Diabo State Park in São Paulo state. "We are very encouraged by what they have learned with the golden lion tamarins."

Another endangered tamarin species, the golden-headed lion, is to benefit shortly from a community environmental education program modeled after the one here. Restricted largely to the Una Biological Reserve in Bahia State, these monkeys live alongside three other endangered species: the buff-headed tufted capuchin, the northern masked titi and Weid's marmoset.

The woolly spider monkey, also known as the muriqui, has recently been chosen by the World Wildlife Fund to be Brazil's conservation symbol. The drive to save this monkey is coming just in time. Only 375 are believed to survive, largely in southern Bahia.

Russell A. Mittermeier, director of the World Wildlife Fund primate program, says the conservation, introduction and education program under way to save the golden lion tamarins may point the way for future species survival efforts in Brazil.

"The prospects for the survival of wild populations of this spectacular and uniquely Brazilian species are better than they have been at any time during the last 15 years," he wrote recently.

from *The New York Times*

When Poço das Antas Biological Reserve opened in 1974, only 100 golden tamarins survived in area.

BOLIVIAN INDIANS PROTEST WRECKING OF RAIN FOREST

Hundreds trek 400 miles to La Paz to stop logging on tribal land

BY JAMES PAINTER

from *The Christian Science Monitor*

LA PAZ, BOLIVIA—More than 700 Indians from Bolivia's Amazonian basin were due to arrive yesterday in the 12,000-foot-high capital La Paz, completing a 400-mile "march for dignity and territory."

The Indians are demanding the return of 1.5 million acres which they say have been "invaded" by logging companies, settlers, and cattle ranchers. On August 15 the marchers set out from the northern tropical town of Trinidad, in the center of the rain forests where they and their ancestors have lived for centuries.

"We want to live as we lived before," explains Tomas Ticuasi, the leader of the Siriono Indians, one of the 10 ethnic groups represented on the march. "[We are marching] to demand back what the 'caravanas' [whites] have taken away from us."

Many have left their forest homes for the first time to walk to La Paz to discuss their demands with President Jaime Paz Zamora, whom they call "the white chief." The last stage of their journey involved an exceptionally arduous climb over the eastern range of the Andes, which reaches a height of 15,000 feet and registers subzero temperatures.

Wearing Western dress and carrying long wooden spears, the marchers have kept up their morale and energy by playing traditional music. Villages on the way have opened their arms to welcome them. Help has come from church groups and dozens of support organizations, especially for the 12 pregnant women and 90 child marchers.

For the first time in Bolivia's history, Indians from the jungle lowlands are big news. Daily newspaper headlines have followed the Indians' march and highlighted their plight. The groundswell of popular support and wide media coverage forced President Paz Zamora and most of his Cabinet to travel last week to meet marchers in mid-route.

The government repeated its offer to recognize as Indian territory most of the land the marchers are seeking. But the sticking point remains 400,000 acres of land in the heart of the Chimane Forest, which the government legally handed over to four Bolivian logging companies in 1987.

The Indians want loggers out, saying they are ruining flora and fauna and threatening Indian culture. "Money and money, they squeeze the land dry, they exploit it until it cries out, they kill the trees—we don't understand it," complains Ernesto Noe, of the local Indigenous Peoples' Council.

The government is trying to walk a tightrope between logger and Indian interests—"the two 'logics' of exploiting the forest and living with it," says Zulema Lehm, a Bolivian specialist on the Chimane Forest.

The latest government offer is to re-zone areas given over to timber company operations, but not to revoke all timber rights. Critics say concessions to the companies

---

arduous (är′jü əs) *adj.* requiring great effort or energy; difficult.

plight (plīt) *n.* bad situation or condition.

flora (flôr′ə) *n.* plant life of a particular region or environment.

fauna (fô′nə) *n.* animals of a particular region or environment.

492

have led to rapid depletion of mahogany, as the companies are not reforesting as Bolivian law demands. Paz Zamora acknowledges "irrational" <u>exploitation</u> of the Chimane Forest has occurred. He estimates 93,000 cubic meters of mahogany have been taken in the last four years, though some dispute this.

Guillermo Mann, former vice-president of science for the US environmental group Conservation International, estimates each of three large timber companies working the forest make $1.3 million in profit a year, but only pay $70,000 each to the state in taxes. "The difference is <u>appalling</u>, and has to be changed," he says.

The companies say it would be perfectly possible to live <u>harmoniously</u> with the Indian groups in the Chimane Forest. They also claim any revision of the concessions would cut the foreign exchange of South America's poorest country. Wood exports totaled $44 million last year, roughly 5 percent of the country's total.

The companies and their supporters place hopes on a new three-year $1.2 million management plan for the Chimane Forest funded by Conservation International, the International Tropical Timber Organization, and the companies themselves. The plan aims to <u>integrate</u> three elements of forestry use: protection of flora and fauna, participation of Indian communities, and forestry.

Paz Zamora also promises a law to protect Bolivia's indigenous peoples—about 200,000 Indians. Experts say the move is overdue since current law considers Indians to be, in essence, part of forest flora and fauna. ■

INDIANS SEEK REVISION OF DEBT-FOR-NATURE SWAP

LA PAZ, BOLIVIA—Part of the 3-million-acre Chimane Forest is covered by a precedent-setting debt-for-nature swap signed by Bolivia and Conservation International (CI) in July 1987.

CI bought $650,000 of Bolivia's bank debt, in exchange for a government agreement to set aside funds to conserve rapidly diminishing rain forests. According to Lidema, a Bolivian environmental group, Bolivia will lose half its forests by the year 2000.

About 40 percent of Bolivia's forests are controlled by timber companies, including 1.4 million Chimane acres. CI says the forest's best hope is a new management plan—the Amazon basin's "first exercise in regional planning."

Indians marching to La Paz to protest forest destruction want a "complete restructuring" of the plan. "CI will only continue with the plan if the Indians participate," says María Teresa Ortiz, a CI official in Bolivia.

Rain Forest • SOUTH AMERICA • PERU • Trinidad • BRAZIL • La Paz • Chapare River • Marchers' route • South Pacific Ocean • BOLIVIA • PARAGUAY • CHILE • ARGENTINA

exploitation (ek′sploi tā′shən) *n.* unjust or unfair use for selfish reasons.

appalling (ə pô′ling) *adj.* horrible; shocking; dreadful.

harmoniously (här mō′nē əs lē) *adv.* in agreeable combination.

integrate (in′ti grāt′) *v.t.* bring together into a whole.

WOODMAN, SPARE THOSE BRAZILIAN TREES

an editorial from the Atlanta *Constitution*

Brazil's President Jose Sarney is feeling the heat, and not from the high tropical sun his country customarily basks in.

He has been the lightning rod for a succession of environmentalist thunderbolts in response to his countrymen's appalling despoliation of the great Amazon rain forests, nature's biggest factory for making oxygen. He has been blistered by ecologists the world over, by the foreign ministries of the industrialized nations, by some of his country's creditors and, most recently and most usefully, by a group of prominent Latin Americans, who give the lie to his jingoist contention that the First World is ganging up on his poor little Third World country.

Earlier this month, with much fanfare, Mr. Sarney announced "Our Nature," a government program to rescue Brazil's precious forests from the encroachments of cattle barons, mining companies and hundreds of thousands of poor squatters hoping to scratch out a living on Brazil's equivalent of our Western frontier.

Sad to say, many environmentalists fear Mr. Sarney is more intent on finding a way to insulate himself from criticism than dealing effectively with the crisis. It's a tall order for him to persuade his Congress to allocate $350 million for what seems to many Brazilians a frivolous save-the-trees program and to marshal the forces to patrol a 2-million-square-mile wilderness. It's especially tall considering his term is running out and his political stock has plummeted alongside Brazil's hyper-devalued currency.

Outsiders have alerted Brazil's leadership to the gravity of the problem. Now they must find ways to help it raise the funds and the public will to complete the task. It may take the form of donations to Brazil's new National Environmental Fund. It may be more emphasis on debt-for-nature swaps. It may be increased support for Brazil's beleaguered environmental organizations.

However it is proffered, the outside encouragement must disabuse the average Brazilian of the notion that the rain forest question is an us-vs.-them proposition. When it comes to the planet's air quality, we're all involved and we all have a say. ■

SAVE THE BRAZILIAN RAIN FORESTS

MEANWHILE, BACK IN THE PACIFIC NORTHWEST....

Paul Conrad Copyright, 1989, *Los Angeles Times*

---

prominent (prom′ə nənt) *adj.* well-known or important.
allocate (al′ə kāt′) *v.t.* set aside (for a specific purpose).

by Mark Sigel
from
The Christian Science Monitor

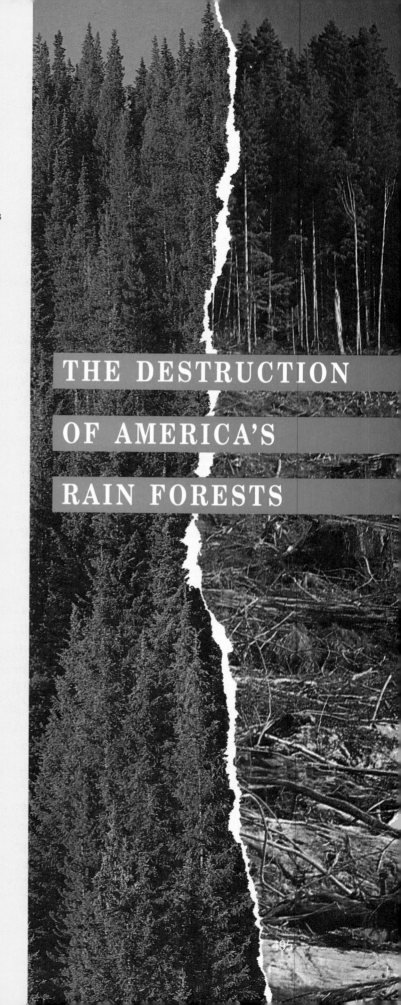

THE DESTRUCTION

OF AMERICA'S

RAIN FORESTS

The conifer forests of the Pacific Northwest contain the largest stands of temperate, old-growth rain forest south of Alaska. These stands are being liquidated faster than the tropical rain forests of South America. At least 90 percent of the Pacific Northwest's old-growth forests have been eliminated, compared to 40 percent of the world's tropical rain forests and 15 percent of the Amazon's.

Some argue that protecting these forests and the animals that inhabit them will come at the expense of mill employment. But both old-growth rain forest and forestry jobs can be protected if Congress, the US Forest Service, and the Bureau of Land Management (BLM) take the right steps.

Compared with the Amazon rain forest, the Northwest conifer forests contain double the biomass, or plant and animal weight per acre. These forest ecosystems also support species of birds, amphibians, flowering plants, and mushrooms found nowhere else in the world.

Biologists have identified 64 vertebrate species that are associated with the mature forests of western Oregon and Washington. The marten and fisher, predators from the weasel family, are disappearing as these ancient forests on which they depend are fragmented and destroyed.

The northern flying squirrel, primary food source for the endangered northern spotted owl, feeds on the lichen and fungi that grow on old-growth trees. Some 5,000 remaining spotted owls are found only in the conifer forests of the Pacific Northwest.

Less than 2 million acres of old-growth forest remain of the nearly 20 million acres that blanketed Oregon prior to European settlement. The situation is similar in Washington. The disappearance of these forests is being aided by the Forest Service and the BLM, which are pursuing a policy of selling off as much of the old growth as possible. If this practice continues, these ancient ecosystems will be eliminated or hopelessly fragmented in as little as five years.

Among the proponents of these policies are the region's mill workers, who mistakenly blame court injunctions protecting the old-growth stands for the closure of lumber mills. Court-ordered protections, however, are only a minor factor in the Northwest's declining mill employment.

The primary reason is that one in every four logs cut in the Northwest is shipped overseas. Most are purchased in Japan, Korea, and other Asian nations that are willing to spend twice what domestic mills will pay for unprocessed logs. Consequently, the largest United States timber companies are posting record profits by exporting raw logs—and thousands of mill jobs.

The gradual modernization of Northwest timber companies, which must now compete with state-of-the-art mills in Canada and the southeastern US, is another major cause of rising unemployment among mill workers. Modernized mills employ about half the former labor force. The older mills, equipped to cut only mature logs, will be forced to retool or close down in the next few years. Mill jobs will be lost regardless of whether conifer forests are cut or preserved for their wilderness value.

Yet the Forest Service and the BLM still view their primary organizational goal as providing the maximum number of timber jobs possible. And while long-range management plans are currently being finalized for many districts in the Northwest, it is likely their forest plans will call for cutting the majority of the old growth in the next decade.

A congressional directive extending National Park protection to significant stands of old-growth, temperate rain forests in the Pacific Northwest is desperately needed to preserve these rare and ancient ecosystems. The protection of rain forests and biological diversity is already accepted worldwide as a primary environmental goal, and Congress can make an important statement to the American people and to industrializing nations by protecting these environmental resources.

At the same time, Congress can soften the transition the timber industry is undergoing by investing in retraining programs for displaced mill workers.

When Congress holds oversight hearings on the management of the Pacific Northwest forests, the American people must demand protection for this priceless and irreplaceable ecological treasure.

Mark Sigel, associate director of the program in public policy analysis at Pomona College in Claremont, Calif., was a researcher at the Oregon National Resources Council. ■

---

proponents (prə pō′nənts) *n., pl.* people who propose or support something.

Guarding the Forests Begins at Home

an editorial from the *Chicago Tribune*

Brazilian officials have a persuasive response when other countries, notably the United States, pummel them to do something about saving the precious Amazon rain forest. Look to your own back yard, they say, or to what is left of it.

The fact is that the American back yard, as measured by the vast virgin forests that once covered much of the continent, is pretty much gone. Most of what is left is on federal land in our own rain forests in Washington and Oregon, and at the rate they are disappearing to logging—60,000 acres a year—they too could be gone in perhaps no more than 30 years.

The magnitude is not the same as what is happening in Brazil, where in 1987 alone 20 million acres of Amazon were burned to clear the way for ranching. The effects aren't quite the same, either. Besides the immediate destruction of the rain forest and its unique plant and animal life, the slash-and-burn technique pours enormous amounts of carbon gases into the atmosphere, while decreasing the amount of oxygen produced by the trees. That contributes to the so-called greenhouse effect, the presumed gradual and destructive warming of the Earth.

But the final measure—when these forests are gone, they are gone—is very much the same. It is enough to challenge the piety of U.S. ecological lectures to the rest of the world, and to suggest it is time for the U.S. Forest Service to re-examine where it is heading with its policy of administering the public forests.

The Forest Service is under increasing criticism from conservationists for being increasingly generous to the lumber industry—allowing more timber to be cut and more roads to be built through former wilderness areas, at a price that doesn't even cover the cost of managing the forests. Tree-cutting is at an all-time high in the 156 national forests, including a record 12.7 billion board feet in 1987, with almost half of it coming from the ancient stands in Washington and Oregon. The Service stirred new controversy in February with a proposal that could double the trees cut and almost double the network of roads in six southern Appalachian forests.

The Forest Service argues that its job isn't just to preserve forests, but to manage them for a mixed use of lumbering and recreation, while preserving wildlife habitat and certain valuable ecosystems. The mission is sound; the question is whether the balance has tipped too far to the business end. If the government is too generous in letting the forests be cut, and in the ways it allows them to be cut, the day will come when there will be little left to manage. ■

RESPONDING TO *Literature*

THINK • TALK • WRITE

1 Did these articles change your ideas about rain forests? Why or why not?

2 What do you think James Painter's purpose was in writing his article? How might the article have been different if his purpose had been to persuade you to believe one point of view?

3 Why are golden lion tamarins being threatened by extinction? Why is the program to save them so important?

4 Try to express in your own words why it is a tragedy when a species disappears forever.

5 What did you learn about the indigenous peoples of the Bolivian rain forest? Why are they protesting the destruction of the rain forest?

ACTIVITIES

- **Write About Author's Purpose** Write a letter to the editor taking a side on one aspect of the rain forest debate. Through the use of facts and arguments, try to make your letter as persuasive as possible.

- **Design a T-shirt** Think of a short message you could print on a T-shirt that would encourage people to help save the rain forests. Choose a picture or photograph to put on your T-shirt as well.

VOCABULARY PRACTICE

On a separate sheet of paper, write the vocabulary word from the list that is the best substitute for each italicized word or phrase.

mortality   appalling
degenerate   harmoniously
reluctant   integrate
arduous   prominent
plight   allocate

1 The *sad situation* of the rain forest makes me depressed and angry.

2 The quality of our air will *become worse* if the rain forests are cut down.

3 It would be best to *bring together* the needs of rain forests and the needs of emerging countries.

4 The *death rate* of tropical species is increasing each year.

5 The loss of so many species is *horrifying*.

6 We must *distribute* our efforts to save rain forests everywhere.

7 The president is a *well-known* citizen whose help we need.

8 Some people are *unwilling* to get involved in the rain forest debate.

9 A rain forest is a delicate world where all life forms get along in a *well-balanced way*.

10 It can be *very difficult* to hike through parts of a rain forest.

498

BEFORE READING

....

GENTLE GIANT

CONNECT TO LITERATURE

What is your favorite animal? How can you describe it so that others might understand your interest and excitement? In your journal, write a few lines describing the animal and explaining why it's your favorite. Then, as you read "Gentle Giant," note how Tsuneo Nakamura uses words and photographs to excite your interest in whales.

THINKING ABOUT SENSORY LANGUAGE

You know about the five senses: sight, hearing, touch, taste, and smell. When writers want to describe something vividly, they often use words that help you to see, hear, touch, taste, or smell it. This is called *sensory language*. For instance, in "Polar Night," Norah Burke writes, "All that the bear could hear was the wash of blue water against grinding ice." This is an example of sensory language, because it involves the senses of sight and hearing.

DID YOU KNOW?

Although they live in the oceans, whales are not fish; they are mammals. Mammals are warm-blooded animals that breathe with lungs, give birth to live animals, and feed their young with milk produced by the mother. There are about 75 different kinds of whales. One kind, the blue whale, can grow to be 100 feet (30 m) long; it is the largest animal that has ever lived.

Whales are among the most intelligent of all the world's creatures. They communicate through a complicated variety of sounds, which can travel up to 50 miles (80 km) through the water. The best-known whale "songs" are those of the humpback whale; each song is made up of a series of sounds that lasts from 7 to 30 minutes and is then repeated. Every humpback whale sings a distinct song.

GENTLE
GIANT

At Sea with the Humpback Whale

By Tsuneo Nakamura

In 1977 in Alaska's Glacier Bay, I saw the breaching of a humpback whale for the first time. I was so taken by surprise that quite unintentionally I cried out. Since that time, I have become very interested in whales, and whenever I hear that I can view them by going to the Bering Sea or the Arctic or Antarctic oceans or any ocean or sea around the world, I grab my camera and go. And no sooner had I begun to think that I wanted to meet whales in their underwater world than I became acquainted with Professor Louis Herman, and he let me join his whale project team at the University of Hawaii. Day after day, riding in a tiny rubber raft, we chased whales in the open seas around Hawaii from sunrise to sunset. In that way, I gathered my pictures of the humpback whales.

■ **breaching** (brē′ching) *v.i.* breaking the water by leaping out.

501

Gentleness Concealed in a Giant Body

February 6

The Aloha Airlines Boeing 737, only just lifted off from Honolulu Airport, readied for landing at Kahului Airport situated on the plain between Maui's Haleakala and Puukukui mountains. The seat belt light came on, and I figured that the plane was about to go in for a landing, when the pilot announced, "Whales on the right." The plane went into a sharp turn.

During the commotion among my fellow passengers, I rushed to the window to look down. I saw three whales swimming along beneath the surface, like three great shadows in the sea. While we all looked at the whales, the plane continued to circle around. As soon as the whales disappeared, the plane changed its position and landed at Kahului.

It was a good start for me, for I had just arrived in Hawaii to investigate humpback whales by joining the Marine Mammals Study Team of the University of Hawaii.

February 8

At 8:30 in the morning we arrived at Lahaina, formerly a whaling port. All the trawlers and the whalers had left, and only a $3\frac{1}{2}$-meter-long rubber raft, sitting off to the side, occupied the quiet port.

Near the raft was parked a station wagon several times bigger than the boat. The vehicle bore on its side the message: OFFICIAL USE ONLY, UNIVERSITY OF HAWAII. A pile of goods had been removed from the wagon: gasoline tanks, life preservers, a wireless radio, batteries, an underwater recorder, an antenna, a permit flag, camera bags, food, recording paper, oars, polytanks, diving instruments, and so on.

The marine survey team's membership for the day consisted of Tom, a lecturer at the university; a volunteer named Budgie; Jim from Earthwatch; and me. After a brief exchange of morning pleasantries, we began to load the equipment into the raft. I wondered if this tiny craft had sufficient capacity to hold the four of us plus the large load; for on top of all that gear, each of us had a sack containing a change of clothes, and I also had three underwater cameras, two regular cameras, a number of interchangeable lenses, and my diving equipment.

In this "giant pod," whales are threatening one another by taking short submersions, surfacing, and spouting.

The load was somehow fit onto the floor of the boat, and we were all forced to make a seat for ourselves on the inflated <u>pontoons</u> that formed the sides of the craft, with our legs resting on the load.

Just on time at 9:00. With the raft full of people and equipment, we set out for the open sea. The sound of the raft's twenty-five-horsepower outboard motor echoed all around the port. Before us in the channel was Lanai Island, toward which we were slowly heading. To the right was Molokai, and to the left was Kahoolawe.

Under Tom's leadership, everyone was assigned an area of the ocean's surface to keep watch over. After all, no one could be sure just when and where a whale would spout or put in an appearance.

Here and there were floating other whale-watching boats filled with curious spectators. Although there were no doubt whales near those boats, we decided to look for our whales elsewhere.

We were only ten minutes into our run when Budgie cried out, "Two o'clock spray!" Everyone looked in the direction she was pointing, and there they were: two whales beginning their dives, their flukes (the lobes of their tails) raised high into the air. We immediately opened <u>throttle</u> and headed for the spot where the animals had dived. Our raft bucked over the churning surface while we all clung to the <u>lanyards</u> strung along the side of the small boat to keep from being dumped overboard.

---

pontoons (pon tünz´) *n., pl.* flat-bottomed boats used as floating supports.
throttle (throt´əl) *n.* fuel supply valve.
lanyards (lan´yərdz) *n., pl.* short ropes used on ships to fasten things.

Five minutes later, we arrived at the place where we estimated the whales had begun their dives, but of course there were no whales, nor even their shadows, to be found. So we cut the engine and waited for the whales to resurface.

Just twelve minutes after the first sighting, two whales spouted 500 meters ahead of us. Then another two appeared. It was a pod, or group, of four whales headed straight for Molokai. We recorded the amount of time the pod spent underwater when it dove and the distance it traversed, as well as the course the pod was taking. After starting up the engine, we followed the course the whales were taking and adjusted our speed to match that of the pod.

Ten more minutes passed, and Budgie murmured, "Just another few minutes. It'll be soon now." The four of us on the raft concentrated on the surface of the ocean that surrounded us.

Exactly twelve minutes later, two whales surfaced just 100 meters away from us; ten seconds later, the other two came up. The whales spouted three times, as they had before, and then dove back into the water. Throughout this time, I was standing on the violently bucking raft, frantically focusing my camera lenses, and taking shots of the whales' flukes (straight-on shots that could be used in identifying the animals).

I wondered if the time had at last arrived. I glanced over at Tom, and he, looking in the direction of my diving gear, nodded at me, telling me it was a go. Hurriedly, I removed the long-sleeved jacket and long pants I wore to protect myself from sunburn, and donned my diving gear.

I was tense with the mixed feelings that had welled up in me. The excitement at the thought that after a year's <u>hiatus</u> I would encounter whales beneath the ocean's surface once again was mingled with the <u>trepidation</u> I felt in the face of the whales' awesomeness and power. I put on my face mask, grabbed my camera, and, straddling the side of the raft, assumed a standby position. The raft was moving in concert with the whales' direction and speed. I imagined the great animals gliding along right under my legs.

---

hiatus (hī ā'təs) *n.* break or gap, as in time.

trepidation (trep'i dā'shən) *n.* nervous or fearful anticipation; anxiety.

A pod of whales. Inset photos: The shape of the whales' flukes and their patterns are used for identification.

505

Ten minutes, eleven minutes. . . . I was growing more and more tense. Controlling my breathing, I kept a lookout all around the raft. It had been exactly twelve minutes. Then, only twenty meters behind our raft, two whales broke the surface with a resounding "bwoosh." As soon as I heard it, I dove into the sea, with the raft continuing on ahead. The water around me was white with the bubbles from my breathing apparatus and from the raft's propeller. I immediately dove deeper, and as soon as I exited the curtain of bubbles, two great shadows passed together below my legs. They looked like submarines. The whales slid through the sea by moving their flukes slowly up and down and extending their flippers.

They were massive. Even though I was using a wide-angle lens, one whale extended beyond the camera's frame. In about two seconds, the heads of the two whales passed out of my view, and their flukes disappeared soon after. <u>Exhilarated</u>, I returned to the surface. As I was gaining my breath, I again heard "bwoosh" sounding all over the ocean, and the heads of the two whales came into view. Hurriedly, I dove back down. The whales threw a quick glance my way, but quietly they passed me by and again disappeared.

February 15

Tom shouted, "Floating whale!" When I turned my binoculars to where he was pointing, I found a whale floating with just a bit of its dorsal fin showing, looking almost like a wave. We brought our raft up quietly to within 200 meters of the whale, which was stretched out near the surface, its great length visible from blowhole to dorsal fin. Keeping its position, the whale breathed in and out a few times, making a noise but not spraying.

"It's probably a singing whale," Tom said. He unpacked the <u>hydrophone</u> and put it into the water. Through the earphones, I heard a sound like a cross between a purring cat and an angry pig, repeating itself over and over.

Within a quarter of an hour, the sound from the hydrophone grew louder. No sooner had Tom shouted, "The whale's coming up!" than the great animal rose to the surface, breaking through the water some 200 meters ahead of us.

---

exhilarated (eg zil′ə rā′tid) *adj.* joyfully excited.
hydrophone (hī′drə fōn′) *n.* device used for hearing underwater sounds.

After it had stretched itself and settled its breathing down as before, it cried out and sank into the water. I kept still and tried to listen carefully. Ever so gently, the whale's cry came to me through the water. I placed the oar, which we had brought along in case of engine trouble, into the water, just as the Eskimos do to listen for the sounds of seals. I could hear the whale's cry much more clearly as it <u>resonated</u> through the oar's handle.

Who on earth could describe the ocean as "the silent world," we wondered as we listened to the whale's voice. Meanwhile, the whale surfaced again as before.

I finished recording the whale's voice, prepared myself and my equipment for underwater photography, and slid quietly into the water. Holding my head above the water and without splashing, I swam slowly toward where the whale had sunk below the surface. Drenched in the ocean's waters, I heard the whale's strange <u>ambiguous</u> cries echoing louder and louder. When I looked back to the raft to see if I had swum far enough, Tom waved at me to continue. So I swam on, not only hearing the whale's song but actually feeling it throughout my whole body.

When I figured I had come close to where the whale had gone down, I was suddenly shaken by that booming sound we had

---

resonated (rez'ə nā'tid) *v.i.* echoed with full, rich sound.
ambiguous (am big'ū əs) *adj.* unclear; vague.

A curious calf swims close to me.

heard before, as the whale crashed through the surface of the sea. I altered my threatened position and looked toward where the sound originated. Only thirty meters ahead of me, the whale was floating, its side turned toward me. I was maneuvering myself around to face the whale when it again headed down into the depths, its flukes fluttering before my eyes. I immediately gave a big kick with my flippers and dove after the whale. With my snorkeling gear I descended more than ten meters, but quickly lost the huge beast in the murky sea.

I resurfaced and decided to wait for the whale to come back up, listening to its song as I waited. Ten minutes passed and I was expecting it to come up at any minute.

Suddenly, two large open-sea sharks over three meters in length silently appeared and began to circle beneath my legs. "Danger!" I thought. Without taking my eyes off the sharks, I raised my left hand above the water and made a fist, a signal to those aboard the raft to come and get me. Meanwhile, the sharks drew closer, ever shrinking the diameter of their circling. They seemed to be moving convulsively, a known sign that a shark is closing in on its prey. I listened carefully for the approach of the boat, but I heard no engine sounds at all. At some point unnoticed by me, the whale had ceased its cries.

Desperately hoping that the raft would arrive quickly, I raised and lowered my hands in the air over and over, making the signal for rescue. My camera, which I had lifted out of the water, had grown heavy.

Suddenly, one shark stopped circling, and, coiling its body like a snake, rushed at me. I decided to photograph this shark that was, I thought, about to devour me. I readied my camera and took the shot. The shark slowed down just a bit, probably bothered by the click of the shutter. But it continued to come at me.

The shark's snout was only fifty centimeters or so away from me. I shouted, "Damn you!" and shoved my camera out at the monster, striking it squarely on its nose. Even so, I thought the shark had gotten a piece of me. But at the

Breaching humpback whale

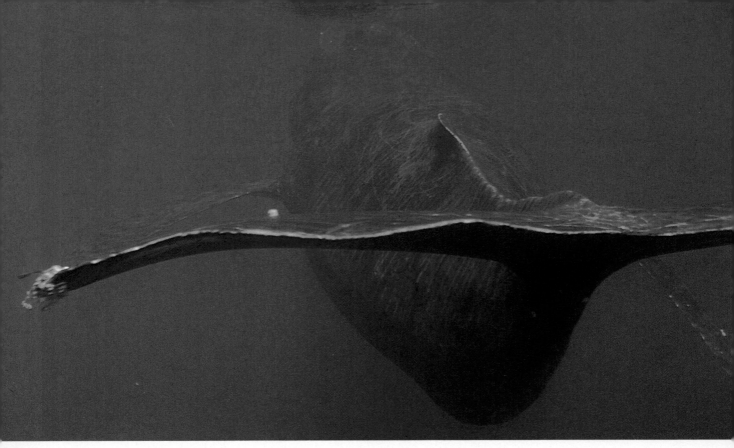

After this whale passed by our raft, I dove into the water right after it.

sound of the dull thud, the shark broke off its attack, took a U-turn away from me, and, with its companion, disappeared into the sea's dark depths.

The danger had passed. As I raised my head above the water and calmed my breathing down, I heard the raft's engine start up and saw the small craft move toward me. When I looked up, my crewmates, who knew nothing of what had <u>transpired</u> beneath the surface of the water, were eyeing me quizzically as if to say "What happened?" Perhaps they thought I had driven the singing whale away. I shouted at them, "Sharks! Sharks! I was attacked by sharks!" At that, they all raised a commotion, and in an instant, I was pulled up into the raft.

February 19

It was 3 P.M. I was thinking that the morning and early afternoon had not been very productive. After departing Lahaina at 8:15 in the morning, we had not come across any whale pods, and I had had no opportunity for any more "fluke" shots.

---

transpired (tran spīrd′) *v.i.* happened; occurred.

We were all gazing aimlessly out to sea, almost ready to give it up for the day, thinking "Today's not a good day. Let's hope for tomorrow." But we kept on going, and the wind came up, blowing straight through Maui's deep valley in the peculiar way it does, partially roughening up the surface of the water, but leaving a clearly distinct area of calm. We were headed for Lanai, traveling over calm waters about fifty meters away from the rough stuff.

"Spray!" Jim yelled out. The sighting was about a mile away. It took us five minutes to get to the area. We shut down the engine and waited on the next spouting. Fifteen minutes . . . twenty minutes . . . nothing yet. The roughened water was swinging toward us; the wind was changing its direction.

Pierre murmured, "We must have lost it." We began to stow away the equipment that had been scattered around the bottom of the raft—cameras, underwater speaker, and diving gear—and prepared to head back to port. At that moment, it happened. "Whoa!" I blurted out. A huge black shadow hove into view only two or three meters below the surface.

On our raft, <u>pandemonium</u>: "It's a whale!" "It's a whale-shark!" "It's a submarine!" A few seconds later, flukes appeared above the water. By then, I had already jumped into my gear, grabbed my camera, and was diving into the water. The enormous flukes were waving up and down, as if they meant to stroke my face, even as they receded away from me. I went down deeper, swimming under the boat, and chased after the great beast. The whale made a U-turn, sank a little lower, and again came toward the raft.

"Good," I thought, and took a deep breath, intending to dive down and meet the whale face to face. The whale continued to come slowly in my direction, about ten meters below the surface. I grew impatient and started to take some photographs. The whale sped up a bit and sank deeper again. I knew whales did not like the sound of the camera's shutter, but my impatience got the better of me, and I shot anyway. I regretted my slip-up immediately.

Pierre, the raft's pilot, donned his mask and fins and came to join me. While we were exchanging eye signals, the whale drew closer again, to within fifteen meters right under us. Immediately, Pierre dove toward the whale. In order to get a picture of Pierre with the whale, I followed behind him, keeping my camera ready.

---

pandemonium (pan'də mō'nē əm) *n.* wild disorder or uproar.

The whale did not seem to mind us, but started to slowly sink deeper into the sea. Out of breath, the two of us returned to the surface. We removed our snorkels and began to talk excitedly about what had just happened.

But rough seas came on fast, and a strong wind blew up around us. In an instant, the highly buoyant rubber raft had been blown away from us. On the raft, Jim and Ronnie did not know how to restart the engine and just looked at us helplessly over the side of the retreating raft. Pierre, still in his snorkeling equipment, swam with great vigor, chasing after the boat, with me following after.

After ten or fifteen minutes of swimming, I put my face up and looked in the direction the wind was blowing. The distance between the raft and me was not lessening. I could not increase my speed because of the resistance caused by my underwater camera. I was growing impatient, as well as a bit worried about the possible arrival of a shark upon this scene.

Meanwhile, Pierre at last reached the raft. I saw him being pulled up into the boat by the two others. Greatly relieved, I stopped swimming and struggling against the muscle strain that was coming on in my legs. I floated there on the surface. In about five minutes, I heard the engine draw close. As I climbed aboard, Jim and Ronnie welcomed me with faces lit up in smiles.

February 22

Five in the morning. I was awakened by the morning call bell. It was still very dark outside. Rubbing the sleep out of my eyes, I hurriedly got myself going. Within forty minutes, the car arrived at Lahaina. Already the staff from the university was loading our equipment into the raft. The night had not yet given way to dawn; by the lights of the harbor, I also loaded my gear—cameras and diving equipment—aboard the raft. Leaving a trail on the quiet sea-face of the lonely harbor, our raft headed toward the open sea. The jet-black figure of Haleakala was silhouetted against the freshly brightening morning sky.

During the night whales are barely active, and the pace of their breathing slows down remarkably to one breath every fifteen or twenty minutes. So the great animals are not easily seen. "Come

---

buoyant (boi′ənt) *adj.* able to float.
vigor (vig′ər) *n.* active power or force; healthy strength.

on, whales," I wished to myself, "show us where you are." The sky continued to grow brighter.

I was afraid we had woken up so early in vain. I very much wanted to get a picture of a spouting whale backed by a dawning sky. The day before we had left port at 6:40 A.M., but it was not until 7:50, when the sun had fully risen over the top of the mountain, that we found any whales. During the daytime they showed themselves so much, I thought, why were we so unlucky in the early morning. We departed Lahaina and headed for Molokini.

"Spray!" The first person to call out was the Earthwatcher, the wife of Jim the reporter. The whale spouted a few times while floating on the surface, then kicked his flukes up high and dove into the water. I heard that familiar "bwoosh" sound again and turned to see two more whales spouting just 100 meters away. I realized that today I would be able to take as many pictures as I wanted before the sun rose over the mountain's shadow.

We moved a bit toward the open sea, and I readied my camera for some pictures of spouting whales against the deep black mountain shadow and the dawn-reddened sky. The first pod sprayed a few times, and at the moment they kicked their flukes up, a whale

A mother whale and her calf

513

from another pod sent a <u>plume</u> of spray high into the sky. The scene from my imagination spread out to fill the viewfinder of my camera. Whales floated on the water's surface, taking in relaxed and leisurely breaths, and then submerged. I grew tired watching the ocean's surface, and then I heard the sound of a whale spouting once again and saw it all in the distance. Photography itself is rather easy, so I grew anxious and irritated waiting for an opportunity to take some early morning shots.

When the whale came up for the third time, the sun was shining through the clouds that floated over the mountain peak. And so ended this particular session of early morning photography. . . .

Reflections on the Whale

"Gentle Giant." I like to use this phrase in referring to whales, not just because it sounds nice, but because of the impressions I have of them through my close association with some 150 humpbacks over the eight years since I became interested in whales.

From the whales' point of view, I have never been a friendly neighbor or close companion to them although we live on the same planet. To the whales, I suppose, I was an invader, coming unusually deep into their territory with the noises of motorboats or small aircraft. I was a strange and unidentifiable creature, who did not swim very well, but eagerly drew close to them, with legs flapping and a weird object of some kind attached to my front.

Indeed, there were only three whales that came close to the rafts I have been aboard. Most of them hated the approaching boat, changing again and again the direction of their swimming or remaining underwater longer in order to avoid it.

When I dove into the water from the raft to photograph them underwater, many whales went deeper into the sea or veered away at the sound of my dive. After I discovered that the whales were trying to avoid me, I waited for them to draw closer to the raft with the engine shut off. I was also

---

plume (plüm) *n.* large, fluffy, showy feather.

In order to get this photo, I chased the whale until sunset.

careful to slip noiselessly into the water whenever I dove. I did not swim and chase after them, but waited for them to come close to me as I floated like a log.

On one occasion a calf became interested in a piece of drift-wood and came to within two meters of it. When I began to photo-graph the scene, the mother whale hurried up to the calf as though she were scolding a child. She swam between me and her calf, and I quickly moved back to avert the near miss. The mother whale and her calf then swam out of my field of view as though nothing had happened. This was the only instance in which I had to get out of the way of an approaching whale.

There was another time when we found our entire raft was on a whale's back, riding high in the air. I still do not know how it happened—whether our raft went over the whale's back or whether the whale accidentally rose up under the raft. Again, the surprised parties were the human beings, while the indifferent whale <u>non-chalantly</u> swam away.

Although the whales, with the tremendous power hidden in their huge bodies, were quite capable of easily knocking away the raft or me with their flukes, I never felt in such danger. Once after I had dived into the water and ended up, quite by chance, directly in front of a group of whales, they avoided a collision by moving away.

In fact, I felt most insecure and hesitant while still in the raft, before diving in. But once in the ocean, with the whales in plain sight, my insecurity evaporated. All I saw were these huge, tran-quil, and sympathetic creatures, who are most accurately described as "Gentle Giants."

"Let's show these whales to our children and grandchildren." Five years ago I read this statement in Hawaii. I still recall that when I read it, the blood drained from my body. Years from now, I thought, when I have grandchildren who are grown, will whales still be swimming through this ocean where once I rafted around, in such excitement, searching for them?

There are species that my grandparents could have come upon easily that are now on the <u>verge</u> of extinction. Only in very secluded ocean redoubts can they be found. This knowledge fills me with apprehension for the future of these gentle giants.

---

nonchalantly (non′shə länt′lē) *adv.* with casual indifference.
verge (vûrj) *n.* edge; border; point beyond which something happens or begins.

MEET Nakamura

A photographer of oceanic subjects for many years, Tsuneo Nakamura was born in Tokyo, Japan, in 1949. Although he continues to live there, he spends more than half of each year in other parts of the world taking photographs and collecting information. Nakamura has traveled to both the North and South poles to photograph whales and other marine animals. He is also well known for his published photographs and writings on sailboats and passenger ships.

RESPONDING TO *Literature*

THINK • TALK • WRITE

1 Would you ever want to go on an expedition to photograph whales? Why or why not? Explain your opinion.

2 Why does Nakamura have mixed feelings when he first encounters the whales? How do these feelings change after he's been in the water? What might have caused this?

3 How would you describe Nakamura's character? What do you learn about him from the way he handles the incident with the shark?

4 What are some of the qualities a person might need to be a good photographer of whales? What makes you think so? Use story details in your response.

5 Nakamura quotes the statement "Let's show these whales to our children and grandchildren." Do you think whales will still exist two generations from now? Explain your opinion.

ACTIVITIES

- **Write About Sensory Language**
  Write a description of a whale chase. Use language that appeals to all five senses.

- **Make a Whale Chart** Research a particular species of whale. Find a picture of it, then list its home waters, its size, and its unusual characteristics. Also find out if it is endangered, and why.

VOCABULARY PRACTICE

Each of the numbered words below is either a *synonym* or an *antonym* of one of the vocabulary words. On a separate sheet of paper, write the vocabulary word that completes each pair. Then write whether the two words are synonyms or antonyms.

trepidation	pandemonium
exhilarated	vigor
resonated	plume
ambiguous	nonchalantly
transpired	verge

1 feather:

2 definite:

3 stillness:

4 fear:

5 strength:

6 exhausted:

7 edge:

8 echoed:

9 attentively:

10 occurred:

BIRDFOOT'S GRAMPA

by Joseph Bruchac

The old man
must have stopped our car
two dozen times to climb out
and gather into his hands
the small toads blinded
by our lights and leaping,
live drops of rain.

The rain was falling,
a mist about his white hair
and I kept saying
you can't save them all,
accept it, get back in
we've got places to go.

But, leathery hands full
of wet brown life,
knee deep in the summer
roadside grass,
he just smiled and said
*they have places to go to
too.*

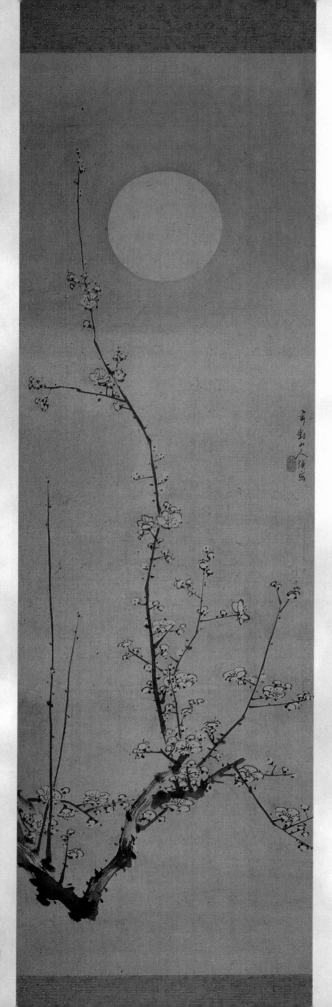

TWO HAIKU

TRANSLATED BY HARRY BEHN

Behind me the moon
brushes a shadow of pines
lightly on the floor.

—*Kikaku*

■

The red sun sinks low
beyond a dead tree clutching
an old eagle's nest.

—*Boncho*

Prunus Blossom in Moonlight
Gentai   British Library, London

520

BEFORE READING

. . . .

RESTORING OUR EARTH

CONNECT TO LITERATURE

What do you picture when you hear the words *swamp* or *marsh?* Do you think of slime and crawly creatures? In your journal, jot down some ideas about what you think swamps and marshes are like. As you read "Restoring Our Earth," check your journal to see how accurate your predictions were.

THINKING ABOUT EXPOSITION

Exposition is a type of writing that explains or informs; the writer knows a great deal about a topic and wants to share the information with readers. In an expository essay the writer will often give a thesis statement, a sentence or two near the beginning of the work that directly expresses the essay's main idea. Often, the first sentence of a paragraph states a new idea; the rest of the paragraph's sentences provide supporting details for that idea. Occasionally the writer will restate the main idea in new words at the end of the essay.

DID YOU KNOW?

Salt marshes exist on many of our shorelines. They act as protection from storms by absorbing and then slowly releasing the floodwater; in this way they stabilize the shoreline. These marshes are extremely fertile and provide a home to such sea animals as clams, mussels, oysters, crabs, sole, flounder, and striped bass, all of which eat the food provided by the marsh. Many types of birds also make their nests in these marshes.

Even so, filling in salt marshes was long considered an environmental improvement; they were seen as breeding grounds for mosquitoes and as useless for farming or grazing. By 1970 marshes were being filled in at a rate of 300,000 acres (121,410 hectares) per year. Only recently has the value of these marshes been appreciated with the result that support has grown for preserving them.

Meet Laurence Pringle

Growing up in farm country near Rochester, New York, Laurence Pringle often rambled through the woods and fields near his home. His love of the outdoors inspired his choice of a college major in wildlife conservation. He also studied journalism and photography as ways to communicate his enthusiasm for nature to other people.

After teaching high school science for a year, Pringle spent seven years as a writer/editor at *Nature and Science,* a magazine published by the American Museum of Natural History. Since then, he has written many acclaimed books about nature and the environment.

Pringle has been honored with a Special Conservation Award by the National Wildlife Federation "for his numerous environmental books for children and young adults." *Restoring Our Earth* was selected as an Outstanding Science Trade Book for Children.

Restoring Our Earth

by Laurence Pringle
Illustrated by Michael Rothman

REASSEMBLING NATURE

In San Francisco Bay and Chesapeake Bay, men and women slog through deep mud to plant cordgrasses and create new marshes. In the Midwest, people search in old cemeteries for patches of native prairie plants and collect some of their seeds for propagation. In Florida, a straightened river may be restored to its old meandering channel.

Salt Marsh Grasshopper

All over North America people are working to restore marshes, prairies, rangelands, forests, lakes, rivers, and other damaged environments. A new scientific field, ecological restoration, is emerging. As defined by John Berger in his book *Restoring the Earth,* "Restoration is an effort to imitate nature in all its artistry and complexity by taking a degraded system and making it more diverse and productive."

Restoration is *not* reclamation. A developer may boast of "reclaiming" land when he fills or drains a marsh in order to create dry land for homesites. Strip-mined land may be said to be reclaimed when it is covered with a growth of grasses, probably species from Europe or Asia rather than plants native to the area. The land may be reclaimed, but it isn't restored.

Given time, a disturbed piece of land or body of water will often restore itself to some extent. In Great Britain, a beautiful natural area called the Norfolk Broads was discovered to be a former peat-industry site. Over four centuries, until about the year 1500, peat was dug from the area, leaving several steep-walled basins that eventually filled with water. No doubt it was an ugly landscape when first abandoned. Today the area is a complex of shallow lakes, marshes, and forests, rich with wildlife, and has been declared a nature reserve.

A weedy city lot can also become a forest if undisturbed for a few decades, although it will lack many plants and animals that are natives of that region. Restoration ecologists seek to influence this process of change and to speed it up. They encourage and also reintroduce plants and animals that are native to an area. They try to wipe out and keep out organisms from other regions that are not native.

■ ——————————————

peat (pēt) *n.* rotted plant matter found in bogs and swamps, and used as fertilizer or burned for fuel.

Canvasback Duck

In a sense, a damaged piece of land or body of water is like a fine watch that someone <u>blithely</u> took apart and cast aside. The restoration challenge: to reassemble the parts and make the complex device work again. (Reclamation of the parts would produce something useful but not the same intricate timepiece.) Restoration often calls for knowledge of ecology, botany, zoology, agriculture, engineering, and agronomy, or soils science. It has been called the "acid test of ecological understanding," because it asks humans, with their imperfect knowledge, to imitate nature.

Restoration of lands and waters also gives ecologists an opportunity to test ideas, to reassemble an environment piece by piece, and to observe the effects. This basic research could lead to a new understanding of how living and nonliving things depend on one another.

No less important are the immediate <u>tangible</u> results of restoration—formerly degraded places made into prairies, marshes, forests, and other natural places with their diverse plant-animal communities. As these healed wounds delight our senses, they remind us that we have the ability to refashion our landscape in positive as well as negative ways.

---

blithely (blīth′lē) *adv.* thoughtlessly; with no concern.
tangible (tan′jə bəl) *adj.* definite; capable of being measured.

Various native seeds

Eel Grass

Squid (Loligo)

525

"The ribbon of green marshes, part solid land, part mobile water, has a definite but elusive border, now hidden, now exposed, as the tides of the Atlantic fluctuate. . . . The marsh reaches as far inland as the tides can creep and as far into the sea as marsh plants can find a roothold and live in saline waters."

JOHN AND MILDRED TEAL
*Life and Death
of the Salt Marsh*

Flounder

Great Egret

Striped Bass

MARSH BUILDERS

Of all marshes, swamps, and other wetlands, saltwater marshes produce the most living matter. These wet meadows are washed daily by tides. Outgoing tides carry bits of dead grass and other <u>edible</u> organic matter into the deeper waters of a bay—food for oysters and other shellfish. Incoming tides allow fish, crabs, and squid to reach the low parts of the marsh. Salt marshes serve as feeding grounds, spawning beds, and nurseries for marine fish and crustaceans. Destruction of salt marshes spells the end of many kinds of seafood valued by humans.

People have so far wiped out about half of the ribbon of green marshes that once <u>flourished</u> along the coastal United States. California, for example, once had 381,000 acres of coastal wetlands; now it has about 105,000 acres. Former salt marshes are now covered by cities, housing tracts, airports, landfills, or simply by soil washed off the land and carried by rivers into bays and lagoons. The human impact includes diking and draining marshes, and changing the amount and content of fresh water flowing into bays and other estuaries.

In the 1960s increasing numbers of people learned to appreciate the value of salt marshes and to protect them. One book, published in 1969, played a role in changing public attitudes toward salt marshes. *Life and Death of the Salt Marsh,* by John and Mildred Teal, eloquently explained that salt marshes are one of nature's great gifts, a <u>bounty</u> being <u>squandered</u> by humanity.

Sometimes a person's life is changed by a book. *Life and Death of the Salt Marsh* had a great effect on a man named Edgar Garbisch, Jr. In 1970 Garbisch took a temporary leave from the University of Minnesota, where he was a successful research chemist and teacher. He was looking for work with more

Blue Crab

---

edible (ed′ə bəl) *adj.* fit to eat.
flourished (flûr′isht) *v.i.* grew or developed strongly; thrived.
bounty (boun′tē) *n.* gift generously given.
squandered (skwon′dərd) *v.t.* spent or used in a wasteful manner.

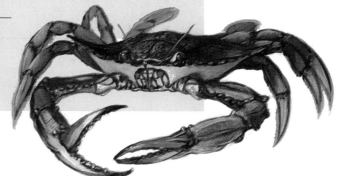

tangible results. Although Garbisch had spent boyhood summers beside Chesapeake Bay, he had never paid much attention to its salt marshes. Now, living by the bay again at age thirty-seven, he began to learn about the marshes, their value, and their destruction by people.

Garbisch felt we could do more than just protect the marshes that remained. There were opportunities to restore marshes in places where they had been damaged and to create marshes where they had never existed. In fact, the authors of *Life and Death of the Salt Marsh* had written: "There seems to be no reason why the construction of new marshland would be an impossibility. . . . It might be possible to get a new marsh well established within only a few years if it were adequately planted. We know of no case in which this has been tried."

Ed Garbisch was fascinated. After further study and success with a small-scale planting of marsh grasses, he resigned from his university job. He became a marsh builder.

At first he believed a staff of scientists would be needed to learn how to restore salt marshes. But most of the problems that arose did not require long study or complex research. They were mainly technical problems, such as finding or adapting machinery or equipment for the peculiar job of marsh-building. When planting grass seedlings by hand, for example, workers sometimes needed to wear plastic-covered snowshoes to keep from sinking deep into the gooey marsh mud.

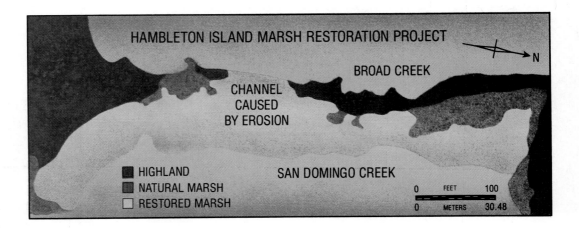

HAMBLETON ISLAND MARSH RESTORATION PROJECT

N

BROAD CREEK

CHANNEL CAUSED BY EROSION

SAN DOMINGO CREEK

■ HIGHLAND
■ NATURAL MARSH
□ RESTORED MARSH

0   FEET   100

0   METERS   30.48

In 1972 Garbisch created a nonprofit organization, Environmental Concern, Inc., with headquarters in the fishing village of St. Michaels, Maryland, on the eastern shore of Chesapeake Bay. That spring he also began the first known full-scale attempt to create a salt marsh. The site was Hambleton Island, a mile from St. Michaels. In the mid-1800s the island had been 55 acres in size, but waves and currents had eroded about half of it away. Erosion had also cut the uninhabited island in two.

To halt erosion, Garbisch decided to plant a new marsh in the channel that bisected the island. The channel was too deep for marsh grasses to grow, so the first step was to partly fill it with sand. Three hundred bargeloads of sand were needed to raise the channel bottom to the desired level. Then Ed Garbisch and his work crew, along with friends and volunteers, began to hand-transplant a quarter million seedlings of marsh grasses. The job took five months to complete. The grasses took hold and began to flourish. Then they were flattened by

LEFT: Environmental Concern, Inc., planted a new marsh, comprised of thousands of marsh grass seedlings and tons of new sand. This marsh reversed the erosion that had caused a channel to bisect Hambleton Island.

RIGHT: *Spartina* seedlings are raised in peat pots (top) until they are ready for planting. The planting of seedlings (middle and bottom) is done during low tide when the marsh floor is exposed.

Duck Potato

Arrow Arum

Pickerelweed

Spartina alterniflora

Spartina patens

the high winds and waves of a hurricane. For a few days the situation looked grim, but the grasses recovered. The new Hambleton Island marsh grew thick and tall, slowing erosion and attracting animal life both above and below water.

The success of this first human-made marsh led to new opportunities. Environmental Concern each year restores or creates dozens of marshes for communities, government agencies, corporations, and private land-owners. Most of the projects are located along the East Coast, but Environmental Concern has also restored freshwater marshes as far inland as Ohio.

To build a marsh one needs native marsh plants—duck potato, arrow arum, and pickerelweed for freshwater sites, and the two species of cordgrass that <u>dominate</u> eastern saltwater marshes. Cordgrasses have the scientific name *Spartina,* from the Greek word for cord, because people used to twist similar grasses into thin ropes. One species of cordgrass, *Spartina alterniflora,* grows up to 10 feet high in low marsh areas that are

dominate (dom′ə nāt′) *v.t.* have the main influence or control over.

This diagram shows how tides and the gentle slope of the coastal terrain determine the type of marsh. Duplicating the natural grade of the marshland's floor is essential to the successful restoration of a marsh.

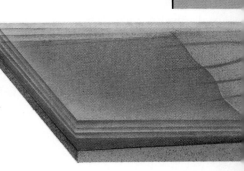

EXTREME LOW TIDE

flooded twice daily by tides. The other common eastern species, *Spartina patens,* sometimes called salt hay, grows about 2 feet tall in marsh areas that are <u>inundated</u> by only the highest tides.

Each year Ed Garbisch grows as many as a half million *Spartina* seedlings in a wetland nursery. These plants are raised from seeds, and many salt marshes are restored by direct planting of seeds. So in early autumn each year the staff of Environmental Concern harvests about 500 gallons of *Spartina* seeds from existing marshes.

Compared with the challenge of restoring a forest, prairie, or other land ecosystem, salt marsh restoration is relatively easy. Once *Spartina* grasses are established, other saltwater organisms are carried in by the tides. Within five years cordgrasses lay down a peatlike layer of dead leaves and stems. Soon it is hard to tell a new marsh from one that has existed for scores of years.

Nevertheless, getting a new marsh off to a good start can be difficult. The grade, or height of land in relation to the tides, is critical for cordgrasses. Marsh plants fail to survive if the grade is off by a few inches. Establishing a favorable grade at a site requires knowledge of the tides, surveying, and careful work with earth-moving equipment. Even with an ideal grade, however, cordgrasses fail to survive if the land rises too steeply. A steep slope invites erosion; the incline toward higher ground must be very gentle to <u>minimize</u> wave impact. Even then waves

■

inundated (in′ən dā′tid) *v.t.* covered with a flood.
minimize (min′ə mīz′) *v.t.* make as small as possible.

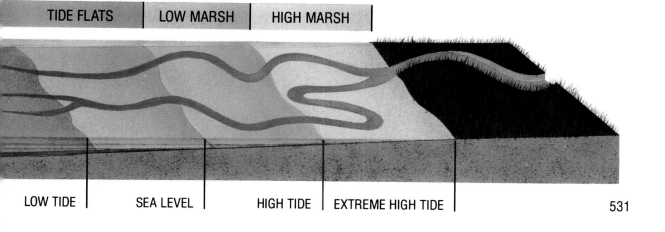

TIDE FLATS	LOW MARSH	HIGH MARSH

LOW TIDE   SEA LEVEL   HIGH TIDE   EXTREME HIGH TIDE

may wash away newly planted *Spartina*. Temporary baffles, or low stone walls, may be needed to tame the waves. Given a few months' protection, *Spartina* seedlings grow into a thick mat of soil-trapping vegetation.

One benefit of salt marshes, whether natural or planted by people, is that they control erosion. Environmental Concern is frequently asked by landowners to stop shoreline erosion. The conventional but expensive remedy is to line the shore with a wall of stones. At many sites Environmental Concern established a 25-foot-wide strip of wave-taming marsh for one tenth the cost of a stone barrier. The lush ribbon of green, more attractive than stones, is also a habitat for fish, <u>crustaceans</u>, and other wildlife.

Environmental Concern is often hired to repair or replace marshes that have been harmed by construction or draining. Usually a utility or corporation is allowed by government to destroy some marsh only on the condition that an equal or greater area of marsh is created elsewhere. (A larger area is usually demanded, on the assumption that human-made marsh does not match the value of the original wetland.) This tradeoff is called mitigation, and mitigation projects make up 60 percent of Environmental Concern's work.

In the mid-1970s, the U.S. Army Corps of Engineers began an effort to establish marshes and other natural habitats on the mud and silt <u>dredged</u> from harbors and shipping channels.

---

crustaceans (kru stā′shənz) *n., pl.* shellfish such as lobsters, shrimp, clams, and barnacles.
dredged (drejd) *v.t.* cleared out with a large mechanical scoop or net.

Spartina grasses grow from both seeds and rhizomes— creeping stems that run horizontally under the soil with aerial shoots at their tips. Over several years, the grasses deposit a layer of dead leaves and stems (detritus) that provides a home for marine life and prevents erosion.

Spartina seed

Growth from rhizome

Diamondback Terrapin

Detritus

Spartina flower

Tides and currents continually carry silt into these channels, and nationwide the Corps of Engineers dredges up more than 350 million cubic yards a year. The bottom muck is commonly dumped back into the water, away from the channel, where it may kill bottom-dwelling shellfish and may also be gradually swept back into the channel. Hauling the dredged material to land is costly, and few landowners want the stuff anyway. In Chesapeake Bay the Corps of Engineers has hired Ed Garbisch and his staff to make salt marshes on dredged material.

After successfully establishing salt marshes up to 10 acres in size on dredged sediments, in 1982 Environmental Concern tackled the largest project of this kind. The corps dredged a channel near Barren Island in Chesapeake Bay, and Ed Garbisch had the 180,000 cubic yards of sediments deposited in a huge, nearly flat pile near the island. Garbisch directed the dumping of the silt and mud so that about 27 acres of land were exposed at low tide. The new island sloped very gently up toward a crown that was

3–6 feet
(1–2 meters)

Growth from rhizome

---

sediments (sed′ə mənts) *n., pl.* solid materials that settle to the bottom of a body of water.

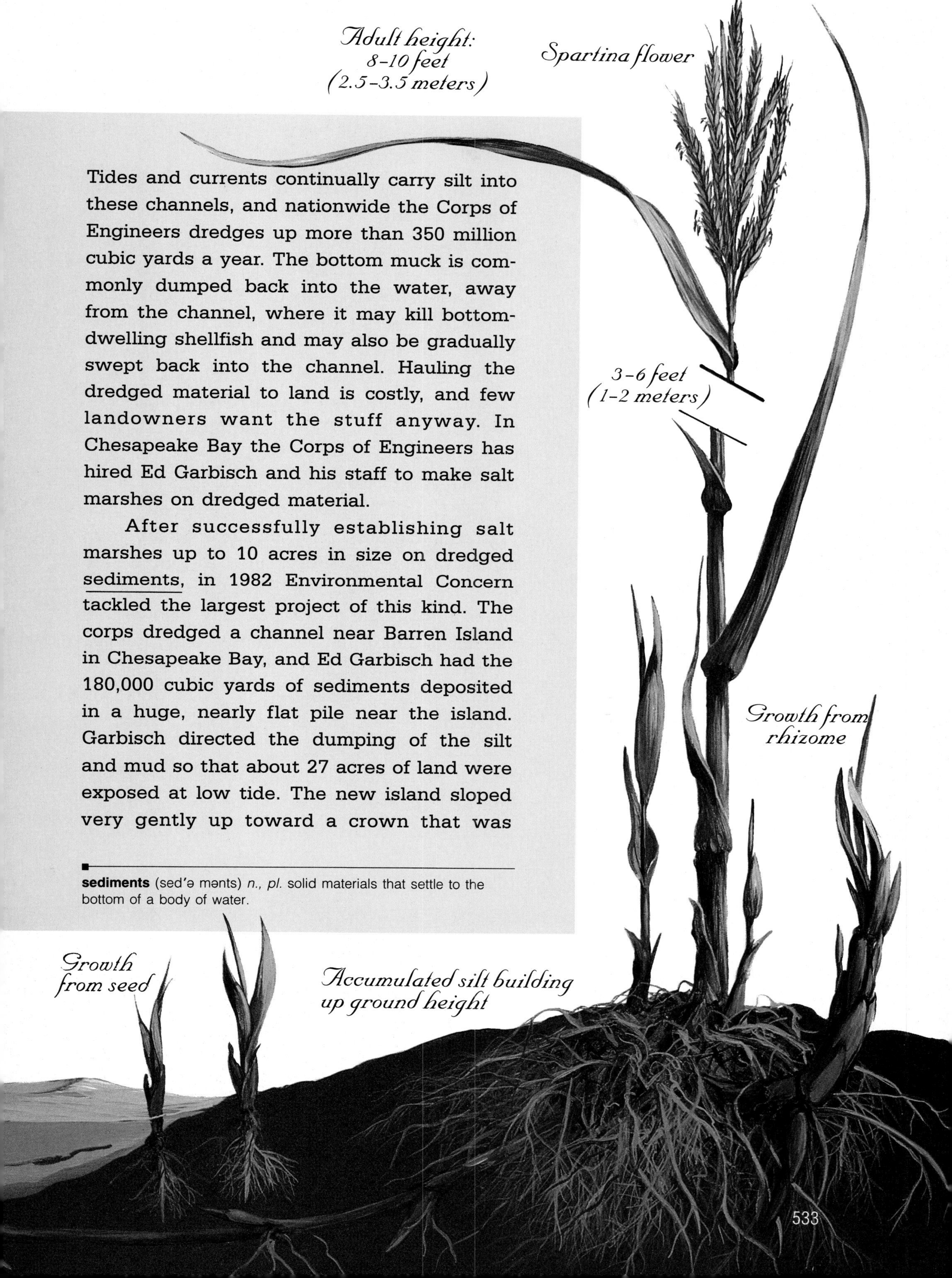

Growth from seed

Accumulated silt building up ground height

533

27 inches above normal high spring tides, an elevation that was needed for nesting by least terns, an endangered species whose production the corps wanted to encourage.

The following spring Environmental Concern's work crews scattered *Spartina* seeds and planted *Spartina* seedlings on 25 acres of the island. The plants began to grow, to trap silt, and to stabilize the dredged material. By midsummer of 1982 the new island's crown was adorned with a large nesting colony of least terns.

Although Ed Garbisch is considered the master marsh builder on the eastern seaboard, marsh restoration efforts are being made all along the U.S. coast. The basic operating principles remain the same, but may involve the use of different native plants. Near Tampa, Florida, for example, red mangroves were planted with cordgrasses along 10 miles of shoreline to help stabilize the soil in front of a housing development.

In Southern California, the cordgrass *Spartina foliosa* dominates the lowest areas of salt marshes, while pickleweed is most common in the middle and high marshes. Such plants as saltwort and arrow grass are also <u>abundant</u> in the middle marsh elevations. As part of their effort to make salt marshes as natural as possible, ecologists try to exclude or discourage <u>exotic</u> plants. In Southern California these include the white mangrove from New Zealand and sickle grass from Europe.

The simplest and least expensive way to restore a marsh calls for no planting but simply returning tidal flows to areas that were drained or somehow blocked from the ocean's tides. In 1980, full tidal flow was restored to Pine Creek Marsh in Fairfield, Connecticut. Upland plants that could not tolerate salt water disappeared, and the area was quickly colonized by salt-marsh plants.

Ecologists recognize that they cannot restore a salt marsh to conditions that existed before Europeans settled in North America. We don't even know what salt marshes were like then; old maps reveal only their locations, not detailed accounts of their plant-animal communities. Also, even without the impact of humans, marshes have been altered by floods, droughts, hurricanes, and other natural calamities. By reversing the human damage whenever possible and by replacing native plants and animals that have been lost, marsh builders aim to create the most natural coastal wetlands possible today.

---

abundant (ə bun′dənt) *adj.* more than enough; plentiful.
exotic (eg zot′ik) *adj.* of or belonging to another part of the world.

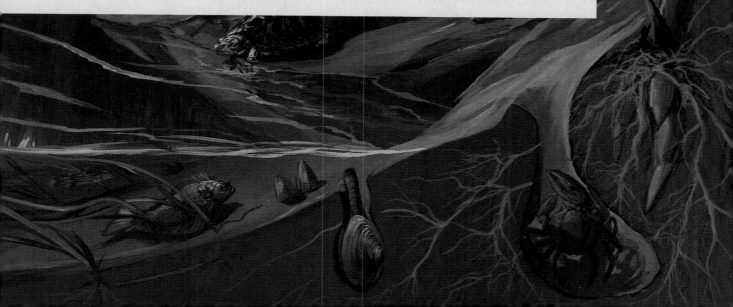

RESPONDING TO Literature

1 What did you find most interesting in this selection? Jot down some ideas in your journal.

2 What does Laurence Pringle mean by "restoration of the environment"? How does it differ from "reclamation"? Would turning a vacant lot into a park be restoration or reclamation?

3 Why does Pringle compare a damaged marsh to a broken watch? What skills are required to make it work again?

4 Write a character sketch of Ed Garbisch. What kind of person is he? Use story details in your response.

5 Pringle writes that "Restoration . . . asks humans, with their imperfect knowledge, to imitate nature." Why is our knowledge imperfect? How does restoration imitate nature? How does it differ from nature?

ACTIVITIES

- **Write About Exposition** Write letters urging your congressional representatives and the president to save endangered salt marshes. Be sure to include information that will make your letters as persuasive as possible.

- **How Do You Make a Marsh?** Write a "recipe" for rebuilding a marsh. List what tools are needed. Arrange the instructions in a step-by-step format.

VOCABULARY PRACTICE

On a separate sheet of paper, write the letter of the answer that best completes the sentence.

1 If a mushroom is **edible,** it is
   a. poisonous **b.** delicious
   c. safe to eat

2 People who **dominate** an industry are its
   a. losers **b.** leaders **c.** enemies

3 If a plant **flourished,** it probably
   a. died **b.** altered **c.** thrived

4 If a species is **abundant,** it is
   a. plentiful **b.** rare **c.** endangered

5 When a restoration's results are **tangible,** they are
   a. eroding **b.** healthful **c.** definite

6 An example of nature's **bounty** is a
   a. thunderstorm **b.** harvest
   c. toxic spill

7 An **exotic** bird is one that is
   a. common **b.** foreign **c.** beautiful

8 If tides **inundated** marshes, the marshes were
   a. flooded **b.** drained **c.** restored

9 If we **squandered** a fortune, we have
   a. lots of money **b.** no money
   c. more money

10 If we try to **minimize** damage to the environment, we are trying to make it
   a. better **b.** small **c.** sufficient

THE TIME WE CLIMBED SNAKE MOUNTAIN

Kathleen Norris Cook

Seeing good places
    for my hands
I grab the warm parts of the cliff
       and I feel the mountain as I climb.
Somewhere   around here
     yellow spotted snake is sleeping   on his rock
       in the sun.

So
   please, I tell them
      watch out,
don't step on the spotted yellow snake
      he lives here.
The mountain is his.

             —*Leslie Marmon Silko*

S P O on T

ESSAY

Suppose you're an issues-minded person and there's a topic that's important to you. If you wanted to express your viewpoint, how would you choose to do it? The person who drew the cartoon below chose to make his statement through art.

Drawing by Mulligan; © 1970 The New Yorker Magazine, Inc.

Look at the cartoon. Where does the scene take place?

What is the boy doing? What other details do you notice?

What do you think is the main idea of the cartoon?

Why might the artist have drawn this cartoon?

Think about other cartoons you have seen. What points were the artists trying to make? Now think about essays you have read. What were the writers trying to say? In what ways are cartoons like the one above and some essays alike?

LIGHT

ELEMENTS OF AN ESSAY

An essay is a short work of nonfiction that focuses on a single subject. There are two general types of essays.

- **Formal essays** are objective, or impersonal, and serious in tone.
- **Informal essays** are subjective, or personal, and light in tone.

FACTS AND OPINIONS are details the author uses in writing about the subject of the essay.

- **Facts** are statements that can be proved.
- **Opinions** are statements about beliefs, feelings, or other ideas that cannot be proved.

MAIN IDEA is the single most important idea in the essay. The main idea can be stated directly in the essay or suggested by the essay's tone or details.

POINT OF VIEW is the perspective from which an essay is written.

- In the **first-person point of view,** the speaker is a person in the essay. Pronouns such as *I, me,* and *mine* indicate this point of view.
- In the **third-person point of view,** the speaker is outside the essay. Pronouns such as *he, she,* and *they* indicate this point of view.

PURPOSE is the author's reason for writing. An essay can have one or more purposes:

- to entertain
- to explain
- to share personal feelings and opinions
- to persuade

TONE suggests how the essay writer feels toward his or her subject matter. It can reflect any feeling that a writer has about a subject.

In the selections that follow, you will learn more about essays. What you discover will add to your understanding and enjoyment of essays and will help you in writing your own essay.

ESSAY

ANIMAL CRAFTSMEN

CONNECT TO LITERATURE

Have you ever studied a butterfly's cocoon? Did you know that beaver dams can alter the courses of rivers? Did you ever wonder what goes on inside a beehive? In your journal, jot down some ideas about animals and the homes they build. As you read "Animal Craftsmen," see if the author shares any of your ideas.

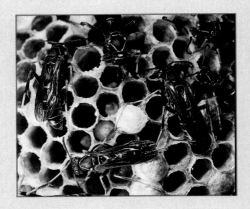

INTRODUCTION TO THE MODEL ESSAY

When you read the essays in this unit, you will find that all of them have certain elements in common. For example, each essay has an author's purpose, a main idea, and details that support the main idea.

As you read "Animal Craftsmen," use the notes in the margin. The notes will help you see the structure of the essay and show you how the basic elements of the essay are connected to each other. As you read the essay, you might like to note your own thoughts and impressions in your journal.

DID YOU KNOW?

You may have heard of the "Seven Wonders of the World." These were ancient buildings that were considered architectural marvels. Many kinds of animals produce architectural marvels every day.

For example, did you know that beavers use logs, stones, and mud to build dams that may be as much as 1,000 feet (305 m) long? Equally impressive is the fact that spiders produce their own silk for their webs; for its diameter, a thread of this silk is one of the strongest fibers in the world.

Paper wasp building its nest

ANIMAL CRAFTSMEN

by Bruce Brooks

One evening, when I was about five, I climbed up a ladder on the outside of a rickety old tobacco barn at sunset. The barn was part of a small farm near the home of a country relative my mother and I visited periodically; though we did not really know the farm's family, I was allowed to roam, poke around, and conduct sudden studies of anything small and harmless. On this evening, as on most of my jaunts, I was not looking for anything; I was simply climbing with an open mind. But as I balanced on the next-to-the-top rung and inhaled the spicy stink of the tobacco drying inside, I *did* find something under the eaves—something very strange.

---

jaunts (jôntz) *n., pl.* short trips, especially taken for pleasure.

It appeared to be a kind of gray paper sphere, suspended from the dark planks by a thin stalk, like an apple made of ashes hanging on its stem. I studied it closely in the clear light. I saw that the bottom was a little ragged, and open. I could not tell if it had been torn, or if it had been made that way on purpose—for it was clear to me, as I studied it, that this thing had been *made.* This was no fruit or fungus. Its shape, rough but trim; its intricately colored surface with subtle swirls of gray and tan; and most of all the uncanny adhesiveness with which the perfectly tapered stem stuck against the rotten old pine boards—all of these features gave evidence of some intentional design. The troubling thing was figuring out who had designed it, and why.

I assumed the designer was a human being: someone from the farm, someone wise and skilled in a craft that had so far escaped my curiosity. Even when I saw wasps entering and leaving the thing (during a vigil I kept every evening for two weeks), it did not occur to me that the wasps might have fashioned it for themselves. I assumed it was a man-made "wasp house" placed there expressly for the purpose of attracting a family of wasps, much as the "martin hotel," a giant birdhouse on a pole near the farmhouse, was maintained to shelter migrant purple martins who returned every spring. I didn't ask myself why anyone would want to give wasps a bivouac; it seemed no more odd than attracting birds.

As I grew less wary of the wasps (and they grew less wary of me), and as my confidence on the ladder improved, I moved to the upper rung and peered through the sphere's bottom. I could see that the paper swirled in layers around some secret center the wasps inhabited, and I marveled at the delicate hands of the craftsman who had devised such tiny apertures for their protection.

I left the area in the late summer, and in my imagination I took the strange structure with me. I

---

intricately (in′tri kit lē) *adv.* very involved or complicated.

uncanny (un kan′ē) *adj.* strange and eerie; weird.

bivouac (biv′ü ak′) *n.* temporary camp or shelter.

apertures (ap′ər chərz) *n., pl.* holes, gaps, or other openings.

envisioned unwrapping it, and in the middle finding—what? A tiny room full of bits of wool for sleeping, and countless manufactured pellets of scientifically determined wasp food? A glowing blue jewel that drew the wasps at twilight, and gave them a cool infusion of energy as they clung to it overnight? My most definite idea was that the wasps lived in a small block of fine cedar the craftsman had drilled full of holes, into which they slipped snugly, rather like the bunks aboard submarines in World War II movies.

Wasp nest

As it turned out, I got the chance to discover that my idea of the cedar block had not been wrong by much. We visited our relative again in the winter. We arrived at night, but first thing in the morning I made straight for the farm and its barn. The shadows under the eaves were too dense to let me spot the sphere from far off. I stepped on the bottom rung of the ladder—slick with frost—and climbed carefully up. My hands and feet kept slipping, so my eyes stayed on the rung ahead, and it was not until I was secure at the top that I could look up. The sphere was gone.

I was crushed. That object had fascinated me like nothing I had come across in my life; I had even grown to love wasps because of it. I sagged on the ladder and watched my breath <u>eddy</u> around the blank eaves. I'm afraid I pitied myself more than the apparently homeless wasps.

Consider the depth and honesty with which Brooks reveals his feelings. Writing in which authors share their feelings and impressions is **subjective writing.**

But then something snapped me out of my sense of loss: I recalled that I had watched the farmer taking in the purple martin hotel every November, after the birds left. From its spruce appearance when he brought it out in March, it was clear he had cleaned it and re-painted it and kept it out of the weather. Of course he would do the same thing for *this* house, which was even more fragile. I had never mentioned the wasp dwelling to anyone, but now I decided I would go to the farm, introduce myself, and inquire about it. Perhaps I

---

eddy (ed′ē) *v.i.* move in a circular or whirling motion.

would even be permitted to handle it, or, best of all, learn how to make one myself.

I scrambled down the ladder, leaping from the third rung and landing in the frosty salad of tobacco leaves and windswept grass that collected at the foot of the barn wall. I looked down and saw that my left boot had, by no more than an inch, just missed crushing the very thing I was rushing off to seek. There, lying dry and separate on the leaves, was the wasp house.

I looked up. Yes, I was standing directly beneath the spot where the sphere had hung—it was a straight fall. I picked up the wasp house, gave it a shake to see if any insects were inside, and, discovering none, took it home.

My awe of the craftsman grew as I unwrapped the layers of the nest. Such beautiful paper! It was much tougher than any I had encountered, and it held a curve (something my experimental paper airplanes never did), but it was very light, too. The secret at the center of the swirl turned out to be a neatly made fan of tiny cells, all of the same size and shape, reminding me of the heart of a sunflower that had lost its seeds to birds. The fan hung from the sphere's ceiling by a stem the thickness of a pencil lead.

The rest of the story is a little embarrassing. More impressed than ever, I decided to pay <u>homage</u> to the creator of this <u>habitable</u> sculpture. I went boldly to the farmhouse. The farmer's wife answered my knock. I showed her the nest and asked to speak with the person in the house who had made it. She blinked and frowned. I had to repeat my question twice before she understood what I believed my mission to be; then, with a gentle laugh, she <u>dispelled</u> my illusion about an ingenious old papersmith fond of wasps. The nest, she explained, had been made entirely by the insects themselves, and wasn't that amazing?

Well, of course it was. It still is. I needn't have been so embarrassed—the structures that animals

Paper wasp

---

homage (hom′ij) *n.* honor, respect, or reverence.
habitable (hab′i tə bəl) *adj.* suitable for living in.
dispelled (di speld′) *v.t.* drove away or caused to disappear.

build, and the sense of design they display, *should* always astound us. On my way home from the farmhouse, in my own defense I kept thinking, "But *I* couldn't build anything like this! Nobody could!"

The most natural thing in the world for us to do, when we are confronted with a piece of animal architecture, is to figure out if we could possibly make it or live in it. Who hasn't peered into the dark end of a mysterious hole in the woods and thought, "It must be pretty weird to live in there!" or looked up at a hawk's nest atop a huge sycamore and shuddered at the thought of waking up every morning with nothing but a few twigs preventing a hundred-foot fall. How, we wonder, do those twigs stay together, and withstand the wind so high?

It is a human tendency always to regard animals first in terms of ourselves. Seeing the defensive courage of a mother bear whose cubs are threatened, or the cooperative determination of a string of ants dismantling a stray chunk of cake, we naturally use our own behavior as reference for our <u>empathy</u>. We put ourselves in the same situation and express the animal's action in feelings—and words—that apply to the way people do things.

Sometimes this is useful. But sometimes it is misleading. <u>Attributing</u> human-like intentions to an animal can keep us from looking at the *animal's* sense of itself in its surroundings—its immediate and future needs, its physical and mental capabilities, its genetic instincts. Most animals, for example, use their five senses in ways that human beings cannot possibly understand or express. How can a forty-two-year-old nearsighted biologist have any real idea what a two-week-old barn owl sees in the dark? How can a sixteen-year-old who lives in the Arizona desert identify with the muscular jumps improvised by a waterfall-leaping salmon in Alaska? There's nothing wrong with trying to empathize with an

By using the pronouns *us* and *we*, Brooks makes you feel as though the two of you were having a conversation. This is one way authors involve their audience in their writing.

---

empathy (em′pə thē) *n.* a sharing of another's feelings or state of mind without actually going through the same experiences.

attributing (ə trib′ūt ing) *v.t.* considering as belonging to, produced by, or resulting from.

animal, but we shouldn't forget that ultimately animals live *animal* lives.

Animal structures let us have it both ways—we can be struck with a strange wonder, and we can empathize right away, too. Seeing a vast spiderweb, taut and glistening between two bushes, it's easy to think, "I have no idea how that is done; the engineering is awesome." But it is just as easy to imagine climbing across the bright strands, springing from one to the next as if the web were a new Epcot attraction, the Invisible Flying Flexible Space Orb. That a clear artifact of an animal's wits and <u>agility</u> stands right there in front of us—that we can touch it, look at it from different angles, sometimes take it home—inspires our imagination as only a strange reality can. We needn't move into a molehill to experience a life of darkness and digging; our creative wonder takes us down there in a second, without even getting our hands dirty.

But what if we discover some of the mechanics of how the web is made? Once we see how the spider works (or the hummingbird, or the bee), is the engineering no longer awesome? This would be too bad: we don't want to lose our sense of wonder just because we gain understanding.

And we certainly do *not* lose it. In fact, seeing how an animal makes its nest or egg case or food storage vaults has the effect of increasing our amazement. The builder's energy, concentration, and athletic <u>adroitness</u> are qualities we can readily admire and envy. Even more startling is the recognition that the animal is working from a precise design in its head, a design that is exactly replicated time after time. This knowledge of architecture—knowing where to build, what materials to use, how to put them together—remains one of the most intriguing mysteries of animal behavior. And the more *we* develop that same knowledge, the more we appreciate the instincts and intelligence of the animals.

Think about the subject of this piece of writing. A short piece of nonfiction that focuses on a single subject is called an **essay.** An essay in which an author shares his or her feelings about a subject is called an **informal,** or **personal, essay.**

An author's reason for writing a particular piece is called the **author's purpose.** Here Brooks's purpose is to share his feelings of awe regarding the things animals build.

---

agility (ə jil′i tē) *n.* quickness and ease in motion or thought; nimbleness.
adroitness (ə droit′nes) *n.* act of being smoothly skillful; deft; clever.

Meet Bruce Brooks

Bruce Brooks (born 1950) wrote his first story at the age of ten. It wasn't until he read the classic book *Great Expectations,* however, that Brooks decided he wanted to become a novelist. A graduate of the University of North Carolina at Chapel Hill, Brooks went from there to the University of Iowa's Writers' Workshop. After graduating from the workshop in 1980, Brooks held many jobs, including reporter, writer, editor, movie critic, teacher, and lecturer.

A successful author of both fiction and nonfiction, Brooks has said that writing "gives me an excuse to be interested in everything new and small and analytical and funny." In addition to writing, Brooks speaks at schools and conferences around the country. He lives in Maryland with his wife and two sons.

More Essays

- *The Rescue of Miss Yaskell and Other Fine Dreams* by Russell Baker (Penguin, 1990). Russell Baker writes an often hilarious column for the *New York Times.* Everyday events take on a new slant when seen through Baker's eyes. Many of his columns are collected in this book.

- *The Best of James Herriot* (St. Martin's Press, 1989). A country vet must be capable of treating a variety of animals—from the most massive bulls to the tiniest kittens. Herriot learned his job well, and, with the help of his essays, you can join him on his rounds.

- *The Essays of E. B. White* by E. B. White (Harper & Row, 1979). E. B. White, the author of *Charlotte's Web* and *Trumpet of the Swan,* lived in New England, where he wrote these sensitive and witty essays about nature, farming, and rural life, among other things.

RESPONDING TO *Literature*

THINK • TALK • WRITE

1 Which "animal craftsmen" would you like to know more about? What would you like to know? Jot down some questions in your journal.

2 Why do you think the wasps' nest so fascinated the author when he was a boy?

3 Why does the author believe it is a mistake to use human terms when describing the habits of animals? Do you agree? Explain your opinion.

4 What does the author mean when he writes, "We needn't move into a molehill to experience a life of darkness . . . our creative wonder takes us down there in a second"?

5 What do you think is the main idea of this selection? Why do you think the author chose to begin it with the anecdote about the wasps' nest? How does it relate to the main idea?

ACTIVITY

● **Write About Essay** Copy and complete this chart for "Animal Craftsmen." You may add detail boxes.

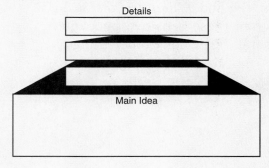

Details

Main Idea

VOCABULARY PRACTICE

On a separate sheet of paper, write the vocabulary word that best completes each sentence.

jaunts	dispelled
intricately	empathy
uncanny	attributing
homage	agility
habitable	adroitness

1 My family likes to take _____ in our new car.

2 Scholars are now _____ the anonymous painting to Leonardo.

3 When the truth about the case finally came out, it _____ all the whispered rumors.

4 The spider web was _____ constructed of delicate silk.

5 Because it once happened to us, we felt great _____ for the family whose house was destroyed by the storm.

6 All of the soldiers gathered to pay _____ to their slain comrade.

7 The cousins bear an _____ resemblance to each other.

8 The gymnast's _____ is a product of years of training.

9 Her _____ in doing card tricks drew admiring praise from the onlookers.

10 A constant interior temperature makes a beehive _____ year round.

ESSAY

TWO ESSAYS BY ALICE WALKER

CONNECT TO LITERATURE

Do you know what a *vegetarian* is? Do you know anyone who is a vegetarian? What are some of the advantages and disadvantages of being a vegetarian? Discuss your thoughts with a classmate. Then as you read Alice Walker's essays, note in your journal her thoughts about vegetarianism.

THINKING ABOUT AUTHOR'S POINT OF VIEW

In personal essays an author writes to convey his or her opinions about a particular subject; this is the *author's point of view.* The author provides details to support his or her point of view in an attempt to persuade readers to agree with it. For example, in the following essays, Alice Walker has some strong opinions about food. She gives details that support her point of view and that she hopes will convince her readers of her ideas.

HAVE YOU EVER?

Have you ever thought about the food you eat and whether or not it is good for you? Doctors and other health professionals recommend eating a balanced diet—including plenty of fruits and vegetables. This does not mean you should never have your favorite soft drink or snack cake, it just means that you should limit how much of these types of food you eat.

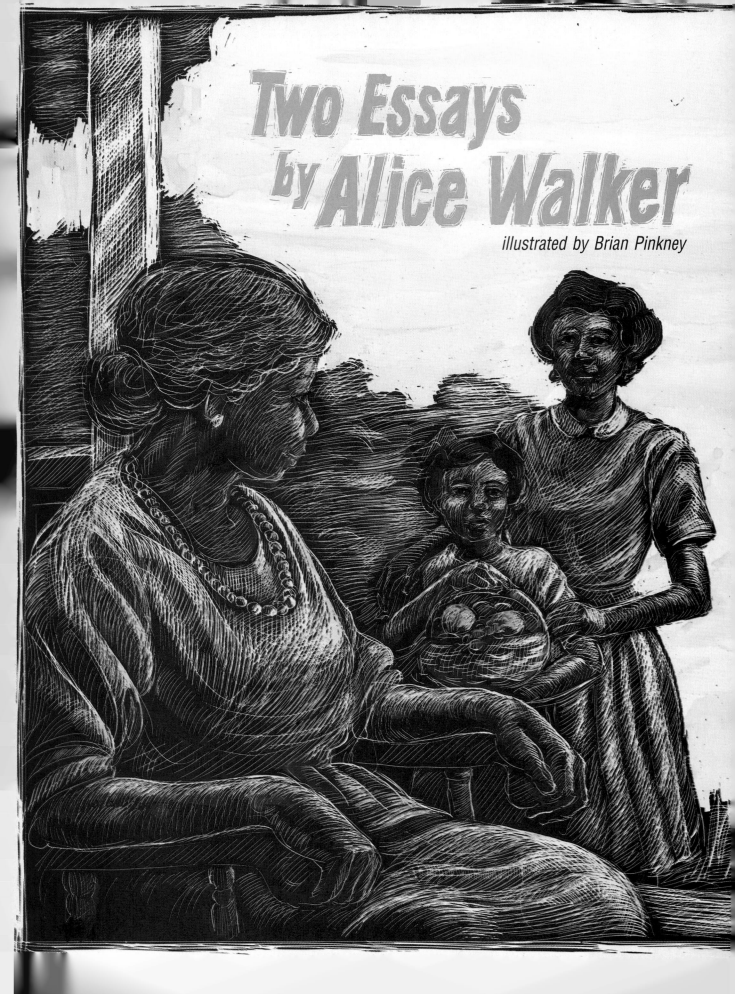

Two Essays
by Alice Walker

illustrated by Brian Pinkney

Longing to Die of Old Age

Mrs. Mary Poole, my "4-greats" grandmother, lived the entire nineteenth century, from around 1800 to 1921, and enjoyed exceptional health. The key to good health, she taught (this woman who as an enslaved person was forced to carry two young children, on foot, from Virginia to Georgia), was never to cover up the pulse at the throat. But, with the benefit of hindsight, one must believe that for her, as for generations of people after her, in our small farming community, diet played as large a role in her longevity and her health as loose clothing and fresh air.

For what did the old ones eat?

Well, first of all, almost nothing that came from a store. As late as my own childhood, in the fifties, at Christmas we had only raisins and perhaps bananas, oranges, and a peppermint stick, broken into many pieces, a sliver for each child; and during the year, perhaps, a half-dozen apples, nuts, and a bunch of grapes. All extravagantly expensive and considered rare. You ate *all* of the apple, sometimes, even, the seeds. Everyone had a vegetable garden; a garden as large as there was energy to work it. In these gardens people raised an abundance of food: corn, tomatoes, okra, peas and

beans, squash, peppers, which they ate in summer and canned for winter. There was no chemical fertilizer. No one could have afforded it, had it existed, and there was no need for it. From the cows and pigs and goats, horses, mules, and fowl that people also raised, there was always ample organic manure.

Until I was grown I never heard of anyone having cancer.

In fact, at first cancer seemed to be coming from far off. For a long time if the subject of cancer came up, you could be sure cancer itself wasn't coming any nearer than to some congested place in the North, then to Atlanta, seventy-odd miles away, then to Macon, forty miles away, then to Monticello, twenty miles away. . . . The first inhabitants of our community to die of acknowledged cancer were almost celebrities, because of this "foreign" disease. But now, twenty-odd years later, cancer has ceased to be viewed as a visitor and is feared instead as a resident. Even the children die of cancer now, which, at least in the beginning, seemed a disease of the old.

Most of the people I knew as farmers left the farms (they did not own the land and were unable to make a living working for the white people

■ **longevity** (lon jev′i tē) *n.* long life.
extravagantly (ek strav′ə gənt lē) *adv.* wastefully; beyond reasonable limits.

551

who did) to rent small apartments in the towns and cities. They ceased to have gardens, and when they did manage to grow a few things they used fertilizer from boxes and bottles, sometimes in improbable colors and consistencies, which they rightly suspected, but had no choice but to use. Gone were their chickens, cows, and pigs. Gone their organic manure.

To their credit, they questioned all that happened to them. Why must we leave the land? Why must we live in boxes with hardly enough space to breathe? (Of course, indoor plumbing <u>seduced</u> many a one.) Why must we buy all our food from the store? Why is the price of food so high—and it so tasteless? The collard greens bought in the supermarket, they said, "tasted like water."

The United States should have closed down and examined its every intention, institution, and law on the very first day a black woman observed that the collard greens tasted like water. Or when the first person of any color observed that store-bought

tomatoes tasted more like unripened avocados than tomatoes.

The flavor of food is one of the clearest messages the Universe ever sends to human beings; and we have by now eaten poisoned warnings by the ton.

When I was a child growing up in middle Georgia in the forties and fifties, people still died of old age. Old age was actually a common cause of death. My parents <u>inevitably</u> visited dying persons over the long or short period of their decline; sometimes I went with them. Some years ago, as an adult, I accompanied my mother to visit a very old neighbor who was dying a few doors down the street, and though she was no longer living in the country, the country style lingered. People like my mother were visiting her constantly, bringing food, picking up and returning laundry, or simply stopping by to inquire how she was feeling and to chat. Her house, her linen, her skin all glowed with cleanliness. She lay propped against pillows so that by merely turning her head

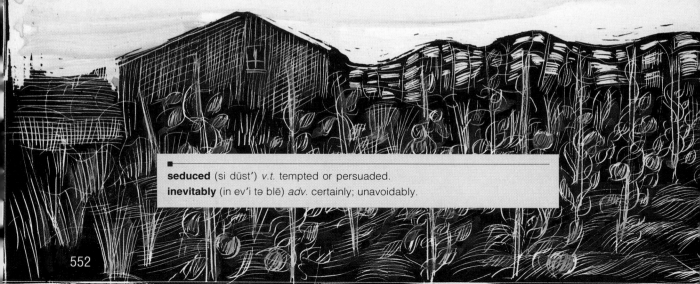

seduced (si düst′) *v.t.* tempted or persuaded.
inevitably (in ev′i tə blē) *adv.* certainly; unavoidably.

she could watch the postman approaching, friends and relatives arriving, and, most of all, the small children playing beside the street, often in her yard, the sound of their play a lively music.

Sitting in the dimly lit, spotless room, listening to the lengthy but warm-with-shared-memories silences between my mother and Mrs. Davis was extraordinarily pleasant. Her white hair gleamed against her kissable black skin, and her bed was covered with one of the most intricately patterned quilts I'd ever seen—a companion to the dozen or more she'd stored in a closet, which, when I expressed interest, she invited me to see.

I thought her dying one of the most reassuring events I'd ever witnessed. She was calm, she seemed ready, her affairs were in order. She was respected and loved. In short, Mrs. Davis was having an excellent death. A week later, when she had actually died, I felt this all the more because she had left, in me, the indelible knowledge that such a death is possible. And that cancer and nuclear annihilation are truly obscene alternatives. And surely, teaching this very vividly is one of the things an excellent death is supposed to do.

To die miserably of self-induced sickness is an aberration we take as normal; but it is crucial that we remember and teach our children that there are other ways.

For myself, for all of us, I want a death like Mrs. Davis's. One in which we will ripen and ripen further, as richly as fruit, and then fall slowly into the caring arms of our friends and other people we know. People who will remember the good days and the bad, the names of lovers and grandchildren, the time sorrow almost broke, the time loving friendship healed.

It must become a right of every person to die of old age. And if we secure this right for ourselves, we can, coincidentally, assure it for the planet. And that, as they say, will be excellence, which is, perhaps, only another name for health.

1985

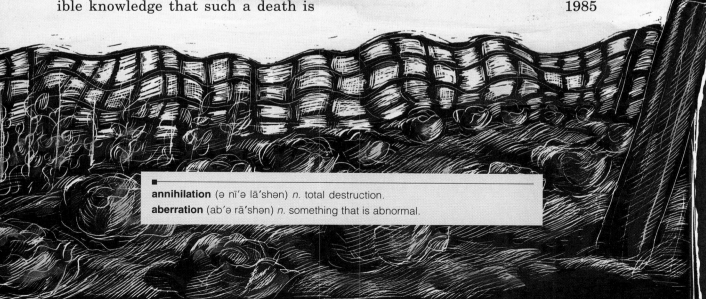

annihilation (ə nī'ə lā'shən) *n.* total destruction.
aberration (ab'ə rā'shən) *n.* something that is abnormal.

Why Did the Balinese Chicken Cross the Road?

"Why do you keep putting off writing about me?" It is the voice of a chicken that asks this. Depending on where you are, you will laugh, or not laugh. Either response is appropriate. The longer I am a writer—so long now that my writing finger is periodically numb—the better I understand what writing is; what its function is; what it is supposed to do. I learn that the writer's pen is a microphone held up to the mouths of ancestors and even stones of long ago. That once given permission by the writer—a fool, and so why should one fear?—horses, dogs, rivers, and, yes, chickens can step forward and <u>expound</u> on their lives. The magic of this is not so much in the power of the microphone as in the ability of the nonhuman object or animal to *be* and the human animal to *perceive its being*.

This then is about a chicken I knew in Bali. I do not know her name or that of her parents and grandparents. I do not know where she was from originally. Suddenly on a day whose morning had been rainy, there she was, on the path in front of us (my own family, on our way back to our temporary shelter), trying to look for worms, trying to point out other possible food items to her three chicks, and trying at the same time to get herself and her young ones across the road.

It is one of those moments that will be engraved on my brain forever. For I really *saw* her. She was small and gray, flecked with black; so were her chicks. She had a healthy red comb and quick, light-brown eyes. She was that proud, chunky chicken shape that makes one feel always that chickens, and hens especially, have personality and *will*. Her steps were neat and quick and authoritative; and though she never touched her chicks, it was obvious she was shepherding them along. She clucked impatiently when, our feet falling ever nearer, one of them, especially self-absorbed and perhaps hard-headed, ceased to respond.

When my friend Joanne—also one of my editors at *Ms.* magazine for nearly fifteen years—knew I was going to Bali, she asked if I would consider writing about it. There was so much there to write about, after all: the beautiful Balinese, the spectacular countryside, the ancient myths, dances, and rituals; the food, the flowers, the fauna, too. When I returned, with no word on Bali, she asked again. I did not know how to tell her that my

---

expound (ek spound´) *v.t.* set forth in detail; explain.

strongest experience on Bali had been to really be able to see, and identify with, a chicken. Joanne probably eats chicken, I thought.

I did, too.

In fact, just before going to Bali I had been fasting, drinking juices only, and wondering if I could give up the eating of meat. I had even been looking about in San Francisco for an animal rights organization to join (though it is the animal liberationists, who set animals free, who actually take my heart); in that way I hoped to meet others of my kind, i.e., those who are beginning to feel, or have always felt, that eating meat is <u>cannibalism</u>. On the day my companion pointed out such an organization, in an Australian magazine we found at a restaurant in Ubud, I was slow to speak, because I had a delicious piece of Balinese-style chicken satay in my mouth.

I have faced the distressing possibility that I may never be a "pure" vegetarian. There is the occasional stray drumstick or slice of prosciutto that somehow finds its way into my mouth, even though purchased meat no longer appears in my kitchen. Since Bali, nearly a year ago, I have eaten several large pieces of Georgia ham (a cherished delicacy from my childhood, as is fried chicken; it is hard to consider oneself Southern without it!) and several pieces of chicken prepared by a long-lost African friend from twenty years ago who, while visiting, tired of my incessant chopping of vegetables to stir-fry and eat over rice and therefore cooked a chicken and served it in protest. There have been three crab dinners and even one of shrimp.

I console myself by recognizing that this diet, in which ninety percent of what I eat is nonmeat and nondairy, though not <u>pristinely</u> vegetarian, is still completely different from and less barbarous than the one I was raised on—in which meat was a mainstay— and that perhaps if they knew or cared (and somehow I know they know and care), my chicken and fish sister/ fellow travelers on the planet might give me credit for effort.

I wonder.

Perhaps I will win this struggle, too, though. I can never *not* know that the chicken I absolutely *saw* is a sister (this recognition gives a whole different meaning to the expression "you chicks"), and that her love of her children definitely resembles my love of mine. Sometimes I cast my <u>quandary</u> about it all in the form of a <u>philosophical</u> chicken joke: Why did the Balinese chicken cross the road? I know the answer is, To try to get both of us to the other side.

It is not so much a question of whether the lion will one day lie down with the lamb, but whether human beings will ever be able to lie down with any creature or being at all.

1987

cannibalism (kan′ə bə liz′əm) *n.* act or practice of eating the flesh of one's own kind.

pristinely (pris tēn′lē) *adv.* purely.

quandary (kwon′də rē) *n.* state of hesitation or uncertainty; dilemma.

philosophical (fil′ə sof′i kəl) *adj.* accepting life and its problems with calmness and understanding.

Meet Alice Walker

As the youngest of eight children in a family of share-croppers, Alice Walker always felt different. "Sometimes I thought I'd gotten into the family by mistake," she says. "I always seemed to need more peace and quiet than any-body else." She was often outdoors. "I found what pri-vacy I had by walking in the fields," she recalls. "We had to get our water from a spring, so that was a time to be alone too. I spent so much time out of doors that when I started writing—and I found myself writing my first book of poems, *Once,* under a tree in Kenya—it seemed quite normal."

A novel, *The Color Purple,* drew on her memories and impressions of the close com-munity of strong African-American women she had known from childhood. It won both the Pulitzer Prize and the American Book Award in 1983 and became an award-winning motion picture.

Happiest out of doors, Walker feels "ecstatic . . . simply lying on a hillside in the sun." But the earth, she says, "cannot tolerate much longer the old ways of humans that batter it so unmercifully." Many of her essays are a plea for a return to harmony with nature.

RESPONDING TO *Literature*

THINK • TALK • WRITE

1 Do you agree with everything in these essays? Write some notes in your journal telling how you would reply to Alice Walker's essays.

2 Why does Walker state that Mrs. Davis's death was "one of the most reassuring events I'd ever witnessed"? Support your response with story details.

3 What do you think Walker means by the statement "A writer's pen is a microphone held up to the mouths of ancestors and even stones of long ago"? Do you agree? Why or why not?

4 What do you think Walker means when she writes that the Balinese chicken crossed the road "to try to get both of us to the other side"?

5 Alice Walker describes the life led by her African American grandmother many years ago in a rural town in the American South. What did you learn about this life from her essay?

ACTIVITIES

• **Write About Author's Point of View** Write a letter to Alice Walker. In your letter, tell her why you agree or disagree with her opinion about vegetarianism. Be sure your point of view is clear and well supported.

• **Make a Menu** Create a menu for a vegetarian restaurant. Refer to cookbooks if you need help. Try to make your menu as interesting as possible.

VOCABULARY PRACTICE

Decide if the word in color is used correctly or incorrectly in each sentence below. On a separate sheet of paper, write *correct* or *incorrect* for each sentence. Then write a sentence explaining why you think so.

1 Elizabeth missed her train, and was in a **quandary** about how to get home.

2 **Inevitably,** we have a birthday every year.

3 The Olympic athlete's excellent diving was an **aberration.**

4 Her **extravagantly** decorated dress had many ribbons and jewels on it.

5 The speaker began to **expound** her theory about atomic power.

6 The soldiers were **seduced** and refused to listen to the mutineers.

7 The **annihilation** of the city was complete; not a building remained.

8 The tortoise has impressive **longevity;** it can live as long as a hundred years.

9 The dying man was **philosophical** as he screamed and complained all the time.

10 The **pristinely** dressed children were covered with filthy rags.

ESSAY

·····················

HAVASU

CONNECT TO LITERATURE

Have you ever found yourself in a dangerous or very difficult situation? How did you feel? How did you get out of the situation? What did you learn from it? Write about the incident in your journal. Then as you read "Havasu," compare your own thoughts and feelings to Edward Abbey's.

THINKING ABOUT DESCRIPTIVE DETAILS

Writers use *descriptive details* to create specific and vivid images in the minds of their readers. For instance, in the previous selection, Alice Walker uses descriptive details to paint a picture of the chicken crossing the road in Bali: "She was small and gray, flecked with black; so were her chicks. She had a healthy red comb and quick, light-brown eyes. . . . Her steps were neat and quick and authoritative."

As you read "Havasu," note the many descriptive details that Edward Abbey uses to bring his experience to life.

DID YOU KNOW?

The Grand Canyon cuts through 277 miles (446 km) of northwest Arizona; at points it is as much as 1 mile (1.6 km) deep and 18 miles (29 km) wide. The canyon was formed over millions of years, as the Colorado River slowly eroded the layers of granite, limestone, sandstone, and shale that now make up the walls of the canyon.

Havasu Canyon, the setting of the next selection, is a branch of the Grand Canyon, about 165 miles (265 km) from Flagstaff, Arizona.

HAVASU

by Edward Abbey

Phantom Ranch, Grand Canyon   1925   Gunnar Widforss   Santa Fe Railway Collection

M OST OF MY WANDERING IN THE DESERT I'VE DONE ALONE. Not so much from choice as from necessity—I generally prefer to go into places where no one else wants to go. I find that in con-templating the natural world my pleasure is greater if there are not too many others contemplating it with me, at the same time. However, there are special hazards in traveling alone. Your chances of dying, in case of sickness or accident, are much improved, simply because there is no one around to go for help.

---

contemplating (kon′təm plāt′ing) *v.t.* giving a great deal of attention to; looking at or thinking about long and carefully.

Exploring a side canyon off Havasu Canyon one day, I was unable to resist the temptation to climb up out of it onto what corresponds in that region to the Tonto Bench. Late in the afternoon I realized that I would not have enough time to get back to my camp before dark, unless I could find a much shorter route than the one by which I had come. I looked for a shortcut.

Nearby was another little side canyon which appeared to lead down into Havasu Canyon. It was a steep, shadowy, extremely narrow defile with the usual <u>meandering</u> course and overhanging walls; from where I stood, near its head, I could not tell if the route was feasible all the way down to the floor of the main canyon. I had no rope with me—only my walking stick. But I was hungry and thirsty, as always. I started down.

For a while everything went well. The floor of the little canyon began as a bed of dry sand, scattered with rocks. Farther down a few boulders were wedged between the walls; I climbed over and under them. Then the canyon took on the slickrock character—smooth, sheer, slippery sandstone carved by erosion into a series of scoops and potholes which got bigger as I descended. In some of these basins there was a little water left over from the last flood, warm and <u>fetid</u> water under an oily-looking scum, condensed by prolonged evaporation to a sort of broth, rich in dead and dying organisms. My canteen was empty and I was very thirsty but I felt that I could wait.

I came to a lip on the canyon floor which overhung by twelve feet the largest so far of these <u>stagnant</u> pools. On each side rose the canyon walls, roughly perpendicular. There was no way to continue except by dropping into the pool. I hesitated. Beyond this point there could hardly be any returning, yet the main canyon was still not visible below. Obviously the only sensible thing to do was to turn back. I edged over the lip of stone and dropped feet first into the water.

Deeper than I expected. The warm, thick fluid came up and closed over my head as my feet touched the muck at the bottom. I had to swim to the farther side. And here I found myself on the verge of another drop-off, with one more huge bowl of green soup below.

This drop-off was about the same height as the one before, but not overhanging. It resembled a children's playground slide, concave and S-curved, only steeper, wider, with a vertical pitch in the middle. It did not lead directly into the water but ended in a series of steplike ledges above the pool. Beyond the pool lay another edge, another drop-off into

---

meandering (mē an'dər ing) *adj.* following a winding course.
fetid (fet'id) *adj.* having a bad smell; stinking.
stagnant (stag'nənt) *adj.* still or motionless, as air or water.

an unknown depth. Again I paused, and for a much longer time. But I no longer had the option of turning around and going back. I eased myself into the chute and let go of everything—except my faithful stick.

I hit rock bottom hard, but without any physical injury. I swam the stinking pond dog-paddle style, pushing the heavy scum away from my face, and crawled out on the far side to see what my fate was going to be.

Fatal. Death by starvation, slow and <u>tedious</u>. For I was looking straight down an overhanging cliff to a rubble pile of broken rocks eighty feet below.

After the first wave of utter panic had passed I began to try to think. First of all I was not going to die immediately, unless another flash flood came down the gorge; there was the pond of stagnant water on hand to save me from thirst and a man can live, they say, for thirty days or more without food. My sun-bleached bones, dramatically sprawled at the bottom of the chasm, would provide the diversion of the picturesque for future wanderers—if any man ever came this way again.

My second thought was to scream for help, although I knew very well there could be no other human being within miles. I even tried it but the sound of that anxious shout, cut short in the dead air within the canyon walls, was so inhuman, so detached as it seemed from myself, that it terrified me and I didn't attempt it again.

I thought of tearing my clothes into strips and <u>plaiting</u> a rope. But what was I wearing?—boots, socks, a pair of old and ragged blue jeans, a flimsy T-shirt, an ancient and rotten sombrero of straw. Not a chance of weaving such a wardrobe into a rope eighty feet long, or even twenty feet long.

How about a signal fire? There was nothing to burn but my clothes; not a tree, not a shrub, not even a weed grew in this stony cul-de-sac. Even if I burned my clothing the chances of the smoke being seen by some Hualapai Indian high on the south rim were very small; and if he did see the smoke, what then? He'd shrug his shoulders. Furthermore, without clothes, the sun would soon bake me to death.

There was only one thing I could do. I had a tiny notebook in my hip pocket and a stub of pencil. When these dried out I could at least record my final thoughts. I would have plenty of time to write not only my epitaph but my own <u>elegy</u>.

But not yet.

There were a few loose stones scattered about the edge of the pool. Taking the biggest first, I swam with it back to the foot of the slick-

---

tedious (tē′dē əs) *adj.* causing weariness and boredom because of length, dullness, or the like.
plaiting (plāt′ing) *v.t.* braiding.
562   **elegy** (el′i jē) *n.* sad poem or musical work written to mourn someone who has died.

rock chute and placed it there. One by one I brought the others and made a shaky little pile about two feet high leaning against the chute. Hopeless, of course, but there was nothing else to do. I stood on the top of the pile and stretched upward, straining my arms to their utmost limit and groped with fingers and fingernails for a hold on something firm. There was nothing. I crept back down. I began to cry. It was easy. All alone, I didn't have to be brave.

Through the tears I noticed my old walking stick lying nearby. I took it and stood it on the most solid stone in the pile, behind the two topmost stones. I took off my boots, tied them together and hung them around my neck, on my back. I got up on the little pile again and lifted one leg and set my big toe on the top of the stick. This could never work. Slowly and painfully, leaning as much of my weight as I could against the sandstone slide, I applied more and more pressure to the stick, pushing my body upward until I was again stretched out full length above it. Again I felt about for a fingerhold. There was none. The chute was smooth as polished marble.

No, not quite that smooth. This was sandstone, soft and <u>porous</u>, not marble, and between it and my wet body and wet clothing a certain friction was created. In addition, the stick had enabled me to reach a higher section of the S-curved chute, where the angle was more favorable. I discovered that I could move upward, inch by inch, through adhesion and with the help of the leveling tendency of the curve. I gave an extra little push with my big toe—the stones collapsed below, the stick clattered down—and crawled rather like a snail or slug, oozing slime, up over the rounded summit of the slide.

The next obstacle, the overhanging spout twelve feet above a deep plunge pool, looked impossible. It *was* impossible, but with the blind faith of despair I slogged into the water and swam underneath the dropoff and floundered around for a while, scrabbling at the slippery rock until my nerves and tiring muscles convinced my numbed brain that *this was not the way*. I swam back to solid ground and lay down to rest and die in comfort.

Far above I could see the sky, an irregular strip of blue between the dark, hard-edged canyon walls that seemed to lean toward each other as they towered above me. Across that narrow opening a small white cloud was passing, so lovely and precious and delicate and forever inaccessible that it broke the heart and made me weep like a woman, like a child. In all my life I had never seen anything so beautiful.

---

porous (pôr′əs) *adj.* having or full of many small holes.

Grand Canyon   1911   William Robinson Leigh   The Newark Museum, Newark, New Jersey

The walls that rose on either side of the drop-off were literally perpendicular. Eroded by weathering, however, and not by the corrasion of rushing floodwater, they had a rough surface, chipped, broken, cracked. Where the walls joined the face of the overhang they formed almost a square corner, with a number of minute crevices and inch-wide shelves on either side. It might, after all, be possible. What did I have to lose?

When I had regained some measure of nerve and steadiness I got up off my back and tried the wall beside the pond, clinging to the rock

---

corrasion (kə rā′zhən) *n.* act in which rocks and soil are worn away by materials pushed along the surface by wind, waves, streams, or glaciers.

with bare toes and fingertips and inching my way crabwise toward the corner. The watersoaked, heavy boots dangling from my neck, swinging back and forth with my every movement, threw me off balance and I fell into the pool. I swam out to the bank, unslung the boots and threw them up over the drop-off, out of sight. They'd be there if I ever needed them again. Once more I attached myself to the wall, tenderly, sensitively, like a <u>limpet</u>, and very slowly, very cautiously, worked my way into the corner. Here I was able to climb upward, a few centimeters at a time, by bracing myself against the opposite sides and finding sufficient <u>niches</u> for fingers and toes. As I neared the top and the overhang became noticeable I prepared for a slip, planning to push myself away from the rock so as to fall into the center of the pool where the water was deepest. But it wasn't necessary. Somehow, with a skill and <u>tenacity</u> I could never have found in myself under ordinary circumstances, I managed to creep straight up that gloomy cliff and over the brink of the drop-off and into the flower of safety. My boots were floating under the surface of the little puddle above. As I poured the stinking water out of them and pulled them on and laced them up I discovered myself bawling again for the third time in three hours, the hot delicious tears of victory. And up above the clouds replied—thunder.

I emerged from that treacherous little canyon at sundown, with an enormous fire in the western sky and lightning overhead. Through sweet twilight and the sudden dazzling flare of lightning I hiked back along the Tonto Bench, bellowing the *Ode to Joy*. Long before I reached the place where I could descend safely to the main canyon and my camp, however, darkness set in, the clouds opened their bays and the rain poured down. I took shelter under a ledge in a shallow cave about three feet high—hardly room to sit up in. Others had been here before: the dusty floor of the little hole was littered with the droppings of birds, rats, jackrabbits and coyotes. There were also a few long gray pieces of scat with a curious twist at one tip—cougar? I didn't care. I had

---

limpet (lim′pit) *n.* brownish green saltwater shellfish that clings to rocks.
niches (nich′əz) *n., pl.* hollowed out spaces in a wall.
tenacity (tə nas′i tē) *n.* state or quality of being stubborn or obstinate.

some matches with me, sealed in <u>paraffin</u> (the prudent explorer); I scraped together the handiest twigs and animal droppings and built a little fire and waited for the rain to stop.

It didn't stop. The rain came down for hours in alternate waves of storm and drizzle and I very soon had burnt up all the fuel within reach. No matter. I stretched out in the coyote den, pillowed my head on my arm and suffered through the long long night, wet, cold, aching, hungry, wretched, dreaming claustrophobic nightmares. It was one of the happiest nights of my life.

---

paraffin (par′ə fin) *n.* waxy, white substance obtained from petroleum and used for making candles and waxed paper and for sealing jars for preserves.

Meet Edward Abbey

Edward Abbey (1927–1989) grew up in Pennsylvania, the son of a farmer and a teacher. From 1956 to 1971, Abbey worked as a park ranger and fire lookout for the National Park Service in the Southwest. His experiences there greatly affected his writing. He became concerned about the future of wilderness areas in Arizona, New Mexico, and Utah, and often used these areas as the settings for his novels and essays.

"Havasu" is one of the essays in *Desert Solitaire*, a collection that helped make Abbey one of America's best-known nature writers. One reviewer wrote, "No one should visit southeastern Utah without first reading this book."

More Essays About Nature

- *Desert Solitaire: A Season in the Wilderness* by Edward Abbey (Simon & Schuster, 1968). During the time Edward Abbey spent working as a park ranger in Utah, he observed the impact the oil, mining, and tourist industries had on the natural environment. The essays in this book are his warning cry.

- *Father Water, Mother Woods: Essays on Fishing and Hunting in the North Woods* by Gary Paulsen (Delacorte Press, 1994). Gary Paulsen, the award-winning author of adventure-packed survival stories, has written a series of essays about his own adventures in the wilderness.

RESPONDING TO *Literature*

THINK • TALK • WRITE

1 What did you find most memorable in this selection? Write a few lines about it in your journal.

2 Edward Abbey writes, "In contemplating the natural world my pleasure is greater if there are not too many others contemplating it with me." Do you feel the same way? Why or why not?

3 What kind of person does Abbey reveal himself to be in this selection? Use story details in your response.

4 Why do you think Abbey is so moved by the sight of the cloud above the canyon? What kind of meaning does it have for him?

5 Imagine that you are Edward Abbey. Write a paragraph describing what you were thinking about during your night in the cave.

ACTIVITIES

- **Write About Descriptive Details** Think about a place that has great personal meaning for you. Write a description of it, using details that will paint a vivid picture. If you wish, include yourself as a character in the place.

- **Draw a Map** Based on the details Abbey includes in this selection, draw a map of his wanderings through Havasu Canyon. Include as many details as possible.

VOCABULARY PRACTICE

contemplating	plaiting
meandering	elegy
fetid	porous
stagnant	niches
tedious	tenacity

On a separate sheet of paper, write the word that is *least* like the others in each set.

1 meandering   wandering
   winding   hurrying

2 elegy   editorial
   farewell   mourning

3 tedious   exciting
   thrilling   exhilarating

4 niches   recesses
   hollows   corners

5 stagnant   steaming
   motionless   inert

6 porous   leaky
   melted   hole-filled

7 tenacity   flexibility
   commitment   stubborness

8 contemplating   canceling
   considering   pondering

9 plaiting   tying
   braiding   snipping

10 fetid   aromatic
    pleasing   fragrant

WRITING

There are millions of species of plants and animals on the earth. No one person can know everything about all of these life forms. So people *specialize*. You can specialize, too. Choose a plant or animal species to describe in an essay.

PREWRITE

After you choose your plant or animal species, do some planning. What is the main idea of your essay? What supporting details will help readers understand this main idea? How can you arrange your essay to make the ideas flow smoothly?

The writer of our sample decided to write about honeybees. Before he started to write, he made a chart to organize his ideas.

Once you've selected your topic, try using a chart like the one here.

MAIN IDEA:

Each honeybee has a specialized function.

SUPPORTING DETAILS:

The queen lays eggs to maintain bee population.

Workers gather pollen, feed young, build hive.

Drones help the queen reproduce, but do no work.

DRAFT

Read the first paragraph of the essay about bees. Can you suggest any improvements?

This writer relates his subject to an experience most of us have had. Keep your audience in mind as you begin your opening.

Honeybees

When a bee buzzes near your picnick

do you ever think about the life it leads.

Bees are intelligent creatures.

Now it's time to begin your draft. Don't hesitate to talk about your opening paragraph with a partner. It might help you to organize your thoughts.

AN ESSAY

REVISE

The writer of the sample essay felt he had to focus more clearly on his topic and make it more interesting for the reader. He made some revisions to his draft.

The writer has selected honey-bees, but realizes he has forgotten to use the term here.

The writer realizes he has not stated his main idea—the special-ized functions of honeybees. Remember to revise your opening to hint at the ideas you will de-velop in your essay.

> When a *honey* bee buzzes *dangerously* near your picnick
>
> do you ever think about the life it leads.
>
> Bees are *highly organized* intelligent creatures.

Revise your own draft. Have you given the reader too many details? Have you included enough? Has the purpose of your essay changed?

PROOFREAD

The writer made a couple of proofreading corrections in the opening paragraph of his essay.

All your major revisions should be included at this point. Reread your essay looking for spelling, punc-tuation, and grammar mistakes.

> When a *honey* bee buzzes *dangerously* near your (picnick) *picnic,*
>
> do you ever think about the life it leads, ?
>
> Bees are *highly organized* intelligent creatures.

PUBLISH

The author included with his essay a diagram of a hive.

How will you present your work? Ask some other students if they'd like to combine their essays with yours to create an anthology of essays about the world of nature.

WRITING

BRIGHTENING UP WRITING WITH INTERJECTIONS

ENRICH YOUR WRITING OF **ESSAYS.**

An interjection is a word or phrase that expresses strong feeling. For interjections that stand alone, use an exclamation mark.

Hey! That's a beautiful shirt!

Use interjections when you want to add color and energy to your writing, but don't overuse them.

Read the two paragraphs. Which seems more enthusiastic?

Paragraph 1

There is a way to beat stress and also make the world more beautiful. Try working in a garden. Start early in the day when the flowers are still covered with sparkling dew. You'll love the fresh air and the soft crunch of wet earth against your trowel.

Paragraph 2

Hey! Want a way to beat stress and also make the world more beautiful? Try working in a garden. Start early in the day when the flowers are still covered with sparkling dew. You'll love the fresh air and the soft crunch of wet earth against your trowel.

PRACTICE 1 Respond on a separate sheet of paper.

1 In which paragraph does the writer involve the reader more directly? How does the writer do this?

2 Rewrite the second paragraph using a different interjection. Your purpose is to get your reader to consider the joys of gardening.

570

PRONOUNS IN PREPOSITIONAL PHRASES

REMEMBER THESE RULES ABOUT PRONOUNS IN PREPOSITIONAL PHRASES WHEN YOU ARE WRITING **ESSAYS.**

- When the object of a preposition is a pronoun, the pronoun should be an object pronoun.

- A preposition can also take a compound object, which is two or more words joined by a conjunction.

- The pronoun *me* comes last in a compound object.

PRACTICE 2 Complete each sentence with the correct word or phrase. Write your answers on a separate sheet of paper.

1 Using an insecticide could be dangerous for (we, us).

2 She bought two rose bushes and planted one of (them, they).

3 They gave the gardening tools to (me and Tim, Tim and me).

4 Take some fertilizer and give the rest to (her, she).

SUBJECT-VERB AGREEMENT WITH COMPOUND SUBJECTS

USE THESE RULES ABOUT SUBJECT-VERB AGREEMENT WHEN YOU ARE WRITING **ESSAYS.**

- With compound subjects, the conjunction determines whether the verb should be singular or plural.

- When two or more subjects are joined by *and* or by *both . . . and,* the verb should be plural.

- When two or more subjects are joined by *or, nor, either . . . or,* or *neither . . . nor,* the verb agrees with the simple subject closer to it.

PRACTICE 3 Complete each sentence with the correct form of the verb. Write your answers on a separate sheet of paper.

1 Both roses and azaleas (grow, grows) well here.

2 Neither the lilac nor the tulip (bloom, blooms) without a frost.

3 Either the shrubs or the tree (need, needs) to go.

4 Carlos or Sandra (help, helps) the gardener on Saturdays.

WRITING A SCIENCE REPORT

How much do you know about the world around you? Research a problem that requires a scientific solution. Then explain everything to your reader in a well-organized report.

PREWRITE

How will you get your ideas? Read about a subject having to do with the natural world. Gather some data. Then focus on a specific topic. Organize your information in a chart.

Problem	Cause	Solution
Big cats (lions, tigers, leopards, jaguars, pumas, cheetahs) are endangered.	hunted for sport	Support laws to stop sale and use of these cats.
	demand for fur coats	
	as more land taken from wild, less room for cats to live	Help wildlife organizations.

DRAFT Just before you write, complete the following sentence in your mind: My report will help my readers to understand _____.

REVISE You've done the research for your science report, but someone else's opinion may clarify your argument. Show your piece to a friend.

PROOFREAD Try proofreading twice—once when you finish revising and once just before you publish.

PUBLISH How controversial is your report? Try reading it to friends or even to a nature or ecology group. Ask for comments.

▶ *Proofreading Alert!*

Use commas with addresses, dates, and names. Check page 206 in *Writing and Language Handbook.*

PROJECTS

CREATE A NATURAL-WORLD MURAL

REMEMBER TO: • PREWRITE • DRAFT • REVISE • PROOFREAD • PUBLISH

Work with a team to create for your school a mural about the natural world. Include scenes of plants and animals in their natural habitats. First work with a partner to choose two similar animals and to research them. Organize your information in a Venn diagram. Then get together with other partner-pairs to plan the entire mural using the information you have gathered. Create each piece of the mural. Ask permission to display it in the school hallway or auditorium.

BIRDS   BATS

feathers;   eat insects   fur;
2 legs and wings; or fruit;   4 legs and flaps;
lay eggs;   warm blooded;   young born live;
nest in trees   fly   nest in caves

CREATE A COMIC STRIP STORY

REMEMBER TO: • PREWRITE • DRAFT • REVISE • PROOFREAD • PUBLISH

Create a comic strip story for a second-grade class about animals in their natural habitat. Work with a partner to brainstorm the characters, setting, and the problem and events for your story. Use a chart to organize your ideas. Keep your comic strip clear and simple. Then draw your strip, putting character dialog in speech balloons.

Characters and Setting	What's the Problem?	What's the Solution?
Freddy Fish	Big waves are coming; Susie doesn't know how to surf.	Freddy shows Susie how to ride waves.
Susie Starfish		The two fish have fun.
underwater	Freddy is cast ashore by wave.	Two children return Freddy to water.

573

VIEWP

COMMUNITY LAND USE

Because the population of the United States continues to increase, land is at a premium in many areas of our country. Every day we read about controversies in communities over how to use their available land. Should it be used for housing, schools, or other necessary community services? Or is it just as important to preserve our undeveloped land in its natural state? Resolving this issue is never easy.

CONSIDER THIS ISSUE: There's a large tract of undeveloped land in your community. Your city is considering a proposal to build much-needed middle-income housing on the site. Opponents want to preserve the land as a wilderness area for hiking and camping. Many students are taking sides in the controversy. What do you think?

- Isn't building affordable housing more important than creating hiking trails?
- If we continue to sacrifice our undeveloped land, won't we eventually lose all of our natural heritage?
- Isn't it important to provide people with an opportunity to enjoy nature?

Read the following viewpoints about how to use undeveloped land in the community. Decide which one is closest to your own opinion. Think of some arguments of your own to support the position you choose.

VIEWPOINT 1

I think the land should be used for housing.

- Shelter is more important than recreation.
- People in the community already have access to public parks.
- New housing fills an immediate need.

VIEWPOINT 2

I think it's more important to leave the land as a wilderness area.

- We should preserve our natural environment wherever it's endangered, or we will lose it entirely.
- Giving people an opportunity to enjoy the wonders of nature is as important as providing them with housing.
- Using the land as a wilderness area sends an important message about the ecological concerns of our community.

VIEWPOINT 3

I think part of the land should be used for housing and the rest can be left as a public park.

- We have to create a balance between our concern for nature and the needs of our citizens.
- Creating a park will preserve at least some of the disputed land.
- Using the land in this way is a realistic approach to a problem that will get worse as our population grows.

WHAT DO YOU THINK?

Spend time thinking about this issue. Do you agree with one of the viewpoints above, or do you have another? Discuss your views with a group. Then role-play a community meeting where representatives from both sides debate the issue of land use.

real life CONNECT

THE NATURAL WORLD: It's the world of plants and animals and all of the natural wonders that surround us.

We continue to study our natural world and to be amazed by its order and beauty. It is the natural beauty of the humpback whales that Tsuneo Nakamura captures in his photo journal "Gentle Giant." His sensitive observation of these mammals helps us to understand that Earth is a delicately balanced world in which every species has an important place.

The greatest threat to this delicate balance is human misuse of our natural resources. The selection "Rain Forests" highlights this important environmental issue. Another way to present important information about the destruction of the tropical rain forests is with a bar graph, such as the one here.

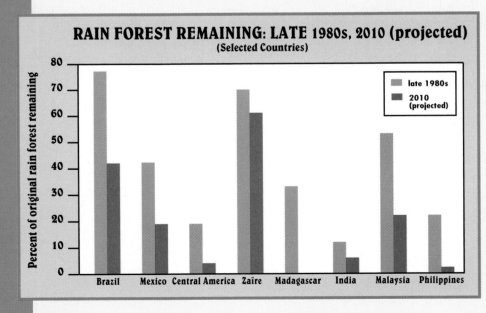

RAIN FOREST REMAINING: LATE 1980s, 2010 (projected)
(Selected Countries)

Percent of original rain forest remaining

late 1980s
2010 (projected)

Brazil Mexico Central America Zaire Madagascar India Malaysia Philippines

A **bar graph** uses parallel bars of different lengths to present information on a particular topic. Some bar graphs display information about two or more related topics so that comparisons can be made. The title sums up the main idea of the bar graph. Labels at the side tell the units of measure used in the bar graph.

IONS

Here are three activities in which you use bar graphs. Think of other situations in which a bar graph is a good way to display data. Then choose an activity below or one of your own and talk or write about it.

PROJECT 1

BAR GRAPH STUDY A bar graph visually represents key facts about a particular topic. Find a bar graph in a national news or business magazine or in a newspaper. Study the bar graph. On a sheet of paper, list all the facts you find about the topic on the bar graph. Compare and discuss your list with a partner.

PROJECT 2

CREATE A BAR GRAPH Use a library index to find a recent magazine article about an environmental issue, such as the fight to save the rain forests. Read the article carefully. Then make a bar graph that includes key facts and ideas from the story. Include a title for your bar graph. Label the units of measurement. Display and discuss your bar graphs in small groups.

PROJECT 3

LETTER TO THE EDITOR Information from a bar graph can be used in a variety of ways. Select a current social or environmental issue. Use a library index to locate a bar graph in a news article about the topic. Write a letter to a local newspaper editor. Express your personal opinion about the issue. Use facts from the bar graph to support your point of view. Read your letter in class. How did the facts in the bar graph strengthen your position?

UNIT 6

Flower Vendor 1949 Diego Rivera Museo Nacional Centro de Arte Reina Sofía, Madrid

Perspectives

have calloused her hands,
brightly colored crepe paper: turquoise,
yellow, magenta, which she shapes
into large blooms for bargain-hunting tourists
who see her flowers, her puppets, her baskets,
but not her—small, gray-haired woman
wearing a white apron, who hides behind
blossoms in her stall at the market,
who sits and remembers collecting wildflowers
as a girl, climbing rocky Mexican hills
to fill a straw hat with soft blooms
which she'd stroke gently, over and over again
with her smooth fingertips.

—Pat Mora

UNIT 6

$\mathcal{P}erspectives$

BEFORE READING

....

THE WAKING OF THE PRINCE

CONNECT TO LITERATURE

Do you like fairy tales? Some modern fairy tales have "twists"—they've taken fairy tale traditions and altered them in surprising and often amusing ways. Discuss some fairy tale traditions with a classmate. Then as you read "The Waking of the Prince," note in your journal examples of twists in this modern fairy tale.

THINKING ABOUT PARODY

The story you're about to read, "The Waking of the Prince," is an example of a *parody*. A parody closely imitates an author's style or a literary form in order to produce a comic effect. The parody resembles the original work, but with just enough of a difference to poke fun at it.

DID YOU KNOW?

Fairy tales exist in virtually every world culture. "Cinderella," for example, is told in over a hundred different versions. In many fairy tales from Europe, the hero or heroine leaves home to seek fortune or adventure; after conquering various obstacles—such as dragons or giants—he or she returns home and is rewarded.

"The Waking of the Prince" is a parody of one of the most famous fairy tales of all time—"Sleeping Beauty." This tale has been the subject of countless plays, a ballet, and several movies. The basic plot is familiar: a beautiful princess is condemned to sleep for a hundred years until she is awakened by a kiss from a handsome prince. In this case, though, there are some unexpected—and funny—changes in the plot!

THE WAKING OF THE PRINCE

BY WILLIAM J. BROOKE

Ducking under a gout of flame, the Prince threw himself forward into a double roll and with the last of his strength thrust the sword upward into the soft underbelly of the dragon. He staggered back from the blast of steam and blood that boiled forth as the creature sank to the ground. When the mists cleared, the dragon had crumbled into dust, the forest of thorns had melted into the ground, and a newly bright sun shone down upon castle and countryside.

The Prince took a moment to thrill at the adventure of it all. Then he spun and charged beneath the portcullis, into the gloom of the staircase spiraling up into the tower. He ignored the sleeping forms that made the castle grounds seem a bloodless battlefield. Up and up through the last twist into the topmost chamber where, facedown before a simple spinning wheel, lay a still, feminine figure in regal <u>attire</u>.

Willing his heart to still its pounding, the Prince gently turned her over and gasped.

Here was beauty beyond beauty! Her hair was deep brown, almost black, like the last of twilight yielding to night, a starry night shot through with many a dancing gleam. Her face was a snowfield reflecting moonlight amid that star-shot night, each feature precisely etched, yet soft and glowing as if from within. Her mouth lolled slightly open in the sweet abandon of her childlike sleep, so totally helpless and trusting that a man might happily give his life to protect that slumber that the Prince was about to end.

He drank her in for a moment, then leaned forward and pressed his lips to hers. Never was there such a kiss! In his mind he could hear the echo of this moment in the songs of all ages to come.

He felt warmth awaken in her mouth and saw color rushing to the curve of her cheeks. Her eyes fluttered and opened, and his heart was lost in those deep-green pools set in <u>alabaster</u> and arched over with <u>ebony</u>.

She looked at him in dreamy confusion as he spoke.

"I am Prince Valorian. I have won my way past the forest of thorns and the evil fairy who guarded your bower in dragon shape to awaken you from your hundred-year slumber."

Her eyes came into sharper focus. She seemed to really see him then. She spoke and her voice was music.

"Do you have any form of identification with you?" she asked.

---

attire (ə tīr′) *n.* clothes.
alabaster (al′ə bas′tər) *n.* smooth, whitish stone.
ebony (eb′ə nē) *n.* hard, black wood, used especially for piano keys.

"Identification?"

"Well, you don't look particularly like a Prince. Your clothes are a mess."

"I had some little difficulty in getting here, as I said."

"Where are my guards? They should be here. Particularly to-day. It's my twenty-first birthday and I'm supposed to be extra careful. . . . I don't mean to be rude, but I shouldn't be talking to strange men today."

"It's not your twenty-first birthday, actually," the Prince said, a little put out. "It's your hundred-and-twenty-first."

She looked at him a moment, then tried a sincere smile, which didn't work. "You didn't happen to notice any guards on your way up, did you?"

"Yes, but they're all asleep, or just beginning to wake up, I suppose. Listen to me—you've been asleep for a hundred years. I have just awakened you."

Her smile grew brittle. "No, that's what I'm supposed to be on guard against, a curse or something. I had to stay away from spin-ning wheels until my twenty-first birthday."

The Prince gestured to the wheel. "Didn't quite make it, did you?"

"Well, I found this one and touched it and I guess I was so nervous that I fainted for a moment, but now I'm fine."

The Prince sighed with some exasperation. This was not work-ing out as he had expected.

"The curse worked," he said shortly. "You slept a hundred years. The whole kingdom slept a hundred years. A forest of thorns grew up. A dragon guarded the entry. I fought my way through. I awakened you. And here we are."

She smiled again in that way that was beginning to irritate him. "Did you say you had some identification? Just out of curiosity?"

He held out his hand. "My signet ring."

She scrutinized it. "Very attractive. I don't seem to recognize the seal."

"I am Prince Valorian of Swederbaum, the son of Silarion, the grandson of Hilarion."

"Swederbaum," she mused. "I don't know it."

"Well there *have* been some changes in the old neighborhood in the last hundred years."

There was a clatter on the stairs, and a great panting and puffing, and twelve armed guards finally rushed into the room. The Captain knelt at the Princess's feet and began, "Your Highness, I am deeply sorry we were not with you, but . . ." Suddenly his eyes went round. He spun to his men and screamed, "Attack!"

They leaped fearlessly at the spinning wheel and wrestled it to the ground, tangling themselves considerably in the wool. The Captain stood between the Princess and the battle with sword drawn to protect her, presumably against any sudden moves by the spinning wheel.

At last the tangle of men made its way to a window, and the wheel was hurled out. The Captain turned and saluted smartly, clapping his sword hilt to his forehead. "All clear!" he shouted. "The room is secured."

"Thank you, Captain," the Princess said sweetly. "Now could you please find my father, the King, and tell him that I wish to see him."

"At once, Your Highness. Fall in! Right face! Double time! One, two, three, four!" The twelve men struggled themselves into some order and started to rush out.

"One of you!" the Princess called. "One of you can take the message. The others should stay and . . ." She glanced sideways at the Prince, then finished innocently, ". . . keep an eye out for any possible trouble."

"Shmendrick!" the Captain bellowed. One of the guards untangled from his fellows and stepped forward, saluted, missed, and struck the man behind him. "Double time! To the King! Tell him . . ." But Shmendrick was already out of the room and racing down the stairs.

"Tell him his daughter is in good hands and wants to see him!" the Captain shouted.

There were the sounds of metal crashing repeatedly against wood and stone, then "Good hands" and "See him" echoed weakly upward.

"A farce," thought the Prince. "I am a hero trapped in a comedy."

"Captain," said the Princess.

"Your Highness!" snapped the Captain.

"Have you or any of your men," she began, glancing slyly at the Prince, "been sleeping lately?"

Among the guards, eyes widened and sweat started. <u>Furtive</u> glances were cast and avoided. "You mean since we came on duty?"

furtive (fûr′tiv) *adj.* secretive; sly.

"Yes, Captain."

"Certainly not, Your Highness! Right, men?" Elaborate pantomimes of innocence. "May I ask who has been spreading such unwarranted rumors about us?"

"Oh, no one of any importance, Captain. Tell me," and now she was grinning sarcastically at the Prince, "did you and your men see the forest of thorns?"

"Forest of thorns?" The Captain and his men looked at each other, trying to decide if this was some form of subtle accusation.

"Yes, it's all over the castle, I've heard."

Was all over the castle," the Prince tried to correct her, but he couldn't be heard for the clatter of the guards rushing to the windows to see this wonderful sight.

"And, of course, the dragon," the Princess concluded, grinning triumphantly.

"Dragon?" the Captain gulped, as his men froze.

"Yes, at the gates. Big and fire breathing, I assume?" She raised eyebrows at the Prince, but he declined to confirm.

The men at the windows were suddenly cured of all curiosity, having acquired instead a sudden intense interest in the center of the room.

The Princess strolled to the window and idly glanced out. "No, no dragons in sight, no forest of thorns. I must have been misinformed."

The Prince was beginning to regret the whole episode. Still, she *was* quite beautiful and he owed it to himself to establish his own position in this adventure. "I slew the dragon. The forest of thorns melted away."

"And why did you do that?"

"So that I could awaken you. The whole world knows your story, the beauty sleeping in the tower, unreachable, unattainable. I had to see you for myself and become a part of this greatest adventure of all."

The Princess was not displeased by this answer. She twirled a lock of hair playfully around one finger, dark silky threads on an ivory bobbin. "And how did you wake me from my hundred-year catnap? Did you crow like a cock or did you toss pebbles at my window?"

"I kissed you."

For a moment she was silent, but her mouth dropped open into a perfect O. Her cheeks flushed most becomingly. She stepped close and looked up into his face. She raised one dainty hand toward his cheek. Her eyelids drooped and her head tilted back. The Prince smiled down at her, pleased that she was finally appreciating him. He just had time to notice her hand accelerating before it slapped his face with surprising force.

"Kissed me," she said, turning coldly away. "Did it occur to you that I might not wish to be kissed?"

The Prince rubbed his chin in surprise. "No, it didn't. I just made the assumption that a young, beautiful, vibrant Princess would also like to include consciousness among her <u>attributes</u>."

The Princess softened a bit at the adjectives, but retained her haughtiness. "I have read of many entirely satisfactory rulers who never demonstrated any <u>overt</u> signs of consciousness at all."

"I can't believe you would be like that. For you, the world should blossom anew each morning. Every day should be an adventure waiting to unfold."

The Princess was <u>pensive</u> and the Prince thought again how nice she looked when she wasn't being thoroughly unpleasant. "Adventure," she <u>mused</u>. "Adventure is what happens in stories, not in real life. Real life is dressing properly and needlepoint and preparing myself to be a suitable consort."

The Prince smiled ruefully at that, and she noticed he had a very nice smile.

"You have slept," he said, "even longer than I thought. I have come just in time. The world lies open before us! Pack a bag! We'll be off by nightfall!"

"Off where?"

"To the mountains where dawn awakens! To the land where men grow tails and women spin gold! To the home of the cyclops and the haunt of the basilisk! Wherever fancy and the four winds take us!"

For a moment, a light glowed in her eyes, then she blinked and recovered. "Captain!" she snapped.

The guardsmen had been pretending not to listen, while maneuvering as close as possible. The Captain now clanged a salute from just behind the Princess that made her jump.

"Arrest this man," she instructed him, turning away with a show of indifference.

---

attributes (at′rə būts′) *n., pl.* qualities; characteristics.

overt (ō vûrt′) *adj.* not hidden; easily observed.

pensive (pen′siv) *adj.* deep in serious thought, often about matters of a sad nature.

mused (mūzd) *v.i.* said thoughtfully.

The Captain raised his sword and stepped toward the Prince. "Sirrah, I command you to yield yourself to my sword." He held the point to the Prince's breast.

"This sword?" the Prince asked, grabbing the flat of the blade, jerking the Captain forward, striking his forearm, twisting the sword away and throwing it out the window.

The Captain rubbed his arm and stared out the window. A distant clang echoed up from the courtyard. "Well, that was the one I had in mind."

"Go get it and I'll consider yielding to it."

The Captain started for the stairs . . . then shook his head and ordered his men, "Seize him!"

Before they could move, the Prince slammed one man against the wall, jerked his sword from his scabbard, and threw it out the window. Another man drew, and the Prince spun him to the window, rapped his wrist on the sill, and sent his blade to join the others. Turning, striking, twisting, the Prince made quick work of most of the guards, then stood out of the way so the last three could get to the window to throw their swords out in a gesture of friendship and <u>conciliation</u>.

The Prince stood, arms folded, facing the Princess. He was breathing slightly heavier than before, but his smile was broader. This was more like it! "I hope," he said, "the Princess will reconsider her order and offer me better hospitality."

The Princess drew herself up. "Perhaps I was hasty," she said at last. "May I offer you the hospitality of this chamber until my father arrives."

The Prince looked around the bare room. "Since you offer so graciously, how can I refuse?"

"Captain," said the Princess. There was a movement, which might have been an attempted salute, near the bottom of a pile of bodies. "I rescind my order. This gentleman is not to be bothered."

"If Your Highness wishes," a muffled voice responded.

The Prince leaned against the wall while the Princess <u>feigned</u> nonchalance at the window. The guards stood up and arranged themselves as close to the stairs as possible.

After a few moments of silence, the Prince started to say ironically, "Lovely weather we're . . ." The Princess stamped her foot and turned on him.

---

conciliation (kən sil'ē ā'shən) *n.* act of overcoming hostility; truce.
feigned (fānd) *v.t.* pretended; put on a false appearance.

"No!" she blurted, "I will not listen to the weather! When a man talks about the weather to a woman it is because he thinks her incapable of understanding anything else." Her eyes burned with an emerald fire.

The Prince bowed slightly. "I would never so insult you, but when I speak of *you,* you strike me, and when I speak of *me,* you order me arrested. The weather seemed the only safe subject." The Princess smiled slightly, so he hurried on. "If I could speak my mind, I would say that your eyes are the most beautiful I have ever . . ."

"I know flattery when I hear it." The Princess smiled at him.

"Then you also know truth," he replied, smiling in turn.

And suddenly that sleeping softness returned to her face as she asked, "Has your life been filled with adventures?" And though her face was gentle, her eyes fixed his with a strength he could not master, and he was drawn down into their depths, into a hollow place he couldn't fathom. How lucky a man might be, he thought, if he could only find the thing to fill that void. Or *be* the thing himself.

Before he could find breath to answer, there was a sound of feet upon the stairs, then the sound of wheezing. A voice echoed up, "I'm coming, my dear, just a moment more, I'll be there, oh, my goodness."

"Papa is not as young as he used to be," the Princess said, and turned her eyes away from the Prince.

"By a hundred years," the Prince agreed. The Princess gave a little sniff, and her look turned from snow and ocean depth back to alabaster and jade.

At last a florid face framed in bushy side-whiskers and crowned with snow-white hair and a golden coronet appeared above the edge of the stairwell. "My dear? Are you all right?"

She hurried to help him up the last few stairs. "I'm fine, Daddy, but what took you so long?"

"We would have been here sooner, but it was raining swords in the courtyard."

The Prince bowed civilly to the King. "Your Majesty."

"Who's this?" the King whispered loudly to his daughter.

"This man claims to be a Prince. He broke into the castle, he resisted arrest and . . ."

"Slew the dragon," interjected the Prince, "melted the forest of thorns, awakened the Princess and the populace from their enchanted sleep . . ."

---

jade (jād) *n.* mineral used for jewelry and carved ornaments, often green.
coronet (kôr′ə net′) *n.* small, decorated crown.

"And kissed me!" the Princess finished decisively.

The King stared, befuddled. Finally, he spoke to the Prince. "Do you happen to have any form of identification?"

The Prince's brow knit and he stamped his foot. "What is this insistence upon who I am?" he stormed. "A man is what he does! Judge me by my deeds, not by my name! Forgive my ill temper, Your Majesty, but it has been a long day."

He then repeated his whole story to the King, while the Princess stared out the window and snorted occasionally to show her <u>disdain</u>. But in fact she was listening with some care.

When the Prince was finished, the Princess said, "You see, Father, this ridiculous man is . . ."

"Now, daughter," he said soothingly, "we mustn't be impolite. In fact, what he describes is exactly what we were warned might happen. However," he addressed the Prince, "our difficulty is that there is no proof of what you say. One would certainly think that a hundred-year sleep would leave some kind of evidence."

"Well, if Your Majesty would just confer with my father, Silarion of Swederbaum, he can confirm . . ."

"No, no, if there has been some sort of disruption in the neighboring kingdoms, I don't think we can take their word for what might have happened. This could be a plot to <u>usurp</u> our power, after all. Tell me, what is it you wanted in coming here?"

The Prince was taken aback. "Well, the idea was that the Princess would, well, love me and—"

"Love you!" the Princess exploded. "Of all the conceited . . ."

"Love me and we would marry and live hap—"

"Father! Are you going to let this man talk of . . ."

"Now, Daughter, if he is a Prince and if he has done all he says and if you really slept a hundred years, then . . ." He paused in thought.

"Then what?"

"I'm not sure."

"If he really awakened me from a hundred-year sleep with a kiss, wouldn't I have fallen in love with him on the spot? That's what happens in stories. It seems to me that would be part of the enchantment."

"Me, too," said the Prince. There was a clatter of mail and metal as the guards nodded their agreement.

disdain (dis dān´) *n.* dislike for something or someone thought of as unworthy or beneath one; scorn.
usurp (ū sûrp´) *v.t.* take possession of by force.

"Well, I *didn't* fall in love with him. In fact, I don't like him at all," the Princess insisted stubbornly.

The King turned to the Prince. "What are your feelings toward my daughter?"

The Prince thought. "I guess I love her. I have thought about her for so long and I have gone through so many hardships to win her. Yes, I love her. Of course I love her! That is part of the adventure!"

The Princess started to respond to that, but the King silenced her with a look. "I think the only thing to do is ask for some proof of your love. You must perform a heroic deed." He stopped the Prince's protest. "I know, I know, you already have, but we don't have any proof of that. Humor us."

After a moment's struggle with himself, the Prince asked, "What sort of deed?"

"Oh, a dragon would be acceptable, I think. That's sort of standard."

"I just slew the only dragon I know of!"

"That was an evil fairy masquerading as a dragon, according to your story, so I don't think it counts. Now there is a very famous dragon in the kingdom of Farflungia that would fit the bill nicely. Ignispirus Magnus is his name."

"I've never heard of him," the Prince said. "He must have died in the last hundred years."

"Well, I'm sure you'll find him if you look carefully. Now bring us back his head and we'll talk some more. If you've really done all you claim, this will be child's play."

The Prince strode thoughtfully to the stairs, the guards giving way before him. He stopped and looked at the Princess, who refused to return his look but flushed very prettily at his attention.

"Actually, after the events of the last hour, fighting a dragon might be a pleasant change." He proceeded down the stairs.

There was silence for a moment, then the King cleared his throat in the dry way he always did when he was about to start on one of his father-daughter talks that were meant to be firm but were in fact extremely timid.

The Princess swept out before he could get started. "I'm tired," she announced. "I'm going to take a nap."

The King was left to sigh and stare out the window at his domain, and to wonder why it was easier to rule a kingdom than a daughter.

Ducking under a gout of flame, the Prince threw himself forward into a double roll and with the last of his strength thrust the sword upward into the soft underbelly of the dragon.

Or, rather, what *should* have been the soft underbelly of the dragon, but was in fact empty space. The dragon looked down at him from where it hovered, wings flapping, just a foot out of reach.

"Nice moves," it said, its throaty rasp making it hard to tell if sarcasm was intended.

Swinging his arm in a wide circle, the Prince quickly released the sword, hurling it upward into the soft underbelly of the, well, no, what *should* have been the soft underbelly of the dragon. The sword arced upward through empty space, where a twisted claw plucked it neatly from the air and added it to the cascading pile of treasure in the corner.

The Prince feinted toward the cave entrance, then threw himself on the treasure heap and scrambled upward toward his sword. He felt a tug at the back of his neck, an upward rush, and found his feet churning a lot of nothing.

"This is not going well," he thought. Out loud, he said, "Give me back my sword," but a flick of a claw sent him sprawling into a tight corner, where the dragon settled in front of him. The Prince watched in dismay as the dragon drew itself up to tower over him. He saw the great body expand, then the swelling of the neck as what he assumed was the flame for his funeral pyre rushed up the throat.

"You can keep the sword!" he shouted as the great jaws gaped open before him.

He was surrounded by a terrible rush of hot air, and the ground shook. He closed his eyes and tried to think of the Princess in what was probably his last moment. Somehow, he could not conjure up her face. He could remember all the stories and he could remember the years of thinking about her, but he could not quite picture her face.

He had been wondering about this for a while when he noticed that he was still alive and not even particularly warm. He opened his eyes. The dragon was looking at him from behind one of its stubby wings and fluttering the wiry lashes of its bug eyes. If the green face could have turned red, he would have described it as embarrassed.

"Excuse me," the dragon rasped.

"What happened?" the Prince managed to get out.

595

The dragon looked away. "Heartburn. I'm sorry. I'm not used to this kind of activity." It rose into the air again and settled atop its treasure. The Prince found that his knees were more than a little shaky and seated himself on a rock.

"Not that it wasn't fun," the dragon added. "Haven't had a good set-to in decades. That double roll of yours is especially picturesque."

"I killed a dragon with it just recently, as a matter of fact," the Prince said defensively, before realizing that might not be a very polite thing to say. But the dragon took no offense.

"Must have been a young one."

"Well," the Prince allowed, "it was really an evil fairy masquerading as a dragon."

"Ah." The dragon breathed happily, settling back and scrunching down into its treasure comfortably. "You don't live long as a dragon without learning to cover your belly."

"How old *are* you?" Now that his shock was over, the Prince was sliding toward the entrance, trying to cover his movement with polite conversation.

"About three hundred years, as you reckon it. I used to be the terror of three kingdoms, stealing maidens, burning villages, you name it." The dragon sat up suddenly and fixed the Prince with its gaze, stopping his progress toward the exit. "I'm being thoughtless, aren't I? You must be upset by my mention of such things. It's just that I have so little company, I've lost all sense of good manners."

"No, not at all. I'm rather interested in such things, adventures and so forth."

"Yes," the dragon mused, settling back again, "you're young, aren't you? Sometimes it's hard to tell, humans look so much alike. But, then, who else but a youngster would make the effort to try to slay an old has-been like me?"

The Prince reached the cave entrance and ran out as fast as he could.

"Wait!" the dragon wailed behind him. "Don't go!"

The Prince concealed himself behind some rocks just as the grisly head on its snaky neck thrust out from the cave. The big eyes turned in every direction, then the lids lowered in disappointment.

"I was going to make us tea," the dragon said.

The Princess leaned back from her needlepoint and sighed.

The Queen looked at her with a measuring eye. It was one of her best expressions.

"Thinking of that young Prince again, I expect. You and your father might have had the courtesy to introduce him to me."

"I was not thinking *of* him," the Princess said. When the Queen continued to scrutinize her, she admitted, "I was thinking *about* him. There is a great difference!" she finished.

The Queen gave a little "Hem!" just to show that there was much she could have said on the subject if she wished, then asked, "What were you thinking *about* the young Prince, then?" Her hands did not pause in their turning of an embroidery hoop, passing the needle from one side to the other.

The Princess gestured at the screen before her. "Here we sit, creating scenes of <u>chivalry</u>, unicorns, dragons, deeds of valor. And there he is out there living those same scenes. It doesn't seem fair."

The Queen pursed her lips in consideration. "No, I daresay it isn't fair, but I'm sure he has learned to live with it."

The Princess blinked twice. "I mean it isn't fair to *us!*"

The Queen blinked three times. "What an extraordinary idea! Do you really think you'd rather be out there facing hardship and danger than tucked up cozy here by the fire?"

"Of course I'd prefer that! Oh, my life is so boring!" She paced back and forth before the mantel. "I sit and sew, I practice on the lute, I wave to the people from the balcony . . ."

"You dress magnificently, you eat splendidly, someday you will be given in marriage to a great family . . ."

"And then I'll get to watch my sons go off to adventures and I'll raise my daughters to be as dull as I am."

The Queen clicked her tongue to show that that did not deserve comment. "If what this Prince says is correct," she said, "you've already had your great adventure."

"And I slept all the way through it." The Princess stared into the fire. "I wish . . ." she whispered.

"That you were with him?" the Queen inquired, arching her eyebrows and lowering her eyelids. It was a difficult expression, but she practiced it mornings in the looking glass.

"That I *was* him," the Princess whispered to herself expressionlessly.

---

chivalry (shiv′əl rē) *n.* qualities of an ideal knight, such as honor, courtesy, and skill in battle.

"**O**h Ignispirus!" the Prince warbled in what he hoped was a conciliatory tone.

There was silence from the cave mouth.

"Yoo hoo, Ignispirus!"

Still nothing.

"Iggy!"

There was a burst of flame closely followed by a huge green head with flashing eyes.

"Unauthorized nicknames are exceedingly rude!"

"I'm deeply sorry," the Prince said. "I came here to apologize for yesterday."

"Apologize?" The dragon curled its neck into a great S, for "suspicion," perhaps.

"For leaving so <u>abruptly</u>. I want to apologize and take you up on your offer of tea." He froze as the great face dropped down and an eyeball bigger than his head glared into his eyes from a foot away.

"And why *did* you leave so abruptly?" This close, the Prince could feel the dragon's voice vibrating in all the hollow spaces of his own body.

It took several efforts to get it out, but finally the Prince sputtered, "I was somewhat concerned . . ."

"Concerned?"

"A little nervous . . ."

"Nervous?"

A deep breath. "I was frightened out of my wits."

The dragon laughed at that.

The Prince was a bit annoyed. "After all, you are a fire-breathing dragon. It's no sign of weakness to experience a little natural . . ."

"But I didn't hurt you a bit. I was very careful not to hurt you. I could have, you know"—it winked coyly—"but I didn't. Why do people insist on thinking that just because one is a dragon . . ."

"You told me yourself you had <u>pillaged</u> and burned."

"Mere childish shenanigans."

"You shot fire at me!"

"Because you came in here swinging that sword. You'd have been disappointed if I didn't give you a little show."

The Prince was speechless for a moment. He had forgotten to be conciliatory or even normally cautious. He stamped his foot.

---

abruptly (ə brupt′lē) *adv.* suddenly; without warning.
pillaged (pil′ijd) *v.t.* robbed by force, as during a war.

"'Swinging that sword!' I was coming here to slay you! And I would have if you had fought fair. I slew a dragon just the other day."

"A fake dragon! I'm beginning to doubt you're even a real prince. Do you have any form of identification?"

The Prince sputtered and shook his fist at the dragon. "Of course I'm a real prince! And it may have been a fake dragon but at least it gave me a good fair fight. It didn't go flying off like a clumsy, overgrown bird. It stood there and fought its best and died like all dragons should. . . ."

The dragon darted its head forward, gaped its jaws, and the Prince disappeared between them.

For a while the dragon sat there, enjoying the feel of the morning sun on its scales and ignoring the muffled sounds coming from inside its mouth. After these quieted, it sat awhile longer enjoying the stillness. Birdsong came from a nearby stand of trees and the ripple of water could be heard. Finally, after what seemed like a hundred years to at least one of those involved, the dragon opened its jaws and deposited a damp and <u>chastened</u> Prince on the ground.

"I'd like to rephrase some of my last statements," he said.

"No," said the dragon. "I think you're a little overexcited. Just sit there quietly and dry out while I talk.

"Now, there's a lot about this dragon-prince stuff that doesn't make much sense to me. Take those maidens, for instance. I mean, what was I supposed to do with a maiden? They were too small for a good meal and too ugly for romance. I tried to get some of them to do a little work around the cave, but they were too high-class to be much use. I carried them off anyway—it was expected of me. But the only thing they were good for was prince bait."

"When the princes rescued them, did the maidens automatically fall in love with them?" the Prince asked, a bit wistfully.

The dragon looked at him sadly. "No prince ever survived long enough to find out. And then I'd let the maidens go so they wouldn't clutter up the place. So what was the point of it all?"

"Adventure?" The Prince didn't sound too sure.

"Adventure. Yes, I guess it was, for me. It's always adventure for the winner. The princes might call it by another name, if they had the chance."

---

chastened (chā′sənd) *adj.* brought under control by punishment.

They sat in silence awhile. Things seemed different to the Prince than they had before . . . "Well," he laughed ruefully to himself, "before the dragon kissed me."

"I think you've come," said the dragon suddenly, "to try to steal back your sword. Perhaps even still to slay me with it, if you get the chance."

The Prince looked deeply hurt. "I'm sorry you think such a thing. Perhaps I should just go and not bother you any longer. You don't seem to like me."

The dragon raised a claw and scratched behind an ear. "I'm beginning another molt and I'm not fit for company these days. Not that I ever get much anyway." A couple of scales were dislodged by the scratching and crashed to the ground, narrowly missing the Prince. "I'm sorry. Now don't go off in a huff. Come in and have that tea."

So they went into the cave and the dragon heated a great cauldron of water with a breath or two and dumped in several tea plants to steep.

The Prince was staring into the corner of the cave. The dragon smiled, after its fashion.

"You're staring at my treasure," it purred.

The Prince gave a start. "No! Well, yes, but I was just noticing it doesn't look right. It's all golden, but the shapes are wrong. It's not coins and jewels and crowns and necklaces, it looks like . . ."

"Yes?"

"Well, junk. I'm sure I'm wrong!" he added quickly as he noticed spines and bristles rising up all over the dragon like hair on a cat's back.

"Junk," the dragon breathed, leaving a sulfurous tang in the air. "Go closer. Look carefully. Judge again."

The Prince moved forward, hesitantly, glancing with some longing at the sunlit cave entrance he was leaving farther behind. He reached the great heap of treasure and stood looking. Everything was vaguely familiar, yet made strange by the gold and jewels. He was startled to recognize an eggbeater with solid gold whisks and an emerald the size of a pigeon's egg for a handle.

"Did you ever sleep on gold? It is most uncomfortable. It is hard and lumpy and you mostly lie awake. When I was young, I

cauldron (kôl′drən) *n.* large kettle or boiler.

spent those hard golden nights thinking of maidens and princes and treasure. As I got older, I thought about what on earth I could do with all that gold. So I taught myself to make things. I needed no fire but my own, no <u>bellows</u>, no tools but claw and tail to <u>forge</u> whatever I wanted. I wasted a century on useless ornaments and swords and such things. Then one sleepless night I got the idea for a wonderful labor-saving device. It would carve, slice, dice, knead dough . . ."

The dragon began digging through the heap of golden objects, hunting excitedly. "I know it's here somewhere." It tossed aside glittering masses, all jewel encrusted. "Astrolabe, anemometer, potato peeler, barometer . . ."

The Prince retreated from the shower of priceless gadgets. The dragon forgot him in its excitement.

"You'll love this! It takes the place of knives, rolling pin, mortar and pestle . . ." It stopped for a moment and stared, bewildered, at an elaborate device. "What on earth was that? Oh, well." It tossed the thing aside and went back to digging. "Compass, sword, apple corer . . ."

With a clank, the Prince's sword landed at his feet. He looked at it. The dragon had been right. This was what he had come back for. A rush of contradictory thoughts and feelings swept through him, but his sword hand knew no doubts as it yearned toward its lost mate.

He looked at the dragon with its head stuck deep into its pile of treasures and its belly exposed. He grabbed the sword and threw himself forward into a double roll.

The King, the Queen, and the Princess were engaged in a royal audience. The King smiled benignly on the loyal vassals who sought his judgment. The Queen bestowed upon them her most beneficent expression. The Princess stared out a window.

Suddenly, there were approaching footfalls and the Prince ran into the Throne Room. The guards started forward from their niches on either side, saw who it was, and continued straight across the floor to the opposite niches.

The Prince stopped before the <u>dais</u> and hurled down two large green objects. He drew his sword and laid it atop them.

---

bellows (bel′ōz) *pl. n.* device that produces a strong air current, used for making a fire burn faster.
forge (fôrj) *v.t.* make or form.
dais (dā′is) *n.* slightly raised platform, as for a throne.

"Having slain the great and terrible dragon Ignispirus Magnus and endured hardship and privation, I claim the hand of the Princess, whom I awakened from enchanted sleep and had already slain a dragon to reach in the first place anyway."

Everyone was startled into silence. Then the Princess gave a little sigh. She pointed at the scales. "What are those things?"

"Scales hewn from the rocklike hide of the terrible dragon."

"Rocklike, eh? Yes, I think very much like rocks." The Princess sniffed.

The Prince drew himself up. "You don't believe me?"

"Now, now," said the King, "it's not that. We just wonder why you didn't bring back the head as we had discussed."

"It was a very inconvenient journey as it was. You have no idea how awkward a dragon's head can be in difficult terrain."

"Well, a claw then."

"Dangerous to tote around. You could poke an eye out."

"Well, the ears then."

"Damaged in battle. Terrible, ragged, bloody things, not fit for ladies to see."

The Queen rolled her eyes up and nodded her agreement.

The Princess was staring deliberately out the window.

The King rubbed at his chin for a while. "Well, you see my problem here."

"No," said the Prince.

The King started at that. "Well," he said, "we still don't have proof of anything. Much talk of hundred-year sleeps and dead dragons but all we can put a finger on is some big green things."

"Scales! They're scales! Look at them! Did you ever see anything like them before? Doesn't that prove something?"

"Now, now, I daresay there are many things I've never seen, and almost none of them are dragon scales."

"Almost none," the Queen put in, smiling <u>beatifically</u>.

"Wasn't there anything else you could have brought?" asked the King wistfully.

"Only kitchen gadgets," the Prince muttered.

"What?"

"Nothing, never mind."

The King sighed. "I think we shall have to find some disinterested proof. Captain!"

---

beatifically (bē′ə tif′ik lē) *adv.* with great happiness; blissfully.

The startled Captain marched quickly forward and saluted tentatively. "My <u>liege</u>?"

"Take your men," the King began. Immediately the Captain barked out a series of orders that brought the guards tumbling into formation.

"Take your men!" the King repeated, shouting to make himself heard over the din. "And seek out the dragon's lair to be sure that . . ." The King stopped as he realized he was shouting into an absolute stillness, the guards having frozen in terror.

"To be sure that . . . ?" the Captain prompted with a quaver in his voice.

"That the dragon is dead—which I am sure it is," the King added for the Prince's benefit. The guards breathed easier. "And if it is not dead . . ." Silence. ". . . To finish the job yourselves."

---

liege (lēj) *n.* lord or ruler.

The Captain began to call out commands and the guards shaped up, wheeled about, and marched back to their niches.

After some uncomfortable moments, the King called out, "Oh, Captain?"

The Captain marched smartly forward and saluted. "Sire!"

The King lowered his voice, just in case he was asking something foolish. "Why aren't you going?"

"Oh!" barked the Captain in surprise. "Did you mean right now?"

"Yes, now," ordered the King sternly.

"Don't bother," the Prince cut him off.

"So it's not dead!" the Princess snapped, eyes flashing.

"No, just offended. I stood it up for tea. I couldn't slay it. It took all my best moves just to make my escape with the scales. So there's no need to send your guards to . . ." The rest of his sentence was drowned out by the noise of the guardsmen dropping to their knees before the Prince and clapping their swords to their foreheads with such fervor that they all fell unconscious to the ground.

"Sorry," said the Prince. "If you'll excuse me, I have a dragon to apologize to. I was just beginning to learn from him that life is not the simple story I expected it to be, and then I forgot it all in a moment's excitement. I have failed at hero. Maybe I'll be better at doing odd jobs around the cave, if he'll let me." He turned on his heel and marched toward the door.

The Princess watched him go, then called out, "Wait!"

The Prince turned back and eyed her coldly.

"You're going to see the supposed dragon again?"

"Yes. So?"

The Princess started to say something, then sighed and lowered her eyes to the floor. "Nothing. Never mind."

The Prince looked at her. She was very sad and very beautiful. Suddenly he remembered his first sight of her and couldn't bear not to see those eyes again.

"Come on, then," he said.

She looked at him very hard, then around the Throne Room at all the appurtenances of royal life. Decisively, she jumped up and kissed her mother and father. "Perhaps he's not so bad after all," she said, tossing her coronet onto her chair as she ran out, pausing only to give the Prince a quick peck on the cheek.

The Prince looked back at the King, questioningly. "She's your problem now," said the King. The Prince bowed and started out. "By the authority of divine right, I pronounce you husband and wife," the King called after them, as an afterthought.

When the Prince was gone, the King contemplated his unconscious guardsmen and decided he liked them that way. He looked at his wife, who, having run out of suitable expressions, had fallen into a light sleep.

"Now *this* is the way a kingdom should run!" the King thought as he scrunched himself into a corner of his throne and closed his eyes.

MEET WILLIAM J. BROOKE

When William J. Brooke decided to write a book of stories, he turned to well-known folk tales for inspiration. "One of the stories I thought about was 'The Sleeping Beauty,'" he explains. "The question that struck me was, 'Would a person know if they were in an enchanted sleep?' If I woke up one morning and there was someone in my room saying, 'You slept for a hundred years and I awakened you. Let's get married,' would my immediate response really be, 'Okay, sure'?"

Since many of the characters in "The Waking of the Prince" do so much talking, Brooke felt the need for some action to move the story along. "I would imagine myself in the scene and create comic business the way I would in a play. This helped me make the story as physical and visual as possible. This was particularly true for the fight scenes, the slapstick guards, and the Queen's expressions." "The Waking of the Prince" and four other tales with fresh perspectives can be found in *A Telling of the Tales: Five Stories*.

RESPONDING TO *Literature*

THINK • TALK • WRITE

1 Did you find this story amusing? Explain why or why not in your journal.

2 How does the Princess's attitude toward the Prince change in the course of the story? Why do you think this is so?

3 How do you think the Prince obtained the dragon's scales?

4 What do you think the Prince means when he says that "life is not the simple story" he expected? Why do you think the story was called "The Waking of the Prince"?

5 In what ways is the Princess not a typical fairy tale princess? Use story details to explain your answers.

ACTIVITIES

• **Write About Parody** Choose a familiar fairy tale. Write a parody in which the characters behave in unexpected ways. Read your finished parody to the class.

• **Sing a Parody** You can make a parody of any form of writing. Think of a familiar song. How could you write a parody of it? How would you make your parody humorous? Share your parody with the class.

VOCABULARY PRACTICE

Use your understanding of the meanings of the words in color to complete the following sentences. Write the correct word on a separate piece of paper.

1 **Furtive** gestures probably won't be:
   a. polite **b.** noticed **c.** forgotten

2 All of these are **attributes** except:
   a. bravery **b.** kindness **c.** illness

3 A proud person would **disdain:**
   a. help **b.** respect **c.** admiration

4 One gesture of **conciliation** is the:
   a. insult **b.** handshake **c.** snub

5 An **overt** movement would be:
   a. hidden **b.** repeated **c.** obvious

6 The bored listener **feigned:**
   a. conversation **b.** interest **c.** yawning

7 A **pensive** person would look:
   a. thoughtful **b.** careless **c.** desperate

8 "Adventure," **mused** the Princess; this means she said it:
   a. thoughtfully **b.** carelessly
   c. happily

9 A soldier's **attire** includes a:
   a. handbook **b.** duffel bag **c.** helmet

10 A message that arrives **abruptly** comes:
   a. late **b.** by mail **c.** suddenly

BEFORE READING

....

THE ROCKET

CONNECT TO LITERATURE

What was the best vacation you ever had? What did you do? What made it so special? Share your memories with a classmate. As you read "The Rocket," note in your journal how Fiorello Bodoni gives his children the most unforgettable vacation they will ever have.

THINKING ABOUT SCIENCE FICTION

Ray Bradbury, the author of the story you are about to read, is a famous writer of science fiction. *Science fiction,* as you would guess from its name, is fiction that is based on real or imaginary developments in science or technology—for example, interplanetary travel or time machines. Often, science fiction is set on other planets or in the future. Sometimes writers will use science-fiction stories set in the future as a way of discussing problems in today's world, such as war or overpopulation or environmental destruction.

Wherever or whenever the story is set, it is the job of the science-fiction writer to convince the reader of the authenticity of the world in which the story is set.

HAVE YOU EVER?

Have you ever seen photographs of the surface of other planets? The National Aeronautics and Space Administration (NASA) has sent a variety of rockets into space to photograph the planets. The pictures the rockets have sent back to Earth of Mars's reddish, barren surface, Saturn's luminous rings, and Jupiter's atmosphere full of whirling gases have become familiar to most Americans.

THE ROCKET

by Ray Bradbury

Illustrated by Nicholas Jainschigg

KET

Many nights Fiorello Bodoni would awaken to hear the rockets sighing in the dark sky. He would tiptoe from bed, certain that his kind wife was dreaming, to let himself out into the night air. For a few moments he would be free of the smells of old food in the small house by the river. For a silent moment he would let his heart soar alone into space, following the rockets. ■ Now, this very night, he stood half naked in the darkness, watching the fire fountains murmuring in the air. The rockets on their long wild way to Mars and Saturn and Venus! ■ "Well, well, Bodoni." ■ Bodoni started. ■ On a milk crate, by the silent river, sat an old man who also watched the rockets through the midnight hush. ■ "Oh, it's you, Bramante!" ■ "Do you come out every night, Bodoni?" ■ "Only for the air." ■ "So? I prefer the rockets myself," said old Bramante. "I was a boy when they started. Eighty years ago, and I've never been on one yet." ■ "I will ride up in one someday," said Bodoni. ■ "Fool!" cried Bramante. "You'll never go. This is a rich man's world." He shook his gray head, remembering. "When I was young they wrote it in fiery letters: THE WORLD OF THE FUTURE! Science, Comfort, and New Things for All! Ha! Eighty years. The Future becomes Now! Do *we* fly rockets? No! We live in shacks like our ancestors before us." ■ "Perhaps my *sons*—" said Bodoni. ■ "No, nor *their* sons!" the old man shouted. "It's the rich who have dreams and rockets!" ■ Bodoni hesitated. "Old man, I've saved three thousand dollars. It took me six years to save it. For my business, to invest in machinery. But every night for a month now I've been awake. I hear the rockets. I think. And tonight I've made up my mind. One of us will fly to Mars!" His eyes were shining and dark. ■ "Idiot," snapped Bramante. "How will you choose? Who will go? If you go, your wife will hate you, for you will be just a bit nearer God, in space. When you tell your amazing trip to her, over the years, won't bitterness <u>gnaw</u> at her?" ■ "No, no!" ■ "Yes! And your children? Will their lives be filled with the memory of Papa, who flew to Mars while they stayed here? What a senseless task you will set your boys. They will think of the rocket all their lives. They will lie awake. They will be sick with wanting it. Just as you are sick now. They will want to die if they cannot go. Don't set that goal, I warn you. Let them be content with being poor. Turn their eyes down to their hands and to your junkyard, not up to the stars." ■ "But—" ■ "Suppose your wife went? How would you feel, knowing she had *seen* and you had not? She would become holy. You would think of throwing her in the river. No, Bodoni, buy a new wrecking machine, which you need, and pull your dreams apart with it, and smash them to pieces." ■ The old man <u>subsided</u>, gazing at the river in which, drowned, images of rockets burned down the sky.

■ "Good night," said Bodoni.

■ "Sleep well," said the other.

---

gnaw (nô) *v.i.* cause constant discomfort, pain, or trouble to.
subsided (səb sī′did) *v.i.* decreased in activity or intensity.

When the toast jumped
from its silver box, Bodoni almost
screamed. The night had been sleepless. Among his nervous children, beside
his mountainous wife, Bodoni had twisted and
stared at nothing. Bramante was right. Better to
invest the money. Why save it when only one of the
family could ride the rocket, while the others remained
to melt in frustration? ■ "Fiorello, eat your toast," said his
wife, Maria. ■ "My throat is shriveled," said Bodoni. ■ The
children rushed in, the three boys fighting over a toy rocket,
the two girls carrying dolls which duplicated the inhabitants
of Mars, Venus, and Neptune, green <u>mannequins</u> with three yellow eyes and twelve fingers. ■ "I saw the Venus rocket!" cried
Paolo. ■ "It took off, *whoosh!*" hissed Antonello. ■ "Children!"
shouted Bodoni, hands to his ears. ■ They stared at him. He seldom shouted. ■ Bodoni arose. "Listen, all of you," he said. "I have
enough money to take one of us on the Mars rocket." ■ Everyone
yelled. ■ "You understand?" he asked. "Only *one* of us. Who?"
■ "Me, me, me!" cried the children. ■ "You," said Maria. ■ "You,"
said Bodoni to her. ■ They all fell silent. ■ The children recon-
sidered. "Let Lorenzo go—he's oldest." ■ "Let Miriamne go—she's
a girl!" ■ "Think what you would see," said Bodoni's wife to
him. But her eyes were strange. Her voice shook. "The meteors, like fish. The universe. The Moon. Someone should go
who could tell it well on returning. You have a way with
words." ■ "Nonsense. So have you," he objected.
■ Everyone trembled. ■ "Here," said Bodoni unhappily.
From a broom he broke straws of various lengths.
"The short straw wins." He held out his tight fist.
"Choose." ■ Solemnly each took his turn.
■ "Long straw." ■ "Long straw." ■ Another.
■ "Long straw." ■ The children finished.
The room was quiet. ■ Two straws re-
mained. Bodoni felt his heart
ache in him.

■─────────────────────────────────────

mannequins (man'i kinz) *n., pl.* little men; dwarves.

"Now," he whispered. "Maria." ■ She drew. ■ "The short straw," she said. ■ "Ah," sighed Lorenzo, half happy, half sad. "Mama goes to Mars." ■ Bodoni tried to smile. "Congratulations. I will buy your ticket today." ■ "Wait, Fiorello—" ■ "You can leave next week," he murmured. ■ She saw the sad eyes of her children upon her, with the smiles beneath their straight, large noses. She returned the straw slowly to her husband. "I cannot go to Mars." ■ "But why not?" ■ "I will be busy with another child." ■ "What!" ■ She would not look at him. "It wouldn't do for me to travel in my condition." ■ He took her elbow. "Is this the truth?" ■ "Draw again. Start over." ■ "Why didn't you tell me before?" he said incredulously. ■ "I didn't remember." ■ "Maria, Maria," he whispered, patting her face. He turned to the children. "Draw again." ■ Paolo immediately drew the short straw. ■ "I go to Mars!" He danced wildly. "Thank you, Father!" ■ The other children edged away. "That's swell, Paolo." ■ Paolo stopped smiling to examine his parents and his brothers and sisters. "I *can* go, can't I?" he asked uncertainly. ■ "Yes." ■ "And you'll *like* me when I come back?" ■ "Of course." ■ Paolo studied the precious broomstraw on his trembling hand and shook his head. He threw it away. "I forgot. School starts. I can't go. Draw again." ■ But no one would draw. A full sadness lay on them. ■ "None of us will go," said Lorenzo. ▪ "That's best," said Maria. ▪ "Bramante was right," said Bodoni.

With his breakfast <u>curdled</u> within him, Fiorello Bodoni worked in his junkyard, ripping metal, melting it, pouring out usable <u>ingots</u>. His equipment flaked apart; competition had kept him on the insane edge of poverty for twenty years. ▪ It was a very bad morning. ▪ In the afternoon a man entered the junkyard and called up to Bodoni on his wrecking machine. "Hey, Bodoni, I got some metal for you!" ▪ "What is it, Mr. Mathews?" asked Bodoni, listlessly. ▪ "A rocket ship. What's wrong? Don't you want it?" ▪ "Yes, yes!" He seized the man's arm, and stopped, bewildered. ▪ "Of course," said Mathews, "it's only a mockup. *You* know. When they plan a rocket they build a full-scale model first, of aluminum. You might make a small profit boiling her down. Let you have her for two thousand—" ▪ Bodoni dropped his hand. "I haven't the money." ▪ "Sorry. Thought I'd help you. Last time we talked you said how everyone outbid you on junk. Thought I'd slip this to you on the q.t. Well—" ▪ "I need new equipment. I saved money for that." ▪ "I understand." ▪ "If I bought your rocket, I wouldn't even be able to melt it down. My aluminum furnace broke down last week—" ▪ "Sure." ▪ "I couldn't possibly use the rocket if I bought it from you." ▪ "I know." ▪ Bodoni blinked and shut his eyes. He opened them and looked at Mr. Mathews. "But I am a great fool. I will take my money from the bank and give it to you." ▪ "But if you can't melt the rocket down—" ▪ "Deliver it," said Bodoni. ▪ "All right, if you say so. Tonight?" ▪ "Tonight," said Bodoni, "would be fine. Yes, I would like to have a rocket ship tonight."

---

curdled (kûr′dəld) *adj.* soured.

ingots (ing′gəts) *n., pl.* masses of metal cast into bars or blocks.

There was a moon. The rocket was white and big in the junkyard. It held the whiteness of the moon and the blueness of the stars. Bodoni looked at it and loved all of it. He wanted to pet it and lie against it, pressing it with his cheek, telling it all the secret wants of his heart. ■ He stared up at it. "You are all mine," he said. "Even if you never move or spit fire, and just sit there and rust for fifty years, you are mine." ■ The rocket smelled of time and distance. It was like walking into a clock. It was finished with Swiss <u>delicacy</u>. One might wear it on one's watch fob. "I might even sleep here tonight," Bodoni whispered excitedly. ■ He sat in the pilot's seat. ■ He touched a lever. ■ He hummed in his shut mouth, his eyes closed. ■ The humming grew louder, louder, higher, higher, wilder, stranger, more exhilarating, trembling in him and leaning him forward and pulling him and the ship in a roaring silence and in a kind of metal screaming, while his fists flew over the controls, and his shut eyes quivered, and the sound grew and grew until it was a fire, a strength, a lifting and a pushing of power that threatened to tear him in half. He gasped. He hummed again and again, and did not stop, for it could not be stopped, it could only go on, his eyes tighter, his heart furious. "Taking off!" he screamed. *The jolting concussion! The thunder!* "The Moon!" he cried, eyes blind, tight. "The meteors!" *The silent rush in volcanic light.* "*Mars.* Oh, Yes! Mars! Mars!" ■ He fell back, exhausted and panting. His shaking hands came loose of the controls and his head tilted wildly. He sat for a long time, breathing out and in, his heart slowing. ■ Slowly, slowly, he opened his eyes. ■ The junkyard was still there. ■ He sat motionless. He looked at the heaped piles of metal for a minute, his eyes never leaving them. Then, leaping up, he kicked the levers. "Take off, blast you!" ■ The ship was silent. ■ "I'll show you!" he cried.

---

delicacy (del'i kə sē) *n.* fineness of structure, quality, or form.

■ Out in the night air, stumbling, he started the fierce motor of his terrible wrecking machine and advanced upon the rocket. He maneuvered the massive weights into the moonlit sky. He readied his trembling hands to plunge the weights, to smash, to rip apart this <u>insolently</u> false dream, this silly thing for which he had paid his money, which would not move, which would not do his bidding. "I'll teach you!" he shouted. ■ But his hand stayed. ■ The silver rocket lay in the light of the moon. And beyond the rocket stood the yellow lights of his home, a block away, burning warmly. He heard the family radio playing some distant music. He sat for half an hour considering the rocket and the house lights, and his eyes narrowed and grew wide. He stepped down from the wrecking machine and began to walk, and as he walked he began to laugh, and when he reached the back door of his house he took a deep breath and called, "Maria, Maria, start packing. We're going to Mars!" ■ "Oh!" ■ "Ah!" ■ "I can't *believe* it!" ■ "You will, you will." ■ The children balanced in the windy yard, under the glowing rocket, not touching it yet. They started to cry.
■ Maria looked at her husband. "What have you done?" she said. "Taken our money for this? It will never fly." ■ "It will fly," he said, looking at it. ■ "Rocket ships cost millions. Have you millions?" ■ "It will fly," he repeated steadily. "Now, go to the house, all of you. I have phone calls to make, work to do. Tomorrow we leave! Tell no one, understand? It is a secret."
■ The children edged off from the rocket, stumbling. He saw their small, feverish faces in the house windows, far away. ■ Maria had not moved. "You have ruined us," she said. "Our money used for this—this thing. When it should have been spent on equipment." ■ "You will see," he said.
■ Without a word she turned away.
■ "God help me," he whispered, and started to work.

---

insolently (in′sə lənt lē) *adv.* with offensive rudeness.

Through the midnight hours trucks arrived, packages were delivered, and Bodoni, smiling, exhausted his bank account. With blowtorch and metal stripping he assaulted the rocket, added, took away, worked fiery magics and secret insults upon it. He bolted nine ancient automobile motors into the rocket's empty engine room. Then he welded the engine room shut, so none could see his hidden labor. ■ At dawn he entered the kitchen. "Maria," he said, "I'm ready for breakfast." ■ She would not speak to him. ■ At sunset he called to the children. "We're ready! Come on!" The house was silent. ■ "I've locked them in the closet," said Maria. ■ "What do you mean?" he demanded. ■ "You'll be killed in that rocket," she said. "What kind of rocket can you buy for two thousand dollars? A bad one!" ■ "Listen to me, Maria." ■ "It will blow up. Anyway, you are no pilot." ■ "Nevertheless, I can fly *this* ship. I have fixed it." ■ "You have gone mad," she said. ■ "Where is the key to the closet?" ■ "I have it here." ■ He put out his hand. "Give it to me." ■ She handed it to him. "You will kill them." ■ "No, no." ■ "Yes, you will. I *feel* it." ■ He stood before her. "You won't come along?" ■ "I'll stay here," she said. ■ "You will understand; you will see then," he said, and smiled. He unlocked the closet. "Come, children. Follow your father." ■ "Good-bye, good-bye, Mama!" ■ She stayed in the kitchen window, looking out at them, very straight and silent. ■ At the door of the rocket the father said, "Children, this is a swift rocket. We will be gone only a short while. You must come back to school, and I to my business." He took each of their hands in turn. "Listen. This rocket is very old and will fly only *one* more journey. It will not fly again.

This will be the one trip of your life. Keep your eyes wide." ■ "Yes, Papa." ■ "Listen, keep your ears clean. Smell the smells of a rocket. *Feel. Remember.* So when you return you will talk of it all the rest of your lives." ■ "Yes, Papa." ■ The ship was quiet as a stopped clock. The airlock hissed shut behind them. He strapped them all, like tiny mummies, into rubber hammocks. "Ready?" he called. ■ "Ready!" all replied. ■ "Blast-off!" He jerked ten switches. The rocket thundered and leaped. The children danced in their hammocks, screaming. "We're moving! We're off! Look!" ■ "Here comes the Moon!" ■ The moon dreamed by. Meteors broke into fireworks. Time flowed away in a serpentine of gas. The children shouted. Released from their hammocks, hours later, they peered from the ports. "There's Earth!" "There's Mars!" ■ The rocket dropped pink petals of fire while the hour dials spun; the child eyes dropped shut. At last they hung like drunken moths in their cocoon hammocks. ■ "Good," whispered Bodoni, alone. ■ He tiptoed from the control room to stand for a long moment, fearful, at the airlock door. ■ He pressed a button. The airlock door swung wide. He stepped out. Into space? Into inky tides of meteor and gaseous torch? Into swift mileages and infinite dimensions?

■ No. Bodoni smiled. ■ All about the quivering rocket lay the junkyard. ■ Rusting, unchanged, there stood the padlocked junkyard gate, the little silent house by the river, the kitchen window lighted, and the river going down to the same sea. And in the center of the junkyard, manufacturing a magic dream, lay the quivering, purring rocket. Shaking and roaring, bouncing the netted children like flies in a web. ■ Maria stood in the kitchen window. ■ He waved to her and smiled. ■ He could not see if she waved or not. A small wave, perhaps. A small smile. ■ The sun was rising. ■ Bodoni withdrew hastily into the rocket. Silence. All still slept. He breathed easily. Tying himself into a hammock, he closed his eyes. To himself he prayed, Oh, let nothing happen to the illusion in the next six days. Let all of space come and go, and red Mars come up under our ship, and the moons of Mars, and let there be no flaws in the color film. Let there be three dimensions; let nothing go wrong with the hidden mirrors and screens that mold the fine illusion. Let time pass without crisis. ■ He awoke. ■ Red Mars floated near the rocket. ■ "Papa!" The children thrashed to be free. ■ Bodoni looked and saw red Mars and it was good and there was no flaw in it and he was very happy. ■ At sunset on the seventh day the rocket stopped shuddering. ■ "We are home," said Bodoni. ■ They walked across the junkyard from the open door of the rocket, their blood singing, their faces glowing. Perhaps they knew what he had done. Perhaps they guessed his wonderful magic trick. But if they knew, if they guessed, they never said. Now they only laughed and ran. ■ "I have ham and eggs for all of you," said Maria, at the

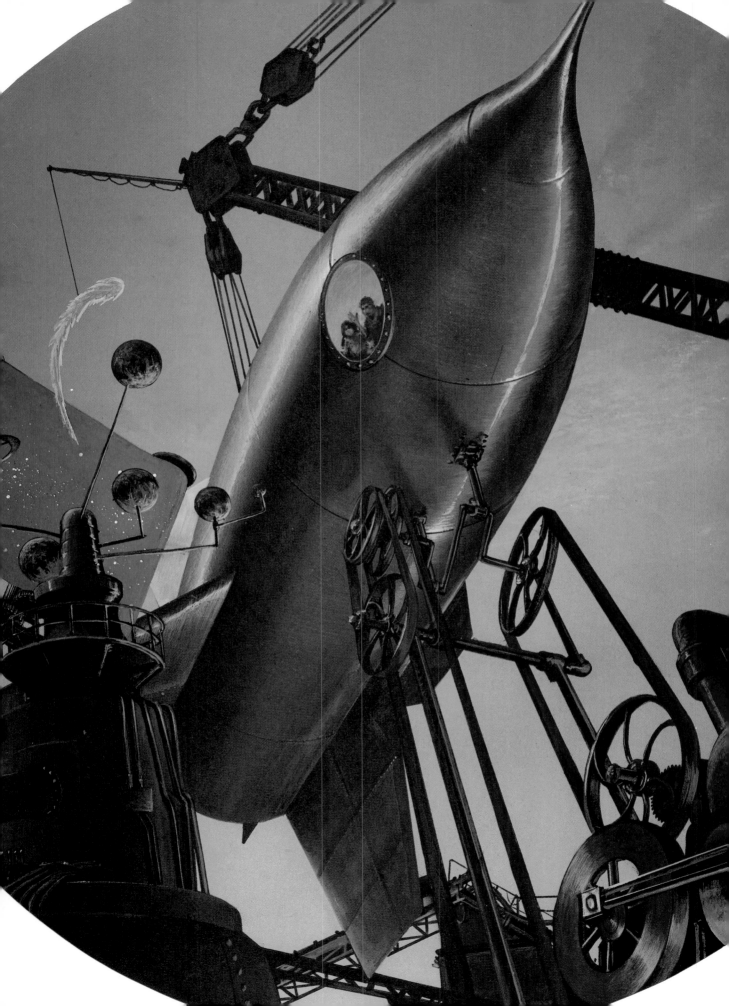

kitchen door. ■ "Mama, Mama, you should have come, to see it, to see Mars, Mama, and meteors, and everything!" ■ "Yes," she said. ■ At bedtime the children gathered before Bodoni. "We want to thank you, Papa." ■ "It was nothing." ■ "We will remember it for always, Papa. We will never forget."

Very late in the night Bodoni opened his eyes. He sensed that his wife was lying beside him, watching him. She did not move for a very long time, and then suddenly she kissed his cheeks and his forehead. ■ "What's this?" he cried. ■ "You're the best father in the world," she whispered. ■ "Why?" ■ "Now I see," she said. "I understand." ■ She lay back and closed her eyes, holding his hand. "Is it a very lovely journey?" she asked. ■ "Yes," he said. ■ "Perhaps," she said, "perhaps, some night, you might take me on just a little trip, do you think?" ■ "Just a little one, perhaps," he said. ■ "Thank you," she said. "Good night." ■ "Good night," said Fiorello Bodoni.

Meet
Ray Bradbury

When Ray Bradbury was in high school, space travel was the stuff of science fiction. "I was the only person at Los Angeles High School who knew the Space Age was coming," he claimed. "Totally alone among 4,000 students, I insisted we were going to get the . . . rocket off the ground, and that made me the class kook, of course. I said, 'Well, we're going to do it anyway.'" ■ That young dreamer has become one of the world's foremost science fiction writers. Bradbury believes that science fiction is "the most important fiction ever invented because it dares to dream things that are not yet possible." ■ Ray Bradbury has written novels, short stories, and movie and television scripts. Many works, such as *The Martian Chronicles*, are considered science fiction classics. *R Is for Rocket*, which includes "The Rocket," and *S Is for Space* are short story collections written especially for young adults. His compelling novel *Fahrenheit 451* became a hit movie. The numerous awards he has won include the Grand Master Award from the Science Fiction Writers of America and the World Fantasy Award for Lifetime Achievement.

RESPONDING TO *Literature*

THINK • TALK • WRITE

1 If you were offered the chance to travel to Mars on a rocket, would you want to go? Why or why not? Write a few lines in your journal.

2 Why do you think Bodoni buys the rocket ship? Why does he get so angry at it later?

3 Why does Paolo finally decide not to go to Mars? Why does the rest of the family also not want to go?

4 Why do you think Bodoni's wife says "I understand" at the end of the story? What does she "understand"?

5 Describe the future world depicted in this story. Which aspects are different from today's world? Which are similar?

ACTIVITIES

• **Write About Science Fiction** Write a brief newspaper story about the time the first tourists from Earth landed on Mars. Describe who they are, how they got to Mars, and what they did and saw there.

• **Design a Poster** Imagine that you have been hired by the company that arranges flights to Mars in "The Rocket." Design a poster that will make people want to buy a ticket for the flight.

VOCABULARY PRACTICE

gnaw   delicacy

subsided   insolently

curdled

On a separate sheet of paper, write the vocabulary word that best answers each question. Then write a sentence that explains your answer.

1 During low tide, have the waves *subsided* or have they *curdled*?

2 Did the urge to go to Mars *gnaw* at Bodoni or did it leave him *curdled*?

3 Is a powerful mini-computer constructed with *delicacy* or *insolently*?

4 If your milk has gone bad, has it *curdled* or *subsided*?

5 Would a rude teenager speak to a teacher with *delicacy* or *insolently*?

BEFORE READING

UFOS

CONNECT TO LITERATURE

Have you ever heard of UFOs? What image does the word *UFO* bring to your mind? Do you think UFOs really exist? Discuss your ideas with a classmate. As you read "UFOs," note in your journal information that makes you believe or disbelieve in UFOs.

THINKING ABOUT ANECDOTE

An *anecdote* is a brief and entertaining account of a true event. Authors use anecdotes to amuse, to help illustrate a main idea, or to reveal an aspect of a character's personality.

In this selection, you will read several anecdotes—brief stories about people who think they have seen UFOs. As you read, ask yourself why the author has chosen to include them.

DID YOU KNOW?

Interest in extraterrestrials (life from other planets) is not new. As far back as 2,000 years ago, the Roman poet Lucretius wrote, "So we must realize that there are other worlds in other parts of the universe." In the nineteenth century, the astronomer Joseph von Littrow proposed digging huge ditches in the Sahara desert in various geometric shapes, then filling them with kerosene and lighting them on fire so that they would be visible from space.

Meet *Melvin Berger*

Making a career choice is not easy for anyone, and Melvin Berger was no exception. Music was Berger's first love; but to be practical, he started college majoring in electrical engineering. Eventually, his intense interest in both science and music led him to write books on these subjects for young people.

Berger has provided readers with fresh perspectives on a rich range of topics: *Bizarre Crimes*; *Jobs That Save Our Environment*; and *Quasars, Pulsars, and Black Holes in Space* are just a few of the more than eighty books Berger has written. "I am especially proud of the science books," he said. ". . . I try to provide the reader with a depth of understanding that will make him or her scientifically aware, better able to participate as an informed citizen."

To keep up with the latest findings in science, Berger visits science labs, talks to researchers, and observes them at work. He is the first to admit, however, that not every event can be explained in logical, scientific terms. He tries to present the facts objectively, "allowing the readers to draw their own conclusions."

Berger's books have been honored by the National Science Teachers' Association and the Child Study Association.

UFOs

by Melvin Berger
Collages by George Baquero

UFOs: abbreviation of Unidentified Flying Objects.
Objects seen in the air or on land but of unknown source or origin.

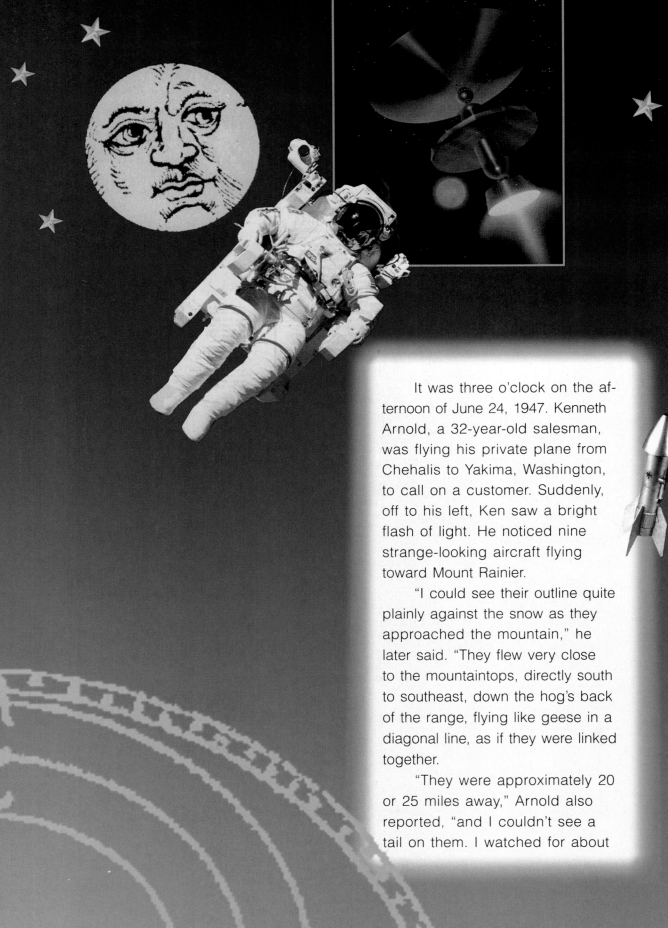

It was three o'clock on the afternoon of June 24, 1947. Kenneth Arnold, a 32-year-old salesman, was flying his private plane from Chehalis to Yakima, Washington, to call on a customer. Suddenly, off to his left, Ken saw a bright flash of light. He noticed nine strange-looking aircraft flying toward Mount Rainier.

"I could see their outline quite plainly against the snow as they approached the mountain," he later said. "They flew very close to the mountaintops, directly south to southeast, down the hog's back of the range, flying like geese in a diagonal line, as if they were linked together.

"They were approximately 20 or 25 miles away," Arnold also reported, "and I couldn't see a tail on them. I watched for about

three minutes . . . a chain of saucerlike things at least 5 miles long, swerving in and out of the high mountain peaks. They were flat like a pie pan and so shiny they reflected the sun like a mirror."

The startled pilot estimated that each silvery craft was 45 to 50 feet long. They seemed to be flying at a height of about 9,500 feet. And he put their speed at 1,700 miles an hour—about three times swifter than any existing plane! "I never saw anything so fast," he said later.

As Arnold watched in amazement, the strange-looking aircraft dove, soared and scooted this way and that before disappearing out of sight. After locating the point on his map, he continued his flight to the Yakima airport.

Arnold's account of the mysterious sightings created an absolute sensation. Newspapers and magazines around the world rushed to print stories about what he had seen. Using the pilot's words, they reported that the unidentified craft looked "like a saucer would if you skipped it across the water." That name caught on, and soon everyone was talking about "flying saucers."

The news reached the ears of officials in the U.S. Air Force. Since it is their job to protect the United States from air attack, they decided to investigate. After all, the craft that Arnold saw might threaten the nation's security.

An expert in military intelligence questioned Arnold at great

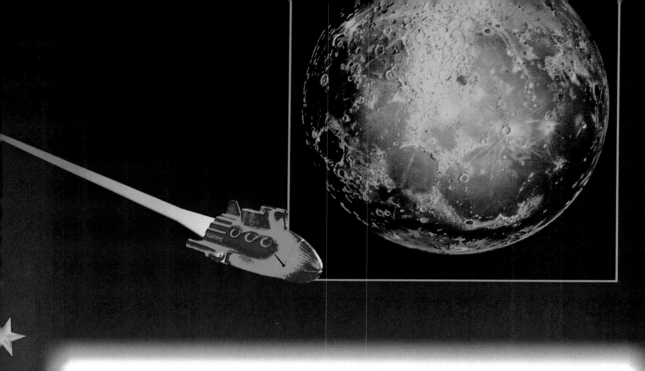

length. He reported: "It is the personal opinion of the interviewer that Mr. Arnold actually saw what he stated that he saw. It is difficult to believe that a man of Mr. Arnold's character and apparent integrity would state that he saw objects and write up a report to the extent that he did if he did not see them."

In the little town of Maysville, Kentucky, on January 7, 1948, a number of people noted a strange-looking object in the sky overhead. Someone called the State Police. Several officers rushed out to look, and they, too, noticed something moving across the sky that they could not recognize. The police called the Godman Air Force Base near Louisville, Kentucky, for more information. The control tower could offer no explanation. But they agreed to help identify the flying object.

Meanwhile, other reports of the same craft began pouring in. People from many different locations described it in similar terms: It was round, between 250 and 300 feet in diameter, metallic in color and glowing brightly. Everyone also said that it was heading westward at great speed.

By now the top commanders at Godman were at the control tower. None of them could identify the object. But while they were trying to decide what to do next, a flight of four F-51 jets from the Air National Guard passed nearby on a routine training flight. Since these very fast planes were already in the air, the officers at Godman asked the lead pilot, Captain Thomas Mantell, to investigate.

Captain Mantell banked his plane south to look for the

---

integrity (in teg'ri tē) *n.* moral uprightness; honesty; sincerity.

object. Very soon he radioed the control tower, "Object traveling at half my speed and directly ahead of me and above. I'm going to take a closer look. It appears metallic and tremendous in size. I'm going to 20,000 feet." Then silence.

At 3:20 P.M. the Godman control tower got word that Captain Mantell's plane had crashed. Based on first reports, some said that he had made contact with the mysterious object. Others suspected that the unidentified object had somehow caused his plane to go down.

➤

Clarence C. Chiles and John B. Whitted, two Eastern Airlines pilots, were flying from Houston, Texas, to Atlanta, Georgia, on the night of July 24, 1948. At 2:45 A.M., when they were a few miles

southwest of Montgomery, Alabama, Captain Chiles noticed a red glow in the sky. Thinking it was some sort of advanced military plane, he told his copilot to look at the "new Army jet."

For ten seconds, as the two pilots watched, the craft advanced toward them from above and to the right. They later described it to FAA authorities as a huge cigar-shaped object, about 1,000 feet long and 30 feet across, without wings. Across its smooth surface were two rows of lighted windows. Chiles said, "You could see right through the windows and out the other side." The bottom of the craft glowed a dark blue, and red-orange flames shot out the rear section.

Horror-struck, Chiles and Whitted watched the object come to within 700 feet of their plane. To avoid a collision, Captain Chiles

pulled the plane sharply to the left. But despite his desperate maneuver, it still looked as if a midair crash was inevitable. Then, at the last possible instant, the "thing" veered to the right, just missing the passenger plane. Still flying at about 600 miles per hour, the craft suddenly rose up and disappeared in the clouds.

The pilots reported their sighting to the Air Force. Officials added this message to two other reports they had just received about the same craft. Observers at Robbins Air Force Base in Macon, Georgia, had described a brilliant light that flashed across the sky from north to south at about the same time. And two Air Force pilots who were flying near the Virginia–North Carolina state line had also seen a strange object flying in the direction of Montgomery, Alabama!

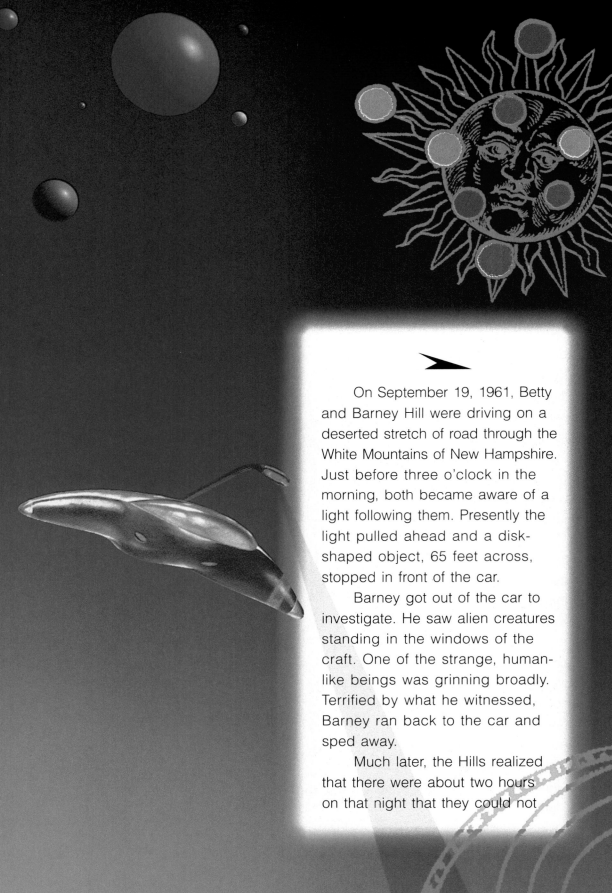

On September 19, 1961, Betty and Barney Hill were driving on a deserted stretch of road through the White Mountains of New Hampshire. Just before three o'clock in the morning, both became aware of a light following them. Presently the light pulled ahead and a disk-shaped object, 65 feet across, stopped in front of the car.

Barney got out of the car to investigate. He saw alien creatures standing in the windows of the craft. One of the strange, human-like beings was grinning broadly. Terrified by what he witnessed, Barney ran back to the car and sped away.

Much later, the Hills realized that there were about two hours on that night that they could not

account for. Both of them became very anxious. Betty began suffering from frightening nightmares. Barney developed an ulcer.

In December of 1962, the Hills went to psychiatrist Dr. Benjamin Simon in Boston for treatment. Dr. Simon decided to hypnotize the couple as a way of relieving their mental stress. While under hypnosis, the Hills were helped to recall what happened during those "missing" two hours. What came out, separately, from each of their stories, proved to be amazingly similar and one of the most exciting—and baffling—of all UFO stories.

Both Betty and Barney told of being brought inside the "silver metal" craft by "short, grotesque" creatures who were about 5 feet tall, had "grayish" skin, very large

---

psychiatrist (sī kī'ə trist) *n.* physician who specializes in the treatment of emotional and mental disorders.

"dark black" eyes, no ears and tiny noses. The creatures examined the two of them, but did neither any harm. The Hills were also shown the maps the aliens had used to find Earth from their home in the Zeta Reticuli star system. Just before the aliens departed, they released the Hills and warned them to forget all that had happened.

Dr. Simon's medical report included Betty's re-creation of the creatures' map. As soon as the report was made public, a number of researchers tried to <u>plot</u> the location on published star maps. Several possible matches were suggested, but experts could not agree on the home port of the mysterious spaceship.

On December 13, 1961, George E. Weber was walking across the parking lot of George Washington University in Washington, D.C., when a guard pointed out a strange-looking object in the sky. Meanwhile, William John Meyer, Jr., who was driving his car and waiting for a traffic light to change, also noted the same object overhead.

All three descriptions of the object were similar—dark gray in color, diamond-shaped, about 20 feet long and moving silently at a height of about 1,500 feet.

Weber mentioned a light shining from the bottom of the object. Meyer told of an orange-brown glow from the center area. The craft had neither wings nor propellers and left no <u>vapor</u> trail in the air. The two men in the parking lot had it in view for about three minutes. Meyer could watch only for a minute before the beeping horns of the cars he was blocking

plot (plot) *v.t.* locate on a map or diagram; chart.
vapor (vā′pər) *n.* tiny particles suspended in the air, such as mist or smoke.

forced him to move along with the traffic.

Just before six o'clock on the evening of April 24, 1964, Sergeant Lonnie Zamora of the Socorro, New Mexico, Police Department spotted a speeding black Chevrolet. Zamora began chasing the car south near the city limits when, in the police-man's words, "I heard a roar and saw a flame in the sky to the southwest, some distance away, possibly a half-mile or a mile." He said the flame was "bluish and sort of orange, too." Giving up the chase, Zamora de-cided to investigate the mysterious object instead.

To reach the source of the noise and the flame, the officer pulled off the highway and drove along a rough gravel road. About 150 or 200 yards south of the road, Zamora saw an object that looked like an overturned car, but was all bright and shiny as though made of aluminum. There was no sign of the flames he had seen before.

Standing next to the craft were two figures in white coveralls. Zamora said they were "normal in shape, but possibly they were small adults or large kids." When one turned to look at the police car, the creature "seemed startled, seemed to quickly jump somewhat."

As Zamora steered his car toward the craft, the figures scampered back into the ob-ject. A burst of blue and orange flame shot out from under the craft and it <u>emitted</u> the same loud roar he had heard before. As it rose up into the air slowly, Zamora noticed that it had no visible doors or

emitted (i mi'tid) *v.t.* sent forth; gave off.

windows, only some red markings on the side.

Terrified by the noise and flame, the officer turned and started to pull away. The object's roar rose to a high-pitched whine and then stopped altogether. When Zamora looked back, he saw the object skimming away about 15 feet above the ground.

Zamora radioed in an account of his experience and Sergeant Sam Chavez of the New Mexico State Police appeared on the scene. The two men took note of the scorched ground and burned bushes where Zamora had encountered the craft. They also found four shallow holes in the ground—about 12 inches long and 1 inch deep—arranged in a diamond pattern. The bushes had been burnt, they assumed, by the flames, and they

also assumed the four holes had been created by the landing feet of the craft.

Launched on July 16, 1969, the Apollo 11 space shot had three astronauts on board—Neil Armstrong, Edwin Aldrin and Michael Collins. The historic flight was the first to place a human being on the moon.

After their return, certain stories began circulating about bizarre happenings on their trip. On the second day, when they were about halfway to the moon, it was said, the crew observed some shiny white objects flying alongside their ship and keeping pace with them. They supposedly photographed the objects. Two days later, they again saw the objects

and again recorded the sighting on film.

According to some reports, the astronauts noted two objects flying together in close formation. At times they would come close together. Then they would separate. Both appeared to be emitting some sort of liquid. After watching their movements in space, the astronauts decided the objects were under intelligent control.

The report of astronaut sightings of unidentified objects was taken very seriously. Because astronauts are highly trained as pilots and scientists, they are considered very reliable observers. In this case, not only had they presumably sighted the objects, but they had also taken photos of them. It had long been expected that if there are intelligent beings

elsewhere in the universe, they would be very interested in our space shots.

>

It was just about 4:00 A.M. in the pre-dawn hours of September 20, 1977. In Leningrad, Helsinki and many places in between, residents who were awake at that hour observed something absolutely terrifying. One eyewitness said that it looked like a glowing "jellyfish" hovering over the Russian city of Petrozavodsk. Shaped like a huge star, it glowed brightly in the almost pitch-dark sky. And pouring out and down from this disk were fine rays of light, which some said looked like a shower of shiny raindrops.

After a while the rays disappeared. The object changed its shape, becoming more like a semicircle. And it began heading off in the direction of Lake Onega. The half-circle shone with a bright light—red in the middle and white at the sides. Observers reported that they could see it for as long as 12 minutes.

The rumors and stories that followed this sighting were quite amazing. People reported that the hanging arms of the so-called jellyfish had dug holes in the sidewalks of the various cities over which it had passed. Some home owners complained that those same rays had drilled holes in the glass of their windows. A number of Russian dockworkers took it as a signal of the beginning of an American invasion of Russia. One doctor grumbled that the object passing overhead made his ambulance go out of control. Large groups of people said they smelled ozone in the air for days after the sighting.

---

ozone (ō'zōn) *n.* form of oxygen with a distinctive odor, formed when an electric discharge passes through the air.

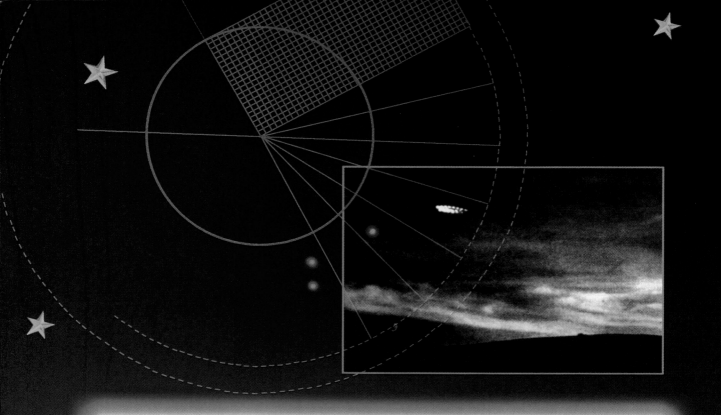

Colonel Osires Silva is a trained aeronautical engineer as well as the head of Brazil's state-owned oil company. Because of his background and position everyone listened very carefully to what he had to say when his private plane landed at the airport at São José dos Campos on May 19, 1986.

Silva told how he and his pilot had seen a strange light in the air. He described "a dancing point in the sky." The two observers estimated the object's speed at about 900 miles per hour.

On checking with the control tower, it was learned that some unidentified objects were also being picked up on the radar screen. The airport authorities quickly called the Brazilian Defense Center. They sent up six of their fastest jets to locate and identify these mysterious lights.

Although all the pilots saw the lights, the planes they were flying could not catch up with the objects emitting them. After some three hours the pilots lost sight of the lights entirely. They also disappeared from the radar screen. Even though the Brazilian Air Force investigated the incident, they never released their findings.

These have been among the best-known sightings of UFOs in recent years. At first, the accounts were generally accepted to be true.

Later, however, a number of investigators tried to discover whether or not these reports were accurate.

The Kenneth Arnold Case

This case proved to be one of the simplest to understand. Bright sunlight shining on clouds among mountain peaks frequently creates optical illusions, making things seem real that are not. One effect that has been noted often is the <u>optical</u> illusion of disks of light that seem to be floating in the air. There is every reason to believe that such round, flat, thin objects are what Arnold saw. The nine disks were merely a false impression of "flying saucers" caused by the particular relationship of the sun, clouds and mountains at the time.

The Captain Mantell Case

Investigators of the Mantell incident found that the captain had been chasing a Skyhook balloon. The incident occurred, however, at a time when the Skyhook balloon was still a military secret. No one outside the program knew that it even existed.

The balloon, it was discovered, had a metallic surface, measured 100 feet across and carried various scientific measuring instruments. Captain Mantell did not crash because of any encounter with a UFO. The Air Force authorities said that he flew too high without oxygen and blacked out.

The Eastern Airlines Case

For nearly twenty years, the report by the two Eastern Airlines pilots puzzled experts. Then, on March 3, 1968, three observers in Tennessee, six in Indiana and three in Ohio reported a UFO that looked exactly like the one Chiles and Whitted had seen. It even included the row of windows lit from within!

When experts from the Air Force started working on this case, they discovered that the Russians had put a spacecraft into orbit on March 2, 1968. The day of the "sighting," one of the rocket boosters fell back down toward earth and burned up in the atmosphere. What appeared to be a spaceship was the booster shell. And what seemed to be a row of lit windows was the red-hot fragments breaking off the burning shell. Since the Chiles–Whitted UFO looked the same, it was probably the falling booster from a secret space shot.

The Hill Case

The 1961 encounter of Betty and Barney Hill with "alien creatures" was very convincing. How else could one explain their identical stories of <u>abduction</u> by creatures from the spaceship? In fact, this case was so persuasive that it became the basis for a book, *Interrupted*

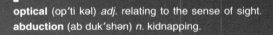

optical (op'ti kəl) *adj.* relating to the sense of sight.
abduction (ab duk'shən) *n.* kidnapping.

Journey (1966), by John Fuller, and a TV movie, *The UFO Incident,* aired on NBC in 1975.

However, a breakthrough came in 1975. Dr. Simon, the psychiatrist who spent hundreds of hours treating the Hills, broke his silence. At long last, he gave his professional opinion of the case.

The doctor pointed out that Betty had been an <u>avid</u> reader of science fiction magazines. Her sister was also very interested in tales of interplanetary travel and adventure. Often the two women would discuss some of the more terrifying UFO stories together. So it seemed obvious, Dr. Simon concluded, that Betty's nightmares originated in these fictional stories.

As the doctor also learned, Betty retold many of these stories to her husband. Since they had the same frightening UFO tales in the back of their minds, it was not surprising that they both imagined the same encounter with the UFO and its creatures.

Robert Sheaffer, a UFO investigator, took another tack in researching the Hill case. He studied the weather records and the positions of stars and planets on the night of the event. What the Hills saw, he believes, was the planet Jupiter bursting forth from behind some clouds. This sight, combined with the fact that it was late and they were tired, convinced the couple that something was chasing them. According to other experts, this strange illusion has been reported a number of times before.

➤

The Weber–Meyer Sightings

The 1961 Weber–Meyer sighting in Washington, D.C., is still listed as an unsolved case. After nearly thirty years, no one has been able to confirm it either as a known object, a natural event or a true encounter with a UFO.

avid (av′id) *adj.* eager; enthusiastic.

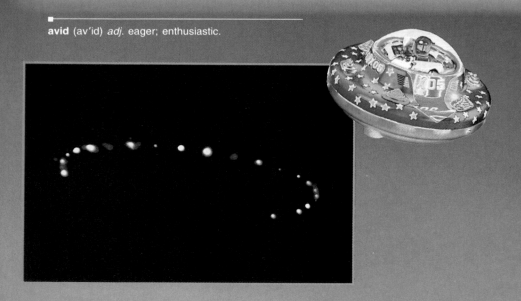

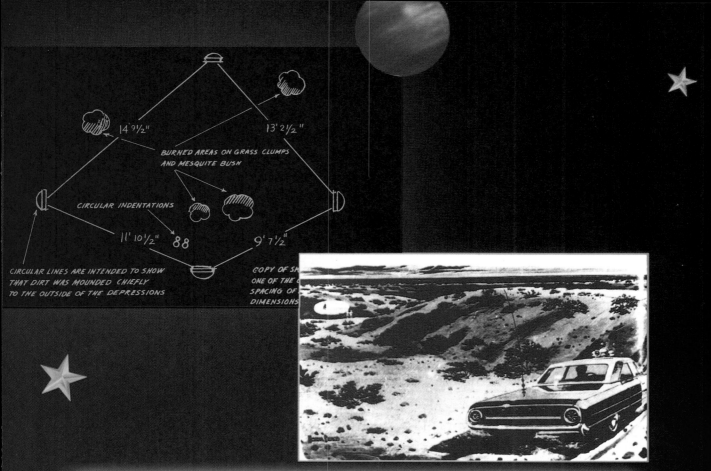

Burned areas on grass clumps and mesquite bush

14' 9½" 13' 2½"

Circular indentations

11' 10½" 88 9' 7½"

Circular lines are intended to show that dirt was mounded chiefly to the outside of the depressions

Copy of sk... one of the c... spacing of... dimensions...

The Zamora Case

The Lonnie Zamora sighting in the New Mexico desert is, according to UFO expert Major Hector Quintanilla of the U.S. Air Force, "the best-documented case in the Air Force files." Dr. J. Allen Hynek (1911–1986), an astronomer, consultant on UFOs to the Air Force, founder of the Center for UFO Studies and the leading UFO researcher, has said that "a real physical event occurred on the outskirts of Socorro that afternoon."

Philip Klass, an electrical engineer, and also a student of UFOs, has come up with one possible explanation. Klass thinks that Zamora may have seen an unusual form of lightning. This type appears as a bright, shiny ball, not as the usual streak of light across the sky. A lightning ball can be several feet across and so appear to be a solid object. And it may be seen at any height—from just above the ground to high in the air.

Klass also says that Zamora's description of the "bluish and sort of orange" flame also fits the color of a ball of lightning. As for the two figures in white that Zamora noticed, Klass says they could have been wisps of electrified gas coming from the lightning. To the frightened police officer, however, they looked like small men.

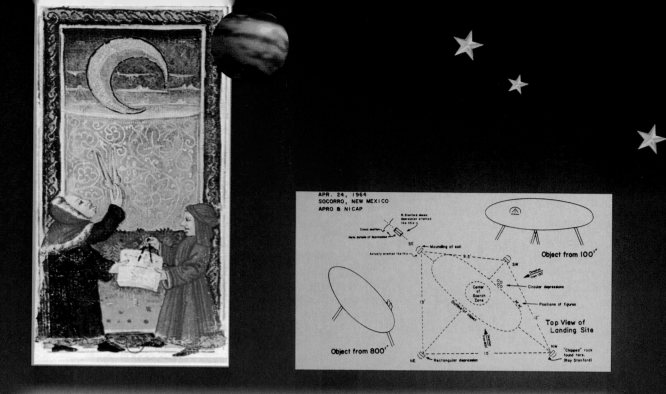

APR. 24, 1964
SOCORRO, NEW MEXICO
APRO & NICAP

The Apollo 11 Incident

The Apollo 11 incident proved to be an out-and-out fake. When Neil Armstrong was asked about seeing UFOs, he answered, "We didn't see them, and with what we . . . are doing in space, that's a real wonder." NASA official Charles Redmond adds, "We don't have any UFO secrets."

One photograph of Earth taken from Apollo 11 did, however, show a bright white object floating in the air. But upon further investigation, it proved to be nothing more than a piece of metal that had broken off when the lunar module was released. In the same way, movie film shot from inside the spacecraft reveals a number of strange lights and shapes. All the experts agree, however, that they are simply reflections and glares in the window.

It now seems clear that the early reports of UFOs involving Apollo 11 were based on false quotes and <u>transcripts</u> of conversations between the crew and Mission Control. Also, it was discovered that someone had retouched the photos to make them look as though UFOs were present. Nevertheless, the desire to believe in UFOs is very strong in some people. Even when NASA released the original transcripts and the original photos, which did not show UFOs, some Americans continued to think that the Apollo 11 crew had seen UFOs. A few even charged that NASA was hiding the truth!

---

transcripts (tran'skripts) *n., pl.* written copy.

The "Jellyfish" UFO

A study of the records shows that at 3:58 on the morning of the "jellyfish" sightings, Russia launched an artificial satellite from a secret base near Plesetsk. Since this was a <u>covert</u> operation, there was no public mention of the launch. Previous launchings from the same site had never been seen due to the fact that a pre-dawn mist usually covers the area.

The morning was very clear, however, when the glowing mass with flowing <u>tentacles</u> appeared near Plesetsk. The unusual weather made the rocket quite visible in the dark sky. And the booster's five separate sets of jets sent out vapor trails that could be seen clearly—and closely resembled the trailing feelers of a jellyfish!

The Colonel Silva Sighting

The results of the Brazilian Air Force investigation of the "dancing point" of light that Colonel Silva watched have never been made public. Nor have any other scientists been able to explain what the colonel, his pilot and the six pilots of the Air Force jets observed or what the radar screen showed that night.

James Oberg, a leading UFO researcher, points out that radar can be fooled by birds, insects or certain weather conditions. But neither he nor any of the others who have looked into the case has succeeded in identifying the mysterious lights. Colonel Silva's sighting, therefore, remains another significant case of an unsolved UFO encounter.

---

covert (kō′vert) *adj.* secret; hidden.

tentacles (ten′tə kəlz) *n., pl.* long, slender, flexible growths used for feeling, grasping, and moving.

UFOs in Perspective

Sightings of UFOs are nothing new. As long ago as A.D. 98, a number of ancient Romans reported seeing a round burning shield flashing across the sky. Another sighting from around that time was of a giant globe, brighter than the sun, coming down to Earth and then flying off again. In fact, all through the Middle Ages people related tales about strange objects and unexplained lights that they saw in the sky—and sometimes on land as well.

What *is* new are the efforts of scientists to study UFOs. Soon after Kenneth Arnold reported seeing flying saucers in 1947, the U.S. Air Force set up an office to investigate all such sightings to make sure they were not part of a military attack or invasion. The inquiry was later given the name Project Blue Book. In 1969 the project was brought to a close when the Air Force concluded that UFOs did not threaten the nation's security.

Besides the Air Force, many private organizations set up UFO investigations. Some of them are still in operation. Worldwide, reports on UFO sightings still pour in at the rate of about 100 a day!

To help in the study of UFOs, scientist J. Allen Hynek divided UFO sightings into six types.

The first three are distant observations:

1. Bright lights seen in the night sky.
2. Bright ovals or disks seen in the daytime sky.
3. Objects detected only by radar.

The final three are much closer and thus more exciting:

4. Close encounters of the first kind—sighting an unidentified object on Earth.
5. Close encounters of the second kind—sighting an unidentified object on Earth and tracing its physical effects on things or beings.
6. Close encounters of the third kind—sighting an unidentified object on Earth and making physical contact with the object or its occupants.

Most UFO reports fall into one of the first three of Dr. Hynek's categories. But experts find eventually that most of them, perhaps 90 percent or more, are not true UFOs. They are really IFOs—Identified Flying Objects.

According to these experts, people may be fooled into thinking they are making a Type One sighting when they catch an unusual or unexpected view of a plane, a meteor, the very bright planet Venus or one of the other planets. Weather balloons, particular cloud formations, artificial satellites and blimps account for a large percentage of Type Two observations. False radar signals can come either from flocks of birds, swarms of insects or unexplained radar waves, called "angels."

When Project Blue Book stopped operating, it had studied over 12,000 UFO sightings. Of the total number, the experts were able to explain well over 90 percent of the reported incidents. In over 2,000 of the cases, the observers were found to be seeing Venus or another planet, a particularly bright star or some other natural astronomical body or event. In another 1,500 cases, the object sighted proved to be an airplane. Nearly 800 more were glimpses of artificial satellites, and about 500 were balloons. A total of about 6,500 were false reports, posed or retouched photos, strange cloud formations, birds, insects and just plain human error.

When all was said and done, however, there remained about 700 events for which no explanation could be found, either natural or man-made. What do the experts say about these?

Major Hector Quintanilla, former director of Project Blue Book, insists that there are no UFOs. He cites the absence of even one fully confirmed report of a UFO sighting. Astronomer Carl Sagan concurs. A true sighting, he expects, would have many reliable witnesses all coming forward at the same time.

Other experts make these points: UFOs could not land and then take off without leaving significant evidence of the tremendous force needed to launch or slow down a spaceship. Since a spaceship would have to travel an <u>immense</u> distance to arrive on Earth, it would not just appear in a remote area, stay for a few minutes and then quickly fly away. Most likely it would stay for a period of time and make better contact with the Earth's inhabitants. And with all the military air defense and civilian air traffic systems now operating, it is <u>virtually</u> impossible for any aircraft to enter the Earth's air space without being detected.

Still, in a February 1987 Gallup poll, almost half of all Americans said they believe in UFOs. Some had had UFO experiences themselves and don't accept the scientists' explanations. Many more had read or seen very dramatic accounts of the most exciting of these encounters. For all these people, the unsolved, unexplained UFO events are enough to convince them that there are living beings that have come to Earth from the outer reaches of space in what we call UFOs.

---

immense (i mens´) *adj.* very large; huge.
virtually (vûr´chŭ ə lē) *adv.* in almost every way; practically.

RESPONDING TO *Literature*

THINK • TALK • WRITE

1 After reading this selection, you think about UFOs? Jot down some thoughts in your journal.

2 Which do you find more convincing, the Hills's story about their encounter with aliens, or Melvin Berger's explanation of what happened? Why do you think this?

3 If many people see the same object, does this make the sighting more believable? Explain your opinion.

4 Sergeant Zamora found scorched grass and four holes in the soil. Does this make his story more believable? Why or why not?

5 Why do you think humans have always been so fascinated by the idea of life in outer space? Write a few lines giving some ideas.

ACTIVITIES

- **Write About Anecdote** Turn one of the UFO sightings into a personal anecdote. Rewrite the experience as a first-person narration. Remember to use language which reveals the speaker's feelings.

- **An Outer Space Capsule** Imagine that a capsule is being sent into outer space to introduce our species to aliens. What objects would you include in the capsule to represent the achievements of the human race? Make a list.

VOCABULARY PRACTICE

On a separate sheet of paper, write the vocabulary word that best answers each question.

integrity	avid
plot	transcripts
vapor	covert
emitted	immense
optical	virtually

1 Which word is an adverb?

2 Which word is a verb that means "to locate on a map"?

3 Which word is a past-tense verb?

4 Which word is an adjective meaning "relating to the sense of sight"?

5 Which word is a name for the written copies of a phone conversation?

6 Which word is a quality an honest person would have?

7 Which word is a synonym for *huge* or *enormous*?

8 Mist and smoke are examples of which word?

9 Which word might describe a secret mission?

10 Which word is an adjective describing someone who is eager or enthusiastic?

SOUTHBOUND ON THE FREEWAY

BY MAY SWENSON

Corporate Rise   1986   James Doolin

A tourist came in from Orbitville,
parked in the air, and said:

The creatures of this star
are made of metal and glass.

Through the transparent parts
you can see their guts.

Their feet are round and roll
on diagrams—or long

measuring tapes—dark
with white lines.

They have four eyes.
The two in the back are red.

Sometimes you can see a 5-eyed
one, with a red eye turning

on the top of his head.
He must be special—

the others respect him,
and go slow,

when he passes, winding
among them from behind.

They all hiss as they glide,
like inches, down the marked

tapes. Those soft shapes,
shadowy inside

the hard bodies—are they
their guts or their brains?

METEORO

Sobre la mesa
un vaso
se desmaya,
  rueda,
    cae.

Al estrellarse
contra el piso,
una galaxia
      nace.

METEOR

On the table
a glass
faints,
    rolls,
        falls.

It shatters
on the floor;
a galaxy
      is born.

— ELÍAS NANDINO

650

BEFORE READING

THE INN OF LOST TIME

CONNECT TO LITERATURE

If you lost your watch, would you try to remember every place you might have left it? If a friend didn't seem as cheerful as usual, would you try to figure out the reason? When something puzzles you, you probably use what you know and observe to unravel the mystery. As you read "The Inn of Lost Time," keep track in your journal of clues that help the narrator find the answers to puzzling events.

THINKING ABOUT FORESHADOWING

Authors often increase suspense with *foreshadowing*—clues that hint at events occurring later in the story. The use of foreshadowing teases readers, excites their curiosity, and makes them wonder what will happen next. In "The Inn of Lost Time" the narrator notices certain details about the inn the first time he visits it. These details foreshadow—and might even help you guess—what the narrator discovers later.

DID YOU KNOW?

"The Inn of Lost Time" is set in a period when the actual governing of Japan was done by a *shogun,* or general. The most powerful families kept private armies of warriors, called *samurai.* In the 1550s many of these private armies fought one another, and Japan was in a state of chaos. By 1603 the Tokugawa family had gained control of the country. They ruled until 1867, when a powerful emperor ended shogun rule.

In 1549 Portuguese traders arrived in Japan. These were the first Europeans to do so, and they were not welcomed by the Japanese. After 1630 the shoguns closed Japan to the rest of the world. This isolation lasted for 250 years.

THE INN OF LOST TIME

By LENSEY NAMIOKA

Illustrated by YOSHIKAZU OGINO

"Will you promise to sleep if I tell you a story?" said the father. He pretended to put on a stern expression.

"Yes! Yes!" the three little boys chanted in unison. It sounded like a nightly routine.

The two guests smiled as they listened to the exchange. They were wandering ronin, or unemployed samurai, and they enjoyed watching this cozy family scene.

The father gave the guests a helpless look. "What can I do? I have to tell them a story, or these little rascals will give us no peace." Clearing his throat, he turned to the boys. "All right. The story tonight is about Urashima Taro."

Instantly the three boys became still. Sitting with their legs tucked under them, the three little boys, aged five, four, and three, looked like a descending row of stone statuettes. Matsuzo, the younger of the two ronin, was reminded of the wayside half-body statues of Jizo, the God of Travelers and Protector of Children.

Behind the boys the farmer's wife took up a pair of iron chopsticks and stirred the ashes of the fire in the charcoal brazier. A momentary glow brightened the room. The lean faces of the two ronin, lit by the fire, suddenly looked fierce and hungry.

The farmer knew that the two ronin were supposed to use their arms in defense of the weak. But in these troubled times, with the country torn apart by civil wars, the samurai didn't always live up to their honorable code.

Then the fire died down again and the subdued red light softened the features of the two ronin. The farmer relaxed and began his story.

The tale of Urashima Taro is familiar to every Japanese. No doubt the three little boys had heard their father tell it before—and more than once. But they listened with rapt attention.

Urashima Taro, a fisherman, rescued a turtle from some boys who were battering it with stones. The grateful turtle rewarded Taro by carrying him on his back to the bottom of the sea, where he lived happily with the Princess of the Undersea. But Taro soon became homesick for his native village and asked to go back on land. The princess gave him a box to take with him but warned him not to peek inside.

---

stern (stûrn) *adj.* severe or strict; grim or forbidding.
unison (ū′nə sən) *n.* union, as when two or more voices speak as one.
brazier (brā′zhər) *n.* metal container to hold charcoal, used for heating, lighting, or cooking.
rapt (rapt) *adj.* deeply absorbed.

When Taro went back to his village, he found the place quite changed. In his home he found his parents gone, and living there was another old couple. He was stunned to learn that the aged husband was his own son, whom he had last seen as a baby! Taro thought he had spent only a pleasant week or two undersea with the princess. On land, seventy-two years had passed! His parents and most of his old friends had long since died.

Desolate, Taro decided to open the box given him by the princess. As soon as he looked inside, he changed in an instant from a young man to a decrepit old man of more than ninety. ❀

At the end of the story the boys were close to tears. Even Matsuzo found himself deeply touched. He wondered why the farmer had told his sons such a <u>poignant</u> bedtime story. Wouldn't they worry all evening instead of going to sleep?

But the boys recovered quickly. They were soon laughing and <u>jostling</u> each other, and they made no objections when their mother shooed them toward bed. Standing in order of age, they bowed politely to the guests, and then lay down on the mattresses spread out for them on the floor. Within minutes the sound of their regular breathing told the guests that they were asleep.

Zenta, the older of the two ronin, sighed as he glanced at the peaceful young faces. "I wish I could fall asleep so quickly. The story of Urashima Taro is one of the saddest that I know among our folk tales."

The farmer looked proudly at his sleeping sons. "They're <u>stout</u> lads. Nothing bothers them much."

The farmer's wife poured tea for the guests and apologized. "I'm sorry this is only poor tea made from coarse leaves."

Zenta hastened to reassure her. "It's warm and heartening on a chilly autumn evening."

"You know what I think is the saddest part of the Urashima Taro story?" said Matsuzo, picking up his cup and sipping the tea. "It's that Taro lost not only his family and friends, but a big piece of his life as well. He had lost the most precious thing of all: time."

The farmer nodded agreement. "I wouldn't sell even one year of my life for money. As for losing seventy-two years, no amount of gold will make up for that!"

---

poignant (poin′yənt) *adj.* deeply moving; sad; touching.
jostling (jos′ə ling) *v.t.* bumping, pushing, or shoving roughly.
stout (stout) *adj.* having courage; brave; strong.

Zenta put his cup down on the floor and looked curiously at the farmer. "It's interesting that you should say that. I had an opportunity once to observe exactly how much gold a person was willing to pay for some lost years of his life." He smiled grimly. "In this case the man went as far as one gold piece for each year he lost."

"That's bizarre!" said Matsuzo. "You never told me about it."

"It happened long before I met you," said Zenta. He drank some tea and smiled <u>ruefully</u>. "Besides, I'm not particularly proud of the part I played in that strange affair."

"Let's hear the story!" urged Matsuzo. "You've made us all curious."

The farmer waited expectantly. His wife sat down quietly behind her husband and folded her hands. Her eyes looked intently at Zenta.

"Very well, then," said Zenta. "Actually, my story bears some resemblance to that of Urashima Taro. . . ."

It happened about seven years ago, when I was a green, inexperienced youngster not quite eighteen years old. But I had had a good training in arms, and I was able to get a job as a bodyguard for a wealthy merchant from Sakai.

---

ruefully (rü′fə lē) *adv.* with sorrow or regret.

As you know, wealthy merchants are relatively new in our country. Traditionally the rich have been noblemen, landowners, and warlords with thousands of followers. Merchants, considered as <u>parasites</u> in our society, are a despised class. But our civil wars have made people unusually mobile and stimulated trade between various parts of the country. The merchants have taken advantage of this to conduct businesses on a scale our fathers could not imagine. Some of them have become more wealthy than a warlord with thousands of samurai under his command.

The man I was escorting, Tokubei, was one of this new breed of wealthy merchants. He was trading not only with outlying provinces but even with the Portuguese from across the sea. On this particular journey he was not carrying much gold with him. If he had, I'm sure he would have hired an older and more experienced bodyguard. But if the need should arise, he could always write a message to his clerks at home and have money forwarded to him. It's important to remember this.

The second day of our journey was a particularly <u>grueling</u> one, with several steep hills to climb. As the day was drawing to its close, we began to consider where we

---

parasites (par′ə sīts) *n., pl.* people who live off others for their own gain but give nothing in return.

grueling (grü′ə ling) *adj.* very difficult; exhausting.

should spend the night. I knew that within an hour's walking was a hot-spring resort known to have several attractive inns.

But Tokubei, my employer, said he was already very tired and wanted to stop. He had heard of the resort, and knew the inns there were expensive. Wealthy as he was, he did not want to spend more money than he had to.

While we stood talking, a smell reached our noses, a wonderful smell of freshly cooked rice. Suddenly I felt ravenous. From the way Tokubei swallowed, I knew he was feeling just as hungry.

We looked around eagerly, but the area was forested and we could not see very far in any direction. The tantalizing smell seemed to grow and I could feel the saliva filling my mouth.

"There's an inn around here, somewhere," muttered Tokubei. "I'm sure of it."

We followed our noses. We had to leave the well-traveled highway and take a narrow, winding footpath. But the mouth-watering smell of the rice and the vision of fluffy, freshly aired cotton quilts drew us on.

The sun was just beginning to set. We passed a bamboo grove, and in the low evening light the thin leaves turned into little golden knives. I saw a gilded clump of bamboo shoots. The sight made me think of the delicious dish they would make when boiled in soy sauce.

We hurried forward. To our delight we soon came to a clearing with a thatched house standing in the middle. The fragrant smell of rice was now so strong that we were certain a meal was being prepared inside.

Standing in front of the house was a pretty girl beaming at us with a welcoming smile. "Please honor us with your presence," she said, beckoning.

There was something a little unusual about one of her hands, but, being hungry and eager to enter the house, I did not stop to observe closely.

You will say, of course, that it was my duty as a bodyguard to be suspicious and to look out for danger. Youth and inexperience should not have prevented me from wondering why an inn should be found hidden away from the highway. As it was, my stomach growled, and I didn't even hesitate but followed Tokubei to the house.

Before stepping up to enter, we were given basins of water to wash our feet. As the girl handed us towels for drying, I saw what was unusual about her left hand: she had six fingers.

Tokubei had noticed it as well. When the girl turned away to empty the basins, he nudged me. "Did you see her left hand? She had—" He broke off in confusion as the girl turned around, but she didn't seem to have heard.

The inn was peaceful and quiet, and we soon discovered the reason why. We were the only guests. Again, I should have been suspicious. I told you that I'm not proud of the part I played.

Tokubei turned to me and grinned. "It seems that there are no other guests. We should be able to get extra service for the same amount of money."

The girl led us to a spacious room which was like the principal chamber of a private residence. Cushions were set out for us on the floor and we began to shed our traveling gear to make ourselves comfortable.

The door opened and a grizzled-haired man entered. Despite his vigorous-looking face his back was a little bent and I guessed his age to be about fifty. After bowing and greeting us he apologized in advance for the service. "We have not always been innkeepers here," he said, "and you may find the accommodations lacking. Our good intentions must make up for our inexperience. However, to compensate for our inadequacies, we will

charge a lower fee than that of an inn with an established reputation."

Tokubei nodded graciously, highly pleased by the words of our host, and the evening began well. It continued well when the girl came back with some flasks of wine, cups, and dishes of salty snacks.

While the girl served the wine, the host looked with interest at my swords. From the few remarks he made, I gathered that he was a former samurai, forced by circumstances to turn his house into an inn.

Having become a bodyguard to a tight-fisted merchant, I was in no position to feel superior to a ronin turned innkeeper. Socially, therefore, we were more or less equal.

We exchanged polite remarks with our host while we drank and tasted the salty snacks. I looked around at the pleasant room. It showed excellent taste, and I especially admired a vase standing in the alcove.

My host caught my eyes on it. "We still have a few good things that we didn't have to sell," he said. His voice held a trace of bitterness. "Please look at the panels of these doors. They were painted by a fine artist."

Tokubei and I looked at the pair of sliding doors. Each panel contained a landscape painting, the right panel depicting a winter scene and the left one the same scene in late summer.

Our host's words were no idle boast. The pictures were indeed beautiful.

Tokubei rose and approached the screens for a closer look. When he sat down again, his eyes were calculating. No doubt he was trying to estimate what price the paintings would fetch.

After my third drink I began to feel very tired. Perhaps it was the result of drinking on an empty stomach. I was glad when the girl brought in two dinner trays and a lacquered container of rice. Uncovering the rice container, she began filling our bowls.

Again I noticed her strange left hand with its six fingers. Any other girl would have tried to keep that hand hidden, but this girl made no effort to do so. If anything, she seemed to use that hand more than her other one when she served us. The extra little finger always stuck out from the hand, as if inviting comment.

The hand fascinated me so much that I kept my eyes on it, and soon forgot to eat. After a while the hand looked blurry. And then everything else began to look blurry. The last thing I remembered was the sight of Tokubei shaking his head, as if trying to clear it.

When I opened my eyes again, I knew that time had passed, but not how much time. My next thought was that it was cold. It was not only extremely cold but damp.

I rolled over and sat up. I reached immediately for my swords

---

alcove (al′kōv) *n.* small room or recess opening off a larger room.
lacquered (lak′ərd) *adj.* having a clear, glossy coating; varnished.

and found them safe on the ground beside me. *On the ground?* What was I doing on the ground? My last memory was of staying at an inn with a merchant called Tokubei.

The thought of Tokubei put me into a panic. I was his bodyguard, and instead of watching over him, I had fallen asleep and had awakened in a strange place.

I looked around frantically and saw that he was lying on the ground not far from where I was. Had he been killed?

I got up shakily, and when I stood up my head was swimming. But my sense of urgency gave some strength to my legs. I stumbled over to my employer and to my great relief found him breathing— breathing heavily, in fact.

When I shook his shoulder, he grunted and finally opened his eyes. "Where am I?" he asked thickly.

It was a reasonable question. I looked around and saw that we had been lying in a bamboo grove. By the light I guessed that it was early morning, and the reason I felt cold and damp was because my clothes were wet with dew.

"It's cold!" said Tokubei, shivering and climbing unsteadily to his feet. He looked around slowly, and his eyes became wide with disbelief. "What happened? I thought we were staying at an inn!"

His words came as a relief. One of the possibilities I had considered was that I had gone mad and that the whole episode with the inn was something I had imagined. Now I knew that Tokubei had the same memory of the inn. I had not imagined it.

But why were we out here on the cold ground, instead of on comfortable mattresses in the inn?

"They must have drugged us and robbed us," said Tokubei. He turned and looked at me furiously. "A fine bodyguard you are!"

There was nothing I could say to that. But at least we were both alive and unharmed. "Did they take all your money?" I asked.

Tokubei had already taken his wallet out of his sash and was peering inside. "That's funny! My money is still here!"

This was certainly unexpected. What did the innkeeper and his strange daughter intend to do by drugging us and moving us outside?

At least things were not as bad as we had feared. We had not lost anything except a comfortable night's sleep, although from the heaviness in my head I had certainly slept deeply enough—and long enough too.

Exactly how much time had elapsed since we drank wine with our host?

All we had to do now was find the highway again and continue our journey. Tokubei suddenly chuckled. "I didn't even have to pay for our night's lodging!"

As we walked from the bamboo grove, I saw the familiar clump of bamboo shoots, and we found ourselves standing in the same clearing again. Before our eyes was the thatched house. Only it was somehow different. Perhaps things looked different in the daylight than at dusk.

But the difference was more than a change of light. As we approached the house slowly, like sleepwalkers, we saw that the thatching was much darker. On the previous evening the thatching had looked fresh and new. Now it was dark with age. Daylight should make things appear brighter, not darker. The plastering of the walls also looked more dingy.

Tokubei and I stopped to look at each other before we went closer. He was pale, and I knew that I looked no less frightened. Something was terribly wrong. I loosened my sword in its <u>scabbard</u>.

We finally gathered the courage to go up to the house. Since Tokubei seemed unable to find his voice, I spoke out. "Is anyone there?"

After a moment we heard shuffling footsteps and the front door

---

scabbard (skab′ərd) *n.* case or sheath for the blade of a sword, bayonet, or other similar weapon.

slid open. The face of an old woman appeared. "Yes?" she inquired. Her voice was creaky with age.

What set my heart pounding with panic, however, was not her voice. It was the sight of her left hand holding on to the frame of the door. The hand was wrinkled and crooked with the arthritis of old age—and it had six fingers.

I heard a gasp beside me and knew that Tokubei had noticed the hand as well.

The door opened wider and a man appeared beside the old woman. At first I thought it was our host of the previous night. But this man was much younger, although the resemblance was strong. He carried himself straighter and his hair was black, while the innkeeper had been grizzled and slightly bent with age.

"Please excuse my mother," said the man. "Her hearing is not good. Can we help you in some way?"

Tokubei finally found his voice. "Isn't this the inn where we stayed last night?"

The man stared. "Inn? We are not innkeepers here!"

"Yes, you are!" insisted Tokubei. "Your daughter invited us in and served us with wine. You must have put something in the wine!"

The man frowned. "You are serious? Are you sure you didn't drink too much at your inn and wander off?"

"No, I didn't drink too much!" said Tokubei, almost shouting. "I hardly drank at all! Your daughter, the one with the six fingers in her hand, started to pour me a second cup of wine . . ." His voice trailed off, and he stared again at the left hand of the old woman.

"I don't have a daughter," said the man slowly. "My mother here is the one who has six fingers in her left hand, although I hardly think it polite of you to mention it."

"I'm getting dizzy," muttered Tokubei and began to totter.

"I think you'd better come in and rest a bit," the man said to him gruffly. He glanced at me. "Perhaps you wish to join your friend. You don't share his <u>delusion</u> about the inn, I hope?"

"I wouldn't presume to contradict my elders," I said carefully. Since both Tokubei and the owner of the house were my elders, I wasn't committing myself. In truth I didn't know what to believe, but I did want a look at the inside of the house.

---

delusion (di lü′zhən) *n.* false idea or belief.

The inside was almost the same as it was before but the differences were there when I looked closely. We entered the same room with the alcove and the pair of painted doors. The vase I had admired was no longer there, but the doors showed the same landscapes painted by a master. I peered closely at the pictures and saw that the colors looked faded. What was more, the left panel, the one depicting a winter scene, had a long tear in one corner. It had been painstakingly mended, but the damage was impossible to hide completely.

Tokubei saw what I was staring at and he became even paler. At this stage we had both considered the possibility that a hoax of some sort had been played on us. The torn screen convinced Tokubei that our host had not played a joke: the owner of a valuable painting would never vandalize it for a trivial reason.

As for me, I was far more disturbed by the sight of the sixth finger on the old woman's hand. Could the young girl have disguised herself as an old crone? She could put rice powder in her hair to whiten it, but she could not transform her pretty straight fingers into old fingers twisted with arthritis. The woman here with us now was genuinely old, at least fifty years older than the girl.

It was this same old woman who finally gave us our greatest shock. "It's interesting that you should mention an inn, gentlemen," she croaked. "My father used to operate an inn. After he died, my husband and I turned this back into a private residence. We didn't need the income, you see."

"Your . . . your . . . f-father?" stammered Tokubei.

"Yes," replied the old woman. "He was a ronin, forced to go into innkeeping when he lost his position. But he never liked the work. Besides, our inn had begun to acquire an unfortunate reputation. Some of our guests disappeared, you see."

Even before she finished speaking, a horrible suspicion had begun to dawn on me. Her *father* had been an innkeeper, she said, her father who used to be a ronin. The man who had been our host was a ronin turned innkeeper. Could this mean that this old woman was actually the same person as the young girl we had seen?

I sat stunned while I tried to absorb the implications. What had happened to us? Was it possible that Tokubei and I had slept while this young girl grew into a mature woman, got married, and bore a son, a son who is now an adult? If that was the case, then we had slept for fifty years!

---

hoax (hōks) *n.* trick or deception.
crone (krōn) *n.* withered old woman.

The old woman's next words confirmed my fears. "I recognize you now! You are two of the lost guests from our inn! The other lost ones I don't remember so well, but I remember *you* because your disappearance made me so sad. Such a handsome youth, I thought, what a pity that he should have gone the way of the others!"

A high wail came from Tokubei, who began to keen and rock himself back and forth. "I've lost fifty years! Fifty years of my life went by while I slept at this accursed inn!"

The inn was indeed accursed. Was the fate of the other guests similar to ours? "Did anyone else return as we did, fifty years later?" I asked.

The old woman looked uncertain and turned to her son. He frowned thoughtfully. "From time to time wild-looking people have come to us with stories similar to yours. Some of them went mad with the shock."

Tokubei wailed again. "I've lost my business! I've lost my wife, my young and beautiful wife! We had been married only a couple of months!"

A gruesome chuckle came from the old woman. "You may not have lost your wife. It's just that she's become an old hag like me!"

That did not console Tokubei, whose keening became louder.

---

gruesome (grü′səm) *adj.* causing horror, disgust, or fear.

keening (kē′ning) *n.* loud wailing for the dead.

Although my relationship with my employer had not been character-ized by much respect on either side, I did begin to feel very sorry for him. He was right: he had lost his world.

As for me, the loss was less traumatic. I had left home under ex-tremely painful circumstances, and had spent the next three years wandering. I had no friends and no one I could call a relation. The only thing I had was my duty to my employer. Somehow, some way, I had to help him.

"Did no one find an explanation for these disappearances?" I asked. "Perhaps if we knew the reason why, we might find some way to reverse the process."

The old woman began to nod eagerly. "The priestess! Tell them about the shrine priestess!"

"Well," said the man, "I'm not sure if it would work in your case. . . ."

"What? What would work?" demanded Tokubei. His eyes were feverish.

"There was a case of one returning guest who consulted the priestess at our local shrine," said the man. "She went into a trance and revealed that there was an evil spirit dwelling in the bamboo grove here. This spirit would put unwary travelers into a long, unnatural sleep. They would wake up twenty, thirty, or even fifty years later."

"Yes, but you said something worked in his case," said Tokubei.

The man seemed reluctant to go on. "I don't like to see you cheated, so I'm not sure I should be telling you this."

"Tell me! Tell me!" demanded Tokubei. The host's reluctance only made him more impatient.

"The priestess promised to make a spell that would undo the work of the evil spirit," said the man. "But she demanded a large sum of money, for she said that she had to burn some very rare and costly <u>incense</u> before she could begin the spell."

At the mention of money Tokubei sat back. The hectic flush died down on his face and his eyes narrowed. "How much money?" he asked.

The host shook his head. "In my opinion the priestess is a fraud and makes outrageous claims about her powers. We try to have as little to do with her as possible."

---

incense (in'sens') *n.* substance that produces a fragrant aroma when burned.

"Yes, but did her spell work?" asked Tokubei. "If it worked, she's no fraud!"

"At least the stranger disappeared again," cackled the old woman. "Maybe he went back to his own time. Maybe he walked into a river."

Tokubei's eyes narrowed further. "How much money did the priestess demand?" he asked again.

"I think it was one gold piece for every year lost," said the host. He hurriedly added, "Mind you, I still wouldn't trust the priestess."

"Then it would cost me fifty gold pieces to get back to my own time," muttered Tokubei. He looked up. "I don't carry that much money with me."

"No, you don't," agreed the host.

Something alerted me about the way he said that. It was as if the host knew already that Tokubei did not carry much money on him.

Meanwhile Tokubei sighed. He had come to a decision. "I do have the means to obtain more money, however. I can send a message to my chief clerk and he will <u>remit</u> the money when he sees my seal."

"Your chief clerk may be dead by now," I reminded him.

"You're right!" moaned Tokubei. "My business will be under a new management and nobody will even remember my name!"

"And your wife will have remarried," said the old woman, with one of her chuckles. I found it hard to believe that the gentle young girl who had served us wine could turn into this dreadful <u>harridan</u>.

"Sending the message may be a waste of time," agreed the host.

"What waste of time!" cried Tokubei. "Why shouldn't I waste time? I've wasted fifty years already! Anyway, I've made up my mind. I'm sending that message."

"I still think you shouldn't trust the priestess," said the host.

That only made Tokubei all the more determined to send for the money. However, he was not quite resigned to the amount. "Fifty gold pieces is a large sum. Surely the priestess can buy incense for less than that amount?"

"Why don't you try giving her thirty gold pieces?" cackled the old woman. "Then the priestess will send you back thirty years, and your wife will only be middle-aged."

While Tokubei was still arguing with himself about the exact sum to send for, I decided to have a look at the bamboo grove. "I'm going for a walk," I announced, rising and picking up my sword from the floor beside me.

remit (ri mit′) *v.t.* send in payment.
harridan (har′i dən) *n.* mean old woman.

The host turned sharply to look at me. For an instant a faint, rueful smile appeared on his lips. Then he looked away.

Outside, I went straight to the clump of shoots in the bamboo grove. On the previous night—or what I perceived as the previous night—I had noticed that clump of bamboo shoots particularly, because I had been so hungry that I pictured them being cut up and boiled.

The clump of bamboo shoots was still in the same place. That in itself proved nothing, since bamboo could spring up anywhere, including the place where a clump had existed fifty years earlier. But what settled the matter in my mind was that the clump looked almost exactly the way it did when I had seen it before, except that every shoot was about an inch taller. That was a reasonable amount for bamboo shoots to grow overnight.

Overnight. Tokubei and I had slept on the ground here overnight. We had not slept here for a period of fifty years.

Once I knew that, I was able to see another inconsistency: the door panels with the painted landscapes. The painting with the winter scene had been on the *right* last night and it was on the *left* this morning. It wasn't simply a case of the panels changing places, because the depressions in the panel for the handholds had been reversed. In other words, what I saw just now was not a pair of paintings faded and torn by age. They were an entirely different pair of paintings.

But how did the pretty young girl change into an old woman? The answer was that if the screens could be different ones, so could the women. I had seen one woman, a young girl, last night. This morning I saw a different woman, an old hag.

The darkening of the thatched roof? Simply blow ashes over the roof. The grizzled-haired host of last night could be the same man who claimed to be his grandson today. It would be a simple matter for a young man to put gray in his hair and assume a stoop.

And the purpose of the hoax? To make Tokubei send for fifty pieces of gold, of course. It was clever of the man to accuse the shrine priestess of fraud and pretend reluctance to let Tokubei send his message.

I couldn't even feel angry toward the man and his daughter—or mother, sister, wife, whatever. He could have killed me and taken my swords, which he clearly admired. Perhaps he was really a ronin and felt sympathetic toward another one.

When I returned to the house, Tokubei was looking resigned. "I've decided to send for the whole fifty gold pieces." He sighed.

"Don't bother," I said. "In fact we should be leaving as soon as possible. We shouldn't even stop here for a drink, especially not of wine."

Tokubei stared. "What do you mean? If I go back home, I'll find everything changed!"

"Nothing will be changed," I told him. "Your wife will be as young and beautiful as ever."

"I don't understand," he said. "Fifty years. . . ."

"It's a joke," I said. "The people here have a peculiar sense of humor, and they've played a joke on us."

Tokubei's mouth hung open. Finally he closed it with a snap. He stared at the host, and his face became first red and then purple. "You—you were trying to swindle me!" He turned furiously to me. "And you let them do this!"

"I'm not letting them," I pointed out. "That's why we're leaving right now."

"Are you going to let them get away with this?" demanded Tokubei. "They might try to swindle someone else!"

"They only went to this much trouble when they heard of the arrival of a fine fat fish like you," I said. I looked deliberately at the host. "I'm sure they won't be tempted to try the same trick again."

"And that's the end of your story?" asked Matsuzo. "You and Tokubei just went away? How did you know the so-called innkeeper wouldn't try the trick on some other luckless traveler?"

Zenta shook his head. "I didn't know. I merely guessed that once the trick was exposed, they wouldn't take the chance of trying it again. Of course I thought about revisiting the place to check if the people there were leading an honest life."

"Why didn't you?" asked Matsuzo. "Maybe we could go together. You've made me curious about that family now."

"Then you can satisfy your curiosity," said Zenta, smiling. He held his cup out for more tea, and the farmer's wife came forward to pour.

Only now she used both hands to hold the pot, and for the first time Matsuzo saw her left hand. He gasped. The hand had six fingers.

"Who was the old woman?" Zenta asked the farmer's wife.

"She was my grandmother," she replied. "Having six fingers is something that runs in my family."

At last Matsuzo found his voice. "You mean this is the very house you visited? This is the inn where time was lost?"

"Where we *thought* we lost fifty years," said Zenta. "Perhaps I should have warned you first. But I was almost certain that we'd be safe this time. And I see that I was right."

He turned to the woman again. "You and your husband are farmers now, aren't you? What happened to the man who was the host?"

"He's dead," she said quietly. "He was my brother, and he was telling you the truth when he said that he was a ronin. Two years ago he found work with another warlord, but he was killed in battle only a month later."

Matsuzo was peering at the pair of sliding doors, which he hadn't noticed before. "I see that you've put up the faded set of paintings. The winter scene is on the left side."

The woman nodded. "We sold the newer pair of doors. My husband said that we're farmers now and that people in our position

don't need valuable paintings. We used the money to buy some new farm implements."

She took up the teapot again. "Would you like another cup of tea?" she asked Matsuzo.

Staring at her left hand, Matsuzo had a sudden qualm. "I—I don't think I want any more."

Everybody laughed.

---

implements (im′plə mənts) *n., pl.* tools.

MEET LENSEY NAMIOKA

作者紹介・レンズィ波岡

When Lensey Namioka takes readers to "The Inn of Lost Time" in a Japan of long ago, she is an expert guide. Namioka says, "For my writings I draw heavily . . . on my husband's Japanese cultural heritage. My involvement with Japan started before my marriage, since my mother spent many years in Japan."

Namioka has written several novels, which include *Who's Hu* and *Village of the Vampire Cat*. Her young adult novel, *Island of Ogres*, was a 1989 School Library Journal Best Book for Young Adults. Her short play, "Herbal Nightmare," appears in a collection, *Center Stage: One-Act Plays for Teenage Readers and Actors*. Namioka's popular short story, "The All-American Slurp," appears in *Visions*, a collection of short stories for young adults edited by Donald Gallo.

RESPONDING TO Literature

THINK • TALK • WRITE

1 Did you predict the outcome of the story? If so, what clues helped you guess the ending? If not, what did you think the ending would be? Why? Jot some thoughts in your journal.

2 Why does Tokubei need an armed escort? What does this tell you about Japan at the time of the story?

3 The author says that "it is important to remember" that Tokubei could send to his clerks for extra money. What does this fact foreshadow?

4 Why do you think the second host insists that he thinks the priestess is a fraud? Do you trust him? Why or why not?

5 What does "The Inn of Lost Time" tell you about life in Japan in the 1500s? Use details to support your ideas.

ACTIVITIES

- **Write About Foreshadowing** Imagine that you recently visited an inn in an isolated area and had the same experience as the narrator's. Write your own version of "The Inn of Lost Time." Include clues that foreshadow the conclusion.

- **Dramatize a Scene** With a few classmates, choose a favorite scene from "The Inn of Lost Time" and act it out. Use props and costumes in your scene to help you recreate the roles.

VOCABULARY PRACTICE

Decide whether the vocabulary word in color is used correctly in each sentence below. Write *correct* or *incorrect* on a separate sheet of paper and explain your choice.

1 The **grueling** journey left us feeling fresh and rested.

2 She has a **stout** heart and is afraid of nothing.

3 He smiled with genuine delight as he answered me **ruefully.**

4 A hoe, a rake, and a shovel are gardening **implements.**

5 The choir sang beautifully in **unison.**

6 His face was **stern** as he joyfully announced his victory.

7 In his **delusion,** he thought he was a purple rabbit.

8 The **gruesome** war photographs were very disturbing.

9 The chanting crowds of soccer fans made a **poignant** picture.

10 Japanese merchants were once thought of as **parasites** on Japanese society.

Jim 1930 William Johnson
*National Museum of American
Art, Washington, D.C.*

Boy at the Window

Seeing the snowman standing all alone
In dusk and cold is more than he can bear.
The small boy weeps to hear the wind prepare
A night of gnashings and enormous moan.
His tearful sight can hardly reach to where
The pale-faced figure with bitumen eyes
Returns him such a god-forsaken stare
As outcast Adam gave to Paradise.

The man of snow is, nonetheless, content,
Having no wish to go inside and die.
Still, he is moved to see the youngster cry.
Though frozen water is his element,
He melts enough to drop from one soft eye
A trickle of the purest rain, a tear
For the child at the bright pane surrounded by
Such warmth, such light, such love, and so much fear.

— R I C H A R D   W I L B U R

SPOT on

DRAMA

William Shakespeare, perhaps the most famous playwright of all time, wrote, "The play's the thing." Surely there are many actors who would agree. For them, and for anyone else who loves drama, the painting below must have special meaning.

Oil on Canvas   Acc. 1970.43

Parson Weems' Fable   *1939   Grant Wood   Amon Carter Museum, Fort Worth, Texas*

Take a look at the people in this painting. What are they doing? What details does the artist provide?

Where and when do you think this scene is taking place onstage? What details suggest this?

What do you think is happening in this scene? What do you think the characters are saying to one another?

Think about other plays you have read or seen. Maybe you've even performed in a few yourself. What elements of those plays also apply to the one taking place on the stage in this picture?

LIGHT

ELEMENTS OF DRAMA

ACTS AND SCENES are parts of a drama. Acts are like chapters in a book. Scenes are divisions within acts.

CHARACTERS are people or animals who take part in a drama. The playwright can present these characters in different ways.

- *Direct characterization* takes place when the playwright tells you how a character looks, acts, and thinks.
- *Indirect characterization* takes place when the playwright lets you draw your own conclusions about a character based on how others react to him or her.

DIALOG is the conversation in a drama—the words a character says. In the written version of a play, dialog is not indicated by quotation marks. Words spoken by an actor follow the character's name.

PLOT is the series of related events in a drama. A plot is created through conflict, a struggle between opposing forces.

- *External conflicts* occur outside a character, such as with another person or a force of nature.
- *Internal conflicts* occur within a character's mind.

SETTING is the time and place in which the drama's action unfolds. The setting of a drama may be stated outright, or you may have to infer it from details given by the playwright.

STAGE DIRECTIONS tell the actors where and how to move and speak. Stage directions are included in parentheses and/or in italics in the script and often describe *scenery,* objects and painted scenes that help create the setting; *props,* physical items the actors use; *lighting,* the degree and type of light used on the stage.

THEME is the insight into life expressed by the playwright.

- *Stated themes* are mentioned outright in the drama.
- *Implied themes* must be inferred from the characters and their actions, the setting, and the conflict.

The following selection is a teleplay. Use what you've learned so far about drama to help you appreciate the playwright's craft.

DRAMA

THE MONSTERS ARE DUE ON MAPLE STREET

CONNECT TO LITERATURE

Suppose you heard that aliens disguised as humans were living on your street. How would you feel? What would you do? Who would you turn to for help and information? In your journal, jot down some thoughts. Then as you read "The Monsters Are Due on Maple Street," compare your reactions with those of the people in the play.

INTRODUCTION TO THE MODEL DRAMA

Drama is a form of literature meant to be performed. "The Monsters Are Due on Maple Street" is what is known as a *teleplay*, a drama written for television. What you will read is a *script*, the written version of a play. The script includes the *dialog*, the words spoken by the actors, and *stage directions*, instructions that tell the actors where to stand and how to say their lines. Like most plays, this one is divided into *acts*; each act is further divided into *scenes*. These divisions occur when the time or place of the action changes.

As you read this play, use the notes in the margin. The notes will help you see the structure of the play and show you how the basic elements of it are connected to each other.

DID YOU KNOW?

Mass panic occurred in 1938 when the Mercury Theater broadcast a radio play called *The War of the Worlds*. Presented as a news program, the play reported that Martians had landed in a small town in New Jersey. The play was so realistic that many listeners actually believed it; many fled their homes in panic, while thousands more flooded emergency offices with phone calls. Keep this in mind as you read the upcoming selection.

THE MONSTERS ARE DUE ON MAPLE STREET

BY ROD SERLING
ILLUSTRATED BY TIM BOWER

CHARACTERS

Narrator

Tommy

Steve Brand

Don Martin

Myra Brand, *Steve's wife*

Woman

Voice One

Voice Two

Voice Three

Voice Four

Voice Five

Pete Van Horn

Charlie

Sally, *Tommy's mother*

Man One

Les Goodman

Ethel Goodman,
    Les's wife

Man Two

Figure One

Figure Two

Ice cream vendor

Second Boy buying
    ice cream

Charlie's wife

Other Residents of
    Maple Street

The list of characters' names that appears at the beginning of a play is called the **cast of characters.**

ACT ONE

Plays are usually divided into **acts** and **scenes.** These divisions occur when the time or place of the action changes.

In a play, descriptions of the scenery and instructions for the actors and the director are called **stage directions.** Often, as here, stage directions are printed in italics and enclosed within parentheses.

(Fade in on a shot of the night sky. The various heavenly bodies stand out in sharp, sparkling relief. The camera moves slowly across the heavens until it passes the horizon and stops on a sign that reads "Maple Street." It is daytime. Then we see the street below. It is a quiet, tree-lined, small-town American street. The houses have front porches on which people sit and swing on gliders, talking across from house to house. STEVE BRAND *is polishing his car, which is parked in front of his house. His neighbor,* DON MARTIN, *leans against the fender watching him. An ice cream vendor riding a bicycle is just in the process of stopping to sell some ice cream to a couple of kids. Two women gossip on the front lawn. Another man is watering his lawn with a garden hose.*

As we see these various activities, we hear the NARRATOR's *voice.)*

NARRATOR: Maple Street, U.S.A., late summer. A tree-lined little world of front-porch gliders, hopscotch, the laughter of children, and the bell of an ice cream vendor.

(There is a pause, and the camera moves over to a shot of the ice cream vendor and two small boys who are standing alongside just buying ice cream.)

Words such as "the camera moves over," which are included in the stage directions, are called **camera directions.** They indicate that this play is a teleplay, which is a script for a television show.

NARRATOR: At the sound of the roar and the flash of the light, it will be precisely six-forty-three P.M. on Maple Street.

(At this moment TOMMY, *one of the two boys buying ice cream from the vendor, looks up to listen to a tremendous screeching roar from overhead. A flash of light plays on the faces of both boys and then moves down the street and disappears.*

Various people leave their porches or stop what they are doing to stare up at the sky.

STEVE BRAND, *the man who has been polishing his car, stands there transfixed, staring upwards. He looks at* DON MARTIN, *his neighbor from across the street.)*

STEVE: What was that? A meteor?

DON: That's what it looked like. I didn't hear any crash though, did you?

STEVE: Nope. I didn't hear anything except a roar.

MYRA *(from her porch):* What was that?

STEVE *(raising his voice and looking toward the porch):* Guess it was a meteor, honey. Came awful close, didn't it?

MYRA: Too close for my money! Much too close.

(The camera moves slowly across the various porches to people who stand there watching and talking in low conversing tones.)

NARRATOR: Maple Street. Six-forty-four P.M. on a late September evening. *(He pauses.)* Maple Street in the last calm and <u>reflective</u> moment *(pause)* before the monsters came!

(The camera takes us across the porches again. A man is replacing a light bulb on a front porch. He gets off his stool to flick the switch and finds that nothing happens.

Another man is working on an electric power mower. He plugs in the plug, flicks the switch of the mower off and on, but nothing happens.

Through a window we see a woman pushing her finger up and down on the dial hook of a telephone. Her voice sounds far away.)

WOMAN: Operator, operator, something's wrong on the phone, operator! *(MYRA BRAND comes out on the porch and calls to STEVE.)*

MYRA *(calling):* Steve, the power's off. I had the soup on the stove, and the stove just stopped working.

WOMAN: Same thing over here. I can't get anybody on the phone either. The phone seems to be dead.

(We look down again on the street. Small, mildly disturbed voices are heard coming from below.)

VOICE ONE: Electricity's off.

VOICE TWO: Phone won't work.

VOICE THREE: Can't get a thing on the radio.

VOICE FOUR: My power mower won't move, won't work at all.

VOICE FIVE: Radio's gone dead!

(PETE VAN HORN, a tall, thin man, is seen standing in front of his house.)

These lines tell what the characters say to each other and are called **dialog.** Unlike other forms of fiction, the plot of a play and the personalities of the characters are revealed through dialog alone.

---

reflective (ri flek′tiv) *adj.* given to or showing serious or careful thinking; thoughtful.

PETE: I'll cut through the back yard to see if the power's still on, on Floral Street. I'll be right back!

(He walks past the side of his house and disappears into the back yard.

The camera pans down slowly until we are looking at ten or eleven people standing around the street and overflowing to the curb and sidewalk. In the background is Steve Brand's car.)

STEVE: Doesn't make sense. Why should the power go off all of a sudden and the phone line?

DON: Maybe some kind of an electrical storm or something.

CHARLIE: That don't seem likely. Sky's just as blue as anything. Not a cloud. No lightning. No thunder. No nothing. How could it be a storm?

WOMAN: I can't get a thing on the radio. Not even the portable.

(The people again begin to murmur softly in wonderment.)

CHARLIE: Well, why don't you go downtown and check with the police, though they'll probably think we're crazy or something. A little power failure and right away we get all flustered and everything—

STEVE: It isn't just the power failure, Charlie. If it was, we'd still be able to get a broadcast on the portable.

(There is a murmur of reaction to this. STEVE looks from face to face and then at his car.)

STEVE: I'll run downtown. We'll get this all straightened out.

(He gets in the car and turns the key.

Looking through the open car door, we see the crowd watching STEVE from the other side. He starts the engine. It turns over sluggishly and then stops dead. He tries it again, and this time he can't get it to turn over. Then very slowly he turns the key back to "off" and gets out of the car.

The people stare at STEVE. *He stands for a moment by the car and then walks toward them.)*

STEVE: I don't understand it. It was working fine before—

DON: Out of gas?

STEVE *(shakes his head):* I just had it filled.

WOMAN: What's it mean?

CHARLIE: It's just as if *(pause)* as if everything had stopped. *(Then he turns toward* STEVE.*)* We'd better walk downtown.

(Another murmur of <u>assent</u> *to this.)*

STEVE: The two of us can go, Charlie. *(He turns to look back at the car.)* It couldn't be the meteor. A meteor couldn't do this.

(He and CHARLIE *exchange a look. Then they start to walk away from the group.*

TOMMY comes into view. He is a serious-faced young boy in spectacles. He stands halfway between the group and the two men, who start to walk down the sidewalk.)

TOMMY: Mr. Brand—you'd better not!

STEVE: Why not?

TOMMY: They don't want you to.

*(*STEVE *and* CHARLIE *exchange a grin, and* STEVE *looks back toward the boy.)*

STEVE: *Who* doesn't want us to?

TOMMY *(jerks his head in the general direction of the distant horizon):* Them!

STEVE: Them?

CHARLIE: Who are them?

TOMMY *(intently):* Whoever was in that thing that came by overhead.

*(*STEVE *knits his brows for a moment, cocking his head questioningly. His voice is intense.)*

assent (ə sent′) *n.* agreement.

STEVE: What?

TOMMY: Whoever was in that thing that came over. I don't think they want us to leave here.

(STEVE *leaves* CHARLIE, *walks over to the boy, and puts his hand on the boy's shoulder. He forces his voice to remain gentle.*)

STEVE: What do you mean? What are you talking about?

TOMMY: They don't want us to leave. That's why they shut everything off.

STEVE: What makes you say that? Whatever gave you that idea?

WOMAN *(from the crowd):* Now isn't that the craziest thing you ever heard?

TOMMY *(persistent but a little frightened):* It's always that way, in every story I ever read about a ship landing from outer space.

WOMAN *(to the boy's mother,* SALLY, *who stands on the fringe of the crowd):* From outer space yet! Sally, you better get that boy of yours up to bed. He's been reading too many comic books or seeing too many movies or something!

SALLY: Tommy, come over here and stop that kind of talk.

STEVE: Go ahead, Tommy. We'll be right back. And you'll see. That wasn't any ship or anything like it. That was just a . . . a meteor or something. Likely as not—*(He turns to the group, now trying very hard to sound more* optimistic *than he feels.)* No doubt it did have something to do with all this power failure and the rest of it. Meteors can do some crazy things. Like sunspots.

DON *(picking up the cue):* Sure. That's the kind of thing—like sunspots. They raise Cain with radio reception all over the world. And this thing being so close—why, there's no telling the sort of stuff it can do. *(He wets his lips and smiles nervously.)* Go ahead, Charlie. You and Steve go into town and see if that isn't what's causing it all.

(STEVE *and* CHARLIE *walk away from the group down the sidewalk as the people watch silently.*

---

optimistic (op′tə mis′tik) *adj.* inclined to look on the bright side.

TOMMY *stares at them, biting his lips, and finally calls out again.)*

TOMMY: Mr. Brand!

(The two men stop. TOMMY *takes a step toward them.)*

TOMMY: Mr. Brand . . . please don't leave here.

*(*STEVE *and* CHARLIE *stop once again and turn toward the boy. In the crowd there is a murmur of irritation and concern, as if the boy's words—even though they didn't make sense—were bringing up fears that shouldn't be brought up.*

TOMMY *is both frightened and defiant.)*

TOMMY: You might not even be able to get to town. It was that way in the story. Nobody could leave. Nobody except—

STEVE: Except who?

TOMMY: Except the people they sent down ahead of them. They looked just like humans. And it wasn't until the ship landed that—*(The boy suddenly stops, conscious of the people staring at him and his mother and of the sudden hush of the crowd.)*

SALLY *(in a whisper, sensing the* <u>antagonism</u> *of the crowd)*: Tommy, please son . . . honey, don't talk that way—

MAN ONE: That kid shouldn't talk that way . . . and we shouldn't stand here listening to him. Why this is the craziest thing I ever heard of. The kid tells us a comic book plot, and here we stand listening—

*(*STEVE *walks toward the camera and stops beside the boy.)*

STEVE: Go ahead, Tommy. What kind of story was this? What about the people they sent out ahead?

TOMMY: That was the way they prepared things for the landing. They sent four people. A mother and a father and two kids who looked just like humans . . . but they weren't.

(There is another silence as STEVE *looks toward the crowd and then toward* TOMMY. *He wears a tight grin.)*

STEVE: Well, I guess what we'd better do then is to run a check on the neighborhood and see which ones of us are really human.

---

antagonism (an tag′ə·niz′əm) *n.* active opposition or strong feeling against; hostility.

(There is laughter at this, but it's a laughter that comes from a desperate attempt to lighten the atmosphere. The people look at one another in the middle of their laughter.)

CHARLIE *(rubs his jaw nervously)*: I wonder if Floral Street's got the same deal we got. *(He looks past the houses.)* Where is Pete Van Horn anyway? Isn't he back yet?

(Suddenly there is the sound of a car's engine starting to turn over.
We look across the street toward the driveway of Les Goodman's house. He is at the wheel trying to start the car.)

SALLY: Can you get started, Les?

(LES GOODMAN gets out of the car, shaking his head.)

LES: No dice.

(He walks toward the group. He stops suddenly as, behind him, the car engine starts up all by itself. LES whirls around to stare at the car.
The car idles roughly, smoke coming from the exhaust, the frame shaking gently.
LES's eyes go wide, and he runs over to his car.
The people stare at the car.)

MAN ONE: He got the car started somehow. He got *his* car started!

(The people continue to stare, caught up by this revelation and wildly frightened.)

WOMAN: How come his car just up and started like that?

SALLY: All by itself. He wasn't anywheres near it. It started all by itself.

(DON MARTIN approaches the group and stops a few feet away to look toward Les's car.)

DON: And he never did come out to look at that thing that flew overhead. He wasn't even interested. *(He turns to the group, his face taut and serious.)* Why? Why didn't he come out with the rest of us to look?

CHARLIE: He always was an oddball. Him and his whole family. Real oddball.

DON: What do you say we ask him?

(The group starts toward the house. In this brief fraction of a moment, it takes the first step toward changing from a group into a mob. The group members begin to head purposefully across the street toward the house. STEVE *stands in front of them. For a moment their fear almost turns their walk into a wild stampede, but* STEVE'S *voice, loud,* <u>incisive</u>, *and commanding, makes them stop.)*

STEVE: Wait a minute . . . wait a minute! Let's not be a mob!

(The people stop, pause for a moment, and then, much more quietly and slowly, start to walk across the street.
    LES *stands alone facing the people.)*

LES: I just don't understand it. I tried to start it, and it wouldn't start. You saw me. All of you saw me.

(And now, just as suddenly as the engine started, it stops, and there is a long silence that is gradually intruded upon by the frightened murmuring of the people.)

LES: I don't understand. I swear . . . I don't understand. What's happening?

DON: Maybe you better tell us. Nothing's working on this street. Nothing. No lights, no power, no radio, *(then meaningfully)* nothing except one car—yours!

(The people's murmuring becomes a loud chant filling the air with accusations and demands for action. Two of the men pass DON *and head toward* LES, *who backs away from them against his car. He is cornered.)*

LES: Wait a minute now. You keep your distance—all of you. So I've got a car that starts by itself—well, that's a freak thing—I admit it. But does that make me a criminal or something? I don't know why the car works—it just does!

(This stops the crowd momentarily, and LES, *still backing away, goes toward his front porch. He goes up the steps and then stops, facing the mob.)*

LES: What's it all about, Steve?

STEVE *(quietly):* We're all on a monster kick, Les. Seems that the general impression holds that maybe one family isn't what we think

---

incisive (in sī'sive) *adj.* penetrating; sharp.

they are. Monsters from outer space or something. Different from us. Aliens from the vast beyond. *(He chuckles.)* You know anybody that might fit that description around here on Maple Street?

LES: What is this, a gag? *(He looks around the group again.)* This a practical joke or something?

(Suddenly the car engine starts all by itself, runs for a moment, and stops. One woman begins to cry. The eyes of the crowd are cold and accusing.)

LES: Now that's supposed to <u>incriminate</u> me, huh? The car engine goes on and off, and that really does it, doesn't it? *(He looks around at the faces of the people.)* I just don't understand it . . . any more than any of you do! *(He wets his lips, looking from face to face.)* Look, you all know me. We've lived here five years. Right in this house. We're no different from any of the rest of you! We're no different at all. . . . Really . . . this whole thing is . . . just weird—

WOMAN: Well, if that's the case, Les Goodman, explain why— *(She stops suddenly, clamping her mouth shut.)*

LES *(softly):* Explain what?

STEVE *(interjecting):* Look, let's forget this—

CHARLIE *(overlapping him):* Go ahead, let her talk. What about it? Explain what?

WOMAN *(a little reluctantly):* Well . . . sometimes I go to bed late at night. A couple of times . . . a couple of times I'd come out here on the porch, and I'd see Mr. Goodman here in the wee hours of the morning standing out in front of his house . . . looking up at the sky. *(She looks around the circle of faces.)* That's right, looking up at the sky as if . . . as if he were waiting for something, *(pauses)* as if he were looking for something.

(There's a murmur of reaction from the crowd again as LES *backs away.)*

LES: She's crazy. Look, I can explain that. Please . . . I can really explain that. . . . She's making it up anyway. *(Then he shouts.)* I tell you she's making it up!

---

incriminate (in krim′ə nāt′) *v.t.* suggest or show someone's guilt.

*(He takes a step toward the crowd, and they back away from him.
He walks down the steps after them, and they continue to back away.
Suddenly he is left completely alone, and he looks like a man caught in
the middle of a menacing circle as the scene slowly fades to black.)*

ACT TWO
Scene 1

(Fade in on Maple Street at night. On the sidewalk, little knots of people stand around talking in low voices. At the end of each conversation they look toward Les Goodman's house. From the various houses, we can see candlelight but no electricity. The quiet that blankets the whole area is disturbed only by the almost whispered voices of the people standing around. In one group CHARLIE *stands staring across at the Goodmans' house. Two men stand across the street from it in almost sentrylike poses.)*

SALLY *(in a small, hesitant voice):* It just doesn't seem right, though, keeping watch on them. Why . . . he was right when he said he was one of our neighbors. Why, I've known Ethel Goodman ever since they moved in. We've been good friends—

CHARLIE: That don't prove a thing. Any guy who'd spend his time lookin' up at the sky early in the morning—well, there's something wrong with that kind of person. There's something that ain't <u>legitimate</u>. Maybe under normal circumstances we could let it go by, but these aren't normal circumstances. Why, look at this street! Nothin' but candles. Why, it's like goin' back into the Dark Ages or somethin'!

*(*STEVE *walks down the steps of his porch, down the street to the Goodmans' house, and then stops at the foot of the steps.* LES *is standing there;* ETHEL GOODMAN *behind him is very frightened.)*

LES: Just stay right where you are, Steve. We don't want any trouble, but this time if anybody sets foot on my porch—that's what they're going to get—trouble!

STEVE: Look, Les—

LES: I've already explained to you people. I don't sleep very well at night sometimes. I get up and I take a walk and I look up at the sky. I look at the stars!

ETHEL: That's exactly what he does. Why, this whole thing, it's . . . it's some kind of madness or something.

---

legitimate (li jit′ə mit) *adj.* logically correct or valid.

STEVE *(nods grimly):* That's exactly what it is—some kind of madness.

CHARLIE'S VOICE *(shrill, from across the street):* You best watch who you're seen with, Steve! Until we get this all straightened out, you ain't exactly above suspicion yourself.

STEVE *(whirling around toward him):* Or you, Charlie. Or any of us, it seems. From age eight on up!

WOMAN: What I'd like to know is—what are we gonna do? Just stand around here all night?

CHARLIE: There's nothin' else we *can* do! *(He turns back, looking toward* STEVE *and* LES *again.)* One of 'em'll tip their hand. They got to.

STEVE *(raising his voice):* There's something you can do, Charlie. You can go home and keep your mouth shut. You can quit strutting around like a self-appointed judge and climb into bed and forget it.

CHARLIE: You sound real anxious to have that happen, Steve. I think we better keep our eye on you, too!

DON *(as if he were taking the bit in his teeth, takes a hesitant step to the front):* I think everything might as well come out now. *(He turns toward* STEVE.) Your wife's done plenty of talking, Steve, about how odd you are!

CHARLIE *(picking this up, his eyes widening):* Go ahead, tell us what she's said.

*(*STEVE *walks toward them from across the street.)*

STEVE: Go ahead, what's my wife said? Let's get it all out. Let's pick out every <u>idiosyncrasy</u> of every single man, woman, and child on the street. And then we might as well set up some kind of citizens' court. How about a firing squad at dawn, Charlie, so we can get rid of all the suspects. Narrow them down. Make it easier for you.

DON: There's no need gettin' so upset, Steve. It's just that . . . well . . . Myra's talked about how there's been plenty of nights you spent hours down in your basement workin' on some kind of radio or something. Well, none of us have ever seen that radio—

(By this time STEVE *has reached the group. He stands there defiantly.)*

---

idiosyncrasy (id′ē ō sing′krə sē) *n.* unusual or distinguishing characteristic of an individual, such as a habit or mannerism; peculiarity.

CHARLIE: Go ahead, Steve. What kind of "radio set" you workin' on? I never seen it. Neither has anyone else. Who do you talk to on that radio set? And who talks to you?

STEVE: I'm surprised at you, Charlie. How come you're so dense all of a sudden? *(He pauses.)* Who do I talk to? I talk to monsters from outer space. I talk to three-headed green men who fly over here in what look like meteors.

(MYRA BRAND steps down from the porch, bites her lip, calls out.)

MYRA: Steve! Steve, please. *(Then looking around, frightened, she walks toward the group.)* It's just a ham radio set, that's all. I bought him a book on it myself. It's just a ham radio set. A lot of people have them. I can show it to you. It's right down in the basement.

STEVE *(whirls around toward her):* Show them nothing! If they want to look inside our house—let them go and get a search warrant.

CHARLIE: Look, buddy, you can't afford to—

STEVE *(interrupting him):* Charlie, don't start telling me who's dangerous and who isn't and who's safe and who's a menace. *(He turns to the group and shouts.)* And you're with him, too—all of you! You're standing here all set to crucify—all set to find a scapegoat—all desperate to point some kind of a finger at a neighbor! Well now, look, friends, the only thing that's gonna happen is that we'll eat each other up alive—

(He stops abruptly as CHARLIE suddenly grabs his arm.)

CHARLIE *(in a hushed voice):* That's not the only thing that can happen to us.

(Down the street, a figure has suddenly materialized in the gloom. In the silence we hear the clickety-clack of slow, measured footsteps on concrete as the figure walks slowly toward them. One of the women lets out a stifled cry. SALLY grabs her boy, as do a couple of other mothers.)

TOMMY *(shouting, frightened):* It's the monster! It's the monster!

(Another woman lets out a wail, and the people fall back in a group staring toward the darkness and the approaching figure.

---

scapegoat (skāp′gōt) *n.* person or thing made to suffer for or bear the blame for the mistakes or wrongdoings of others.

The people stand in the shadows watching. DON MARTIN *joins them, carrying a shotgun. He holds it up.)*

DON: We may need this.

STEVE: A shotgun? *(He pulls it out of* DON's *hand.)* No! Will anybody think a thought around here! Will you people wise up! What good would a shotgun do against—

(The dark figure continues to walk toward them as the people stand there, fearful, mothers clutching children, men standing in front of their wives.)

CHARLIE *(pulling the gun from* STEVE's *hands):* No more talk, Steve. You're going to talk us into a grave! You'd let whatever's out there walk right over us, wouldn't yuh? Well, some of us won't!

*(*CHARLIE *swings around, raises the gun, and suddenly pulls the trigger. The sound of the shot explodes in the stillness.*
The figure suddenly lets out a small cry, stumbles forward onto his knees, and then falls forward on his face. DON, CHARLIE, *and* STEVE *race forward to him.* STEVE *is there first and turns the man over. The crowd gathers around them.)*

STEVE *(slowly looks up):* It's Pete Van Horn.

DON *(in a hushed voice):* Pete Van Horn! He was just gonna go over to the next block to see if the power was on—

WOMAN: You killed him, Charlie. You shot him dead!

CHARLIE *(looks around at the circle of faces, his eyes frightened, his face <u>contorted</u>):* But . . . but I didn't know who he was. I certainly didn't know who he was. He comes walkin' out of the darkness—how am I supposed to know who he was? *(He grabs* STEVE.*)* Steve—you know why I shot! How was I supposed to know he wasn't a monster or something? *(He grabs* DON.*)* We're all scared of the same thing. I was just tryin' to . . . tryin' to protect my home, that's all! Look, all of you, that's all I was tryin' to do. *(He looks down wildly at the body.)* I didn't know it was somebody we knew! I didn't know—

(There's a sudden hush and then an intake of breath in the group. Across the street all the lights go on in one of the houses.)

---

contorted (kən tôr′təd) *adj.* twisted out of shape.

WOMAN (*in a hushed voice*): Charlie . . . Charlie . . . the lights just went on in your house. Why did the lights just go on?

DON: What about it, Charlie? How come you're the only one with lights now?

LES: That's what I'd like to know.

(*Pausing, they all stare toward* CHARLIE.)

LES: You were so quick to kill, Charlie, and you were so quick to tell us who we had to be careful of. Well, maybe you had to kill. Maybe Pete there was trying to tell us something. Maybe he'd found out something and came back to tell us who there was amongst us we should watch out for—

(CHARLIE *backs away from the group, his eyes wide with fright.*)

CHARLIE: No . . . no . . . it's nothing of the sort! I don't know why the lights are on. I swear I don't. Somebody's pulling a gag or something.

(*He bumps against* STEVE, *who grabs him and whirls him around.*)

STEVE: A gag? A gag? Charlie, there's a dead man on the sidewalk, and you killed him! Does this thing look like a gag to you?

(CHARLIE *breaks away and screams as he runs toward his house.*)

CHARLIE: No! No! Please!

(*A man breaks away from the crowd to chase* CHARLIE. *As the man tackles him and lands on top of him, the other people start to run toward them.* CHARLIE *gets up, breaks away from the other man's grasp, and lands a couple of desperate punches that push the man aside. Then he forces his way, fighting, through the crowd and jumps up on his front porch.*

CHARLIE *is on his porch as a rock thrown from the group smashes a window beside him, the broken glass flying past him. A couple of pieces cut him. He stands there perspiring, rumpled, blood running down from a cut on the cheek. His wife breaks away from the group to throw herself into his arms. He buries his face against her. We can see the crowd* <u>converging</u> *on the porch.*)

VOICE ONE: It must have been him.

---

converging (kən vûrj′ing) *v.i.* coming together or tending to come together at a place or point.

VOICE TWO: He's the one.

VOICE THREE: We got to get Charlie.

(Another rock lands on the porch. CHARLIE *pushes his wife behind him, facing the group.)*

CHARLIE: Look, look I swear to you . . . it isn't me . . . but I do know who it is . . . I swear to you, I do know who it is. I know who the monster is here. I know who it is that doesn't belong. I swear to you I know.

DON (*pushing his way to the front of the crowd*): All right, Charlie, let's hear it!

(CHARLIE's *eyes dart around wildly.*)

CHARLIE: It's . . . it's . . .

MAN TWO (*screaming*): Go ahead, Charlie.

CHARLIE: It's . . . it's the kid. It's Tommy. He's the one!

(*There's a gasp from the crowd as we see* SALLY *holding the boy.* TOMMY *at first doesn't understand and then, realizing the eyes are all on him, buries his face against his mother.*)

SALLY (*backs away*): That's crazy! He's only a boy.

WOMAN: But he knew! He was the only one! He told us all about it. Well, how did he know? How could he have known?

(*Various people take this up and repeat the question.*)

VOICE ONE: How could he know?

VOICE TWO: Who told him?

VOICE THREE: Make the kid answer.

(*The crowd starts to converge around the mother, who grabs* TOMMY *and starts to run with him. The crowd starts to follow, at first walking fast, and then running after him.*

Suddenly Charlie's lights go off and the lights in other houses go on, then off.)

MAN ONE (*shouting*): It isn't the kid . . . it's Bob Weaver's house.

WOMAN: It isn't Bob Weaver's house, it's Don Martin's place.

CHARLIE: I tell you it's the kid.

DON: It's Charlie. He's the one.

(*People shout, accuse, and scream as the lights go on and off. Then, slowly, in the middle of this nightmarish confusion of sight and sound, the camera starts to pull away until, once again, we have reached the opening shot looking at the Maple Street sign from high above.*)

Scene 2

(The camera continues to move away while gradually bringing into focus a field. We see the metal side of a spacecraft that sits shrouded in darkness. An open door throws out a beam of light from the illuminated interior. Two figures appear, silhouetted against the bright lights. We get only a vague feeling of form.)

FIGURE ONE: Understand the procedure now? Just stop a few of their machines and radios and telephones and lawn mowers . . . Throw them into darkness for a few hours, and then just sit back and watch the pattern.

FIGURE TWO: And this pattern is always the same?

FIGURE ONE: With few variations. They pick the most dangerous enemy they can find . . . and it's themselves. And all we need do is sit back . . . and watch.

FIGURE TWO: Then I take it this place . . . this Maple Street . . . is not unique.

FIGURE ONE *(shaking his head):* By no means. Their world is full of Maple Streets. And we'll go from one to the other and let them destroy themselves. One to the other . . . one to the other . . . one to the other—

Scene 3

(The camera slowly moves up for a shot of the starry sky, and over this we hear the NARRATOR's voice.)

NARRATOR: The tools of conquest do not necessarily come with bombs and explosions and <u>fallout</u>. There are weapons that are simply thoughts, attitudes, prejudices—to be found only in the minds of men. For the record, prejudices can kill and suspicion can destroy. A thoughtless, frightened search for a scapegoat has a fallout all its own for the children . . . and the children yet unborn, *(a pause)* and the pity of it is . . . that these things cannot be confined to . . . The Twilight Zone!

(Fade to black.)

■ **fallout** (fôl′out′) *n.* particles that fall to the earth from the atmosphere, such as radioactive dust from a nuclear explosion or ash from a volcanic eruption or forest fire.

Meet Rod Serling

Rod Serling (1924–1975) was a screenwriter and television producer. He is best known for his TV series, *The Twilight Zone,* which ran for five years in the early 1960s and won an Emmy award. Serling created the show, wrote some of the episodes, and also appeared as host. As narrator, his dark suits and distinctive voice became as much a part of the show as the unusual story lines.

Throughout his career, Serling fought to get shows of social importance on TV. With *The Twilight Zone* he was able to tackle social problems by placing events and characters in a fantasy world. Many of his screenplays, including the one you just read, attacked prejudice in all its forms.

More Plays About Perspectives

- *Flowers for Algernon,* a full-length play by David Rogers (The Dramatic Publishing Co., 1969). Based on the poignant novel by Daniel Keyes, this is the story of a man who, as the result of a scientific experiment, undergoes a remarkable change and views the world with new vision.

- *The Miracle Worker* by William Gibson (Samuel French, 1985). It would take a worker of miracles to bring Helen Keller back into the world after disease had robbed her of her sight and hearing. Annie Sullivan is that miracle worker.

- *Great Expectations,* adapted from Dickens's novel by Barbara Field (Dramatists Play Service, 1984). Pip is helped to rise in the rigid class system of nineteenth-century England by a mysterious benefactor. Why has Pip been chosen and who is behind the change in his status?

RESPONDING TO
Literature

THINK • TALK • WRITE

1 Do you think it was reasonable for people to think that monsters had arrived on Maple Street? Jot down your reactions in your journal.

2 How does the crowd first react to the boy's story about aliens? What causes their feelings to change? Why do they eventually turn against Les Goodman?

3 Why do you think Steve Brand refuses to let his neighbors look at his ham radio? Is it because he feels guilty, or does he have some other reason? Use story details in your response.

5 What do you think the author's purpose might have been for writing this play? What would you say is the play's theme?

ACTIVITY

• **Write About Drama** Copy and complete this cause-and-effect pattern for the play "The Monsters Are Due on Maple Street."

CAUSE	EFFECT
Why Something Happens	What Happens

VOCABULARY PRACTICE

Copy these paragraphs on a separate sheet of paper. Replace each italicized word or term with the vocabulary word from the list that is closest to it in meaning.

reflective	incriminate
assent	legitimate
optimistic	idiosyncracy
antagonism	contorted
incisive	converging

On Tuesday, the thief was not feeling *hopeful*. The police were *coming together* around his apartment. Their *hostility* toward him was obvious. And, he had to admit, their contempt was *justified*.

There was enough evidence to *charge* him for a variety of crimes. He also had one *characteristic* which gave him away: his face became *twisted* when he lied.

The thief was in a *thoughtful* mood. Suddenly he had a *sharp* realization; he decided to give his *agreement* when the police came to take him. It would be so much easier that way!

WRITING

When it comes to today's entertainment media, what are your "picks" and "pans"? Do you think you could get others to share your perspective? Write a review of a movie, play, or TV program.

PREWRITE

Jot down the names of a few plays, movies, or programs you've seen, along with the reasons you liked or disliked them.

The writer of the sample here decided to organize her review of a school play as shown.

Now organize your notes. Decide what aspects of the performance to focus on.

> **POSITION STATEMENT:**
> <u>The Sleep-over Party</u> had everything going in its favor.
>
> **Reason:** the theme
> **Explanation:** A giant sleep-over party for teenagers in the school gymnasium was a great idea; everybody could relate to it.
>
> **Reason:** the characters
> **Explanation:** The three main characters are lively and full of

DRAFT

Here's the beginning of the draft about _The_ _over Party._ Does the writer state her positio   n clearly?

The writer states her position in the first sentence. She then proceeds to support her opinion.

> <u>A Review of the School Play</u>
>
> This year's comedy, <u>The Sleep-over Party,</u> was good. Most people were smiling as they left the school auditoryum after seeing this fast-paced delight. The jokes get funnier from act to act until the entire audience was laughing.

Now write your draft. Keep your audience in mind and remember to give reasons to support your opinions.

A REVIEW

REVISE

This writer decided to make her writing more dynamic.

The writer chose a stronger phrase to describe the play. If your purpose is to arouse the reader's enthusiasm, use colorful terms. ------------->

> This year's comedy, <u>The Sleep-over</u>
> *a smash hit*
> <u>Party,</u> was ~~good.~~ Most people were smil-
> ing as they left the school auditoryum af-
> ter seeing this fast-paced delight. The
> jokes get funnier from act to act until
> *howling*
> the entire audience was ~~laughing.~~

Does this change give a more vivid feeling of the audience's enjoyment of the play? ------------->

Revise your draft. Have you supported your position with reasons?

PROOFREAD

The writer proofread her review and caught these errors:

Putting commas where they belong makes sentences easier to read and makes their meaning clearer. ----------->

> This year's comedy, <u>The Sleep-over</u>
> *a smash hit*
> <u>Party,</u> was good. Most people were smil-
> *auditorium*
> ing as they left the school (auditoryum) af-
> ter seeing this fast-paced delight. The
> *got*
> jokes (get) funnier from act to act, until
> *howling*
> the entire audience was ~~laughing.~~

Proofread your piece several times. Use standard proofreading marks.

PUBLISH

What's the best way to present your work? You might want to read it aloud to the class.

WRITING

USING CLAUSES TO VARY SENTENCES

ENRICH YOUR WRITING OF **REVIEWS.**

Simple sentences that are all about the same length can make for dull reading. You will want to vary your sentence structure by adding clauses to some of your sentences.

Read both paragraphs. Notice how the writer combined two sentences by making one a clause of the other.

Paragraph 1

    My sister and I noticed two actors in the second scene of the film. The actors were chatting in the background. They dominated the scene. We knew that one day they would be famous.

Paragraph 2

    My sister and I noticed two actors in the second scene of the film. The actors were chatting in the background, but they dominated the scene. We knew that one day they would be famous.

PRACTICE 1 Respond on a separate sheet of paper.

1 What is the effect of sentence combining in the second paragraph?

2 Rewrite the second paragraph. Add a new sentence that has more than one clause.

SENTENCES AND CLAUSES

REMEMBER THESE RULES ABOUT SENTENCES AND CLAUSES WHEN YOU ARE WRITING **REVIEWS.**

- Each of the simple sentences in a compound sentence is called an independent clause. A comma precedes the conjunction that joins the independent clauses in a compound sentence. A semicolon is used if there is no conjunction.

- In a compound sentence, a semicolon precedes a conjunctive adverb, such as *however,* and a comma follows it.

PRACTICE 2 Underline the independent clauses and add commas and semicolons when necessary.

1 The film wasn't a success it closed after two days.

2 Some people enjoyed it but most left before it ended.

3 We liked the film's beginning however the plot soon became confused.

4 One critic praised the film he loved the action scenes.

ADJECTIVE CLAUSES

USE THESE RULES ABOUT ADJECTIVE CLAUSES WHEN YOUR ARE WRITING **REVIEWS.**

- An adjective clause describes a noun or pronoun in the independent clause of a complex sentence.

- An essential clause is an adjective clause necessary to the meaning of the word it modifies. Don't use commas to set off the clause. A nonessential clause is an adjective clause that is not necessary to the meaning of the word it modifies. Use commas to set it off.

PRACTICE 3 On a separate piece of paper, rewrite the sentences. Underline the adjective clauses and use commas where necessary.

1 This movie which offers a laugh a minute is expertly directed.

2 The films that she starred in were all successful.

3 The film was directed by the man who was also the star.

4 The action scenes which all looked fake made the audience yawn.

WRITING A HOW-TO GUIDE

Think about the times you've explained to someone how to do or make something. Perhaps one of those people even told you what a great teacher you were! If so, then you're a natural writer of how-to guides.

PREWRITE

How will you plan your how-to guide? Think about something you know how to do well and would like to share with others. A flowchart can help you organize your thoughts. If you were instructing a group of eight-year-olds how to make a "blotto" and then to share their designs and tell what they see, your flowchart might look like the one here.

DRAFT Keep your purpose in mind when you write your draft. Think about this sentence: When my audience reads my how-to guide, they'll know how to _____.

REVISE Take some time out before you revise. A fresh eye will help you see places where you need to make changes. Are your steps in the right order?

PROOFREAD Ask a friend to check your how-to guide for mistakes.

PUBLISH Publish a how-to journal. You may wish to prepare your work on a computer and then illustrate the printout.

Gather materials:
paper, spoon, paint.

↓

Cover work area
with newspaper
and yourself with
an old shirt.

↓

Fold paper in half;
then open paper and lay flat.

↓

With spoons sprinkle paint
on one half of paper. Fold
paper along fold line
and press smoothly.

↓

Open paper and show your
design to friends. Ask them
to tell what they see.

┌──────── ▶ *Proofreading Alert!* ────────┐
Use a comma after an introductory participial phrase.
Check page 204 in *Writing and Language Handbook.*
└───┘

PROJECTS

CREATE A BULLETIN BOARD

REMEMBER TO: • PREWRITE • DRAFT • REVISE • PROOFREAD • PUBLISH

Find different ways of looking at the same thing. Use photos, drawings, and writing to show different perspectives.

Work in groups to decide on a subject and a way of presenting it. First talk about what it means to see or know something from different perspectives. Then brainstorm examples. Once you've focused on a topic, organize your information using a diagram like this one:

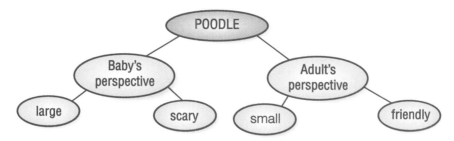

MAKE A POSTER

REMEMBER TO: • PREWRITE • DRAFT • REVISE • PROOFREAD • PUBLISH

Create a poster that will change the way people in your school or community look at an issue. Work in groups with classmates whose viewpoints on an important issue are similar to yours. Discuss how you see things and how others see them differently. Explore how you might change the minds of people with different ideas. You can organize your thoughts using a chart like the one here. Get permission to display your posters at school or at a community center.

Issue	Visual	Verbal
Cleaner streets	1. Dirty, litter-filled street 2. Person walking along street, dropping litter into litter basket 3. Clean street	A small drop in the bucket can make a huge difference.

VIEWP

DOES VIOLENCE IN THE MEDIA AFFECT HOW PEOPLE ACT?

Every day we can witness acts of horrific violence in our own homes—just by turning on our television sets. Critics have accused a variety of media—including television, movies, popular music, and video games—of being too violent. People of all ages, even very young children, experience this violence every day. The question is, how are they affected by what they see and hear?

CONSIDER THIS ISSUE: One of your classmates has written an editorial in the school paper blaming violence in the media for many violent crimes committed by teenagers. The editorial has sparked a debate among students. Do you think media violence influences people's actions? Consider the issue.

- Shouldn't people who commit violent acts accept responsibility for them?
- Isn't there a difference between showing violence and encouraging viewers to be violent?
- If you know the difference between right and wrong, can you really be influenced by violence in the media?
  - Are we more influenced by what our friends do or by what we watch on a movie screen?

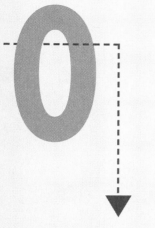

Read the following viewpoints about whether violence in the media affects how people act. Decide which one is closest to your personal opinion. Then think of some arguments of your own to support the position you choose.

VIEWPOINT 1

I don't think violence in the media affects the way people act.

- It takes more than *watching* violence to make people behave in a violent way.
- Millions of people are exposed to violence in the media every day, but only a small percentage of them commit violent acts.
- People know the difference between real life and fiction.

VIEWPOINT 2

I do think that violence in the media influences the way people act.

- Many people who are exposed from an early age to violence in the media have been numbed by what they see and hear, with the result that they are not horrified by violence in real life.
- The media glamorize violence and make it attractive to many viewers and listeners.
- Because the media bring violence into our lives as an almost personal experience, people copy the violent acts they see and hear.

VIEWPOINT 3

I think media violence is just one of many factors that influence some people to behave violently.

- Violence in the media can influence people who are already prone to violence.
- Some people can't distinguish between right and wrong, and they see violently behaving fictional characters as role models.
- Violence in the media reinforces the violence people sense around them.

WHAT DO YOU THINK?

Do you agree with one of the viewpoints above, or do you have another? Discuss your views with a small group. Then write a letter to the editor of your school paper expressing your opinions.

real life
CONNECT

PERSPECTIVES: Your point of view, or perspective, is affected by many factors.

Think about the last time you went to a movie with a friend. You both saw the same film, but you may have had very different reactions to it. In "The Rocket" by Ray Bradbury, the Bodini family learns that it's not a question of *what* you see but of *how* you see it.

Our tendency to experience the same event in different ways is strongly influenced by what we read, hear, and see in periodicals and on television. Each year the advertising industry spends millions of dollars to influence how we feel about the products it represents. The chart at left shows how this money is spent.

A chart or **table** highlights key information about a topic. A chart includes both words and numbers; a table, with the exception of the first column, includes only numbers. The title of the chart or table is a summary of the main idea.

MEDIA SPENDING BY SOME LEADING ADVERTISERS: 1988

ADVERTISER	MEASURED				ESTIMATED UNMEASURED
	PRINT	TV	RADIO	OUTDOOR	
Procter & Gamble	$102,640,000	$684,158,000	$41,311,000	$ 682,000	$678,100,000
General Motors	293,515,000	573,943,000	78,440,000	2,997,000	345,105,000
Eastman Kodak	42,615,000	194,323,000	6,551,000	557,000	491,900,000
McDonald's	6,899,000	387,798,000	5,158,000	6,306,000	322,159,000
PepsiCo	9,425,000	414,802,000	32,140,000	3,080,000	252,900,000
Kellogg	23,335,000	378,411,000	73,000	70,000	281,200,000
Ford Motor	155,574,000	255,383,000	23,870,000	2,157,000	132,800,000
American Telephone and Telegraph	104,021,000	224,627,000	18,494,000	361,000	200,000,000
General Mills	43,623,000	309,120,000	7,020,000	295,000	110,000,000
Johnson & Johnson	38,393,000	195,263,000	1,402,000	77,000	233,700,000
J.C. Penney	87,587,000	54,442,000	11,503,000	49,000	273,000,000
Coca Cola	13,993,000	198,758,000	15,696,000	2,538,000	154,100,000
Mars	15,731,000	163,430,000	8,673,000	23,000	151,800,000
Sara Lee	49,038,000	105,756,000	1,586,000	64,000	170,500,000
Macy's	184,463,000	15,651,000	289,000	376,000	108,100,000
Walt Disney	44,865,000	103,050,000	7,823,000	543,000	144,300,000
Hershey Foods	19,362,000	69,137,000	10,001,000	32,000	200,100,000

IONS

THINK • TALK • WRITE

Here are three activities in which you use a chart or table. Think of other situations in which you might use them. Then choose an activity below or one of your own and talk or write about it.

PROJECT 1

CHARTS AND TABLES Charts and tables highlight important information in magazine and newspaper articles, textbooks, and other reference sources. Each student should bring three examples of charts or tables to class. Work in small groups to answer the following questions: What is the title of each chart or table? How does each graphic relate to the article or chapter it accompanies? What kinds of information does each chart or table compare?

PROJECT 2

CHARTS AND GRAPHS DEBATE The same information can be shown in a variety of ways on a chart or a graph. Choose a topic about advertising for a class debate. Divide into two teams. Each team should research the topic and create charts and graphs to support its position. Elect three students from each side to debate the topic. Each team member speaks for three minutes. Each team has one minute to reply to the other team's arguments. Vote to decide which team won the debate.

PROJECT 3

QUESTIONS AND ANSWERS Find a chart or table in a textbook or in a newspaper or magazine article. Make up six questions based on the information in the chart or table. Then exchange papers with a partner. Use your partner's chart or table to find the answers to the six questions.

Glossary

This glossary can help you to pronounce and find out the meanings of words in this book that you may not know. The meanings given here are the ones that apply to the words as they are used in the selections in this book.

The words are listed in alphabetical order. Guide words tell you the first and last words on the page. The pronunciation respelling is in parentheses following the word. You can understand the pronunciation respelling by using the key that appears at the bottom of every right-hand page.

When a word has more than one syllable, a dark accent mark (′) shows which syllable is stressed. In some words, a light accent mark (′) shows which syllable has a lighter stress.

The following abbreviations are used in this glossary: *n.* noun, *v.* verb, *v.t.* transitive verb, *v.i.* intransitive verb, *adj.* adjective, *adv.* adverb, *prep.* preposition, *pl.* plural, *interj.* interjection.

The entries in the glossary are based on entries in *The Macmillan/McGraw-Hill School Dictionary 2.*

A

abduction (ab duk′shən) *n.* kidnapping.

aberration (ab′ə rā′shən) *n.* something that is abnormal.

abridge (ə brij′) *v.t.* make less; lessen; restrict.

abruptly (ə brupt′lē) *adv.* suddenly; without warning.

abundant (ə bun′dənt) *adj.* more than enough; plentiful.

abusive (ə bū′siv) *adj.* harmful; injurious; mistreating with cruelty or roughness.

accompaniment (ə kum′pə ni mənt) *n.* thing that goes along with something else.

accomplishment (ə kom′plish mənt) *n.* something done successfully; achievement.

adamant (ad′ə mənt) *adj.* not changing position at all; totally unyielding.

adherence (ad hîr′əns) *n.* firm attachment; faithful support.

adjourned (ə jūrnd′) *adj.* ended for the time being.

adroitness (ə droit′nes) *n.* act of being smoothly skillful; deft; clever.

adversaries (ad′vər ser′ēz) *n., pl.* groups that are hostile toward or competing with each other; opponents or enemies.

advocated (ad′və kā′tid) *v.t.* pled in favor of; supported.

agility (ə jil′i tē) *n.* quickness and ease in motion or thought; nimbleness.

alabaster (al′ə bas′tər) *n.* smooth, whitish stone.

alcove (al′kōv) *n.* small room or recess opening off a larger room.

allocate (al′ə kāt′) *v.t.* set aside (for a specific purpose).

allusion (ə lü′zhən) *n.* mention made in passing.

ally (al′i) *n.* person, nation, or group united with another for a common purpose.

ambiguous (am big′ū əs) *adj.* unclear; vague.

ambition (am bish′ən) *n.* strongly desired goal.

analogy (ə nal′ə jē) *n.* comparison or parallel.

anchorage (ang′kər ij) *n.* something that fastens or holds securely.

annihilation (ə nī′ə la′shən) *n.* total destruction.

antagonism (an tag′ə niz′əm) *n.* active opposition or strong feeling against; hostility.

antiseptic (an′ti sep′tik) *adj.* free from germs.

apertures (ap′ər chərz) *n., pl.* holes, gaps, or other openings.

appalling (ə pô′ling) *adj.* horrible; shocking; dreadful.

apparatus (a′pə rat′əs) *n.* a device or mechanism used for a particular purpose.

appellate (ə pel′it) *adj.* having the power to hear and rule on legal appeals and to review the decisions of lower courts.

appointment (ə point′mənt) *n.* act of naming someone to an office or position, or state of having been named.

apprentice (ə pren′tis) *n.* person who works for a skilled worker in order to learn a trade or art.

arduous (är′jü əs) *adj.* requiring great effort or energy; difficult.

aristocrat (ə ris′tə krat′) *n.* person who is considered to be superior or outstanding because of wealth, intelligence, or culture.

arnica (är′ni kə) *n.* medicinal liquid made from the dried flowers and roots of plants bearing clusters of yellow flowers.

arraignment (ə rān′mənt) *n.* appearance before a judge in which charges are formally made.

articulate (är tik′yə lit) *adj.* spoken clearly in distinct syllables and words.

ascribed (ə skribd′) *v.t.* regarded (something) as coming from a particular cause or source.

assent (ə sent′) *n.* agreement.

assert (ə sûrt′) *v.t.* insist upon recognition of.

assess (ə ses′) *v.t.* evaluate.

assiduously (ə sij′ü əs lē) *adv.* attentively, diligently.

attire (ə tīr′) *n.* clothes.

attributes (at′rə būts′) *n., pl.* qualities; characteristics.

attributing (ə trib′ūt ing) *v.t.* considering as belonging to, produced by, or resulting from.

aura (ôr′ə) *n.* distinctive character or atmosphere arising from and surrounding a person or thing.

authentic (ô then′tik) *adj.* being what it appears to be; genuine; real.

avenge (ə venj′) *v.t.* get revenge for.

avid (av′id) *adj.* eager; enthusiastic.

B

barracks (bar′əks) *n.* building or set of buildings for housing soldiers or other military personnel.

beatifically (bē′ə tif′ik lē) *adv.* with great happiness; blissfully.

beckoned (bek′ənd) *v.t.* signaled or summoned (someone) by a sign or gesture.

bellows (bel′ōz) *pl. n.* device which produces a strong air current, used for making a fire burn faster.

benevolent (bə nev′ə lənt) *adj.* doing or desiring to do good; kindly; generous.

bereft (bi reft′) *adj.* deprived.

billy (bil′ē) *n.* short heavy club or stick.

bivouac (biv′ü ak′) *n.* temporary camp or shelter.

blatant (blā′tənt) *adj.* impossible to overlook; very obvious; conspicuous.

blissful (blis′fəl) *adj.* full of great happiness.

blithely (blīth′lē) *adv.* thoughtlessly; with no concern.

board (bôrd) *n.* meals provided regularly for pay.

boggled (bog′əld) *v.i.* hesitated, as from doubt or confusion.

---

at; **ā**pe; **fä**r; **câ**re; **e**nd; **mē**; **i**t; **ī**ce; **p**î**erce; **h**o**t; **ō**ld; **sô**ng, **fô**rk; **oi**l; **ou**t; **u**p; **ū**se; **rü**le; **pu**ll; **tû**rn; **ch**in; si**ng**; **sh**op; **th**in; **th**is; **hw** in **wh**ite; **zh** in trea**s**ure. The symbol **ə** stands for the unstressed vowel sound heard in **a**bout, tak**e**n, penc**i**l, lem**o**n, and circ**u**s.

bounty (boun'tē) *n.* gift generously given.

brazier (brā'zhər) *n.* metal container to hold charcoal, used for heating, lighting, or cooking.

breaching (brē'ching) *v.i.* breaking the water by leaping out.

breed (brēd) *n.* particular strain or variety of a species of plant or animal, produced and maintained by controlled mating.

buoyant (boi'ənt) *adj.* able to float.

burly (bûr'lē) *adj.* big, strong, and sturdy.

C

cannibalism (kan'ə bə liz'əm) *n.* act or practice of eating the flesh of one's own kind.

capacity (kə pas'i tē) *n.* ability or power to do something.

caress (kə res') *n.* light, soothing touch.

carnage (kär'nij) *n.* great and bloody slaughter, as in battle.

cauldron (kôl'drən) *n.* large kettle or boiler.

cervical vertebrae (sûr'vi kəl vûr'tə brē') bones of the upper spine.

chaperones (shap'ə rōnz') *n., pl.* older people who attend and supervise a social gathering of young people.

chastened (chā'sənd) *adj.* brought under control by punishment.

chemises (chə mē'zəz) *n., pl.* loose, shirt-like undergarments worn by women.

chifforobe (shif'ə rōb) *n.* piece of furniture or closet for keeping clothes.

chivalry (shiv'əl rē) *n.* qualities of an ideal knight, such as honor, courtesy, and skill in battle.

choleric (kol'ər ik) *adj.* easily irritated or angered.

civilized (siv'ə lizd') *adj.* brought out of a primitive or savage state or condition; educated in the arts, science, government, or the like.

clemency (klem'ən sē) *n.* mercy in punishing or judging.

colleague (kol'ēg) *n.* fellow member of a profession or other group.

competently (kom'pi tənt lē) *adv.* in a knowledgeable or capable manner.

complied (kəm plīd') *v.t.* acted in agreement, as with a rule.

compulsory (kəm pul'sə rē) *adj.* required.

concessions (kən sesh'ənz) *n., pl.* acts of granting or conceding.

conciliation (kən sil'ē ā'shən) *n.* act of overcoming hostility; truce.

concocted (kon kok'tid) *v.t.* put together; devised.

concurrently (kən kûr'ənt lē) *adv.* at the same time.

confident (kon'fi dənt) *adj.* firmly trusting; certain.

confiscated (kon'fis kā'tid) *v.t.* seized by authority.

confront (kən frunt') *v.t.* face boldly or with defiance.

congealed (kən jēld') *v.i.* changed from a liquid to a solid by cooling or freezing.

conscientious (kon'shē en'shəs) *adj.* guided by a sense of right and wrong.

conspiratorial (kən spir'ə tôr'ē əl) *adj.* secretive, as if planned together.

contemplating (kon'təm plāt'ing) *v.t.* giving a great deal of attention to; looking at or thinking about (something) long and carefully.

contemporaries (kən tem'pə rer'ēz) *n., pl.* people who belong to or live at the same time as another or others.

contended (kən ten'ded) *v.t.* argued.

contorted (kən tôr'tid) *adj.* twisted out of shape; distorted.

contraption (kən trap'shən) *n. Informal.* mechanical device; gadget; contrivance.

convene (kən vēn') *v.t.* cause to assemble.

converging (kən vûrj'ing) *v.i.* coming together or tending to come together at a place or point.

convulsed (kən vulsd') *v.t.* shook or disturbed violently.

coronet (kôr'ə net') *n.* small, decorated crown.

corrasion (kə'ra zhən) *n.* process by which rocks and soil are worn away by materials pushed along the surface by wind, waves, streams, or glaciers.

corrupt (kə rupt') *adj.* influenced by bribery; dishonest.

covert (kō'vərt) *adj.* secret; hidden.

crescendo (kri shen'dō) *n.* gradual increase in loudness or force.

Cro-Magnon man (krō mag'non man) *n.* member of a prehistoric group of humans distinguished by a well-developed brain; tall, erect stature; and the use of stone and bone implements.

crone (krōn) *n.* withered old woman.

crumpets (krum'pits) *n., pl.* soft, unsweetened batter cakes baked on a griddle, then usually toasted and buttered.

crustaceans (kru stā'shənz) *n., pl.* shellfish such as lobsters, shrimp, clams, and barnacles.

curator (kyu̇ rā'tər) *n.* manager of exhibits at a museum or gallery.

curdled (kûr'dəld) *adj.* soured.

curfew (kûr'fū) *n.* order or rule requiring certain persons to be indoors or at home before a fixed time, especially at night.

currency (kur'ən sē) *n.* money that is used in a country.

curtly (kûrt'lē) *adv.* in a rudely brief or abrupt manner.

D

dais (dā'is) *n.* slightly raised platform, as for a throne.

damsels (dam'zəlz) *n., pl.* young girls; maidens.

davenport (dav'ən pôrt') *n.* large, upholstered sofa.

degenerate (di jen'ə rāt') *v.i.* become worse in condition; deteriorate.

delicacy (del'i kə sē) *n.* fineness of structure, quality, or form.

delusion (di lü'zhən) *n.* false idea or belief.

denunciation (di nun'sē ā'shən) *n.* public expression of disapproval; open condemnation.

deplored (di plôrd') *v.t.* disapproved of strongly.

desolate (des'ə lit) *adj.* left alone; without companionship.

dexterity (dek ster'i tē) *n.* skill in using the hands, body, or mind.

diaspora (dī'as pər ə) *n.* scattering.

diatoms (dī'ə tomz') *n., pl.* any of a large group of microscopic, one-celled algae that live in fresh and salt water and have cell walls made up mostly of silica.

dim sum (dim'sum') *n.* in Chinese cooking, a dish consisting usually of steamed or fried dumplings stuffed with meats, fish, or vegetables.

discern (di sûrn') *v.t.* make out or recognize.

discouraged (dis kûr'ijd) *adj.* disheartened.

disdain (dis dān') *n.* dislike for something or someone thought of as unworthy or beneath one; scorn.

dismay (dis mā') *n.* feeling of alarm or uneasiness; frightened amazement.

dispatched (di spacht') *v.t.* sent off quickly to a certain place or for a certain purpose.

dispelled (di speld') *v.t.* drove away or caused to disappear.

dispenses (di spen'səz) *v.t.* gives out in portions; distributes.

dominate (dom'ə nāt') *v.t.* have the main influence or control over.

downtrodden (doun'trod'ən) *adj.* abused or oppressed, as by those in power.

---

at; **ā**pe; f**är**; c**âr**e; **e**nd; m**ē**; **i**t; **ī**ce; p**î**erce; h**o**t; **ō**ld; s**ô**ng, f**ô**rk; **oi**l; **ou**t; **u**p; **ū**se; r**ü**le; p**u̇**ll; t**û**rn; **ch**in; si**ng**; **sh**op; **th**in; **th**is; **hw** in **wh**ite; **zh** in trea**s**ure. The symbol **ə** stands for the unstressed vowel sound heard in **a**bout, tak**e**n, penc**i**l, lem**o**n, and circ**u**s.

dredged (drejd) *v.t.* cleared out with a large mechanical scoop or net.

drought (drout) *n.* long period of dry weather; prolonged lack of rainfall.

E

eavesdrop (ēvz'drop') *v.i.* listen to the private conversation of others without their knowing it.

ebony (eb'ə nē) *n.* hard, black wood, used especially for piano keys.

eddy (ed'ē) *v.i.* move in a circular or whirling motion.

edible (ed'ə bəl) *adj.* fit to eat.

elated (i lā'tid) *adj.* in high spirits.

elegy (el'i jē) *n.* mournful or sad poem or musical work, especially one written to mourn someone who has died.

eloquent (el'ə kwənt) *adj.* having or showing the ability to use language effectively.

eluded (i lü'did) *v.t.* avoided or escaped, as by cleverness or trickery; evaded.

embezzlers (em bez'əl ərz) *n., pl.* people who steal or have stolen money entrusted to their care.

emerged (i mûrjd') *v.i.* came into being or notice.

emigration (em'i grā'shən) *n.* act or process of leaving one place to go live in another.

eminent (em'ə nənt) *adj.* distinguished.

emitted (i mi'tid) *v.t.* sent forth; gave off.

empathy (em'pə thē) *n.* sharing of another's feelings or state of mind without actually going through the same experiences.

epitaph (ep'i taf') *n.* brief statement in memory of a dead person, usually inscribed on a tombstone or monument.

equitable (ek'wi tə bəl) *adj.* fair or just.

ermine (ûr'min) *n.* white winter fur of a weasel whose fur is brown during the rest of the year.

erratically (i rat'i kəl lē) *adv.* acting or moving in an irregular or confused way.

essence (es'əns) *n.* something that makes a thing what it is; necessary and basic part.

essential (i sen'shəl) *adj.* very important or necessary.

evident (ev'i dənt) *adj.* easily seen or understood; clear.

exasperation (eg zas'pə rā'shən) *n.* state of being greatly irritated.

exhilarated (eg zil'ə rā'tid) *adj.* joyfully excited.

exhortation (eg'zôr tā'shen) *n.* act of trying to persuade by appeal, argument, or warning; something that urges strongly.

exile (eg'zīl) *n.* state of being sent away from one's country or home by law.

exotic (eg zot'ik) *adj.* of or belonging to another part of the world.

expiated (ek'spē ā'tid) *v.t.* made amends for; atoned for.

exploitation (ek'sploi tā'shən) *n.* unjust or unfair use for selfish reasons.

exploits (ek'sploits) *n., pl.* heroic deeds or acts.

expound (ek spound') *v.t.* set forth in detail; explain.

extravagantly (ek strav'ə gənt lē) *adv.* wastefully; beyond reasonable limits.

F

fallout (fôl'out') *n.* particles that fall to the earth from the atmosphere, such as radioactive dust from a nuclear explosion or ash from a volcanic eruption or forest fire.

fatal (fā'təl) *adj.* causing death.

fauna (fô'nə) *n.* animals of a particular region or environment.

feasibility (fē'zə bil'i tē) *n.* ability to be done successfully; practicality.

feeble (fē'bəl) *adj.* lacking physical strength.

feigned (fānd) *v.t.* pretended; put on a false appearance.

feloniously (fə lō'nē əs lē) *adv.* in a manner of, relating to, or classified as a criminal act, designated by law to be more serious than a misdemeanor.

fetid (fet′id) *adj.* having a bad smell; stinking.

finesse (fi nes′) *n.* refinement or skill in doing something.

flammable (flam′ə bəl) *adj.* able to be set on fire easily; combustible.

flanked (flangkt) *v.t.* located at the side of.

floes (flōz) *n., pl.* masses or sheets of floating ice.

flora (flôr′ə) *n.* plant life of a particular region or environment.

flourished (flûr′isht) *v.i.* grew or developed strongly; thrived.

forge (fôrj) *v.t.* make or form.

formidable (fôr′mi də bəl) *adj.* causing fear, dread, or awe.

fortitude (fôr′ti tüd′) *n.* courage or strength in the face of pain, danger, or misfortune.

French-seams (french′sēmz) *n.* sewing technique used to reinforce seams.

furrow (fûr′ō) *n.* long, narrow groove or channel made in the ground by a plow.

furtive (fûr′tiv) *adj.* secretive; sly.

futile (fū′təl) *adj.* useless or hopeless; ineffective.

G

gaunt (gônt) *adj.* extremely thin and with sunken eyes, as from hunger or illness; haggard.

gilded (gild′əd) *adj.* covered with a thin layer of gold; sparkling as if covered with a thin layer of gold.

gnarled (närld) *adj.* rough or rugged in appearance.

gnaw (nô) *v.i.* cause constant discomfort, pain, or trouble to.

gratified (grat′ə fīd) *adj.* pleased.

grieving (grē′ving) *v.* mourning; feeling deep sadness.

grievous (grē′vəs) *adj.* causing deep sorrow or great pain.

grueling (grü′ə ling) *adj.* very difficult or punishing; exhausting.

gruesome (grü′səm) *adj.* causing horror, disgust, or fear.

H

habitable (hab′i tə bəl) *adj.* suitable for living in.

haematoma (hē′mə tō′mə) *n.* tumor or swelling containing blood.

harmoniously (här mō′nē əs lē) *adv.* in agreeable combination.

harridan (har′i dən) *n.* mean old woman.

harrowed (har′ōd) *adj.* frightened; distressed.

hearses (hûr′ses) *n., pl.* vehicles for carrying dead people from one place to another before or after a funeral service.

heath (hēth) *n.* flat, open wasteland overgrown with heather or low bushes.

heave (hēv) *v.* lift or raise with force or effort.

hiatus (hī ā′təs) *n.* break or gap, as in time.

hoax (hōks) *n.* trick or deception.

hogsheads (hôgz′hedz′) *n., pl.* large barrels holding from 63 to 140 gallons of liquid.

homage (hom′ij) *n.* honor, respect, or reverence.

honing (hō′ning) *n.* sharpening the edge of.

humanitarian (hū man′i târ′ē ən) *adj.* concerned with or promoting the general welfare of humanity.

humility (hū mil′i tē) *n.* quality of being humble; lack of pride or arrogance.

hydrophone (hī′drə fōn′) *n.* device used for hearing underwater sounds.

---

at; **ā**pe; f**är**; c**â**re; **e**nd; m**ē**; **i**t; **ī**ce; p**î**erce; h**o**t; **ō**ld; s**ô**ng, f**ô**rk; **oi**l; **ou**t; **u**p; **ū**se; r**ü**le; p**ů**ll; t**û**rn; **ch**in; s**i**ng; **sh**op; **th**in; **th**is; **hw** in **wh**ite; **zh** in trea**s**ure. The symbol **ə** stands for the unstressed vowel sound heard in **a**bout, tak**e**n, penc**i**l, lem**o**n, and circ**u**s.

I

idiosyncrasy (id'ē ō sing'krə sē) *n.* unusual or distinguishing characteristic of an individual, such as a habit or mannerism; peculiarity.

ignite (ig nīt') *v.t.* set on fire.

illiteracy (i lit'ər ə sē) *n.* lack of the ability to read or write.

immense (i mens') *adj.* very large; huge.

imparted (im pär'tid) *v.t.* made known; told.

impassioned (im pash'ənd) *adj.* filled with passion or strong feeling; fiery; ardent.

impassive (im pas'iv) *adj.* not feeling or showing emotion.

implements (im'plə mənts) *n., pl.* tools.

implications (im'pli kā'shənz) *n., pl.* indirect suggestions.

impressed (im presd') *adj.* fixed firmly in the mind.

impromptu (im promp'tü) *adj.* done on the spur of the moment.

inadvertently (in'əd vûr'tənt lē) *adv.* in an accidental or unintended manner.

incense (in'sens') *n.* substance that produces a fragrant aroma when burned.

incessantly (in ses'ənt lē) *adv.* continuously; unceasingly.

incisive (in sī'siv) *adj.* penetrating; sharp.

inconspicuous (in'kən spik'ū əs) *adj.* likely to escape notice; not easily seen.

incredulity (in'krə dü'li tē) *n.* refusal to believe; doubt.

incriminate (in krim'ə nāt') *v.t.* suggest or show the guilt of.

incurred (in kûrd') *v.t.* brought something on oneself by one's own actions.

indelible (in del'ə bəl) *adj.* that cannot be removed or taken away.

indulgences (in dul'jən səz) *n., pl.* favors, treats, or pardons allowed (to someone).

inevitably (in ev'i tə blē) *adv.* certainly; unavoidably.

infernal (in fûr'nəl) *adj.* hateful; of, relating to, or characteristic of hell.

infirm (in fûrm') *adj.* physically weak, as from old age.

infuse (in fūz') *v.t.* instill; inspire.

ingenious (in jēn'yəs) *adj.* made with or showing cleverness, originality, or imagination.

ingots (ing'gəts) *n., pl.* masses of metal cast into bars or blocks.

inscription (in skrip'shən) *n.* message or note written on something.

insolently (in'sə lənt lē) *adv.* with offensive rudeness.

integrate (in'ti grāt') *v.t.* bring together into a whole.

integrity (in teg'ri tē) *n.* moral uprightness; honesty; sincerity.

intimate (in'tə mit) *adj.* personal or private.

intoxicated (in tok'si kā'tid) *adj.* greatly excited.

intricately (in'tri kit lē) *adv.* very involved or complicated.

inundated (in'ən dā'tid) *v.t.* covered with a flood.

invariably (in vâr'ē ə blē) *adv.* in an unchanging or unchangeable manner.

irascible (i ras'ə bəl) *adj.* easily irritated or made angry; irritable.

iridescent (ir'i des'ənt) *adj.* displaying shimmering and changing colors, like those reflected by soap bubbles.

J

jade (jād) *n.* green mineral used for jewelry and carved ornaments.

jaunts (jontz) *n., pl.* short trips, especially taken for pleasure.

jeering (jîr'ing) *adj.* scornful or mocking.

jostling (jos'ə ling) *v.t.* bumping, pushing, or shoving roughly.

K

keening (kē'ning) *n.* loud wailing for the dead.

kindling (kind'ling) *n.* small pieces of dried wood or twigs.

L

labyrinth (lab'ə rinth') *n.* place with winding and connected passages or pathways in which it is easy to lose one's way; maze.

lacquered (lak'ərd) *adj.* having a clear, glossy coating; varnished.

lanyards (lan'yərdz) *n., pl.* short ropes used on ships to fasten things.

legacy (leg'ə sē) *n.* heritage; something handed down from previous generations or from the past.

legitimate (li jit'ə mit) *adj.* logically correct or valid.

leniency (lē'nē ən sē) *n.* state or quality of being merciful, tolerant, not severe or harsh.

levying (lev'ē ing) *v.t.* imposing or collecting by force or authority.

liable (lī'ə bəl) *adj.* legally responsible; obligated by law.

liberate (lib'ə rāt') *v.t.* set free; release.

lichen (lī'kən) *n.* any of a large group of plantlike organisms found in all parts of the world, usually growing on tree trunks, rocks, or the ground. Lichens consist of a fungus and an algae growing together.

liege (lēj) *n.* lord or ruler.

limpet (lim'pit) *n.* brownish green saltwater shellfish that has a cone-shaped shell and clings to rocks; used chiefly for bait.

lingered (ling'gərd) *v.i.* stayed on as if reluctant to leave.

lodging (loj'ing) *n.* rented room or rooms.

longevity (lon jev'i tē) *n.* long life.

lumberjacks (lum'bər jaks') *n., pl.* people who cut down trees and get logs ready for transportation to the sawmill.

luminous (lü'mə nəs) *adj.* sending out light of its own; shining.

M

malice (mal'is) *n.* wish to cause harm, injury, or pain to another; spite.

malodorous (mal ō'dər əs) *adj.* having an unpleasant odor.

mannequins (man'i kinz) *n., pl.* little men; dwarves.

mansard (man'särd) *adj.* having two slopes on all sides.

marksmanship (marks'mən ship') *n.* skill in shooting a gun or other weapon.

mead (mēd) *n.* alcoholic drink made from fermented honey and water and flavored with herbs.

meandering (mē an'dər ing) *v.i.* following a winding course.

mediated (mē dē ā'tid) *v.t.* settled (differences or disputes) by coming between and working with disagreeing or opposing parties.

mesquite (mes kēt') *n.* small, thorny tree or shrub that grows in desert regions from the southwestern United States to Chile.

minimize (min'ə mīz') *v.t.* make as small as possible.

mitigate (mit'i gāt') *v.t.* make milder or less severe.

mobilized (mō'bə lizd') *v.* organized or prepared, as for war or an emergency.

monarch (mon'ərk) *n.* hereditary ruler of a state or country, such as a king or queen.

moors (mùrz) *n., pl.* areas of open, rolling, wild land, often covered with heather and having bogs and marshes.

morocco-bound (mə rok'ō bound) *adj.* covered in goatskin leather that originally came from Morocco.

mortality (môr tal'i tē) *n.* death rate.

mortified (môr'tə fīd') *v.t.* shamed, humiliated, or embarrassed.

motivated (mō'tə vā'tid) *v.t.* moved to effort or action as a result of a mental state, inner need, or outward goal.

at; **āpe**; **fär**; **câre**; **end**; **mē**; **it**; **īce**; **pîerce**; **hot**; **ōld**; **sông**, **fôrk**; **oil**; **out**; **up**; **ūse**; **rüle**; **pùll**; **tûrn**; **chin**; **sing**; **shop**; **thin**; **this**; **hw** in **white**; **zh** in **treasure**. The symbol **ə** stands for the unstressed vowel sound heard in **about**, tak**e**n, penc**i**l, lem**o**n, and circ**u**s.

municipal (mū nis′ə pəl) *adj.* of or relating to the local government or affairs of a city, town, or other community.

mused (mūzd) *v.i.* said thoughtfully.

musty (mus′tē) *adj.* stale or moldy.

mutilated (mū′tə lā′tid) *adj.* very damaged or disfigured.

N

niches (nich′iz) *n., pl.* hollowed out spaces in a wall.

nonchalantly (non′shə länt′lē) *adv.* with casual indifference.

O

oblivious (ə bliv′ē əs) *adj.* not aware or conscious; unmindful.

obnoxious (ob nok′shəs) *adj.* extremely annoying, disagreeable, or offensive.

obscured (əb skyürd′) *v.t.* made difficult to understand.

obsession (əb sesh′ən) *n.* state of being occupied or troubled about something.

obvious (ob′vē əs) *adj.* easily seen or understood.

offensive (ə fen′siv) *adj.* unpleasant; disagreeable.

ominously (om′ə nəs lē) *adv.* in a manner suggesting misfortune.

optical (op′ti kəl) *adj.* relating to the sense of sight.

optimistic (op′tə mis′tik) *adj.* inclined to look on the bright side.

orator (ôr′ə tər) *n.* skilled public speaker.

ovation (ō vā′shən) *n.* enthusiastic burst of applause or other demonstration of public approval.

overt (ō vûrt′) *adj.* not hidden; easily observed.

ozone (ō′zōn) *n.* form of oxygen with a distinctive odor, formed when an electric discharge passes through the air.

P

pandemonium (pan′də mō′nē əm) *n.* wild disorder or uproar.

paraffin (par′ə fin) *n.* waxy, white substance obtained from petroleum and used for making candles and waxed paper and for sealing jars for preserves.

parasites (par′ə sīts′) *n., pl.* people who live off or associate with others for their own gain while giving nothing in return.

pathetic (pə thet′ik) *adj.* arousing pity, sadness, or sympathy.

peat (pēt) *n.* rotted plant matter found in bogs and swamps, and used as fertilizer or burned for fuel.

pedestal (ped′ə stəl) *n.* support at the base of a column, statue, or similar upright structure.

pensive (pen′siv) *adj.* deep in serious thought, often about matters of a sad nature.

peril (per′əl) *n.* danger; chance or risk of injury, loss, or destruction.

perpendicularly (pûr′pən dik′yə lər lē) *adv.* straight up and down; vertically.

perplexity (pər plek′si tē) *n.* state or condition of being filled with uncertainty, confusion, or bewilderment.

persistently (pər sis′tənt lē) *adv.* continuing in a firm and steady manner in spite of opposition or difficulty.

petition (pə tish′ən) *v.t.* make a formal request to a person in a position of authority.

philosophical (fil′ə sof′i kəl) *adj.* accepting life and its problems with calmness and understanding.

phonetic (fə net′ik) *adj.* of or relating to speech sounds.

pillaged (pil′ijd) *v.t.* robbed by force, as during a war.

plagiarism (plā′jə riz′əm) *n.* act of copying someone else's work and passing it off as one's own.

plaiting (plā′ting) *v.t.* braiding.

plight (plīt) *n.* bad situation or condition.

plot (plot) *v.t.* locate on a map or diagram; chart.

plume (plüm) *n.* large, fluffy, showy feather.

poignant (poin′yənt) *adj.* deeply moving; sad; touching.

pontoons (pon tünz′) *n., pl.* flat-bottomed boats used as floating supports.

porous (pôr′əs) *adj.* having or full of many small holes.

preceding (pri sē′ding) *adj.* going or coming before.

preclude (pri klüd′) *v.t.* prevent or make impossible.

predominantly (pri dom′ə nənt lē) *adv.* more frequently, commonly, or noticeably.

prehensile (prē hen′sil) *adj.* adapted for grasping or holding, especially by wrapping around.

preoccupation (prē ok′yə pā′shən) *n.* state of being absorbed in deep thought.

prestigious (pre stij′əs) *adj.* having or giving prestige; highly honored or respected.

pretense (prē′tens) *n.* false show or appearance, especially for the purpose of deceiving.

pristinely (pris′tēn lē) *adv.* purely.

privations (prī vā′shənz) *n., pl.* lacks in the comforts or necessities of life.

proclaimed (prə klāmd′) *v.t.* announced officially; declared publicly.

prominent (prom′ə nənt) *adj.* well-known or important.

proponents (prə pō′nənts) *n., pl.* people who propose or support something.

prose (prōz) *n.* everyday written or spoken language that is not like poetry.

psychiatrist (sī kī′ə trist) *n.* physician who specializes in the treatment of emotional and mental disorders.

Q

quandary (kwon′də rē) *n.* state of hesitation or uncertainty; dilemma.

quirt (kwûrt) *n.* flexible riding whip made of knotted rawhide thongs and having a short handle.

quivers (kwiv′ərz) *n., pl.* cases for holding arrows.

R

radiant (rā′dē ənt) *adj.* beaming with joy, contentment, love, or the like; shining brightly.

rapt (rapt) *adj.* deeply absorbed.

rationing (rash′ən ing, rā′shən ing) *n.* government limits on portions or shares.

raucous (rô′kəs) *adj.* disorderly; rowdy.

recessed (rē′sesd) *adj.* set back or indented from the rest.

recipient (ri sip′ē ənt) *n.* person who receives.

reflective (ri flek′tiv) *adj.* given to or showing serious or careful thinking; thoughtful.

refugees (ref′yu̇ jēz′) *n., pl.* people who flee to safety or refuge, especially those who leave home or homeland because of persecution, war, or danger and seek safety in another place.

regime (rə zhem′) *n.* government.

rehabilitative (rē′hə bil′i tā′tiv) *adj.* given to restoring good health.

rejuvenated (ri jü′və nā′tid) *v.t.* made young again.

reluctant (ri luk′tənt) *adj.* unwilling or hesitant.

remit (ri mit′) *v.t.* send in payment.

remorse (ri môrs′) *n.* deep, painful feeling of guilt, sorrow, or distress for wrongdoing.

renounce (ri nouns′) *v.t.* give up or abandon, especially by formal declaration; refuse to recognize as one's own.

resolved (ri zolvd′) *v.t.* decided (to do something); determined.

resonated (rez′ə nā′tid) *v.i.* echoed with full, rich sound.

---

at; āpe; fär; câre; end; mē; it; īce; pîerce; hot; ōld; sông, fôrk; oil; out; up; ūse; rüle; pu̇ll; tûrn; chin; sing; shop; thin; this; hw in white; zh in treasure. The symbol ə stands for the unstressed vowel sound heard in about, taken, pencil, lemon, and circus.

restive (res′tiv) *adj.* stubborn and difficult to manage; unruly.

retained (ri tānd′) *v.t.* continued to have or hold.

rudiments (rü′də mənts) *n., pl.* first or basic principles of something.

ruefully (rü′fə lē) *adv.* with sorrow or regret.

S

sauntered (sôn′tərd) *v.i.* walked in a slow, relaxed way; strolled.

scabbard (skab′ərd) *n.* case or sheath for the blade of a sword, bayonet, or other similar weapon.

scantier (skan′tē ər) *adj.* skimpier; thinner.

scapegoat (skāp′gōt′) *n.* person or thing made to suffer for or bear the blame for the mistakes or wrongdoings of others.

scathing (skā′<u>th</u>ing) *adj.* very severe or harsh.

scones (skōnz) *n., pl.* small, often round biscuits.

scree (skrē) *n.* debris from a landslide lying on a slope at the base of a cliff.

secure (si kyùr′) *adj.* free from worry, care, or fear.

securities (si kyùr′i tēz) *n., pl.* stock or bond certificates.

sediments (sed′ə mənts) *n., pl.* solid materials that settle to the bottom of a body of water.

seduced (si düst′) *v.t.* tempted or persuaded.

seeps (sēps) *v.i.* spreads or flows slowly, as through openings or pores.

segregation (seg′ri gā′shən) *n.* practice of separating one racial group from another or from the rest of society.

shah (shä) *n.* title of the former hereditary ruler of Iran.

significance (sig nif′i kəns) *n.* special value or importance.

silo (sī′lō) *n.* tall, cylindrical tower of metal or other material for the storage and fermentation of green fodder.

simian (sim′ē ən) *adj.* of, relating to, or resembling an ape or monkey.

simultaneous (sī′məl tā′nē əs) *adj.* existing, happening, or done at the same time.

sit-ins (sit′inz′) *n., pl.* protest demonstrations in which persons sit in a public place and stay there until their demands are agreed to or considered.

skeptical (skep′ti kəl) *adj.* showing doubt; disbelieving.

smoldered (smōl′dərd) *v.i.* burned and smoked with little or no flame.

solemn (sol′əm) *adj.* serious and earnest; grave; sober.

sophistication (sə fis′ti kā′shən) *n.* quality of having worldly knowledge and experience.

sound (sound) *adj.* stable or safe; reliable.

sovereign (sov′rən) *n.* supreme ruler of a monarchy.

specious (spē′shəs) *adj.* seemingly true or reasonable, but actually false.

spectral (spek′trəl) *adj.* ghostly.

speculating (spek′yə lā′ting) *v.i.* thinking carefully or seriously.

spellbound (spel′bound′) *adj.* held as if by a magic spell; entranced.

squandered (skwon′dərd) *v.t.* spent or used in a wasteful manner.

stagnant (stag′nənt) *adj.* still or motionless, as air or water.

stalemate (stāl′māt′) *n.* any position or situation in which no further action is possible; deadlock; standstill.

stances (stan′səz) *n., pl.* manners of standing.

stanched (stôncht) *v.t.* brought the flow of blood to a stop.

status (stā′təs) *n.* relative place or rank, especially social or professional standing.

stem (stem) *v.t.* stop or restrain as if by damming.

stern (stûrn) *adj.* severe or strict; grim or forbidding.

stoically (stō′i kə lē) *adv.* in a manner unaffected by pain or pleasure.

stout (stout) *adj.* having courage; brave; strong.

stove (stōv) *v.i.* smashed; broken.

stropping (stro′ping) *v.t.* sharpening on a flexible leather strip.

studded (stud′ed) *v.t.* scattered or spread over.

stupefied (stü′pə fīd′) *adj.* amazed; overwhelmed.

subpoenaed (sə pē′nəd) *v.t.* summoned to a court of law by virtue of having a subpoena, or legal document.

subsided (səb sī′did) *v.i.* decreased in activity or intensity.

succinct (sək singkt′) *adj.* expressed in few words; brief and concise.

suppleness (sup′əl nes) *n.* flexibility; adaptability.

sympathy (sim′pə thē) *n.* ability to share the feelings of another or others.

syndrome (sin′drōm) *n.* group of symptoms that together are characteristic of a particular disease or disorder.

T

tainted (tān′tid) *v.i.* spoiled, blemished, or damaged.

tangible (tan′jə bəl) *adj.* definite; capable of being measured.

tedious (tē′dē əs) *adj.* causing weariness and boredom because of length, dullness, or the like; boring.

tenacity (tə nas′i tē) *n.* state or quality of being stubborn or obstinate.

tentacles (ten′tə kəlz) *n., pl.* long, slender, flexible growths used for feeling, grasping, and moving.

tentatively (ten′tə tiv lē) *adv.* with hesitation or uncertainty.

threshold (thresh′ōld) *n.* point of entry.

throttle (throt′əl) *n.* fuel supply valve.

tiller (til′ər) *n.* bar or handle used to turn the rudder of a boat.

tinder (tin′dər) *n.* any substance that burns easily, especially something used to start a fire from a spark, such as twigs.

transcripts (tran′skripts′) *n., pl.* written copies.

transfixed (trans fikst′) *adj.* motionless as from awe or fear.

transmitted (trans mi′tid) *v.t.* communicated or conveyed from one person to another; handed down.

transpired (tran spīrd′) *v.i.* happened; occurred.

treaty (trē′tē) *n.* formal agreement, especially one between nations.

tremor (trem′ər) *n.* shaking; trembling.

tremulous (trem′yə ləs) *adj.* marked or affected by trembling; shaking.

trepidation (trep′i dā′shən) *n.* nervous or fearful anticipation; anxiety.

tribute (trib′ūt) *n.* anything done, given, or observed as a sign of devotion, gratitude, or respect.

trundle bed (trun′dəl bed) *n.* low, movable bed that may be pushed under another bed for storage.

tureens (tə rēnz′) *n., pl.* deep dishes with covers, used for serving food, especially soup.

tyranny (tir′ə nē) *n.* cruel and unjust use of force, power, or authority.

U

uncanny (un kan′ē) *adj.* strange and eerie; weird.

unfathomable (un fath′ə mə bəl) *adj.* that cannot be measured.

unison (ū′nə sən) *n.* union, as when two or more voices speak as one.

---

at; **ā**pe; f**ä**r; c**â**re; **e**nd; m**ē**; **i**t; **ī**ce; p**î**erce; h**o**t; **ō**ld; s**ô**ng, f**ô**rk; **oi**l; **ou**t; **u**p; **ū**se; r**ü**le; p**ů**ll; t**û**rn; **ch**in; si**ng**; **sh**op; **th**in; **th**is; **hw** in **wh**ite; **zh** in trea**s**ure. The symbol **ə** stands for the unstressed vowel sound heard in **a**bout, tak**e**n, penc**i**l, lem**o**n, and circ**u**s.

unobtrusively (un'əb trü'siv lē) *adv.* inconspicuously.

urn (ûrn) *n.* closed vessel having a spigot, used for making, heating, or serving hot drinks.

usurp (ū sûrp') *v.t.* take possession of by force.

V

vaguely (vāg'lē) *adv.* not definitely or clearly expressed.

valiant (val'yənt) *adj.* brave; courageous.

valid (val'id) *adj.* true; soundly based on facts or evidence.

vapor (vā'pər) *n.* tiny particles suspended in the air, such as mist or smoke.

veered (vîrd) *v.i.* changed in direction or course; shifted; turned.

vehemently (ve'ə mənt lē) *adv.* showing or characterized by intensity of feeling; passionately.

venerable (ven'ər ə bəl) *adj.* deserving respect or reverence, as by reason of age, character, or position.

ventured (ven'chərd) *v.i.* expressed at the risk of objection.

verge (vûrj) *n.* edge; border; point beyond which something happens or begins.

vestibule (ves'tə būl') *n.* entrance hall or passage between the outer door and the interior of a building.

vexation (vek sā'shən) *n.* annoyance.

vicinity (və sin'i tē) *n.* area near or surrounding a particular place.

vigor (vig'ər) *n.* active power or force; healthy strength.

vile (vīl) *adj.* foul; disgusting; repulsive.

vilified (vil'ə fīd') *v.t.* spoke or wrote evil of; slandered.

vindication (vin'di kā'shən) *n.* the state of being cleared of suspicion or charges of wrongdoing.

violate (vī'ə lāt') *v.i.* fail to obey or keep; break.

virtually (vûr'chü ə lē) *adv.* in almost every way; practically.

vital (vi'təl) *adj.* of greatest importance; essential.

voluble (vol'yə bəl) *adj.* with a smooth, easy flow of words; talkative.

W

walkouts (wôk'outs') *n., pl.* strikes in which workers leave their working places; walking out of a meeting or the like, especially as an expression of protest.

whorls (hwûrlz) *n., pl.* patterns resembling coils or spirals.

wincing (win'sing) *v.i.* drawing back or away as if from something painful, dangerous, or unpleasant; flinching.

windfall (wind'fôl') *n.* unexpected advantage or gain.

GLOSSARY OF
Literary Terms

A

Acts The main divisions of a play. There are two acts in *The Monsters Are Due on Maple Street,* page 683. (See also *Drama, Scenes.*)

Allegory A literary work in which different elements, such as characters or settings, have symbolic meanings.

Alliteration The repetition of consonant sounds, usually at the beginnings of words. Note the repetition in these lines from "Birdfoot's Grampa," page 519:

by our lights and leaping,
live drops of rain"

(See also *Poetry.*)

Allusion A reference within a literary work to a character or situation in another literary work or work of art, as when on page 103 of "I Know Why the Caged Bird Sings," Maya Angelou refers to Beowulf and Oliver Twist.

Anecdote A short, often amusing story based on an incident in a person's life. In "The Dog That Bit People," page 107, James Thurber relates anecdotes about dogs he has owned.

Antagonist The character or force that opposes the protagonist, or hero, in a work of literature. The principal is the antagonist in "The Scholarship Jacket," page 274. (See also *Character, Protagonist.*)

Assonance The repetition of a vowel sound in words within a sentence or line of verse. (See also *Poetry.*)

Audience The group of people who read a literary work or watch a play, film, or television program.

Author's Point of View The author's point of view is his or her attitude toward the subject of the written work. (See also *Author's Purpose.*)

Author's Purpose The author's purpose is his or her reason for writing a particular work. An author's purpose may be to inform, to persuade, to entertain, to express an opinion, or a combination of these purposes. In "Crispus Attucks," page 330, Jim Haskins's purpose is to inform. (See also *Author's Point of View.*)

Autobiography The story of a person's life written by that person. (See also *Anecdote, Biography, Narrative Point of View, Subject, Subjective Details.*)

B

Biography The story of a person's life written by another person. (See also *Autobiography, Subject.*)

C

Character A person, an animal, or a personified object that plays a role in the action of a literary work. A **round character** is one for whom an author has created a fully developed physical appearance and personality. A **flat character** is one who is not fully developed. (See also *Antagonist, Hero/Heroine, Protagonist.*)

Characterization The techniques authors use to present and develop characters. In

direct characterization, authors comment in a straightforward manner on the nature of a character. In "A Retrieved Reformation," page 391, O. Henry characterizes Jimmy Valentine directly when he says that "the clerks were pleased to be greeted by the good-looking, agreeable young man who was going to marry Miss Annabel." In **indirect characterization,** authors allow readers to draw conclusions about characters based upon the characters' own words and actions as well as upon how other characters react to them. In "The Joy Luck Club," page 64, Amy Tan uses indirect characterization to make Meimei and her mother come to life. (See also *Character Traits, Character: Motivation.*)

Character: Motivation The reasons fictional characters act, think, or feel certain ways. (See also *Character Traits.*)

Character's Point of View A character's perspective on plot events or other characters.

Character Traits The personal qualities that distinguish one literary character from another. (See also *Character, Characterization, Character: Motivation.*)

Chronological Order The order in which events happen in time.

Circular Story A story that begins and ends with the same or a similar event. (See also *Short Story.*)

Climax (See *Plot.*)

Colloquialisms Expressions that are used in informal conversation, such as when in "With Bert & Ray by William," page 176, William says that "Ma and me got so's people would call us direct and not go through Bert and Ray, and we got so's we could price things out pretty good ourselves." (See also *Dialect.*)

Complications (See *Plot.*)

Conflict The struggle between opposing characters or forces that is central to the action of a literary work. **External conflicts** are those in which a character struggles against another character, society, or force of nature. For example, in "The United States *vs.* Susan B. Anthony," page 341, Anthony engages in an external conflict when she struggles against the system that denies women the right to vote. **Internal conflicts** are those in which a character struggles with an issue or problem within his or her mind. Mike, in "The Moustache," page 406, experiences an internal conflict during his visit to his grandmother in the nursing home. (See also *Plot.*)

Connotation The emotional meaning associated with a word that also adds to its literal meaning. (See also *Denotation.*)

D

Denotation The literal dictionary meaning of a word. (See also *Connotation.*)

Descriptive Details Specific instances in a literary work in which an author uses sensory language to create vivid images of characters, events, or places. In "Havasu," page 560, Edward Abbey uses descriptive details when he says, "The warm, thick fluid came up and closed over my head as my feet touched the muck at the bottom." (See also *Figurative Language.*)

Dialect A form of language spoken by a particular group of people or in a specific geographical area. Dialect differs from standard spoken English in its spelling, word use, and pronunciation. (See also *Colloquialisms.*)

Dialog The conversation between characters in a literary work. Usually, dialog is enclosed in quotation marks and tells the exact words a character says. Sometimes, as in drama, quotation marks are not used to enclose dialog. Instead, the words spoken by the actors come after their characters' names. (See also *Drama, Monolog.*)

Direct Address A literary device that enables an author or a literary character to talk directly to an audience.

Drama A genre of literature meant to be performed before an audience. In drama, the story is told through characters' dialog and actions. (See also *Acts, Dialog, Monolog, Scenes, Stage Directions.*)

E

Episode An event or incident that forms a distinct part of a story and may or may not relate to the plot.

Epistolary Literature Literature that is written in the form of a letter or a series of letters.

Essay A short work of nonfiction that focuses on a single subject. There are two general types of essays: **formal essays** are objective, or impersonal, and serious in tone; **informal essays** are subjective, or personal, and light in tone.

Exaggeration The deliberate overstatement of an idea for emphasis or humorous effect. In "Paul Bunyan's Cornstalk," page 211, for example, Harold Courlander tells of a "Michigan deerfly about the size of a bushel basket."

Exposition Writing that explains, analyzes, or defines. "Rain Forests," page 482, is an example of expository writing.

F

Fables Brief stories that teach morals. Most fables tell about animal characters that behave like people. (See also *Folklore, Moral.*)

Facts Statements that can be proved. (See also *Nonfiction, Opinions.*)

Fairy Tales Stories about fanciful characters with unusual abilities. Typical characters in fairy tales include giants, monsters, dragons, gnomes, evil beings, and talking animals. (See also *Folklore.*)

Falling Action (See *Plot.*)

Fantasy A type of literature that takes place in an unreal, imaginary world characterized by magical or supernatural elements. (See also *Realistic Fiction.*)

Fiction Prose writing that tells an imaginary story in the form of a short story or novel. (See also *Nonfiction, Novel, Short Story.*)

Figurative Language Language that uses imagery and figures of speech to create original and colorful descriptions. Simile, metaphor, and personification are the most commonly used types of figurative language. In "Barrio Boy," page 87, Ernesto Galarza uses figurative language when he says that Miss Hopley had "thin lips that moved like steel springs." (See also *Descriptive Details, Hyperbole, Imagery, Metaphor, Personification, Poetry, Simile, Style.*)

Flashback A scene or an image that interrupts the present action in a story or play to describe an event or events that took place earlier. (See also *Foreshadowing.*)

Folk Hero The major character in a folk tale, whose courageous action and brave deeds are responsible for bringing the story to a happy conclusion. Paul Bunyan in "Paul Bunyan's Cornstalk," page 211, is a folk hero. (See also *Folk Tale.*)

Folklore Stories, songs, and poems that have been handed down within a culture from one generation to another. Kinds of folklore include folk tales, fairy tales, tall tales, fables, myths, and legends.

Folk Tale Entertaining story that has been passed along orally from one generation to the next. These stories usually contain a hero or heroine and common folk who often are shown to have better values than their wealthier, more powerful neighbors. "Bending Willow," page 203, is an example of a folk tale. (See also *Folk Hero, Folklore.*)

Foreshadowing The literary technique authors use to hint at events that will take place later in a story. Foreshadowing occurs in "The Inn of Lost Time," page 652, when Zenta tells his audience it is important for them to remember that Tokubei could always have money forwarded to him. (See also *Flashback.*)

Frame Story A story that contains another story. In "The Inn of Lost Time," page 652, the frame story consists of those parts in which the family and friends are sitting together telling stories. The story about Urashima Taro and the one about Zenta and Tokubei are stories contained within the frame story. (See also *Short Story.*)

G

Genre A category of literature having certain characteristics. Examples of genre include: biography, drama, poetry, and short story.

H

Haiku An unrhymed poem of Japanese origin that usually expresses a single thought about nature. A haiku always consists of three lines made up of seventeen syllables: five syllables in the first and third lines, and seven syllables in the second line. (See also *Poetry.*)

Hero/Heroine The central character in a literary work who is often admired for ex-

emplary personal qualities, such as bravery and nobility. Theseus is the hero of "Theseus," page 219; Bending Willow is the heroine of "Bending Willow," page 203. (See also *Character.*)

Historical Fiction A type of fiction that is based on historical events and characters. "The Man Without a Country," page 246, is an example of historical fiction. (See also *Fiction.*)

Humor The characteristic of writing that makes it funny or amusing. "The Dog That Bit People," page 107, is an example of humorous writing.

Hyperbole A statement that is exaggerated or overstated to emphasize a point or to create a humorous effect, as when Martha describes herself as "pencil-thin" in "The Scholarship Jacket," page 274. (See also *Exaggeration, Figurative Language.*)

I

Imagery Words and phrases that appeal to the senses and that are used to create vivid descriptions. For example, Norah Burke describes the Arctic setting of "Polar Night," page 472, as a landscape containing "lanes and pools of pure cobalt looking-glass opening and closing all the time in the pack ice." (See also *Figurative Language, Sensory Language.*)

Interview A conversation, usually in a question-and-answer format, between a reporter or writer and another person. The person who asks the questions is the **interviewer.** The person who answers the questions is the **subject.**

Irony The effect created when there is a sharp contrast between what is expected to happen and what actually happens, or between what is stated and what is meant. In "The Necklace," page 444, it is ironic that the necklace the Loisels think is so expensive turns out to be worth very little.

L

Legends Stories handed down through generations that describe the heroic actions of characters. Legends sometimes tell about real historical figures in fictionalized situations. (See also *Folklore.*)

Limerick A humorous verse, or poem, written in one five-line stanza with a regular scheme of rhyme and meter.

Lyric Poem A brief poem that expresses a personal thought or emotion, usually through the use of vivid images and a musical rhythm. "I Stepped from Plank to Plank," page 387, is a lyric poem. (See also *Narrative Poem, Poetry.*)

M

Main Idea The main idea is the central idea of a work of nonfiction. The main idea may also refer to the most important idea contained within a paragraph. (See also *Supporting Details.*)

Metaphor Figurative language that suggests a comparison between two things that are not usually considered to be alike. In "Amanda and the Wounded Birds," page 130, Dr. Hart refers to her patients as "wounded birds." (See also *Figurative Language, Poetry.*)

Meter The pattern of rhythm in lines of poetry. (See also *Rhythm.*)

Monolog A long speech delivered by a character in a literary work. (See also *Dialog, Drama.*)

Mood The emotional effect or feeling that an author creates in a literary work. In "Lather and Nothing Else," page 436, the author creates a tense mood, as the reader wonders whether or not the barber will kill Captain Torres.

Moral A lesson about life that is taught in a fable. (See also *Fables.*)

Myths Stories set in ancient times that explain important natural events, such as the formation of the earth or the creation of the seasons. Greek and Roman myths describe the actions of gods, goddesses, and mortal heroes and heroines. "Theseus," page 219, is an example of a Greek myth. (See also *Folklore.*)

N

Narrator The teller of a story. (See also *Narrative Point of View.*)

Narrative Nonfiction A type of writing that tells a story about real people, places, and events. On page 302, "Am I an American?" is an example of narrative nonfiction.

Narrative Poem A poem that tells a story. (See also *Lyric Poem, Poetry.*)

Narrative Point of View The perspective from which an author tells a story. There are two main types of point of view: first person and third person. In the **first-person point of view,** the narrator is a character in the story and uses first-person pronouns, such as *I, me,* and *we.* "The Moustache," page 406, is told from the first-person point of view. In the **third-person point of view,** the narrator is an outside observer, rather than a story character, and uses third-person pronouns, such as *he* and *she.* The third-person point of view can be subdivided into two types: limited and omniscient. In the **limited point of view,** the narrator focuses on the thoughts, actions, and feelings of one character. "Dicey's Song," page 4, is an example of a story told from the limited third-person point of view. In the **omniscient point of view,** the narrator can reveal the thoughts, actions, and feelings of all the characters. O. Henry uses the third-person omniscient point of view in "A Retrieved Reformation," page 391. (See also *Narrator.*)

Nonfiction The type of writing that tells about real people, places, and events. Examples of nonfiction include articles, essays, diaries, news stories, letters, biographies, autobiographies, and reviews. (See also *Facts, Fiction, Opinions.*)

Novel A novel is a fictional story of considerable length containing detailed treatments of characters and/or complicated plots. (See also *Fiction, Short Story.*)

O

Objective Details Small bits of information that can be observed or measured rather than based on an author's thoughts or opinions. (See also *Subjective Details.*)

Onomatopoeia A literary technique involving the use of words in which the sound of a word suggests or imitates its meaning. An example of onomatopoeia is the word *hiss* in "Southbound on the Freeway," page 649. (See also *Poetry.*)

Opinions Statements based on a person's beliefs, feelings, or thoughts about what is true rather than on what can be proved to be true. (See also *Facts, Nonfiction.*)

P

Parody A humorous imitation of a serious literary work or of an author's writing style. "The Waking of the Prince," page 582, is a parody of a fairy tale. (See also *Style.*)

Personification Figurative language in which animals or objects are given human characteristics. In "Boy at the Window," page 679, the snowman is personified.

Persuasion A type of writing in which an author tries to convince an audience to

believe or accept the ideas being presented. "Longing to Die of Old Age," page 551, is an example of persuasive writing. (See also *Propaganda.*)

Play (See *Drama.*)

Plot The series of related events in a literary work. Most plots follow a pattern. The **exposition** introduces the characters and the problems, or **complications,** they face. The part of the story in which the conflict grows is called the **rising action.** The turning point in the story, or the point at which the conflict is resolved and the story outcome is clear, is called the **climax.** The **falling action** describes the events that take place after the climax. The falling action includes the **resolution,** or the outcome of the conflict that is developed in the plot. (See also *Conflict.*)

Poetry A type of literature that expresses ideas and feelings by relying on compact, often musical language that appeals to readers' senses and ignites their emotions. (See also *Alliteration, Assonance, Figurative Language, Haiku, Imagery, Lyric Poem, Metaphor, Narrative Poem, Onomatopoeia, Refrain, Rhyme, Rhythm, Simile, Speaker, Stanza.*)

Propaganda Information and ideas presented in order to persuade people to do or believe something that may or may not be true. (See also *Persuasion.*)

Prose The kind of everyday writing or speech that does not have the rhyme or rhythm patterns of poetry.

Protagonist The central character in a literary work. Martha is the protagonist in "The Scholarship Jacket," page 274. (See also *Antagonist, Character.*)

R

Realistic Fiction A type of fiction that tells an imaginary story about characters and places that could actually exist and events that could actually happen. "The Treasure of Lemon Brown," page 422, is an example of realistic fiction. (See *Fantasy.*)

Refrain A repeated line or phrase in a poem that creates recurring rhythm and produces a musical quality. (See also *Poetry.*)

Repetition A literary technique that involves repeating a word or phrase for emphasis or to create a rhythm or particular emotional effect. The words "Do we" from "What Do We Do with a Variation?," page 158, are an example of repetition.

Resolution (See *Plot.*)

Rhyme A literary technique involving the repetition of the same or similar sounds. When two words rhyme, the accented syllables and all the sounds following these syllables sound the same. The most common form of rhyme, **end rhyme,** occurs when words at the ends of several lines of poetry rhyme, as in "The Armful," page 199. In **internal rhyme,** the rhymes occur within lines of poetry. (See also *Poetry.*)

Rhythm A pattern of sounds or beats created by the arrangement of accented and unaccented words or syllables, especially in poetry. (See also *Poetry.*)

Rising Action (See *Plot.*)

S

Scenes The divisions within acts in a play. (See also *Acts, Drama.*)

Science Fiction A type of imaginary story that involves up-to-date or futuristic scientific developments and technology. "The Rocket," page 608, is an example of science fiction.

Sensory Language Descriptive language that appeals to one or more of the five senses: sight, hearing, smell, touch, and taste. Authors use sensory language to create vivid word pictures that heighten an audience's interest, as when in "Polar Night," page 472, Norah Burke says "Snow water dribbled into pools. Icicles glistened with wet, dropped and broke like glass." (See *Imagery.*)

Setting Setting is the time and place in which the action of a literary work unfolds.

Short Story A brief work of fiction that can usually be read in one sitting. (See also *Circular Story, Fiction, Frame Story, Novel.*)

Simile Figurative language that makes a direct comparison between two apparently unlike things, using the words *like* or *as.* For example, in "UFOs," page 624, an eyewitness says that the UFO "looked like a glowing 'jellyfish.'"

Slang Nonstandard or unconventional speech used by speakers for informal or humorous expression.

Speaker In poetry, the voice that talks to the reader. The speaker is comparable to a narrator in a work of fiction. (See also *Narrator.*)

Stage Directions The means by which actors know where and how to move and speak. Stage directions are set off from dialog by parentheses and/or italics. They often describe scenery, props, and lighting. (See also *Drama.*)

Stanza In poetry, a group of lines arranged in any of various patterns according to meter, rhyme, and the like. In free verse a stanza is more like a paragraph in prose writing. (See also *Poetry.*)

Style The distinctive way an author writes. An author's style is shaped by many elements, including word choice, sentence patterns and length, figurative language, and tone. (See also *Figurative Language, Parody, Tone.*)

Subject The person whose life is presented in an autobiography or a biography or who is profiled in an interview or a news article. A subject may be famous or little known, alive or dead, but he or she is always someone who has actually lived. Eleanor Roosevelt is the subject of "Eleanor Roosevelt: On Her Own," page 321. (See also *Autobiography, Biography, Interview.*)

Subjective Details Small bits of information that are based on personal feelings and opinions rather than on what can be observed and/or proven to be true. (See also *Objective Details.*)

Supporting Details Specific bits of information that directly relate to the main idea in a piece of nonfiction writing. (See also *Main Idea.*)

Surprise Ending The unexpected twist in the ending of any literary work. "A Retrieved Reformation," page 391, contains a surprise ending.

Suspense The feeling of uncertainty about what might happen next in a literary work. "Lather and Nothing Else," page 436, is filled with suspense, as readers wonder whether or not the barber will kill Captain Torres.

Symbolism A literary technique involving the use of an object, event, or character to express an idea more general or broader than itself. In "Scaffolding," page 1, the building of a wall symbolizes the building of a relationship.

T

Tall Tales Humorous stories that exaggerate characters and events beyond belief. "Paul Bunyan's Cornstalk," page 211, is an example of a tall tale. (See also *Folklore.*)

Teleplay A drama written for television. *The Monsters Are Due on Maple Street,* page 683, is a teleplay. (See also *Drama.*)

Theme The underlying idea or message about life or human nature contained in a literary work. A **stated theme** is one the author puts directly into words. An **unstated,** or **implied, theme** is one readers must determine on their own by analyzing other story elements.

Tone An author's attitude toward his or her subject.

Tragedy A dramatic work in which the main character faces a moral struggle and is destroyed because of his or her own actions.

Trickster Tales Stories that describe how clever animals or people play tricks on, or otherwise take advantage of, animals or people. (See also *Folklore*).

INDEX OF
Titles by Genre

INDEX OF
Authors and Titles

The page numbers in *italics* refer to biographical information.

INDEX OF
Fine Art

Acknowledgments

"Restoring Our Earth" from RESTORING OUR EARTH by Laurence Pringle. Copyright © 1985. Published by Enslow Publishers, Inc., 44 Fadem Road, Box 699, Springfield, NJ, 07081-0699 and used with their permission.

"The Rocket" from R IS FOR ROCKET by Ray Bradbury. Reprinted by permission of Don Congdon Associates, Inc. Copyright © 1950, renewed 1977 by Ray Bradbury.

"Scaffolding" by Seamus Heaney. Reprinted by permission.

"The Scholarship Jacket" by Marta Salinas from NOSTRAS: LATINA LITERATURE TODAY. Copyright © 1984. Used by permission of Bilingual Press/Editorial Bilingue, Tempe, Arizona.

"Southbound on the Freeway" reprinted with permission of Simon & Schuster Books For Young Readers from THE COMPLETE POEMS TO SOLVE by May Swenson. Copyright © 1963 May Swenson; copyright renewed 1991 by the Literary Estate of Mary Swenson. First appeared in *The New Yorker.*

"Tableau" by Countee Cullen. Reprinted by permission.

"The Time We Climbed Snake Mountain" by Leslie Marmon Silko. Reprinted by permission.

"To Kill a Mockingbird" chapter 10 from TO KILL A MOCKINGBIRD by Harper Lee. Copyright © 1960 by Harper Lee. Copyright renewed © 1988 by Harper Lee. Reprinted by permission of HarperCollins Publishers, Inc.

"The Treasure of Lemon Brown" reprinted by permission of Walter Dean Myers and *Boy's Life* magazine, published by The Boy Scouts of America. Copyright © 1983 by Walter Dean Myers.

"Two Haiku" by Kikaku and Boncho, translated by Harry Behn. © renewed 1992 by Prescott Behn, Pamela Behn Adams, and Peter Behn.

"UFOs" reprinted by permission of G. P. Putnam's Sons from UFOs, ETs & VISITORS FROM SPACE by Melvin Berger, copyright © 1988 by Melvin Berger.

"Under One Sun" by Neal Beaumont. Reprinted by permission.

Excerpt from "The U. S. *vs.* Susan B. Anthony" from WOMEN OF COURAGE by Margaret Truman. Copyright © 1976 by Margaret Truman Daniel. By permission of William Morrow and Company, Inc.

"The Waking of the Prince" from A TELLING OF THE TALES by William J. Brooke. Text copyright © 1990 by William J. Brooke.

"What Do We Do with a Variation?" from WHEN I DANCE, copyright © 1991, 1988 by James Berry, reprinted by permission of Harcourt Brace & Company.

"Why Did the Balinese Chicken Cross the Road?" from LIVING BY THE WORD: SELECTED WRITINGS 1973–1987, copyright © 1988 by Alice Walker, reprinted by permission of Harcourt Brace & Company.

Cover permission for THE WINTER ROOM by Gary Paulsen. Jacket painting copyright © 1989 by John Ward. Reprinted by permission of the Publisher, Orchard Books, New York.

"With Bert & Ray by William" from THROWING SHADOWS by E. L. Konigsburg. Copyright © 1979 by E. L. Konigsburg. Reprinted with the permission of Simon & Schuster Books For Young Readers.

"Woodman, Spare Those Brazilian Trees" reprinted with permission from *The Atlanta Journal* and *The Atlanta Constitution.*

"Words Like Freedom" from COLLECTED POEMS by Langston Hughes. Copyright © 1994 by the Estate of Langston Hughes. Reprinted by permission of Alfred A. Knopf Inc.

Art & Photo Credits

ILLUSTRATIONS

Unit 1: Iskra Johnson (calligraphy), xvi, i; Jill Enfield, 4,–25; Gary Hagaard, 30–43; Winson Tranz, 64–81; Brent Watkinson, 83; Bonnie Rasmussen (props), 87–93; Stephen Schudlich, 121. **Unit 2:** Kathy McNicholas (calligraphy), 130, 131, 134, 135, 136, 138, 139; Vickie Yiannias, 130–139; Jim Himsworth III, 160, 161, 166–173; Bruce Solotoff (background), 199; Richard High (calligraphy), 203, 208; Jerry Dadds, 211–213, 216; Griesbach/Martucci, 211, 215; Brad Gaber (borders), 219–230. **Unit 3:** J. Craig Hannas (uniform), 246; Lisa Palombo, 274–279, 282, 283; José Ortega (borders, lettering), 274, 283; Steven Karchin (collage), 302; Mark Kaplan (background), 330–338. **Unit 4:** Kim Fraley, 385; Tom Bookwalter, 406, 407, 410, 411, 414, 415, 418, 419; Brad Gaber (background) 422–433; Raul Colon, 436, 442; John Stevens (calligraphy), 445, 446; Stephen Schudlich, 463. **Unit 5:** Iskra Johnson (calligraphy), 468, 469; Bruce Solotoff (background), 537; Dale Verzaal, 482, 483; Michael Rothman, 522–535; Brian Pinkney, 550–557; Stephen Schudlich, 573. **Unit 6:** Neal McPheeters, 587; Nicholas Jainschigg, 608–621; George Baquero (collage), 624–647; Yoshikazu Ozino, 652–677; Tim Bower, 683–704.

PHOTOGRAPHY CREDITS

All photographs are by the Macmillan/McGraw-Hill School Division (MMSD) except as noted below.

Front Matter iv–v: *The Painter's Family* (detail), Henri Matisse, 1911, The Hermitage Museum. Photo courtesy Art Resource. © 1995 Succession H. Matisse, Paris/Artists Rights Society (ARS), NewYork. vi–vii: *Blossoming* (detail), Paul Klee, 1934, Kunstmuseum Winterthur, Switzerland. viii–ix: *Three Flags* (detail: center panel), Jasper Johns, 1958. Encaustic on canvas, 30 7/8 x 45 1/2 x 5 in. (78.4 x 115.6 x12.9 cm.). Collection of Whitney Museum of American Art, 50th Anniversary Gift of the Gilman Foundation, Inc., The Lauder Foundation, A. Alfred Taubman, and anonymous donor, and purchase. 80.32. © 1997 Jasper Johns/Licensed by VAGA, New York. x–xi: *Landscape at Collioure/Study for "Le bonheur de vivre"* (detail), Henri Matisse, 1905, Statens Museum for Kunst, Copenhagen. © 1995 Succession H. Matisse, Paris/Artists Rights Society (ARS), New York. xii–xiii: Orion Press. xiv–xv: *Flower Vendor* (detail), Diego Rivera, 1949. Museo Nacional Centro de Arte Reina Sofía, Madrid. xvi–: I. Art Resource, Inc. **Unit 1:** 16: I. Art Resource, Inc. 25: Walter Voight for MMSD; Walter Voigt. 28: Schomburg Center for Research in Black Culture/The New York Public Library. 30: Gerald Vizenor. 46–47: © by Universal Pictures, a division of Universal City Studios, Inc. Courtesy of MCA Publishing Rights, a division of MCA, Inc. 48: t.l. © by Universal Pictures, a division of Universal City Studios, Inc. Courtesy of MCA Publishing Rights, a division of MCA, Inc./Museum of of Modern Art Movie Stills. 48–49: © by Universal Pictures, a division of Universal City Studios, Inc. Courtesy of MCA Publishing Rights, a division of MCA, Inc./Movie Stills Archive. 50–51: © by Universal Pictures, a division of Universal City Studios, Inc. Courtesy of MCA Publishing Rights, a division of MCA, Inc./Museum of Modern Art. Movie Stills. 51: b.l. © by Universal Pictures, a division of Universal City Studios, Inc. Courtesy of MCA Publishing Rights, a division of MCA, Inc./Museum of of Modern Art Movie Stills. 52–53: © by Universal Pictures, a division of Universal City Studios, Inc. Courtesy of MCA Publishing Rights, a division of MCA, Inc. 56: t.l. © by Universal Pictures, a division of Universal City Studios, Inc. Courtesy of MCA Publishing Rights, a division of MCA, Inc./The Bettman Archives, Inc.; b.l. © by Universal Pictures, a division of Universal City Studios, Inc. Courtesy of MCA Publishing Rights, a division of MCA, Inc./Photofest. 57: t.r. © by Universal Pictures, a division of Universal City Studios, Inc. Courtesy of MCA Publishing Rights, a division of MCA, Inc./The Bettmann Archives, Inc. 58–59: © by Universal Pictures, a division of Universal City Studios, Inc. Courtesy of MCA Publishing Rights, a division of MCA, Inc. 60: © by Universal Pictures, a division of Universal City Studios, Inc. Courtesy of MCA Publishing Rights, a division of MCA, Inc./Movie Still Archives. 61: The University of Alabama News. 81: Robert Foothorap. 87: t.l. Sacramento Archives and Collection Center. 89: Brown Brothers. 90 & 92: Sacramento Archives and Collection Center. 93: University of Notre Dame Press. 104: © Jesse Nemerofsky/Photoreporters. 114: t. Ken Heyman/Woodfin Camp & Associates; b. Copyright © 1966 Helen Thurber. Copyright © 1994 Rosemary A. Thurber. From Thurber & Company, published by HarperCollins. Photograph courtesy Ohio State University Library. 118: Howard Grey/Tony Stone. **Unit 2:** 139: Farrar, Straus and Giroux. 142: t.l Jennifer Ashabranner. 142–143: m. Paul Conklin. 146: Paul Conklin. 148: Paul Conklin. 151: Paul Conklin. 154: Paul Conklin. 173: t.r., m.l., b.r. Richard Chesnut for MMSD; b.l. The Lazar Agency, Inc. Clear Light Publishers. Peabody Essex Musuem. 157: Jane Burton/Bruce Coleman, Inc. 190: *Flower Seller* by Diego Rivera. Private Collection, Diego Rivera Art Library/Bridgeman Art Library. 208: Museum of Mankind, British Museum. Copyright British Museum. 219:

© Sonia Halliday Photographs. 222: © Robert Frerck/Odyssey Productions. 227 & 228: © Erich Lessing/Art Resource. 230: Brown Brothers. 234: Tom McHugh/Photo Researchers. **Unit 3:** 246: Uniform from The Sentry Post/photo by MMSD. 249 & 252: Photo by Richard Bond. 258: Photo by Derek Bayes/Aspect Picture Library. 263: Photo by Richard Bond. 269: I. United States Naval Academy Museum. 299: b.r. Frank Atura/Stewart Tabori & Chang. Photo by Richard Bond; r. Culver Pictures, Inc. 305: r. National Archives. 306–307: t. The Bettmann Archive, Inc. 308–309: Bob Hsiang/The National Japanese American Historical Society. 309: b.r. Baron Goto/Bernice Pavahi Bishop Museum. 310: The Bettmann Archive, Inc. 311: b.r. The National Japanese American Historical Society; t. The Bettmann Archive, Inc. 312–313: b. Eliot Elisofon/Life Picture Service. 313: t.r. Myron H Davis/Life Picture Service; t. Dorothea Lange/National Archives/FPG. 315: National Archives. 317: Warren Ogden; m.l. Krista Kiger; Michael Brown Collection. 318: Archive Photos. 320–321: Franklin Delano Roosevelt Library. 323: Culver Pictures, Inc. 333–334: The Granger Collection. 337: Archive Photos. 341–344 The Granger Collection. 348: Library of Congress. 350: John Barrett/Globe Photos, Inc. 354: The Granger Collection. 302: t.r. Mouchette Films; m.l. Hansel Mieth/Life Picture Service. **Unit 4:** 373: Library of Congress. 375: Heard Musuem. 376: FPG International. 379 & 385: Penguin Books Canada, Ltd. 387: Norman Tomalin/Bruce Coleman; D. P. Hershkowitz/Bruce Coleman.391: Ohio Dept. of Corrections. Photo courtesy of American Correctional Assn. 392: Illinois Dept. of Corrections. 394: Library of Congress. 396: The Bettmann Archive. 400: Wells Fargo Bank. 403: The Bettmann Archive. 406: t.l. Richard Howard. 426: Art and Artifacts Division, Schomburg Center for Research in Black Culture, The New York Public Library, Astor, Lenox and Tilden Foundations. 433: David Godlis/Penguin Books. 450: © Photography by Erich Lessing/Art Resource. 456: Culver Pictures. 460: Tony Freeman/Photo Edit. **Unit 5:** 468–469: Orion Press. 472–478: Dan Guravich 486: t.m. Thomas C. Boyden; t.r. Daniel Cande/Photo Researchers. 487: t.l. Michael Fogden/Animals Animals; t.m. C.B. Frith, D. W. Frith/Bruce Coleman, Inc.; t.r. Thomas C. Boyden 500–517: Volox Inc./Tsuneo Nakamura. 519: Norman Tomalin/Bruce Coleman. 520: The British Library/Bridgeman Art Library. 522: Laurence Pringle. 537: Kathleen Norris Cook. 541: Peter Weimann/Animals Animals. 543: D. Miller/Photo Researchers. 544: Scott Camazine/Photo Researchers. 557: Scott Harvey for MMSD. 573: Newark Museum 570: Cathlyn Melloan/Tony Stone. **Unit 6:** 582–583: Steve Crisp/Artbank. 584–594: Frank & Jeff Lavaty. 595: John Rowe/Artbank. 596–602: Frank & Jefff Lavaty. 603: Paul Davies/Artbank. 604: Frank & Jeff Lavaty. 621: Harry Redl/Black Star. 624: t.r. Scott Harvey for MMSD. 625: t.m. NASA/Superstock; t.r. NASA JPL/Starlight; b.m. The Picture Collection, The New York Public Library; b.r. Cliff Peuner/The Image Bank. 626: t.l. Branch Libraries/The Picture Collection, New York Public Library; t.m. NASA/Superstock; t.r. K. Iwasaki/The Stock Market; m.r. Scott Harvey for MMSD. 627: NASA JPL/Starlight. 628: t.r., b.m. Scott Harvey for MMSD; m.l. David A. Hardy/Science Photo Library/Photo Researchers, Inc.; b.l. Dr. Jean Lorre/Science Photo Library/Photo Researchers, Inc. 629: t.m. Scott Harvey for MMSD; t.r. K. Iwaski/The Stock Market. 630: t.l. Julian Baum/Science Photo Library/Photo Researchers, Inc; t.r. NASA/Superstock. 631: b.l., b.m. Scott Harvey for MMSD. 632: t.r. Branch Libraries/The Picture Collection, New York Public Library; Photofest. 633: t.m. Scott Harvey for MMSD; b.r. Museum of Modern Art–Movie Stills. 634: t.l. Scott Harvey for MMSD; t.m. The Bettmann Archive, Inc; t.r. NASA JPL/Starlight. 635: t., b.r. Scott Harvey for MMSD. 636: t.l. Roger Ressmeyer/Starlight; b.l. Branch Libraries/The Picture Collection, The New York Public Library; t. Scott Harvey for MMSD. 637: t.m. Julian Baum/Science Source/Photo Researchers, Inc; m. The Bettman Archive, Inc; b.r., m.r. Scott Harvey for MMSD. 638: t.l. NASA JSC/Starlight; t.r. K. Iwasaki/The Stock Market; b.r. Scott Harvey for MMSD; b.l. Telegraph Colour Library/International Stock Photography Ltd. 639: t.r. Scott Harvey for MMSD; b.r. Branch Libraries/The Picture Collection, The New York Public Library. 640: t.r. Courtesy of J. Allen Hynek Center for UFO Studies, Chicago. 640–641: Scott Harvey for MMSD. 641: b.r. Masahiro Samo/The Stock Market. 642: b.l. Courtesy of J. Allen Hynek Center for UFO Studies, Chicago; b.r. Scott Harvey for MMSD. 643: t.l., m. Courtesy of J. Allen Hynek Center for UFO Studies, Chicago; b.r. Scott Harvey for MMSD. 644: t.l., b.r. Branch Libraries/The Picture Collection, The New York Public Library; t.r. Courtesy of J. Allen Hynek Center for UFO Studies, Chicago. 645: t.l., b.r. Scott Harvey for MMSD; t.r. NASA JSC/Starlight; m.r. Julian Baum/Science Photo Library/Photo Researchers, Inc. 646: t.l. Branch Libraries/The Picture Collection, The New York Public Library; t.r, b.r. Scott Harvey for MMSD. 647: Scott Harvey for MMSD. 649: Koplin Gallery Corporate Rise. 677: Richard NcNamee/Courtesy of Lensey Namioka. 679: *Jim*, by William Johnson. National Museum/Art Resource, Inc. 704: Photofest. 718: Amon Carter Museum.